CONTENTS

INTRODUCTION   ix

LIST OF MEMBERS   1

LIST OF OFFICE-BEARERS   355

CATALOGUE OF PORTRAITS AND BUSTS
    List of Portraits   365
    List of Busts   368

ILLUSTRATIONS

ENTRANCE HALL AND STAIRCASE, SIGNET LIBRARY   *frontispiece*

THE SIGNET LIBRARY   *facing page* xx

THE UPPER LIBRARY   *facing page* xxiii

INTRODUCTION

The Writers to the Signet have existed as a corporate entity for over 500 years. It is impossible to say precisely when the Society came into being. The earliest entry in this Register is that of Sir John Reid, or "Rede" (before 1460) and there are several other entries which pre-date the year 1500; but the Signet, the seal adhibited by the King to authenticate documents in which he was specially interested, had been in use for at least a century beforehand. The custody and use of the Signet was entrusted to an officer known as the King's Secretary who was "the king's right hand at the pen, the issuer of the royal manuscript authority, whether for the ends of state policy, for transactions of law, or for private purposes."[1] Walter of Wardlaw, who was the King's Secretary in 1369, is the first office-bearer recognised by the Society; and the earliest members of the Society were those who acted as clerks or assistants to the office of the King's Secretary. The first "Writer to the King's Signet" formally so styled was Walter Chapman, or "Chepman" (before 1494).

The immensely long history of the Society, spanning as it does more than half a millenium, has still to be fully chronicled. Various historical accounts have been published from time to time, but they are all of a limited or specialised nature and do not add up to a comprehensive history. The chief purpose of the present volume is to bring up to date the lists of members contained in two earlier publications, *A History of the Society of Writers to Her Majesty's Signet* (1890) and *The Society of Writers to His Majesty's Signet* (1936).[2] For convenience these publications are referred to in this Introduction as the "1890 History" and the "1936 History" respectively.

The list of members contained in the 1890 History is confined to "the names of those Writers to the Signet whose admissions are registered in the existing Minutes of the Society, or who are otherwise recorded therein."[3] This means that no members of a date prior to 1594 are included for it was in that year that the Society's Minutes began with the narrative of a Commission granted by Sir Richard Cockburne of Clerkingtoun, the Lord Secretary, in favour of John Layng, his depute and Keeper of the Signet, and eighteen other members of the Society appointed as Commissioners. The information included under each entry is relatively brief, being confined for the most part to dates of admission, birth and death, along with details of parentage, apprenticeship and any offices, appointments or publications. In many of the early entries, certain of these basic details are lacking. Occasionally, we find additional fragments of biographical information, especially of a notorious nature, but these appear haphazardly and without any evidence of systematic research. Thus, we discover that Archibald Houstoun was killed in a brawl by Gilbert Kennedy in 1706, and that James Stuart of Dunearn killed Sir Alexander Boswell in a duel in 1822 and was later acquitted when tried for murder.

1. 1890 History, p. xii.
2. The full titles of the two volumes are as follows:—*A History of the Society of Writers to Her Majesty's Signet with a List of the Members of the Society from 1594 to 1890 and an Abstract of the Minutes* (1890), and *The Society of Writers to His Majesty's Signet with a List of the Members and Abstracts of the Minutes of the Society, the Commissioners and the Council and the Early History of the Scottish Signet* (1936). It should be noted that the 1936 volume does *not* contain a history of the Society as such and the title on the spine ("A History of the Society of Writers to His Majesty's Signet") is incorrect and inconsistent with the title-page.
3. 1890 History, p.cxxx.

The 1936 History updates the list of members to include all those admitted up to the end of 1935, involving some 500 additional entries. The list was also extended backwards to include all known Writers to the Signet from the earliest times up to 1594. Many further particulars had been gathered between 1890 and 1935 and the entire 1890 list was rewritten. Unfortunately, many details pertaining to members had to be omitted owing to the exigences of space so that the 1936 volume does not in fact contain a significant amount of additional biographical material. The entries for Hamilton Bell and John Bell of Greenhill may be cited as examples. In the case of Hamilton Bell, we are told that an interesting account appears in *Kay's Portraits* of how for a bet he carried a vintner's boy on his back from Edinburgh to Musselburgh; and in the case of John Bell of Greenhill we learn that he was drowned while bathing in the Kirtle on 9th September, 1776.

In this new Register, the entries for members who died before publication of the 1936 History have been reprinted with only very occasional alterations or additions. For those members alive in 1936 and for all subsequent intrants a questionnaire was sent out in April 1974 either to themselves or to relatives, inviting the submission of personal details. From these answers there has been compiled the entries since 1936 and these take their place in the alphabetical sequence, up to the last diet of admission in December 1981. Unfortunately, rather a long time has elapsed since replies to the questionnaire were received. Although every endeavour had been made to amend entries to take account of subsequent events, where known, the information in a few of the entries may be found to be out of date. This is regrettable but for a variety of reasons it has been impossible to publish this volume any sooner.

The 1890 History contains an extended historical introduction running to 126 pages. It is divided into chapters, the first of which, although only forty-five pages in length, provides what is still the longest and most useful general history of the Society. It is particularly informative about the early origins of the Society and in showing how a sense of community and brotherhood evolved out of the possession of common skills and the sharing of common interests. As a chronological account, it is rather unbalanced, the last two centuries before the publication date of 1890 being dealt with in a mere four pages of text and being confined to the picking out of bits and pieces, sometimes trivial, from the Society's Minutes.

This first chapter also deals with a variety of topics under separate headings: the office of the Deputy Keeper; former meeting places of the Society; regulations relating to apprentices and intrants; gowns worn by members; "the box" or common fund in relation to the early finances of the Society; the chair of humanity at Edinburgh University; the Society's involvement with public works and charities; a very brief notice of the element of heredity in the Society's membership; the Society's armorial bearings; and the Society's relationship with the notaries public. The remaining chapters of the 1890 introduction deal with the Library, the Society's finances, the establishment and history of the Widows' Fund, and a very interesting account of the long fight to establish a chair of conveyancing at Edinburgh University under the patronage of the Society in the face of oposition by the Faculty of Advocates.

In 1933, the Society agreed to issue a continuation of the 1890 History and the task was entrusted to a committee set up under the convenership of A. P. Melville. This resulted in the 1936 History, which contains some forty pages of introductory material and a further fifty pages comprising "The Early History of the Scottish Signet" by Professor R. K. Hannay, H.M. Historiographer for Scotland. Professor Hannay's detailed and scholarly article traces the use of the Scottish Signet from earliest times to the end of the sixteenth century, concluding with the granting of the Commission in 1594, the year in which the Society's

formal Minutes begin. It is a distinguished contribution to the history of the origins of the Society.

The introduction to the 1936 History begins with a short outline of the establishment of the Society and goes on to cover in brief the main events since 1890, including service in the 1914-18 war, developments in the Library, and the erection of the West Wing. The Widows' Fund and the various charitable and educational trusts are also dealt with. The setting up of the General Council of Solicitors in Scotland is alluded to, as is the decision of the Society to establish a Council of its own, which met first in 1934.

A feature of both 1890 and 1936 volumes are the Abstracts of Minutes. These form a major part of the earlier work—almost 250 pages—beginning with a complete account of the Commission granted in 1594. Thereafter, there are notes on events for nearly every year until 1887. A narrative selecting the more important and interesting forms part of the 1890 introduction. Most entries are short and factual such as those recording admissions, but others occur in more detail, e.g. a copy of the "Memoriall concerning the rise and constitution of the Society" in 1731 occupying almost six pages. Other entries relate to the happenings of the day, highlighting events of note or that caused concern. In 1767, the Deputy Keeper called members to a meeting "in order to lay before them the wicked incendiary letters sent to my lord president", and he observed, "I humbly think we are called upon to express in the most publick manner our highest indignation of the malicious authors of that hellish performance".[4] The meeting resolved to offer a reward of 300 guineas, upon conviction, to any person able to discover the author—to be raised by imposing a tax on Signet Letters!

Affairs of both local and national importance occupied the Society much and from time to time financial contributions were made, occasionally quite substantial sums. An instance took place in 1798 when it was unanimously decided to subscribe 2,000 guineas (not 200, as stated in the 1890 History at p. xxxvii) towards the support of the state "at the present crisis of affairs", presumably referring to the unrest in Ireland at the time. In 1811, 700 guineas were voted towards the erection of a marble statue to the late Lord President Blair;[5] and frequent sums were given towards the restoration or upkeep of St Giles.

These Abstracts of Minutes give a useful outline of the Society's affairs over the years, but there was no further significant contribution to the history of the Society until 1970, when Dr A. R. B. Haldane contributed an article about the Society for publication in the *Journal of the Law Society of Scotland*.[6] This was, and still is, the only succinct and balanced account of the Society's origins and its subsequent expansion. By kind permission of Dr Haldane, it is reproduced below, with a few amendments to bring it up to date.

> The story of the Society of Writers to the Signet begins far back in the history of Scotland. Many centuries ago when the art of writing was little more than a mystery known to a few, but at a period when the authority of the King was at length growing from shadow to substance, the method of authentication of documents carrying the King's warrant and approval presented a growing problem. Its solution was found

4. 1890 History, p.405.
5. The statue is located in Parliament House.
6. "The Society of Writers to Her Majesty's Signet" by A. R. B. Haldane, C.B.E., D.Litt., W.S., in *Journal of the Law Society of Scotland*, Vol. 15, 1970, pp.35-38. A slightly shortened account appeared as an introduction to *The Signet Library*, by G. H. Ballantyne, published in 1979.

to be in the use of seals, bearing special devices embossed on them, to be attached to documents in evidence of Royal approval, and with or without any signature. As time passed and the number of documents calling for authentication increased, it was found that one seal only was insufficient and it is known that at least by the fourteenth century, if not earlier, the number of seals in use had grown to four. These seals differed in character and design according to the special purpose for which each was used, but one, known as "The Signet," was reserved for the private communications of the King himself or for the authentication of documents in which he was closely concerned or interested. The earliest recorded use of the Signet was in the year 1369.

With multiplication and growing use of seals came the need for officials and staff to supervise such use. Particularly was this apparent in the case of the Signet, the custody of which came to be entrusted to a high Court official known as the King's Secretary. His office was an important and busy one calling for the employment of clerks, discreet, trustworthy and skilled in the still rare art of writing, whose business it was to attend to the public and private correspondence of the King himself and to execute documents such as Royal Charters and Grants issued by the King's authority. Originally these clerks appear to have lacked any corporate entity other than that inherent in a community of calling, but there is evidence that before the end of the fifteenth century a body united by common interests had in fact come into being. At a time when men "wrote with difficulty and spelled by chance" it is hardly surprising to find these clerks referred to first as "Writaries to the Singnet" and slightly later as "Wrettaries to the Signet." Though still lacking any formal corporate existence or constitution these early Writers to the Signet, sharing a knowlege of law and conveyancing, the rare art of penmanship and the still rarer skill in the use of Latin, had much in common with the Guilds linked by the knowledge of trade and craft.

In 1532 James V brought about a major reform of the legal administration of Scotland by the establishment of the College of Justice. With this reform there came into being the Court of Session, superseding the Lords of Council, Lords Auditor and the other ancient Courts which had hitherto possessed limited or specialised jurisdiction. To these old Courts the Writers to the Signet had acted as clerks for some time before 1532, and now as a component part of the College of Justice they came to act in the same capacity in relation to the new Court of Session. The establishment of the College of Justice and the Court of Session had left in being the old Privy Council, which continued to deal with criminal and civil complaints brought by or against persons of high or low degree in all parts of Scotland. To the

Council, sitting in private session originally in the Council Chamber of the Old Tolbooth, Writers to the Signet, as they were increasingly coming to be called, had from early times acted as clerks. After 1532 they continued so to act, and the growing number of cases recorded in the many volumes of the Register of the Council from 1545 up till 1689 can leave no doubt in the mind of the reader that here, too, the Writers to the Signet found busy, useful and no doubt profitable occupation. By this time, too, it seems increasingly evident that besides acting as clerks to the Council, many of the writers were coming to transact business on behalf of persons appearing as litigants before the Council and the Court of Session, or in more private capacities.

In May 1532 immediately following the establishment of the College of Justice by James V, the first Act of Sederunt of the new Court of Session made regulations for the work of Writers or "Clerkis to the Signet." These were aimed at securing the diligence and confidentiality of a body which was coming increasingly to be recognised as a necessary and responsible part of the legal system of Scotland. The same regulations laid down scales of charges which could properly be levied by them for official work in connection with the Court of Session, the Privy Council or for such other work more directly on behalf of the Crown as they continued to carry out.

The earliest minutes of the Society of Writers to the Signet which have survived date from 1594. In that year Sir Robert Cockburn of Clerkington, Lord Secretary to the King and as such Keeper of the King's Signet, granted to John Layng as Deputy Keeper of the Signet and to eighteen other writers the first Commission conferring on them official status for their work as clerks to the Courts. Rules for the qualification and admission of Writers to the Signet were laid down. Provision was made for the remedying, by the Deputy Keeper and certain senior members, of abuses which might occur within the body, while vacancies among the first Commissioners were to be filled from the other most senior and best qualified members. Admission of new members, though virtually in the hands of the Deputy Keeper and Commissioners, still remained, at least in theory, in those of the Lord Secretary.

The regulations laid down in 1594 and subsequent communications from the Lord Secretary during the next half century emphasise the importance attached to the maintenance of the high standards of work and integrity demanded from members of the Society. For this purpose strict limitation in the membership was recognised as being of first importance for the public benefit, increase in members being seen as likely to lead to decrease in earnings and so to increased temptation "to committ falsettis." Sons, apprentices, or even servants of

members might be admitted, but only on the death of a member, while the total number as laid down in 1594 was restricted to twenty-four. A letter dated 1609 for Sir Alexander Hay, then Lord Secretary, refers to anxiety over the "multitude of wrytaries to the Signet," with an exhortation to the Deputy Keeper of the Signet and Commissioners to "Lett not preposterous pitie heirefter move ather you or thame to spair or mitigate the punishment imposed, that so quhome dewtie can not move feare sall inforce to walk warlie in their calling." No doubt happenings within the Society about this time justified these recurrent warnings aimed at those who stepped outside the bounds of proper professional behaviour, for during the first half of the seventeenth century references appear to the impropriety of drinking at taverns during sessions of the Court, failure to keep a true register of apprentices and servants with a record of their signatures, transacting business on terms other than those approved or acting as clerks to craft guilds in the City. It is on record that one member had even so far lowered the status of himself and the Society as to take employment as a waiter in Kirkcaldy, a monstrous iniquity which cost him his membership of the Society. At this time, too, many references appear to repeated efforts to maintain the standard demanded of entrants to the Society and to the tests of knowledge and qualification. How far these efforts were successful seems doubtful, for numbers continued to grow, a tendency which was perhaps not unconnected with the fact that payments by entrants seem, in theory if not always in practice, to have been a perquisite of the Lord Secretary who as Keeper of the Signet had the final say in admission.

The Society suffered its full share of the confusion which the Civil War brought to so much of the administration of Scotland and England alike, but emerged with the Restoration in 1660 under a new Deputy Keeper of the Signet and a membership purged of many officials and others whose appointments dated from the Commonwealth period. Restriction of the size of the Society was still a prime object, and in 1663 the Earl of Lauderdale, as Keeper of the Signet, undertook that the number of members should be limited to sixty. The Revolution of 1688 brought a further brief period of confusion, during which for a short time the work of the Signet Office was in abeyance, but with the new Monarchy firmly in the saddle the position of the Society as an integral part of the Establishment grew firmer year by year. In 1696 the Society entered into what was described as a "bond of association" in support of William III, and the Treaty of Union of 1707 provided that vacancies in the Court of Session could be filled only by advocates or Writers to the Signet. The Rebellion of 1715 appears to have given rise to some anxiety as to the political leanings of some of

the members, for in November of that year they were warned not to take into their Chambers as apprentices or servants any not well disposed to the Government. This warning did not, however, deter one member from fighting for the Chevalier, at Sheriffmuir, while thirty years later another fought for Prince Charles Edward at Prestonpans. Whether, in the years which followed, glasses were sometimes raised in the privacy of Chambers to the King over the Water can never be known, for the minutes contain no hint. Instead, the records show the Society more and more firmly adhering to Crown and Parliament. An address of congratulation, jointly made to the Duke of Cumberland after Culloden by the Society and Lords of Session, was followed over the next half century by both resolutions and contributions by the Society in support of the Government during the American and French Wars, and in 1778 a sum of 500 gns. was contributed towards the raising in Edinburgh of a regiment for overseas. Meantime one important change closely affecting the Society had taken place. In 1746 the ancient office of Lord Secretary was abolished, and since the holder of the Secretaryship was also Keeper of the Signet, the latter office fell vacant. For some years thereafter the Keepership of the Signet was filled by special appointment, but in 1817 this office was combined with that of Lord Clerk Register. The position has remained unchanged up to the present day, the office of Lord Clerk Register being today filled by the Earl of Wemyss and March, K.T. who, in virtue of his position as Keeper of the Signet, is responsible for the work of the Signet Office.

As the years rolled on the membership of the Society grew, at first slowly but later with increasing speed. The efforts made in the earliest years to limit the number of entrants "for the benefit of the public" were never wholly successful. As late as the first year of the Protectorate the membership was still limited to as few as thirty-six, but by 1731 this had grown to 110, "to the great loss of the whole body, for half the members could not possibly live upon their incomes and hence a larger proportion of aged and infirm brethren was brought to depend upon the Society's funds for maintenance." Throughout the eighteenth century the roll of members steadily lengthened, perhaps reflecting both the rise in the level of qualification and the suitability of these seeking admission, and the steady increase in the financial strength of the Society. In the first years of the nineteenth century, following the inauguration in 1803 of the Widows' Fund, the number had grown to 200 thereafter rising to a peak of 685 in 1840 and falling again in the second half of the century. Today the membership numbers just over 800.

Such in brief and bare outline is the story of this ancient body, sketched with a line, faint but continuous and clearly

discernible in the very earliest years, growing in strength and certainty as the centuries pass. But looking back over the long period of the Society's existence and turning the pages of the written records of nearly 400 years, it becomes apparent how abundant is the detail and the colour which even in a short compass may enable us to bring to the eye of the imagination a picture of the men who went before us, the work they did and the surroundings in which they moved. At the time when the earliest "Writtaris to the Signet" began to emerge as professional men from the historical obscurity of the fourteenth century they had, as has been seen, no corporate entity. It is equally clear that they had nothing approaching regular places of business. Even the King's Secretary, in common with other public servants of the time, had no official place of business and it is very certain that his clerks would be no better situated. The work of the King's Secretary and of his clerks for long continued to be done in their own homes, though in the case of the latter, references begin to appear as time passed to "writing booths." The nature and extent of these must be a matter for speculation, but it needs small imagination to realise their necessity when it is recalled that in the fifteenth and sixteenth centuries, and indeed for more than 200 years to come, the dwelling places of the citizens of Edinburgh were situated in tall tenements housing on sucessive floors rich and poor indiscriminately intermixed, living in only slightly varying degrees of squalor, and that till the middle of the eighteenth century the dwellings of even the richest and most aristocratic might contain only three rooms. It would be fascinating indeed to picture, were it possible, the circumstances and the surroundings in which many of the documents of the time, drafted and engrossed by our professional predecessors, first saw the light of day. Till past the middle of the eighteenth century the life and activity of Edinburgh was virtually confined to the Old Town lying between the Castle and Holyroodhouse, but following the adoption in 1765 of James Craig's imaginative plan for development of the city to the north, linked to the Old Town by the North Bridge and the Mound, the New Town grew rapidly. None took fuller and quicker advantage of the improved housing than the lawyers and by the end of the first quarter of the nineteenth century Writers to the Signet and advocates were living and working in George Street, Queen Street and Heriot Row which with the intervening streets, and especially Charlotte Square, were later to become the centre of the legal life of the city.

The same absence of office accommodation which must have tried so sorely our predecessors applied to the Society as a body in its early years, and its meeting places as recorded in the earliest minutes from 1594 vary in character and no doubt in

quality. In 1596 they meet in "the new Kirk" and in the early years of the seventeenth century in the "Laiche" or the "Heiche" Tolbooth. In 1607 they are recorded as meeting in Holyroodhouse, but often in the dwelling house or "Writing Chalmer" of one of their members. A little later appear references to meetings in the "Signet Chalmer" or the "auld session" house, which appear to have been in the Tolbooth; but by 1648 meetings were being held in the session house of the newly-built Parliament House. In the last years of the century the need for premises to house the Signet office and to provide a regular meeting place for the Society had become imperative, and by 1696 the Society had acquired a "new lodging" in what came to be known as "Writer's Court" on the north side of the High Street opposite the Luckenbooths and St Giles' Church. Here were to be the premises of the Society until 1815 when, on the reconstruction of the buildings in Parliament Square to house the courts, accommodation was provided for the Society in what is now the Lower Hall of the Signet Library, the Signet Office moving in 1826 to the Register House and in September 1960 to Parliament House.

From a very early stage in the history of the Society those responsible for its standing and well-being had been faced with two major and allied problems, firstly to limit the number of members to the extent necessary to ensure a reasonable income for those admitted, and secondly to make provision for colleagues or their dependants who fell on evil times. The first rules of the Society served the double purpose of maintaining professional standards and building up a common fund, providing as they did for fines for non-attendance at meetings or even at funerals of colleagues or for lapses in professional conduct. These payments all went into the "box" representing the Common Fund, and here too went the payments from apprentices and entrants, varying in amount but gradually increasing as time passed, and soon to become a valuable source of income. For very many years after the formal constitution of the Society in 1594 the details of its finances must be largely a matter for conjecture. The details of the Society's sources of income whether from fines or dues cannot be known with any certainty, a lack of certainty which is accentuated during that period in the late seventeenth and early eighteenth centuries when for a time money transactions in Scotland were expressed with little discrimination in terms of Scots or English currency. It is clear that for much more than 100 years from its inception the calls on the Common Fund were almost exclusively for the support of old or infirm members or their widows, but in 1695 the acquisition of the property in Writers' Court for the Society's meetings meant a further substantial burden on its resources. While the payments to widows seem to have been

regular and not ungenerous, fore-shadowing the establishment of a separate Widows' Fund in 1803, it is equally clear that well before the middle of the eighteenth century the Society was making substantial donations to charitable and other objects in Edinburgh and elsewhere. Three payments in 1738 go respectively towards the building of the Royal Infirmary, the erection of an observatory for the University and the establishment of an orphan hospital. In 1760 the Burgh of Kinghorn in Fife gets, somewhat surprisingly, a contribution towards the cost of a harbour at Pettycur. Eight years later another goes towards the erection of a church for Gaelic speakers in Edinburgh, while in 1751 a sum of 500 gns. had been given towards a scheme for rebuilding ruinous houses in the capital. The accounts for the next 100 years show a steady increase in the Society's funds and further substantial payments for charitable, religious and educational objects. The list is long and varied, reflecting the wide interests of the Society and its members.

From an early date the knowledge and practice of the art of the conveyancer was looked on by the Society as falling peculiarly within its province and responsibililty. As early as the middle of the eighteenth century proposals were put forward by Mr John Mackenzie, w.s., of Delvine for regular instruction in conveyancing, in addition to that received by apprentices in the ordinary course of apprenticeship. The proposals met originally with some opposition, but this was soon overcome and during the last quarter of the century lectures on conveyancing were being regularly given to apprentices by members of the Society. By 1796, the feeling had grown that the importance of conveyancing as a part of legal education called for the establishment of a Chair in the University of Edinburgh. This, too, met with considerable opposition both from the courts and from the Town Council of Edinburgh, and it was not till the end of 1824 that a Chair endowed by the Society was finally established with Mr Macvey Napier, Librarian of the Signet Library, as the first professor. Up to and including the present time the professor has always been a member of the Society.

But far exceeding pensions to widows or donations to educational or charitable objects, those responsible for the finances of the Society have since the first quarter of the eighteenth century been confronted with what has come to be probably the greatest source of pride and almost certainly the most complex problem in the history of the Society. On 12th November 1722 the Society resolved that all Acts of Parliament passed before and after the Union and all Scots law books in print and others as they came out should be purchased for the use of members. The Scots law books then in existence are believed to have numbered sixty. At that time no separate

library fund existed, but it soon became evident that some new source of revenue for book purchase must be found. The plan which was decided on in 1755 was ingenious. For some time past it had been the custom for entrants to the Society to give entertainments in celebration of their admission. These parties appear to have resulted in what the Commissioners regarded as unseemly behaviour on the part of those present. Such parties were for the future banned, but in view of the saving in expense thus secured to entrants, a payment of £3 from each for purchase of books was imposed, while a fine of 5 gns. on any member attending an entertainment of the sort was to be similarly used. A few years later the payment due by entrants was raised to £10, and as the number of men entering on apprenticeship each year at this time was about forty, this source of revenue was coming to be substantial.

But the ambitions of those responsible for library policy were almost boundless. A proposal for some degree of merger with the Advocates' Library in 1740 had fallen through. Now in 1778 the Society resolved to form a general library on a large scale, collecting for the purpose the best books in every department of literature, and by 1792 the library contained some 3,000 volumes. From now on the growth of the Signet Library to a great extent reflected the interests and genius of a continuous line of outstanding librarians, and no less the interests and generosity of very many members of the Society. Its growth during the first quarter of last century was remarkable, the average sums spent each year on books and binding rising from about £500 between 1808 and 1814 to £1,155 between 1815 and 1822, with a peak of nearly £2,000 in 1824. In 1837 when the librarian, Mr Macvey Napier, himself a Writer to the Signet, retired, he described the library, by then containing over 30,000 volumes, as "one of the choicest and most valuable repositories of learning this part of the Island possesses." During the last 100 years and more the annual expenditure on purchase of books has fluctuated widely reflecting largely the intake of members to the Society, but despite this the size and importance of the library has steadily increased and very many valuable acquisitions have been added whether by purchase or by gift. Though the Signet Library has never been in any sense a public library, the Society has throughout adopted a most generous and liberal policy in making its books available for reference to researchers and writers. Many a writer and student up to the present day has had reason to be grateful to the Society and to those dedicated and kindly men whose life and work has been devoted to the care of the books in their keeping.

For nearly 100 years from the start of the library in 1722 no special accommodation for the books existed. For over fifty years the growing collection was housed in the Society's

premises in Writers' Court, and although in 1782, due partly to the efforts of Mr Walter Scott, father of the future "Author of Waverley," these premises were enlarged, the accommodation for books remained quite inadequate. Finally, the acquisition in 1815 of the Lower Hall in the Parliament Square buildings, already mentioned, went far to solve the problem, while in 1833 the Upper Hall which had been built by the advocates was acquired from the Faculty. Here in these two magnificent halls, designed by William Stark and Robert Reid in the classical style which characterises many of the finest buildings of modern Edinburgh, is housed the Law Library of the Society, its important collection of Scottish books, and a not insignificant residue of what once constituted one of the outstanding general libraries in the British Isles.[7]

Looking back on the early history of this ancient Society it seems certain that among those who first acted as clerks in the office of the King's Signet must have been many possessing skills and interests uncommon at the times in which they lived. Turning today the pages which record the names and such detail as have survived of past members of the Society from the sixteenth century up to recent times it is apparent that variety of knowledge and interests has throughout persisted, a catholicity of taste which shows itself nowhere more than in the wide scope of the library. An early link with the world of letters was forged when at the end of the fifteenth century Walter Chepman, the first to be formally designated as a "Writer to the King's Signet," was the founder of Scottish printing, working under a patent of monopoly of James IV in a printing office in the Cowgate, and from his time forward the list contains the names of very many who were patrons or practitioners of the literary and other arts. The early years of the eighteenth century saw James Anderson, w.s., Postmaster General for Scotland. A century later James Hope from his office in the New Town was working with Thomas Telford on the great task of road and canal building in the Highlands, completed between 1803 and 1823. The roll of members records the admission in 1835 of William Ayton, later to be the author of *Lays of the Scottish Cavaliers*, while greatest of all, Sir Walter Scott served his apprenticeship as a Writer to the Signet before turning to the Bar and the Courts. These are but a handful of names from among many prominent in law, letters and many other spheres. As the years passed, Edinburgh was growing to be the centre of both the legal and cultural life of the country. At the end of the eighteenth century and for very many years to come, nearly all the landed proprietors in Scotland had legal advisers in Edinburgh, Writers to the Signet for the most part, who made

7. A detailed history of the Library is contained in *The Signet Library, Edinburgh, and its Librarians, 1722-1972* by G. H. Ballantyne, published by the Scottish Library Association in 1979.

THE SIGNET LIBRARY

their wills and their complex family trusts, arranged the heritable bonds which were then almost the sole means of investment or estate financing, and guided through the courts the lengthy and involved lawsuits without which, it almost seemed, no gentleman's estate would be complete. For the legal profession, the turn of the century was a notable time; but literature and litigation went almost hand in hand in an age when each was in its glory, and to the Parliament House came litigants and men of letters, men like Scott, Lockhart, Cockburn, Jeffrey and Brougham, who would be no less at home in the courts than in the Signet Library, where each year saw the laying up of more and more volumes reflecting many sides of the cultural life both of Scotland and of the world beyond.

The Society recently has, like all else in our modern world, undergone great changes. For one looking back over the 500 years of its existence it may well seem that the greatest and most rapid of these have come in the century and a half which separates us from the early nineteenth century when great figures walked our streets and when the legal, literary and artistic life of Scotland centred on Edinburgh was in its prime. Modern life and modern conditions seem to have taken much of the colour from a drab and uniform world, and much of the character and personality from us and our fellows. But of this we are far too close to events to form a true judgment. Those who come after us will be better able to assess the true nature and value of the changes which for better or for worse, are taking place today; and it may be that those whom we see as the ordinary and undistinguished fellows of today will in retrospect appear as the characters and personalities of tomorrow. Whether in their own right or as members of an old and respected body, Writers to the Signet play a prominent part in banking, insurance, finance and other spheres. The Society is fully represented on many educational and charitable trusts not a few of them set up by former members of the Society. Interest in the Arts and the world of Letters still lives on, while in the honourable profession of the Law the Society prides itself on the maintenance of those high standards of work and integrity which was the aim and the achievement of those who went before.

The greatest change in recent years concerns the Library. By the beginning of this century it had become probably the finest private library in Scotland, with some 100,000 volumes. But after the 1914-18 war, various considerations, not least financial, lessened the scope and intake of titles, and by the 1950s it had become evident that the Society could no longer afford—nor indeed did it require—to keep up and maintain such a large collection of books as 150,000, the figure to which it had grown. Accordingly, a policy of reduction was drawn up under the guidance of Dr Haldane and in 1959/60 some 14,000 volumes were sold by

Sotheby's in London. Further minor sales took place in Edinburgh so that, together with other disposals during 1958-64, about 27,000 books and 9,000 pamphlets were disposed of, realising a net sum of some £167,000.

The future of the remaining books seemed assured for a time, but by 1976 it was obvious that inflation was having a grave effect on the Society's finances. Therefore, it was decided to reduce the stock further and that the Library should become "a first-rate legal and reference library, incorporating a general library of books of Scottish interest". As a result, Sotheby's held two sales in the Upper Library in April 1978 and March 1979, when approximately 54,000 volumes were auctioned for a net sum of £716,000. Prior to these auctions, arrangements were made to give the National Library of Scotland an opportunity to purchase at valuation any books which it might wish to have, as a result of which it acquired about 1,500 volumes at a total valuation figure of £40,000. In addition the National Library received a donation of 2,500 volumes of valuation rolls and also a deposit on loan of the Society's interesting collection of old maps and charts.

There now remain about 63,000 books, divided into approximately 30,000 legal books, 20,000 Scottish books, 4,000 older works of fiction, 3,500 antiquarian works, and a mixture of 5,500 bibliographical, biographical, reference and general works and pamphlets. The Lower Library is devoted mostly to legal books with the Upper Library housing the greater part of the Scottish material, including biography and genealogy, along with the antiquarian and fiction sections. The basement holds such special collections as periodicals, session papers, parliamentary papers, civil law books, etc., while the Commissioners' Room houses the Roughead Collection on trials and older sets of encyclopaedias. A home reading section is maintained in the Lower Library which includes a small but interesting selection of the latest titles on biography, travel and history, including of course many Scottish books.

Following the 1959/60 sales, most of the Library at ground and upper floor levels was redecorated and recarpeted. After the second series of sales, the basement was completely reorganised. Mobile shelving was installed in the magazine room, the former map room was converted into a consultation room—named the Napier Room—and the various cellars and book stores were refurbished. The coffee room was refurnished and named the Laing Room and the corridor was decorated and carpeted. The heating system, which since 1962 had been connected to that of Parliament House, was converted to gas and designed to run as an independent unit. At ground level, the main vestibule was upgraded and the apartments at the west end were redecorated, in particular the Deputy Keeper's Room, now known as the Minto Room. Externally, the closure of Parliament Square West ('County Square') to vehicles toward the end of 1975 was followed by a complete renovation of the area in 1977-1978, with the result that this part of the Royal Mile is now much more in keeping with its historical background.

After disposal of over 50,000 volumes, it became possible to vacate the West Wing of the Library which had been acquired in 1904 as extra storage space. Ownership has been retained but the premises have been leased to Faculty Services Limited who have converted the lower two flats into office accommodation and set aside the upper two flats for storage of overflow books from the Advocates' Library.

The 1936 History referred to the appointment of Dr C. A. Malcolm during the previous year as Librarian. He had already established his reputation as a scholar, particularly in the study of Old Edinburgh, and he continued to carry out research and to write, broadcast and lecture in this field throughout his period in office. He died in April 1961, aged 85, and was succeeded by the First Assistant, Mr J. A. Christie, who had already served for almost fifty years. About the same time, Mr S. A. F. Easterbrook, W.S., was appointed and he continued

THE UPPER LIBRARY

Photograph by John K. Wilkie, Edinburgh.

to act as First Assistant until 1981. Mr Christie retired in 1968 as Librarian when his place was taken by Mr G. H. Ballantyne, the present Librarian. During the period of the reorganisation of the Library, 1977-80, Mrs C. J. McWilliam joined the staff as an additional assistant. She was succeeded by Mrs J. C. Penney who has now assumed Mr Easterbrook's responsibilities.

The Upper Library was seldom used until the early 1970s except for the occasional Society meeting, lecture or social event, but since then the policy has been to permit fuller use by appropriate non-commercial bodies of what is one of the finest rooms in the country. A variety of events has taken place, including several series of concerts given by the Scottish Baroque Ensemble. During the Edinburgh Festival, exhibitions have been mounted and the B.B.C. has recorded recitals then and at other times. The association with the Knights of the Thistle referred to on p. xxx of the 1936 History continues, although the Knights now assemble in the Lower Library prior to their annual St Andrew's Day service in the Thistle Chapel of the High Kirk of St Giles. Similarly, on the occasion of the investiture of a new Knight, H.M. the Queen and H.R.H. Prince Philip assemble with the Knights in, and return to, the Lower Library. The Commissioners' Room is used for arbitrations, meetings and small dinner parties. The newly refurbished Napier and Minto Rooms are available to all members for consultations and meetings.

Looking to the future, the advent of legal information retrieval by computer is in time bound to revolutionise research techniques, both in office and library. It is too early yet, especially as changes and refinements are so rapid, to predict what effect these developments will have on the Signet Library, but it seems certain that the computer will have a part to play in its day-to-day operations. In turn, this may call into question the provision and storage of legal literature and information in the whole of Parliament House, with consequent changes.

As well as the Library, the Society itself has undergone significant changes in recent times. These were foreshadowed in the 1936 History with the brief references to the setting up in 1922 of a body to represent practising solicitors in Scotland called the Joint Committee of Legal Societies in Scotland, whose members were appointed by representatives of the six largest societies (including the W.S. Society). The Deputy Keeper of the Signet was *ex officio* Chairman of this Committee. Sir George M. Paul acted as Chairman from 1922 to 1925, Sir William Campbell Johnston from 1925 to 1935 and Sir Ernest Wedderburn from 1935 to 1949, when the Committee ceased to function. As a result of the activities of this Committee there was introduced into Parliament and duly passed, the Solicitors (Scotland) Act 1933, which established the General Council of Solicitors in Scotland with power to deal with the admission, education and training of solicitors. The General Council was elected by constituencies consisting of individual legal societies (including the W.S. Society) and groups of smaller societies. Sir William Campbell Johnston acted as Chairman of the General Council from 1934 to 1935 and Sir Ernest Wedderburn from 1935 to 1949 when its duties were transferred to the Law Society of Scotland. Professional opinion generally favoured the establishment of a council with powers to regulate all professional matters and with this object in view a Bill prepared by the General Council was introduced in Parliament in 1938 but no progress was made in that session. The Bill was re-introduced during the next session and made substantial progress but subsequently had to be dropped because of the national emergency. After the 1939-45 war, steps were taken to resuscitate the Bill. To facilitate its passage through Parliament and to save Parliamentary time, the Bill was combined with the Legal Aid (Scotland) Bill and ultimately became law under the title of the Legal Aid and Solicitors (Scotland) Act 1949. The part of the Act which related to and established the Law Society of Scotland was cited separately as the Solicitors (Scotland) Act 1949.

The Law Society came into existence on the passing of the Act, and Mr R. B. Laurie, w.s., was appointed Secretary. He had already acted as Secretary to the General Council from 1946 to 1949, having the use of two rooms in the Signet Library. Upon formation of the new Society, premises were obtained in North Bank Street. Sir Ernest Wedderburn became the first President of the Law Society and during his term of office from 1949 to 1950 he was much involved in drafting its Constitution.

The Joint Committee of Legal Societies in Scotland continued in being for some considerable time after formation of the General Council of Solicitors in 1933 in order to deal with matters outside the scope of the General Council. When the Law Society of Scotland took the place of the General Council, the old Joint Committee no longer had a role, but it was felt that there were matters of special interest to Solicitors practising in Edinburgh which should be discussed by a representative body.

On 19th January 1951 a new Joint Committee of Legal Societies in Edinburgh and Midlothian was formed upon which serve representatives of each of the W.S. Society, the S.S.C. Society and the Society of Procurators of Midlothian. The Office-Bearers of the Committee are the Chairman, who is the Deputy Keeper *ex officio*, and the Secretary, who is the Clerk to the W.S. Society *ex officio*. This Joint Committee meets regularly and continues to make an active and vigorous contribution, particularly on matters affecting Court of Session procedure. The Principal Clerk of Session and the Deputy Principal Clerk of Session attend meetings of the Committee by invitation.

It can be seen, therefore, that the role played by the W.S. Society—or more specifically the role played by the Deputy Keepers who held office between 1922 and 1949—was prominent in the development of affairs leading up to establishment of the Law Society of Scotland. Since that time the office of Deputy Keeper has diminished in importance in relation to matters outside the affairs of the W.S. Society itself; but it may be mentioned that of the 20 Presidents of the Law Society of Scotland who have served between 1949 and 1982, eight have been members of the W.S. Society. The two Societies have always maintained a close liaison, and the younger one frequently holds both social and educational meetings in the Signet Library.

Within the compass of this short introduction it is possible to note but briefly some of the other developments and events which have affected the Society since 1936.

The 1936 History, at page xix, tells of the Memorial erected in honour of those Members and Apprentices who fell in the 1914-18 war. On 30th November 1950, a marble tablet to the memory of the twenty-five Members and Apprentices who died during the Second World War was unveiled by Lord Elphinstone. This tablet, placed beside the others at the west end of the Lower Library, bears the following names:—

Members

ARTHUR NICOL BRUCE
JAMES BLACK CAMERON D.S.O.
JOHN RONALD CAMERON
DAVID EDWARD FERGUS COATES
ALAN ARCHIBALD COWAN
JOHN PATRICK EASON M.B.E.
JOHN RENSHAW GIFFORD
HAROLD DANVERS GILROY
ARTHUR HOOD JAMES
HAROLD KENNEDY MACDONALD

IAN DRUMMOND MACKENZIE
EDWARD FRANCIS ALLARDYCE MORRISON
COLIN ARTHUR PATTULLO M.C.
ERNEST ALEXANDER MACLAGAN WEDDERBURN

Apprentices
GEORGE HOLMES GALLIE M.C.
COLIN ROSS HUNTER
DAVID AUGUSTUS JAMES LEITH-BUCHANAN
DENIS HERIOT ORROCK
HAROLD GRAHAM ROBERTSON
WILLIAM GORDON THOMSON
JAMES GORDON THORBURN
WILLIAM IAN EDWARD THORBURN
JOHN LAURENCE STUART WATSON
WILLIAM KENNETH MACFARLANE WEIR
GEORGE BERTRAM MURE WOOD

Responsibility for the Signet Office never, strictly speaking, rested with the Society as such, but with the Keeper of the Signet and the officials holding commissions under him. Until 1976, such commissions were held only by the Substitute Keeper and Clerk, the Extractor and Assistant Clerks of the Society, and these officials conducted the business of the Signet Office. By 1975 the number of summonses passing the Signet in each year was of the order of 13,000 as compared with 5-6,000 some ten years earlier, and it became apparent that there would be advantage in combining the process of signetting a Summons with that of registration of the cause in the offices of the Court. Consequently the Keeper, in 1976, granted a commission in favour of the Principal Clerk of Session authorising him, by himself or his deputies, to seal writs in use to pass the Signet. This was the first time a commission was granted for this specific purpose in favour of a person other than a Writer, or Clerk, to the Signet. The commission was, however, in addition, and without prejudice, to the commissions in the existing wider terms held by the Substitute Keeper and Clerk, whose office dates back to 1594, and by the Assistant Clerk and Extractor, whose office dates back to 1711. When, in 1979, an industrial dispute regrettably disrupted the business of the Courts, summonses continued to be signetted by the Society's officials and by other members of the Society in whose favour the Keeper granted additional enabling commissions, so that in this respect, at least, the Queen's Writ continued to run.

At a Stated Meeting of the Society held on 5th April 1976, approval was given to the admission of women members, and on 6th December of that year Miss Patricia Stuart was welcomed into membership of the Society as the first woman intrant. At 30th April 1982, the total number of members was 797 of whom twenty-six were women and 386 were Commissioners. The Commissioners are senior members of the Society appointed by the Keeper on the advice of the Deputy Keeper. They are responsible for all matters of discipline affecting members of the Society and a prospective intrant to membership of the Society requires to be nominated by at least one Commissioner. In each year since 1962, the number of members has increased, and in 1976 the total membership passed the previous peak of 685, established as long ago as 1840 when that number must have constituted a much larger

proportion of the total solicitor profession in Scotland than does the present membership. It is present policy that growth of membership over the years should be encouraged, but at a more modest rate than has been seen in recent years.

When the plans of the Law Society were settled for introduction of the Diploma in Legal Practice, followed by in-office training on a training contract, it became necessary to review the Society's procedure for admission of intrants. The old procedure governing W.S. indentures had in any event become cumbersome and rather meaningless in modern conditions, and much thought was given to the form of an alternative procedure for admission which would, on the one hand, be simplified and modernised yet, on the other hand, take full account of the historical status and tradition of the Society whose members hold a commission from the Keeper, the Queen's representative. In 1979, a new procedure was approved by the Society whereby a prospective intrant who holds or is entitled to hold a full practising certificate from the Law Society of Scotland may be nominated for admission on the petition of three members, of whom at least one must be a Commissioner, and (except in special circumstances) at least one of the petitioners must be a person who has employed, or been in partnership with, the prospective intrant for a period of not less than two years. Each prospective intrant is interviewed by a panel of Commissioners who try, among other things, to ascertain what is an applicant's object in seeking membership. If approved on interview the petition then has to be supported by confidential reports from each of the three petitioning members before it is submitted to the Examiners of Intrants for final approval. The fee currently payable by intrants on admission is £500.

It became necessary to adopt new Acts and Regulations of the Society in order to provide for the altered procedures for admission, and to provide for changes in the constitution of the Council and the Committee of Curators of the Library. These were adopted at a Stated Meeting held on 28th May 1979 and the opportunity was taken to revise and modernise the Acts and Regulations in all respects. Amongst other things, a retiral age of 65 was fixed for the Office-bearers and Clerk, and provision was made for members to record their votes by post on the occasion of the election of a new Office-bearer or Clerk.

The Deputy Keeper is entitled to preside at all meetings of the Society but he is not an Office-bearer of the Society. By statute the appointment is a matter solely for the Keeper of the Signet and not for the Society. Nevertheless in 1978, at the instigation of the Deputy Keeper, a Committee of the Council under the chairmanship of the Treasurer was asked to consider (i) whether or not it would be in the best interests of the Society in future to adopt some formal or informal selection procedure before the name of any proposed Deputy Keeper was submitted to the Keeper for his consideration; and (ii) whether—by way of formal or informal arrangement—there should be a restriction on the term of office of a Deputy Keeper or any other restrictions or provisions affecting the holding of this office.

On this matter the Committee reported to the Council in the following terms:

> It was finally agreed to recommend that a retiring Deputy Keeper should submit a short leet of candidates to a Committee to be chaired by himself consisting of the Treasurer, the Fiscal, two Council Members and two Society Members, the last four to be appointed by the Council, to select the person who would be recommended to the Keeper as his future Deputy. In the event of the Deputy Keeper dying in office the Treasurer, as senior Office-bearer, would carry out the functions of the retiring Deputy Keeper. It was agreed that if accepted by

Council these recommendations should be minuted but that it would not be appropriate for them to form part of the Society's Acts and Regulations.

It was also recommended that the term of office of a Deputy Keeper should be limited to ten years and that he should demit office at sixty-five or if he ceased to hold a practising certificate. Again this could not be formally regulated but should be contained in an informal document when an incoming Deputy Keeper agreed to accept the appointment.

These recommendations met with the approval of the Deputy Keeper and the Council, and they were submitted to the Keeper. The Keeper intimated that he considered the arrangements to be appropriate and they will accordingly be adopted on the next occasion on which a Deputy Keeper is to be appointed.

Following upon the sales of books, and after meeting the very substantial costs of upgrading the library premises and installing new heating plant, the Society was left with a reasonably substantial endowment fund of some £865,000, the investment of which is professionally managed. The costs of maintaining and running a building and library of the importance and scale of the Signet Library become increasingly formidable for a private society to bear, and at least eighty per cent of the Society's entire investment and subscription income is devoted to meeting these costs. A policy is currently adopted whereby there will be met out of capital funds the cost of making good the arrears of book-binding which have built up over the years as a result of financial stringency, the cost of purchasing new books which do not fall within the legal or reference or home reading categories (now a relatively small annual sum) and the cost of any *major* repair work to the Library should this at any time become necessary.

In the changed economic circumstances of the present age, the W.S. Widows' Fund—like other similar co-operative funds—can play no more than a minor role towards protecting the dependants of members. At one time the Fund could be regarded as the principal means (apart from whole of life assurance and savings) of protecting a widow and orphaned children, but this is obviously no longer so. Nevertheless in relation to the modest contributions which are charged, the Fund (now worth over £3.5 million) continues to make a worth-while contribution to the security of members' dependants. In recent years, much has been done to improve performance of the Fund by securing such taxation relief as is open to a fund of this nature and by employment of professional fund managers. An application is, at the time of writing, before Parliament for a new Provisional Order which will materially alter the provisions of the current Writers to the Signet Widows' Fund Order 1955. From this, the Fund will, as a result of admission of women members, emerge with the unfamiliar title of the "Writers to the Signet Dependants' Annuity Fund".

In recent years, the work of the Council of the Society has to a large extent been directed to internal affairs connected with the book sales and the consequent reorganisation of the Library, with upgrading the premises and leasing the West Wing, and with revising and up-dating the Society's procedures and regulations. In its consideration of legal topics, such as proposals for law reform, the Council does not seek to duplicate work which is more appropriately done by the various committees of the Law Society of Scotland, upon which so many members of the Society already serve. Nevertheless, if on any issue the Council of the Society takes a view differing from that of the Law Society, that view will be expressed; and whenever it is thought that some distinctive contribution can be made, the Council either

appoints an *ad hoc* committee or enlists the assistance of individual members to prepare reports and to submit views to the Scottish Law Commission or others concerned.

As it has done for centuries, the Society continues to play its part in community as well as legal affairs, and it continues to be represented on all the charitable bodies mentioned on pages xxxii *et seq* of the 1936 History, and others as well. Sadly, John Watson's School, after giving notable service to the community under the control of the Commissioners of the Signet for 148 years, had to be closed in 1975, following a decision by the then Government to phase out Government grants to grant-aided schools from session 1976/77.[8] The school building was sold to the Crown Commissioners, the intended use being to house the Scottish National Gallery of Modern Art, and it became the responsibility of the Secretary of State for Scotland, under the provisions of the Education (Scotland) Acts, to make a new Scheme to regulate the Trust funds. In January 1979, the Governing Body submitted proposals for a new Scheme, and although, at the time of writing, the new Scheme has not yet been made it is expected that the Keepers and Commissioners of the Signet will continue to be the Governing Body (being, as such Governors, an incorporated body under the provisions of an Act of 1822) and that the Governing Body will delegate the detailed administration of the Trust to a Committee of Trustees appointed by them, consisting of six Writers to the Signet, two nominees of Lothian Regional Council, one nominee of the Scottish Council of Independent Schools and one nominee of the Lothian Association of Youth Clubs. The Deputy Keeper will be Chairman of the Trustees. The principal objects of the new Scheme, if it is finally approved, will be to apply up to, but not exceeding, one third of available income in awarding John Watson's Scholarships for the provision of boarding education for orphans or children of one parent families, and to apply the rest of the income for the benefit of children and young persons who are handicapped physically or mentally or by reason of social deprivation. The annual income of the Trust should exceed £68,000 so that John Watson's will continue as a substantial and important charitable trust able to do much good within an area of need akin to the area it has served for the past century and a half.

The social side has always, properly, played an important part in the corporate life of the Society. Each year a formal dinner is held to which members may invite a private guest, and on these occasions other men and women distinguished in the Law, in other professions, in business and in public affairs are entertained as guests of the Society. These dinners are usually attended by the Master and Clerk of the London Solicitors' Livery Company, with which Company the Society maintains a close and valued association, and in turn the Deputy Keeper and the Clerk are privileged to attend Company dinners in London. The three venerable dining clubs, the 1790 Signet Club, the 1808 Signet Club and the 1850 Signet Club have been joined by a robust and enthusiastic youngster, the 1977 Signet Club. Periodically a Society Ball is held in the matchless setting of the Library and in each year the Deputy Keeper, Office-bearers and Council, with others who are actively concerned in the conduct of the Society's affairs, entertain new intrants, with their guests, at a cocktail party. Many other private parties of one kind or another, involving firms or groups of members, are held within the Library premises.

The W.S. Golf Club was founded in 1957 at the instigation of Sir Hugh Watson and, at a dinner in the Library to celebrate its twenty-fifth anniversary, there were numbered among its guests many representatives from its regular adversaries, the Golfing Societies of the Bench and Bar, the London Solicitors, the Royal Faculty of Procurators in Glasgow, the

---

8. A history of John Watson's School written by Miss Isobel Wallis is shortly to be published under the auspices of the John Watson's F.P. Club.

Society of Advocates in Aberdeen and the Royal Institute of Chartered Surveyors in Edinburgh.

Within the scope of a short introduction such as this it is not possible to present more than a brief sketch of the Society's long history and the many activities of its members, past and present. The 1890 and 1936 publications contain much useful historical information (especially the former volume); but they too are limited in scope. It is to be hoped that one day a definitive history of the Society will be written. Such a history will require, as well as chronicling the facts, to evaluate the role of the Society over the centuries in shaping the development of the law and the Solicitors' branch of the legal profession in Scotland, to describe the Society and its members in their social context, and to deal with the special interests and achievement of its members, their inter-relationships, education and background. The Society during its long existence has played an important part in the evolution of Scots Law, in the conduct, ethics and organisation of private legal practice, and in the development of legal education and the provision of legal text books. It has also exerted other powerful influences by its involvement in charitable and educational bodies, by the creation of its great Library and its support for scholarship, and in the widespread influence its members have been able to exert in all sorts of situations just because they *were* Writers to the Signet, and because of the esteem and respect in which the Society has been held.

LIST OF WRITERS
TO HER MAJESTY'S SIGNET

LIST OF WRITERS
TO HER MAJESTY'S SIGNET

Note: Those marked * were admitted following upon nomination and without apprenticeship under the new regulations approved on 28 May 1979.

ABERCROMBIE, GEORGE, OF OVER CARDEN [Before 1583]. Solicitor in Treasury, 1590. Commissary of Aberdeen, 1593.—Uncle to Alexander Abercrombie of Pitmeddan.

ABERCROMBIE, THOMAS [Before 3 July 1607].

ABERCROMBY, ALEXANDER [10 July 1770]. Apprentice to John Syme.—Son of Alexander Abercromby, Merchant in Norway. *Married* 14 April 1776, Mary (*died* 10 July 1798), daughter of Charles Ramsay, Surgeon in Edinburgh. *Died* 9 April 1804.

ABERNETHY, JAMES SMART, M.A., LL.B. [19 December 1932]. Apprentice to John James Herdman of Duncan & Black.—Son of James John Abernethy, Farmer, Balmain, Fettercairn. *Born* 3 October 1907. *Married* (1) 29 April 1936, Winifred Jane, (*died* 1960), daughter of G. Marr, Agent, and (2) 1 December 1960, Margaret Phyllis, daughter of D. Campbell, Bank Manager. Held various Government and legal positions in North Borneo between 1936 and 1948. Interned by Japanese 1942-45. Resident Magistrate and Puisne Judge, Tanganyika 1949-1958. Member of Faculty of Advocates 1950-63. *Died* 25 May 1976. *Firm*—Smith and Abernethy, Montrose (1934-1936).

ABRAM, HENRY CHARLES, LL.B. [6 December 1976]. Apprentice to John Stewart Macfie and Others of Tods, Murray & Jamieson.—Son of H. C. Abram, Shipping Contractor, Kilmacolm. *Born* 11 August 1951. *Married* 25 October 1975, Leslie Anne, daughter of D. K. Hamilton, Consultant Engineer, Kilmacolm. *Firm*—Tods, Murray & Jamieson.

ACHESON, ANDREW [9 July 1680]. Apprentice to John Kennedy.—*Married* 28 April 1676, Louisa Borthwick. *Died* 25 February 1702, aged 54.

ADAIR, CHARLES MURDOCH [28 March 1819]. Apprentice to John Campbell and Andrew Clason.—Son of Dr James M'Kettrick Adair, Physician in Harrogate. *Died* 23 March 1823.

ADAIR, PERCIVAL WILLIAM GORDON, B.L. [18 March 1935]. Apprentice to George F. Dalziel and Another of Tods, Murray & Jamieson.—Son of Percival John Adair, Solicitor, Stranraer. *Born* 4 May 1910. *Married* (1) Ilva Amelia Meyer (*Divorced* 1954), and (2) 10 February 1954, Katherine Mary Campbell or Franklin. Captain, Infantry. Served U.K., India and Middle East 1939-45. H.Q. Scottish Command, Legal Aid Section 1945. Partner with Messrs. Orr, Dignam & Co., Solicitors, Calcutta. *Died* 26 December 1970. *Firm*—W. & J. Burness.

ADAIR, THOMAS, OF LITTLE GENOCH [3 July 1778]. Apprentice to Cornelius Elliot.— Eldest son of Andrew Adair of Little Genoch, Minister of Whithorn. *Born* 5 October 1749. *Married* (1) Jane, daughter of Rev. Andrew Ross of Balsarroch, Wigtownshire; and (2) 29 September 1783, Agnes (*died* 9 March 1807), daughter of John Jameson, Merchant, Leith. *Died* 22 November 1820.

ADAM, ALASDAIR HUGH MACQUEEN, LL.B. [6 December 1971]. Apprentice to L. F. McLaren and Others of Haldanes and McLaren.—Son of Robert James Adam, University Lecturer, St Andrews. *Born* 15 November 1947. *Married* 17 March 1973, Judith Ann, daughter of Dr J. D. T. Steele, F.R.C.P. *Firm*—Gibson and Spears, Dow and Son, Kirkcaldy.

ADAM, ALEXANDER FORSYTH [11 March 1847]. Apprentice to George Maclachlan and William Ivory.—Son of James Adam, S.S.C. *Born* 24 July 1822. *Died* 24 December 1881, unmarried.

ADAM, ARTHUR [25 May 1883]. Apprentice to John Ord Mackenzie, W.R. and John Kermack.—Son of Stephen Adam, Woolbroker in Leith. *Born* 30 April 1860. *Died* 28 June 1910, unmarried.

ADAM, GEORGE SEYMOUR [29 June 1871]. Apprentice to Robert Blair Maconochie.— Son of Patrick Adam, S.S.C. *Born* 26 May 1846. *Died* 13 May 1875, unmarried.

ADAM, JAMES [21 December 1820]. Apprentice to James Drummond of Comrie.—Son of Hamilton Adam of Kersehead, Ayrshire. *Married* 10 August 1807, Jane (*died* 21 June 1863), eldest daughter of John Shedden of Morrishill, Ayrshire. *Died* 3 December 1849, aged 79.

ADAMSON, ROBERT [11 January 1892]. Apprentice to John Ord Mackenzie, H. Cheyne, and J. Kermack.—Son of Samuel Adamson of Drumclyer. *Born* 6 October 1868. Served in France; discharged September 1917, on account of ill-health contracted on active service. Commission, 3rd Batt. K.O.S.B. *Died* 5 April 1945. *Firm*—Adamson & Blacklock, Dumfries.

ADDISON-SMITH, CHILTON LIND, C.B.E. [11 December 1899]. Apprentice to Sir W. S. Haldane, F. G. Haldane and W. Purves.—Son of Robert Addison-Smith, C.V.O., S.S.C., Edinburgh. *Born* 27 April 1875. *Married* 15 January 1927, Katharine Lushington (*died* 13 May 1972), only child of John Ewart, W.S. Served in South African War, 1899-1901. In European War promoted temporary Lieut.-Colonel; raised and commanded 10th Batt. Seaforth Highlanders. Served in France and Flanders with Sherwood Foresters and other regiments. Commandant at Saigneville, Mautort, and St Valery area, 1918-19. Awarded C.B.E.(Mil.), 1928. Mentioned in Dispatches. Commander of the Order of Wen-Hu (Striped Tiger), 1920, conferred by President of Republic of China. Commander of Saxe-Coburg, conferred by H.R.H. the Duke of Saxe-Coburg and Gotha. Registrar of Friendly Societies for Scotland, 1921. Author of *History of 3rd Batt. The Seaforth Highlanders, History of 10th Batt. Seaforth Highlanders during the Great War*, and other works. *Died* 28 May 1955. *Firm*—R. Addison-Smith and Co.

ADIE, CAMPBELL [12 March 1788]. Apprentice to William Campbell of Crawfordton.— Second son of Rev. George Adie, Minister of Carnock. *Born* 18 May 1762. *Married* 1 May 1800, his cousin Penelope (*died* 1842), daughter of William Campbell of Queenshill, Kircudbrightshire. Circuit Clerk of Justiciary. *Died* 29 January 1807.

ADIE, GEORGE, OF WHITEHOUSE [13 June 1702]. Apprentice to Thomas Pringle.—*Married* December 1706, Agnes, daughter of John Menzies of Cammo and Whitehouse, Advocate. *Died* January 1748.

AIKENHEAD, ALEXANDER [22 March 1630]. Apprentice to Andrew Hay.—Son of David Aikenhead, Lord Provost of Edinburgh, 1624, 1626-29, 1634-36. *Married* 16 April 1635, Helen, third daughter of John Trotter of Mortonhall. *Buried* 21 September 1660.

AIKENHEAD, ALEXANDER [26 January 1671]. Apprentice to James Chrystie.—Son of David Aikenhead, Writer in Edinburgh. *Born* 21 April 1643. *Married* Margaret Andro (*died* 22 March 1689). Fiscal, 1678-83. *Died* 4 September 1705.

AIKMAN, ANDREW, OF THURSTON [26 July 1655]. Apprentice to Robert Pringle.—Re-admitted, 14 November 1661. *Married* 27 April 1654, Sybilla Dickson. *Died* January 1691.

AIKMAN, ANDREW MACKINTOSH, B.L. [26 November 1962]. Apprentice to John Baird and Others of Melville and Lindesay.—Son of David Aikman, Grain Merchant, Edinburgh. *Born* 1 September 1938. *Married* 17 September 1965, Jill, daughter of Edwin E. Sweeting, Consultant Civil Engineer. *Firm*—A. M. Aikman & Co.

AIKMAN, THOMAS, OF BRIMBLETON [18 December 1685]. Apprentice to Nicoll Hardy.—Second son of John Aikman of Cairnie, Forfarshire. *Married* (1) Isabel, daughter of Richard Lermont of Whitelawhouse; and (2) 1687, Margaret, daughter of James Winram of Liberton. *Died* before 1754.

AIKMAN, WILLIAM KEITH [10 July 1899]. Apprentice to William Garson.—Son of Andrew Aikman, General Manager of the Commercial Bank of Scotland Ltd., Edinburgh. *Born* 16 February 1874. *Married* 23 April 1912, Mercedes Vida (*died* 5 February 1977), daughter of Laurence Stuart, Manila. *Died* 17 October 1933. *Firm*—Aitken, Methuen, and Aikman.

AINSLIE, JOHN [Before 1606]. Signs Minute of 17 January 1606.—Son of Adam Ainslie, Merchant Burgess of Edinburgh. *Married* 4 July 1604, Elizabeth Ker.

AINSLIE, ROBERT, OF EDINGHAM [9 July 1789]. Apprentice to Samuel Mitchelson.—Eldest son of Robert Ainslie of Darnchester, Berwickshire. *Born* 13 January 1766. *Married* (1) 3 January 1799, Jane (*died* 14 January 1817), daughter of Colonel James Cunningham of the Scots Brigade in the Dutch Service; (2) 18 October 1837, Isabella (*died* 13 March 1862, aged 72), eldest daughter of Rev. Robert Munro of Ullapool. Author of *A Father's Gift to his Children, Life and Adventures of a Guinea*, and other works. Accompanied Robert Burns on Border Tour, 1787. See *Noctes Ambrosianae*. *Died* 11 April 1838.

AINSLIE, ROBERT [18 June 1829]. Apprentice to George Combe.—Eldest son of Archibald Ainslie, Tenant in Peaston, Mid-Lothian. *Born* 7 November 1805. *Died* 11 December 1858, unmarried.

AITCHISON, WILLIAM KER [15 November 1832]. Apprentice to Henry Gordon Dickson.—Son of William Aitchison, Brewer at Kerfield. *Born* 10 March 1807. *Married* 12 July 1830, Jane [*died* 18 October 1890), daughter of William Murray, Merchant, Edinburgh. *Died* 26 February 1854.

AITKEN, JOHN MURRAY CRAIK, B.L. [13 May 1963]. Apprentice to R. F. Shepherd & Others of Shepherd & Wedderburn.—Son of John Abel Aitken, Edinburgh. *Born* 22 December 1932. *Married* 8 February 1957, Joan Donaldson, daughter of Lewis Stewart. *Firm*—J. M. C. Aitken & Co.

ALEXANDER, ALEXANDER BROWN [28 March 1898]. Apprentice to Nelson Briggs Constable.—Son of William Black Alexander, M.D., Edinburgh. *Born* 8 November 1873. *Died* 31 July 1936.

ALEXANDER, CHARLES, T.D. [14 March 1938]. Apprentice to (1) Harold Alexander of Auld & Macdonald; (2) Robert O. Pitman and Another of J. & F. Anderson, and (3) David Coates of J. & J. Miller, Perth.—Son of Harold Alexander, W.S. *Born* 5 November 1912. *Married* 11 October 1957, Evelyn Macgregor, daughter of William A. Ireland, L.D.S. Lieutenant Colonel R.A. Served U.K. and India 1939-45. *Firms*—(1) Auld & Macdonald; (2) Robson, McLean & Paterson.

ALEXANDER, EDWARD MURRAY MAYNE [11 July 1910]. Apprentice to J. P. Wright and T. M. Murray.—Son of Lieut.-Colonel Edward Mayne Alexander of Westerton, Red House, Bridge of Allan. *Born* 19 January 1886. *Married* (1) 25 April 1914, Florence Eleanor Wilson (*died* 5 February 1933), daughter of Wilson Bell, C.E., Fitzroy, Victoria, Australia: (2) 8 February 1938, Eileen Buchanan Njal Neill or Mitchell-Clarke (*died* 17 August 1942) and (3) 21 October 1943, Phyllis Irene Hazel Westwood Henderson or Williams (*died* 30 January 1978). Enlisted in Seaforth Highlanders in 1914, and became a Captain in same regiment; served in France; twice wounded. *Died* 23 March 1963.

ALEXANDER, HAROLD [15 July 1918]. Apprentice to James Macdonald and A. B. Noble.—Son of Frederick Charles Alexander, retired Civil Servant, Hove, Sussex. *Born* 15 August 1882. *Married* 3 October 1911, Isabella Ballantyne (*died* 12 June 1932), third daughter of Charles S. Dods, Bank Agent, Haddington. *Died* 23 September 1956. *Firm*—Auld and Macdonald.

ALEXANDER, JOHN [2 May 1634]. Apprentice to Hew Rose.—Sheriff-Clerk of Selkirk.

ALEXANDER, JOHN [16 June 1655]. Apprentice to James Tinto.—Re-admitted, 11 April 1661. *Married* 16 December 1658, Agnes Anderson. *Died* 1683.

ALEXANDER, JOHN [20 November 1662]. Apprentice to Robert Alexander and John Bayne.—Second son of Thomas Alexander of Skeddoway, Fife. *Married* 24 April 1662, Jean (*died* 14 March 1673), daughter of Sir Michael Arnot of that Ilk. *Died* November 1711.

ALEXANDER, ROBERT [1606]. Signs Minute of 17 January 1606. Keeper of the Signet, 26 December 1627. *Married* Catherine Stirling (*died* 9 March 1667). *Buried* in Canongate, January 1630.

ALEXANDER, ROBERT [2 April 1638]. Apprentice to John Mudie.—Son of John Alexander, Merchant Burgess of Aberdeen. *Married* (1) Jean Cargill; (2) Janet, daughter of Robert Anderson, Bailie of Kintore; and (3) 1662, Anne, daughter of James Charters, Merchant, Linlithgow. Re-admitted, 21 November 1660. *Buried* 7 November 1666.

ALEXANDER, ROBERT, OF NEWTON [30 June 1707]. Apprentice to Ronald Campbell.—Son of James Alexander of Blackhouse, Minister of Kilmalcolm. *Married* (1) Sophia, daughter of John Baird, Minister of Paisley; and (2) 27 May 1716, Margaret, daughter of Robert Alexander, Advocate. Principal Clerk of Session, 14 December 1715 till death. *Died* 23 May 1723.

ALEXANDER, ROBERT GORDON SHIELS [11 July 1932]. Apprentice to Alexander P. Melville and Another of R. R. Simpson & Lawson.—Son of J. Shiels Alexander, C.A., Edinburgh. *Born* 18 April 1904. Lieutenant Colonel, Allied Military Government, Italy. Served U.K., France, North Africa and Italy 1939-45. *Died* 10 November 1975. *Firm*— Macfie & Alexander, Whithorn.

ALEXANDER, WILLIAM [30 November 1819]. Apprentice to John Archibald Campbell.—Son of Forrest Alexander, Merchant in Edinburgh. *Born* 1798. *Married* 18 October 1833, Jessie Mercer (*died* 24 March 1860), eldest daughter of Alexander Gordon. Commissary Clerk of Edinburgh, 1850-59. Author of *Digest of the Bankruptcy Act*, and other legal works. *Died* 21 December 1859.

ALEXANDER, WILLIAM JAMES, B.L. [27 April 1965]. Apprentice to The Hon. D. A. Balfour and Others of Shepherd & Wedderburn.—Son of William Alexander, Grain Merchant, Aberdeen. *Born* 23 February 1933. *Married* 19 July 1963, Ilean Janet Gray, daughter of John Campbell, Master Grocer.

ALISON, JOHN [23 November 1813]. Apprentice to David Wemyss.—Eldest son of Colin Alison, Writer in Montrose. *Died* 14 March 1836, aged 45, unmarried.

ALISON, JOHN [25 June 1829]. Apprentice to Alexander Blair.—Son of John Alison, residing in Dundee. *Died* 19 February 1850, aged 62, unmarried.

ALISON, ROBERT BARCLAY [15 March 1897]. Apprentice to William Stuart Fraser.— Son of Arthur Alison, Advocate. *Born* 2 February 1873. *Married* 10 July 1902, Amy Alexandra (*died* 31 May 1955), youngest daughter of the Hon. Lord Adam, one of the Senators of the College of Justice. Sub-Commissioner for Lothians and Peebles (National Service, Agriculture). *Died* 22 December 1965.

ALISONE, ALEXANDER, OF BIRKHILL [15 June 1698]. Apprentice to John Strachan.— Son of Alexander Alisone of Birkhill, Fife. *Married* (1) Mary Smyth; (2) Janet, daughter of William Dick of Grange, and relict of Mungo Carnegie, Advocate; and (3) Mary Gray, relict of John Gordon, Younger of Edinglassie. *Died* September 1728.

ALISONE, ALEXANDER [10 March 1719]. Apprentice to, and son of, Alexander Alisone, W.S.—*Married* Grizel, daughter of Thomas Wemyss, Advocate. *Died* 1 January 1728.

ALLAN, ALEXANDER [15 January 1819]. Apprentice to George Robertson.—Third son of William Allan, Merchant in Edinburgh. *Died* 1 February 1871, aged 76.

ALLAN, CHARLES BAIRD, M.A., LL.B. [26 July 1954]. Apprentice to Andrew White Young & Others of J. & R. A. Robertson.—Son of Charles Davidson Allan, Medical Practitioner. *Born* 22 December 1923. *Married* 11 January 1960, May Wood, daughter of James Spence. Captain, Madras Regiment 1943-46. Procurator Fiscal at Jedburgh.

ALLAN, HUGH JOSEPH LORRAINE, B.A.(OXON), LL.B. [30 November 1964]. Apprentice to Andrew James Ramsay Bisset and Others of Baillie & Gifford.—Son of Dr W. R. Allan. *Born* 9 June 1935. *Married* 4 October 1969, Anthea, daughter of P. D. Boyd. *Firm*—Biggart, Baillie & Gifford (formerly Baillie & Gifford).

ALLAN, NEIL GEORGE, LL.B. [7 December 1970]. Apprentice to Charles T. Reid and Others of Thomson, Dickson & Shaw.—Son of Neil T. Allan, Insurance Official, Edinburgh. *Born* 11 August 1948. *Married* 2 October 1971, Barbara Joyce, daughter of George T. Pullen, Edinburgh. *Firm*—Allan Macdougall & Co.

ALLANE, JAMES, OF DEWAR [20 June 1649]. Apprentice to Robert Pringle.—Son of James Allane in Winton. *Born* 1619. *Married* 8 February 1649, Isobel Macmath (*died* 6 December 1683). Treasurer, 1659-62. Re-admitted, 21 November 1660. *Died* January 1693.

ALLARDYCE, WILLIAM PATRICK [28 January 1836]. Apprentice to John Mackenzie Lindsay.—Son of Captain William Allardice of Murlingden. *Born* 8 October 1807. *Married* (1) 25 March 1834, Anna Maria (*died* 1 September 1844), daughter of Captain John Macdiarmid; and (2) 12 September 1854, Elizabeth (*died* 24 April 1899), daughter of Hugh Colquhoun, Glasgow. *Died* 12 August 1876.

ALLARDYCE, GAVIN LEITH, M.C. [23 March 1909]. Apprentice to William Pemberton Robertson.—Son of Colonel James Allardyce of Culquoich, Glenkindie, Aberdeenshire. *Born* 12 September 1885. Served in France and Flanders as Lieutenant 7th Gordon Highlanders (T.F.) in the Great War; twice wounded. *Died* 22 June 1958. *Firm*—J. C. and A. Steuart.

ALLEN, CHARLES EDWARD [24 June 1835]. Apprentice to Alexander Pearson.—Son of John Lee Allen of Errol Park. *Born* 16 November 1810. *Died* at Montreal 4 July 1885, unmarried.

ALLESTER, DAVID [28 June 1827]. Apprentice to Thomas Burns.—Son of William Allester, Writer in Edinburgh. *Born* 1802. *Married* 9 August 1838, Agnes (*died* 19 March 1860), eldest daughter of Robert Paul, W.S. *Died* 29 October 1851.

ALSTON, GAVIN [17 November 1851]. Apprentice to John Granger.—Son of John Alston, in Bothwellhaugh, Parish of Bothwell. *Married* 20 August 1817, Jane (*died* 1871), only daughter of Captain Thomson, R.N. *Died* 16 May 1820.

ALSTON, WILLIAM [18 January 1749]. Apprentice to Alexander Stevenson of Montgreenan.—Son of Rev. James Alston, Minister of Dirleton. *Married* January 1740, Janet (*died* 1 July 1791), daughter of William Clark, Portioner of Gilmerton. Deputy Auditor of Exchequer. *Died* 5 April 1775.

ALVES, ANDREW [25 September 1722]. Apprentice to, and son of, William Alves, W.S.—Carried Prince Charles's letter to Lord Provost demanding surrender of the City of Edinburgh, and was imprisoned therefor. *Died* 23 January 1760.

ALVES, WILLIAM [28 June 1700]. Apprentice to William Russell.—*Married* 3 November 1688, Ann, daughter of Rev. Andrew Hamilton, Minister of Middlebie. M.P. for Sanquhar, 1702-7. Commissary of Dumfries, 12 November 1705. Under Keeper of the Signet, 9 November 1709. Joint Deputy Keeper, 1710-11. *Died* 7 September 1722.

AMBROSE, ALEXANDER JACKSON, M.A., LL.B. [14 July 1947]. Apprentice to Kenneth Murray of Macandrew, Wright & Murray.—Son of John Ambrose, Schoolmaster, Edinburgh. *Born* 25 February 1907. *Married* 2 July 1938, Euphemia Brown Donaldson, daughter of George Kilgour of Singapore and Edinburgh. Fiscal of the Society 1964-74. *Firm*—Gillespie Macandrew & Co. (formerly Macandrew, Wright & Murray).

ANDERSON, ALISTAIR ROBERT, LL.B. [26 April 1976]. Apprentice to (1) G. S. Russell and Others of Strathern & Blair, and (2) H. B. W. Macallan of Maclay, Murray & Spens, Glasgow.—Son of Robert McConnachie Anderson, Butcher, Edinburgh. *Born* 1 September 1951. *Married* 3 January 1975, Fiona Susan Allan, daughter of Dr John Jacobs. *Firm*—S. Graham Mickel & Co., Crieff.

ANDERSON, ANDREW MACBETH, T.D. B.A.(Oxon), LL.B., [19 December 1932]. Apprentice to William Henry Fraser and Others of Fraser, Stodart & Ballingall.—Son of Andrew Macbeth Anderson (The Honourable Lord Anderson), Senator of the College of Justice. *Born* 13 July 1908. *Married* 11 October 1941, Cecil Anne Balmain, daughter of Geoffrey Hutchinson, Cheese Merchant. Staff Captain, R.A. 1939-45. *Died* 1 December 1976. *Firm*—Graham Johnston & Fleming (latterly Macandrew, Wright & Murray).

ANDERSON, CECIL WARDHAUGH HORNE, B.L. [14 December 1936]. Apprentice to Ebenezer Denholm-Young of Denholm-Young & M'Vittie.—Son of John Andrew Anderson, Prestonpans. *Born* 12 September 1908. *Married* 25 November 1939, Isobel Condie, daughter of Andrew Blake, Easter Aberdour. *Died* 16 February 1963. *Firm*— Young & Anderson (latterly Anderson & McVie), Haddington.

ANDERSON, CHARLES, D.S.O., M.C. [13 December 1910]. Apprentice to William Garson.—Son of Robert Ballantine Anderson of Glenburn Hall, Jedburgh, J.P., Solicitor and Banker. *Born* 30 July 1886. *Married* 1 September 1921, Mary Greenwood, daughter of George Gunn Bannerman, M.D., Hawick. Treasurer, Roxburgh County Council, 1921-30. Served with Royal Scots and Lovat Scouts, 1914-19; M.C., D.S.O., twice mentioned in Despatches, and rose to rank of Major. *Died* 25 June 1954. *Firm*— Charles and R. B. Anderson, Jedburgh.

ANDERSON, DAVID [Before 1618]. Apprentice to Adam Lawtie.—Commissioner, 26 December 1627. *Married* Margaret Sharp. *Died* 29 April 1635.

ANDERSON, DAVID [18 August 1731]. Apprentice to William Veitch.—Only son of Andrew Anderson, Writer in Edinburgh. *Born* 1707. *Married* 5 November 1745, Mary (*died* 4 October 1781), daughter of John Mitchelson of Middleton, Mid-Lothian, Advocate. *Died* 11 January 1786.

ANDERSON, DAVID BROWN [11 July 1867]. Apprentice to James Mackenzie, J. B. Innes, and C. B. Logan.—Second son of William Anderson of Hallyards, Peeblesshire, Merchant in Leith. *Born* 22 March 1842. *Married* 5 October 1900, Jane Fisher (*died* 13 December 1931), daughter of William Stuart, Attorney in Exchequer, Edinburgh. *Died* 12 August 1919.

ANDERSON, DAVID RAE, M.A., LL.B., LL.M. [27 November 1961]. Apprentice to William Lindsay of Ketchen & Stevens.—Son of David Anderson, Marine Engineer, Stonehaven. *Born* 27 January 1936. *Married* 6 January 1962, Jean, daughter of William D. Strachan, Peterhead. *Firm*—I. Allan Grant & Co., Alloa.

ANDERSON, DAVID SOUTER, LL.B. [2 December 1974]. Apprentice to David Cairns Fulton and Another of Tods, Murray & Jamieson.—Son of Alastair Campbell Anderson, Auctioneer, Perth. *Born* 3 December 1948. *Married* 29 October 1976, Kathleen Elizabeth, daughter of Rev. D. H. Whiteford. *Firm*—Tods, Murray & Jamieson.

ANDERSON, FRANCIS [6 December 1773]. Apprentice to, and son of, David Anderson, W.S.—*Married* (1) Miss Martin; and (2) Jane Easton (*died* 3 April 1828). Deputy Auditor of Exchequer. *Died* 27 April 1823, aged 76. See *Kay's Portraits*, CCLI. His first wife was the daughter of a gate-keeper. He married her because (as he said) "he couldna be fashed courting a lady."

ANDERSON, FRANCIS [1 July 1837]. Apprentice to Thomas Cranston.—Fifth son of John Anderson of Inchyra, Perthshire. *Born* 19 August 1804. *Married* 24 October 1848, Henrietta Maria (*died* 18 November 1892), daughter of Rev. Edward Law, D.D., British Chaplain at St Petersburg. *Died* 18 December 1855.

ANDERSON, HARRY VANS [17 December 1923]. Apprentice to Thomas M. Murray and Kenneth Murray.—Son of Robert Ballantine Anderson, Glenburn Hall, Jedburgh. *Born* 1 October 1898. *Married* 25 October 1932, Marian Estelle (*died* 11 July 1979), daughter of L. F. Smith, Merchant, Tanga, Tanganyika Territory. 2nd Lieutenant R.G.A., 1917, and served in France 1918. Went to Mombasa, Kenya. *Died* 6 November 1964.

ANDERSON, HUGH HODGSON [14 January 1890]. Apprentice to Alexander Paterson Purves.—Younger son of James Anderson, Banker, Leith. *Born* 24 January 1867. *Died* 3 April 1895, unmarried.

ANDERSON, J. [1606]. Signs Minute of 17 January 1606.

ANDERSON, JAMES [6 June 1691]. Apprentice to Robert Richardson.—Son of Rev. Patrick Anderson, Minister of Welstoune. *Born* 5 August 1662. *Married* Jean, daughter of John Ellis of Elliston, Advocate. Author of *Diplomata Scotiae*, and other works. Fiscal, 5 December 1698. Postmaster-General for Scotland from June 1715 to 29 November 1717. *Died* 2 April 1728.

ANDERSON, JOHN [19 May 1629].—Third son of David Anderson, W.S. *Married* (contract dated 7 May 1633) Elizabeth (*died* 21 March 1684), eldest daughter of William Macmath, Merchant Burgess, Edinburgh. Admitted Advocate, 20 July 1647. *Died* 2 January 1673.

ANDERSON, JOHN, OF INCHYRA [12 July 1779]. Apprentice to Samuel Mitchelson.—Third son of David Anderson, W.S. *Born* 4 August 1754. *Married* 10 August 1784, Janet (*died* 18 May 1851), daughter of Samuel Mitchelson, W.S. *Died* 18 June 1814.

ANDERSON, JOHN [24 May 1821]. Apprentice to James Carnegy.—Third son of Peter Anderson, Writer in Inverness. *Born* 1798. *Married* 22 April 1823, Elizabeth (*died* 1869), only daughter of Alexander Mackenzie of Woodside, Agent for British Linen Company Bank, Inverness. *Died* at St Vincent, West Indies, 21 September 1839.

ANDERSON, JOHN [27 May 1824]. Apprentice to Thomas Cranston.—Fourth son of John Anderson, W.S. *Born* 15 June 1799. *Married* 15 October 1833, Harriet (*died* 4 June 1888), second daughter of George Carr of Newcastle. *Died* 4 May 1862.

ANDERSON, JOHN PITTORMIE, B.L. [24 April 1961]. Apprentice to J. C. Walker and Another of Steedman, Ramage & Co.—Son of J. C. L. Anderson, Solicitor, Pittormie, Dairsie, Fife. *Born* 1 December 1938.

ANDERSON, JOHN RAMSAY [21 October 1874]. Apprentice to Frederick Pitman.—Son of Francis Anderson, W.S. *Born* 25 May 1851. *Married* 5 January 1875, Elizabeth Moore (*died* 16 October 1932), only child of Admiral John Hay, of the Seggieden family. *Died* 7 January 1926. *Firm*—J. and F. Anderson.

ANDERSON, JOHN REID [28 April 1952]. Apprentice to Walter Finlay and Another of W. & W. Finlay.—Son of John Anderson, Company Director, Balerno. *Born* 21 May 1914. Flight Lieutenant R.A.F., Middle East 1940-46. *Died* 28 November 1977.

ANDERSON, PATRICK [2 December 1779]. Apprentice to Walter Scott.—Second son of James Anderson of Kingask and Newbigging, Advocate. *Married* 14 September 1786, Susan (*died* 18 July 1821), daughter of Rev. Gilbert Hamilton, D.D., Minister of Cramond. *Died* 24 December 1809, aged 54.

ANDERSON, PETER [11 December 1828]. Apprentice to John Tweedie.—Youngest son of Adam Anderson, Merchant in Edinburgh. *Born* 1803. *Married* (1) 14 October 1834, Frances (*died* June 1838), daughter of Campbell Gardner, Edinburgh; and (2) 2 December 1850, Agnes (*died* 17 February 1895), youngest daughter of John Anderson, Henderland. *Died* 23 November 1855.

ANDERSON, ROBERT BALLANTINE [8 December 1913]. Apprentice to J. P. Wright and T. M. Murray.—Son of Robert Ballantine Anderson of Glenburn Hall, Jedburgh, Solicitor and Banker. *Born* 27 March 1890. Lieutenant K.O.S.B. Killed in action at Gaza, Palestine, 19 April 1917.

ANDERSON, ROBERT BALLANTINE, T.D. [20 December 1948]. Apprentice to Sir Kenneth Murray & Another of Macandrew, Wright & Murray.—Son of Charles Anderson, D.S.O., M.C., W.S., Jedburgh. *Born* 10 April 1923. *Married* 9 June 1949, Christine Adams, daughter of James Butters, Leuchars, Fife. Major, First Battalion, The Gordon Highlanders, North West Europe. *Firm*—Charles & R. B. Anderson, Jedburgh.

ANDERSON, ROBERT PEARSE, M.A., LL.B. [16 July 1928]. Apprentice to William C. Hunter and Another of Bonar, Hunter & Johnstone.—Son of Reginald William Christie Anderson, Farmer, Carterton, Oxford. *Born* 20 February 1905. *Married* 2 October 1946, Beatrice Georgina, daughter of David Smith Cownie. *Died* 15 December 1976. *Firm*—G. & J. Bogie & Anderson, Kinross.

ANDERSON, ROBERT SMITH [16 November 1831]. Apprentice to (1) Hugh Rollo; (2) Robert W. Niven; and (3) Anthony Murray.—Son of Donald Anderson, Macer to the Court of Justiciary. *Born* 23 May 1809. *Married* 2 January 1839, Margaret Kelly, eldest daughter of James M'Farlane of Balwill, Stirlingshire. *Died* 2 February 1868.

ANDERSON, ROBERT TROTTER [29 October 1888]. Apprentice to Graham C. Somervell.—Son of Thomas Anderson, Merchant, Edinburgh. *Born* 25 September 1864. *Died* 9 February 1935, unmarried.

ANDERSON, ROBERT YOUNG [13 November 1816]. Apprentice to William Inglis.—Eldest son of Robert Anderson, sometime Merchant in the Island of Antigua, and afterwards in Edinburgh. *Died* 15 November 1851, aged 59, unmarried.

ANDERSON, RONALD GEORGE, LL.B. [28 April 1969]. Apprentice to James Barron Lloyd and Others of Skene, Edwards & Garson.—Son of George Darling Anderson, Headmaster, Balerno. *Born* 3 July 1945. *Married* 11 July 1970, Fay Brown, daughter of Alexander R. B. Gillies. *Firm*—Murray, Little & Knox, Annan.

ANDERSON, SAMUEL [12 June 1818]. Apprentice to, and second son of, John Anderson, W.S.—*Born* 1791. *Married* (1) 30 August 1824, Anne (*died* 31 October 1826), eldest daughter of James Milnes, Heatherwick House, East Lothian; and (2) 15 May 1833, Charlotte Wilkinson (*died* 1855). Registrar of Affidavits in the Court of Chancery. He was "The Registrar" in *Noctes Ambrosianae*. Became a Wine Merchant, 1823. *Died* in London, 11 July 1849.

ANDERSON, THOMAS SCOTT [24 June 1830]. Apprentice to John Tweedie.—Only son of Archibald Anderson, Merchant in Edinburgh. *Born* 1808. *Married* 15 July 1834, Hannah (*died* 10 February 1896), daughter of James Lowthorp of Welton Hall, Yorkshire. *Died* 14 September 1884.

ANDERSON, WILLIAM [24 June 1774]. Apprentice to Samuel Mitchelson.—Son of Andrew Anderson of Rashiegrain. *Married* 21 March 1775, Jenny (*died* December 1813), daughter of George Clerk Maxwell of Duncrieff, Dumfriesshire. *Died* 28 October 1785.

ANDERSON, WILLIAM [28 November 1791]. Apprentice to William Dick.—Son of James Anderson, Merchant in Glasgow. *Died* 20 October 1796.

ANDERSON, WILLIAM HENRY [15 March 1948]. Apprentice to Patrick Drought North Menzies of Menzies & Thomson.—Son of Henry Anderson, Cashier, Edinburgh. *Born* 7 July 1908. *Married* 20 July 1935, Mary Tweedie Ritchie, daughter of Dr George Ritchie Gilruth. *Died* 9 May 1965. *Firm*—Menzies & Thomson (latterly J. & F. Anderson).

ANDERSON, WILLIAM ROBERTSON [12 January 1891]. Apprentice to John Clerk Brodie, D.K.S. and Thomas Dawson Brodie.—Son of James John Phillips Anderson, Secretary of the Scottish Widows' Fund and Life Assurance Society, Edinburgh. *Born* 2 December 1866. *Died* 12 July 1914.

ANDREW, DOUGLAS GRAHAM, M.A.(CANTAB), LL.B. [28 July 1952]. Apprentice to John Herbert Richardson and Others of Dundas & Wilson.—Son of Ian Graham Andrew, Headmaster, George Watson's College, Edinburgh. *Born* 19 May 1926. *Married* 4 April 1959, Gratian Elizabeth, daughter of Dr C. G. A. Salvesen. Lieutenant XII Royal Lancers. *Firm*—Morton, Fraser & Milligan (formerly Fraser, Stodart & Ballingall).

ANDREW, ROBERT, M.A., LL.B. [22 November 1954]. Apprentice to William Nimmo of Russel & Aitken.—Son of John McDonald Andrew, Watchmaker. *Born* 5 June 1924. *Married* 28 January 1953, Isabella Buchanan, daughter of Alexander Hay. Lieutenant, Argyll & Sutherland Highlanders (attached Second Punjab Regiment 1943-47). *Firms*—(1) Russel & Aitken; (2) Weir & Macgregor.

ANDREWS, WILLIAM DENYS CATHCART, B.L. [27 April 1964]. Apprentice to The Hon. David A. Balfour and Others of Shepherd & Wedderburn.—Son of Eugene Andrews, Solicitor, Girvan. *Born* 3 June 1931. *Married* 11 November 1955, May, daughter of Thomas O'Beirne, Ayr. President of the Law Society of Scotland 1978-79. *Firm*—Shepherd & Wedderburn.

ANDRO, JOHN [Before 1594]. Commissioner, 16 December 1594. Clerk to Privy Council.

ANSTRUTHER, JAMES, OF TREESBANK [22 June 1826]. Apprentice to John Kerr.—Son of Colonel Robert Anstruther of the Royal Tay Fencibles. *Born* 16 September 1803. *Married* (1) 27 March 1828, Marion (*died* 19 June 1859), daughter of Sir John Anstruther, Chief-Justice of Bengal; (2) 11 October 1866, Anabella Agnes (*died* 3 April 1885), eldest daughter of Thomas Anderson of Glendrissaig, Ayrshire, Advocate. *Died* 19 May 1867.

ANTHONE, PATRICK [12 February 1701]. Apprentice to James Carnegy.—*Died* before 1708.

ARBUTHNOT, PETER [13 November 1678]. Apprentice to Henry Graham.—Brother of Alexander Arbuthnot, Merchant, and one of the Bailies of Dundee. *Died* 6 March 1704, aged 52.

ARCHIBALD, HUGH, OF DANKEITH [13 January 1681]. Apprentice to Archibald Nisbet.—Eldest son of Rev. Hugh Archibald, Minister of Avendale. *Married* Margaret Campbell (*died* 1705). *Died* before 1705.

ARMOUR, JAMES [2 December 1723]. Apprentice to (1) Robert Innes; and (2) Andrew Haliburton.—Son of Andrew Armour, Merchant, Glasgow, and Margaret Boyle. *Married* (1) 25 April 1717, Isobel, daughter of James Coulter, Merchant, Glasgow; and (2) June 1736, Euphemia (*died* 30 January 1765), daughter of John Deans of Woodhouselee, Mid-Lothian. *Died* 23 August 1756.

ARMSTRONG, MICHAEL HENRY DAVID, B.L. [25 April 1977]. (By Rule IX (a))— Son of Guy Hepburn Armstrong, Solicitor, Hawick. *Born* 7 November 1936. *Married* 13 June 1964, Patricia Mary, daughter of William T. Dougal, Banker. *Firm*—George & James Oliver, Hawick.

ARNOTT, JAMES, OF LEITHFIELD [21 November 1815]. Apprentice to John Campbell of Annfield.—Son of James Arnott, Farmer in Arbikie, Forfarshire. *Born* 1791. *Married* 31 October 1835, Emily Sophia (*died* 1874), fourth daughter of Edward Fletcher of Corsock. *Died* 21 December 1866.

ARNOTT, JOHN [20 December 1821]. Apprentice to John Campbell.—Son of Alexander Arnott, Farmer. *Died* 5 April 1864, aged 70, unmarried.

ARNOTT, JOHN WALKER [25 June 1829]. Apprentice to Æneas Macbean.—Son of David Walker Arnott, of Arlary, Kinross-shire. *Born* 21 August 1806. *Died* 23 March 1850, unmarried.

ARNOTT, THOMAS, OF CHAPEL [23 June 1817]. Apprentice to John Ferrier.—Eldest son of Robert Arnott of Chapel, Fife. *Married* 13 November 1838, Jane Arnot (*died* 5 October 1846), youngest daughter of Rev. Andrew Grant, D.D., one of the Ministers of St Andrew's Church, Edinburgh. *Died* 27 March 1865, aged 73.

ASHER, SIR AUGUSTUS GORDON GRANT, C.B.E. [15 July 1889]. Apprentice to Charles Morton and John Neilson.—Only son of John Gordon Asher, M.D., Surgeon-Major in Bengal Staff Corps. *Born* 18 December 1861. *Married* 11 September 1895, Emma Berry (*died* 5 February 1942) youngest daughter of Charles George Barclay, Dura, Cupar, Fife. County Clerk of Mid-Lothian, 1896. Knighted, 1927. *Died* 15 July 1930.

ASHTON-CROSS, DESMOND ION CYRIL, M.A.(CANTAB), LL.B. [23 March 1931]. Apprentice to James Mylne and Another of Mylne and Campbell.—Son of John Ashton-Cross, Barrister at Law, London. *Born* 5 August 1896. First World War— Captain, Queen's (West Surrey) Regiment. Served in India and Mesopotamia. Second World War—Temporary Principal in Admiralty. Winner of two Vans Dunlop Scholarships of Edinburgh University. Sometime Lecturer in Scots, Roman and Roman-Dutch Laws, University of Cambridge. *Died* 11 January 1975.

ATHANAS, CHRISTOPHER NICHOLAS, M.A., LL.B. [11 December 1978] (by Rule IXa)—Son of Nicholas Athanas, Company Director. *Born* 26 August 1941. *Married* 30 June 1964, Sheena Anne, daughter of Peter Stewart, Perth. *Firm*—Dundas & Wilson.

AUCHTERLONY, JOHN [27 January 1699]. Apprentice to John Guthrie.—*Married* Marjory Graham. *Died* 21 February 1716.

AULD, HUGH [13 July 1871]. Apprentice to, and eldest son of, John Auld, W.S.—*Born* 25 March 1845. *Married* 22 November 1893, Isabella Pearson (*died* 9 October 1923), daughter of Houston Stewart Wallace, Minden, Peebles. *Died* 13 November 1902.

AULD, JOHN [28 November 1833]. Apprentice to John Mowbray.—Eldest son of Hugh Auld, Cashier of the Commercial Bank. *Born* 2 November 1810. *Married* 11 June 1844, Janè (*died* 7 April 1901), youngest daughter of Robert Johnstone, Merchant, Port Glasgow. *Died* 28 March 1875.

AULD, JOHN CARNEGIE [29 October 1880]. Apprentice to Colin Mackenzie, A. D. M. Black, and J. M. Mackenzie.—Second son of John Auld, W.S. *Born* 17 February 1854. *Died* 20 November 1921, unmarried.

AUSTIN, RICHARD KEITH, LL.B. [13 May 1980*].—Son of Richard Austin, Sales Manager, Edinburgh. *Born* 29 January 1948. *Married* 2 June 1973, Morag Gillespie, daughter of George Campbell Webster, Dental Surgeon, Gourock. *Firm*—Steedman, Ramage & Co.

AUSTIN, ROBERT DAVID JARDINE MEIN, OF BLACK CLACHRIE [14 January 1890]. Apprentice to Archibald Steuart.—Younger son of Rev. John Mein Austin, of St Mungo. *Born* 4 July 1864. *Married* 10 November 1894, Flora (*died* 30 October 1900), younger daughter of Walter C. Brown, Columbus, Ohio. *Died* at Lausanne, 15 August 1910.

AYTOUN, ROBERT, OF CAPLEDRAE [9 June 1825]. Apprentice to James F. Gordon.—Youngest son of Major-General Aytoun of Inchdairnie, Fife. *Born* 17 March 1799. *Married* 17 May 1844, Helene Louisa Adelaide (*died* 16 July 1885), daughter of George Reid Maugham, London. *Died* 9 September 1874.

AYTOUN, ROGER, OF MURIESTON [8 July 1790]. Apprentice to Samuel Mitchelson, Jun.—Eldest son of William Aytoun, W.S. *Married* 9 March 1807, Joan (*died* 1861), daughter of James Keir of Kinmonth, Perthshire. Director in Chancery, 1837-43. *Died* 16 March 1843, aged 76.

AYTOUN, WILLIAM [16 December 1760]. Apprentice to James Graham.—Second son of Roger Aytoun of Inchdairnie, Fife. *Married* 3 June 1766, Isobel (*died* 11 January 1825), only daughter of Colonel Patrick Edmonstone. *Died* May 1780.

AYTOUN, WILLIAM EDMONDSTOUNE [14 May 1835]. Apprentice to, and son of, Roger Aytoun, W.S.—*Born* 21 June 1813. *Married* (1) 11 April 1849, Jane Emily (*died* 15 March 1853), youngest daughter of Professor John Wilson ("Christopher North"); and (2) 24 December 1863, Fearne Jemima (*died* 25 January 1904), second daughter of James Kinnear, W.S. Author of *Lays of the Scottish Cavaliers*, and other poems. Admitted Advocate, 20 November 1840. Professor of Rhetoric and Belles-Lettres in the University of Edinburgh, 1845. Sheriff of Orkney, 1852. *Died* 4 August 1865.

BABINGTON, WILLIAM [17 October 1878]. Apprentice to James Lindesay, Jun.—Second son of Lieut.-Colonel William Babington, 7th Hussars. *Born* 10 January 1856. *Died* 4 March 1938. *Firm*—Melville and Lindesay.

BAILLIE, ANDREW [20 December 1682]. Apprentice to Archibald Nisbet.—*Buried* 24 December 1689.

BAILLIE, DUNCAN GUS, C.M.G., D.S.O., T.D. [15 March 1897]. Apprentice to Sir Thomas Dawson Brodie.—Son of Major-General Duncan James Baillie, Royal Horse Guards. *Born* 23 October 1872. *Married* 27 September 1919, Mary Evelyn (*died* 24 May 1971), daughter of Captain Blair Onslow Cochrane, Vice-Convener of Nairnshire County Council. Served in Boer War, 1900, and in Great War, 1914-19. Commanded the Lovat Scouts. Four times mentioned in Dispatches. Lieut.-Colonel, 1916. *Died* 3 July 1968.

BAILLIE, JAMES, OF HARDINGTON [14 April 1694]. Apprentice to Andrew Baillie.—Son of Alexander Baillie of Hillhouse. *Born* 1660. *Married* (1) Elizabeth, daughter of David Johnston, Merchant Burgess of Edinburgh; and (2) July 1704, Anna, daughter of George Livingstone of Saltcoats, Haddingtonshire. Treasurer, 1710-14. *Died* 28 July 1747.

BAILLIE, JAMES WILLIAM, OF CULTERALLERS [12 November 1847]. Apprentice to James Mackenzie, J. B. Innes, and John Logan.—Son of Robert Granbery Baillie of Culterallers. *Born* 15 October 1824. *Married* 17 March 1857, Wilhelmina (*died* 27 May 1924), daughter of John Ronald, S.S.C. *Died* 30 April 1880.

BAILLIE, JOHN [7 September 1721]. Apprentice to John Stewart.—Son of James Baillie, Sheriff-Clerk of Inverness. *Born* 1689. *Married* Catherine Dunbar. Agent for the Church of Scotland, 1743-54. *Died* 9 January 1754.

BAILLIE, THOMAS, OF POLKEMMET [3 May 1732]. Apprentice to Robert Hepburn.— Eldest son of Thomas Baillie of Polkemmet, West Lothian. *Married* Isobel (*died* 13 August 1777), daughter of Alexander Walker, Minister of Kirkurd. *Died* 3 February 1785. Father of Sir William Baillie, Lord Polkemmet.

BAILLIE, WILLIAM [19 November 1801]. Apprentice to Charles Innes.—Eldest son of William Baillie, Commissary Clerk, of Brechin and Writer, Montrose. *Married* 25 April 1808, Grace Margaret (*died* 20 March 1849), daughter of John Mackenzie of Dolphinton, Lanarkshire. Sheriff-Substitute at Dumfries, 1815-39. *Died* 13 February 1855, aged 82.

BAILLIE, WILLIAM, OF FALAHILL [21 May 1829]. Apprentice to Melville Burd, Thomas Macmillan, and John Millar.—Son of John Baillie, Edinburgh. *Born* 1805. *Died* 3 December 1876, unmarried.

BAILLIE, WILLIAM ROBERT [2 June 1836]. Apprentice to Andrew Storie.—Only son of William Baillie, W.S. *Born* 30 November 1812. *Married* (1) 4 October 1842, Maria Inglis (*died* 6 June 1844), daughter of William Young, Writer in Kilmarnock; and (2) 15 February 1848, Elizabeth (*died* 22 June 1903), daughter of Henry Johnston, Surgeon in Edinburgh. *Died* 9 August 1858.

BAIN, GEORGE STOBIE PRESTON, B.L. [13 March 1939]. Apprentice to (1) Charles Gibson Connell of Connell & Connell and (2) George W. Harvey of E. A. & F. Hunter & Harvey.—Son of George Bain, Builder, Edinburgh. *Born* 4 August 1915. *Married* 15 October 1944, Jean, daughter of Major D. K. Michie. Squadron Leader R.A.F.V.R. Served Home Forces 1939-45. Wounded May 1941. Mentioned in Despatches 1944. Battle of Britain Decoration. *Firm*—Mylne Campbell & Winchester—Amalgamated with Campbell Smith & Co.

BAIRD, JAMES, OF CHESTERHALL [19 July 1697]. Servitor to Sir James Ogilvie, Principal Secretary of State.—Eldest son of John Baird, Bailie in Cullen. *Married* (1) 1 July 1697, Margaret, daughter of John Anderson, Depute Clerk of Justiciary; (2) 15 August 1706, Jean Watson, of the family of Bilton Park, Yorkshire; and (3) Mary (*died* 27 April 1764), daughter of Rev. James Oswald, Minister of Watten. Clerk of Wardrobe, 1696. Clerk of Bullion, 1702. Depute Clerk of Justiciary, 1706. *Died* July 1741.

BAIRD, JAMES JOHN [20 December 1827]. Apprentice to Alexander Young.—Second son of James Baird, of the Shotts Ironworks. *Born* 1804. *Married* 14 April 1829, Ann (*died* 19 June 1835), daughter of Alexander Dallas, W.S. *Died* 11 December 1831.

BAIRD, JOHN [Before 1628]. Commissioner, 18 October 1631. *Married* Margaret, daughter of Peter Forrest of Archerfield, and widow of Alexander Duff, Clerk of Exchequer.

BAIRD, JOHN [26 February 1824]. Apprentice to Æneas Macbean.—Son of John Baird, of Camelon, Stirlingshire. *Died* at Calcutta, 4 September 1842, aged 43, unmarried.

BAIRD, JOHN [15 December 1930]. Apprentice to William Babington, Joseph Inglis, and Joseph Ellis Inglis.—Son of James Baird, Head Gardener, The Gardens, Stobs. *Born* 29 October 1894. *Married* 29 November 1949, Christine Mary Frances Stevenson. Served in Great War with 9th Royal Scots and as 2nd Lieutenant 4th Royal Scots. *Died* 1 June 1965. *Firm*—Melville and Lindesay.

BAIRD, JOHN WARDEN [4 July 1828]. Apprentice to John Ferrier.—Son of Thomas Walker Baird, Advocate. *Born* 25 August 1798. *Died* 1 February 1875, unmarried.

BAIRNSFATHER, HUGH [21 May 1806]. Apprentice to Harry Davidson.—Son of David Bairnsfather, Farmer in Herperdean. *Married* 1806, Catherine (*died* June 1845), daughter of Robert Walker of Whitelaw, Haddington. *Died* at Paradykes, 25 November 1812.

BAIRNSFATHER, PETER, OF DUMBARROW [17 May 1832]. Apprentice to John Russell.—Eldest son of Hugh Bairnsfather, W.S. *Born* 27 May 1809. *Married* 7 July 1840, Sarah Every (*died* 10 March 1913), daughter of William Miller of Dalswinton, Major in Royal Horse Guards, and M.P. for Dumfriesshire, 1790. *Died* 31 May 1890.

BALCANQUALL, DAVID [19 July 1695]. Apprentice to William Thomson.—*Married* Marion Lawrie. *Died* 27 February 1702.

BALDERSTON, WILLIAM [20 November 1778]. Apprentice to Walter Scott.—Son of George Balderston, Surgeon in St Christopher's, and afterwards in Edinburgh. *Married* 29 March 1796, Helen (*died* 12 July 1854), second daughter of William Charles Little Gilmour of Craigmillar, Mid-Lothian. *Died* at Bath, 2 January 1818.

BALDERSTON, WILLIAM CHARLES [25 November 1824]. Apprentice to (1) William Balderston; and (2) William Scott.—Eldest son of William Balderston W.S. *Died* 19 April 1851, aged 52, unmarried.

BALFOUR, ANDREW [3 November 1686]. Apprentice to George Dallas of St Martin's.—*Married* (1) Elizabeth (*buried* 21 December 1686), daughter of George Bayne, Merchant Burgess, Edinburgh; (2) 4 August 1687, Margaret Hope (*buried* 21 April 1689); and (3) 10 July 1690, Margaret, eldest daughter of John Wedderburn of Blackness, Forfarshire. *Buried* 25 November 1697.

BALFOUR, CHARLES [9 July 1821]. Apprentice to Hugh James Rollo.—Son of John Balfour, Merchant in Glasgow. *Born* 4 January 1798. *Married* 1842, Charlotte (*died* 21 December 1890), daughter of Dugald Macgregor, Merchant, Greenock. *Died* 22 May 1856.

BALFOUR, THE HON. CHRISTOPHER PATRICK, LL.B. [8 December 1975]. Apprentice to Sir Alastair C. Blair and Others of Dundas & Wilson, Davidson & Syme.—Son of David Andrew Balfour, 4th Baron Kinross, W.S. *Born* 1 October 1949. *Married* 29 June 1974, Susan Jane, daughter of Ian Robert Pitman, W.S. *Firm*—Shepherd & Wedderburn.

BALFOUR, DAVID, OF SOMERSIDE [19 July 1779]. Apprentice to Samuel Mitchelson.— Third son of William Balfour of Trenaby, Orkney. *Born* 8 November 1754. *Married* 1 September 1782, Marion (*died* 27 March 1813), daughter of George M'Intosh of Dunchattan, Merchant, Glasgow. *Died* 25 May 1813.

BALFOUR, DAVID, OF TRENABY [29 June 1837]. Apprentice to John Mowbray.—Son of William Balfour of Ellwick, Orkney. *Born* 14 October 1811. *Married* 12 December 1844, Eleanor Alder (*died* 19 December 1902), daughter of Captain Samuel Barker Edmeston. Author of *Udal Rights and Feudal Wrongs: A Memorial for Orkney.* Convenor for the County of Orkney, 1854-87. *Died* November 1887.

BALFOUR, GEORGE [12 March 1736]. Apprentice to (1) John Mein; and (2) Alexander Stevenson of Montgreenan.—Fifth son of James Balfour of Pilrig. *Born* 1771. *Married* October 1739, Ann (*died* 24 May 1785), daughter of Alexander Stevenson of Montgreenan, W.S. *Died* 28 March 1751.

BALFOUR, JAMES [26 June 1769]. Apprentice to John Davidson.—Eldest son of George Balfour, W.S. *Died* 24 November 1806.

BALFOUR, JAMES, OF PILRIG [17 February 1800]. Apprentice to James Gibson.—Eldest son of John Balfour, younger of Pilrig. *Born* 7 January 1774. *Married* 24 February 1806, Anne (*died* 29 June 1825), daughter of Captain John Mackintosh of Corribrough, Inverness. *Died* 20 March 1860.

BALFOUR, HON. JAMES MONCRIEFF, O.B.E. [12 December 1904]. Apprentice to John Cowan, James A. Dalmahoy, and E. J. McCandlish.—Second son of the Rt. Hon. John Blair Balfour, Baron Kinross of Glasclune, Lord Justice-General. *Born* 6 July 1878. *Married* 27 June 1908, Madeline Maude Graham (*died* 5 October 1970), elder daughter of James Graham Watson, Manager, Scottish Provident Institution, Kingston Grange, Mid-Lothian. Assistant Secretary, Ministry of National Service, 1918-19. Secretary to Parliamentary Commission for revising Civil Service Exemptions, 1919. Deputy Financial Adviser to Persian Government, 1920-21. Served in Great War with Scottish Horse and General Staff. Author of *Recent Happenings in Persia* (1922). O.B.E.(Mil.). *Died* 30 April 1960.

BALFOUR, JOHN [Before 1599]. Signs Minute of 17 January 1606. *Died* about 1628.

BALFOUR, JOHN LEWIS GRAHAM [1 June 1820]. Apprentice to James Gibson.—Son of John Balfour of Sauchrie. *Married* 5 October 1824, Alexis (*died* 1870), eldest daughter of Charles Mercer, Allan Park, Stirling. *Died* 4 April 1866, aged 71.

BALFOUR, WILLIAM [27 June 1820]. Apprentice to James Hamilton.—Son of William Balfour, Surgeon in Edinburgh. *Born* 1794. *Died* 30 September 1873, unmarried.

BALFOUR-KINNEAR, GEORGE PURVIS-RUSSELL [7 July 1913]. Apprentice to William MacGillivray and Others of Lindsay, Howe & Co.—Son of James Balfour-Kinnear, W.S. *Born* 11 May 1888. *Married* (1) 7 August 1913, Ethel (divorced by him 1919), daughter of Henry James Purvis-Russell-Montgomery of Hattonburn, Kinross, and assumed the name of Purvis-Russell-Balfour-Kinnear; and (2) 8 October 1924, Elfrida Mary (*died* 10 November 1966), daughter of James Duncan Miller, M.R.C.V.S., Trinidad. Served in First World War as Lieutenant in Royal Air Force, Kite Balloon Section. Mentioned in Despatches. *Died* 12 October 1978. *Firm*—Hamilton, Kinnear & Beatson (now Aitken, Kinnear & Co.).

BALFOUR-KINNEAR, GEORGE THOMAS, of Cross [29 November 1855]. Apprentice to Adam Hay and Robert Pringle.—Eldest son of James Kinnear, W.S. *Born* 8 February 1833. *Married* 16 November 1858, Agnes (*died* 24 December 1920), daughter of Harry Gordon, Liverpool. *Died* 28 April 1915.

BALFOUR-KINNEAR, GEORGE WILLIAM [7 December 1903]. Apprentice to G. T. Balfour-Kinnear and James Balfour-Kinnear.—Son of G. T. Balfour-Kinnear, W.S., of Cross. *Born* 16 November 1877. *Married* (1) 27 April 1904, Henrietta Mary (*died* 4 June 1952), (divorced 15 March 1913), daughter of James Burness, W.S.; (2) 7 April 1914, Rita (*died* 12 March 1916), daughter of Rev. Isidore Harris, London. Lieutenant, Canadian Expeditionary Force. *Died* 11 March 1922.

BALFOUR-KINNEAR, JAMES, of Cross [14 July 1884]. Apprentice to A. Hamilton, G. T. Kinnear, and R. Beatson.—Eldest son of George Balfour-Kinnear, W.S. *Born* 24 September 1859. *Married* 26 January 1887, Catherine (*died* 16 July 1962), second daughter of John Fraser of Parkburn, M.D. *Died* 11 October 1938. *Firm*—Hamilton, Kinnear, and Beatson.

BALFOUR-MELVILLE, JAMES, of Mount Melville [6 June 1839]. Apprentice to, and fourth son of, James Balfour of Pilrig, W.S.—*Born* 17 February 1815. *Married* 15 August 1844, Eliza Ogilvy (*died* 1 July 1897), daughter of James Heriot of Ramornie, Fife, W.S. Assumed surname of Melville on succeeding to Mount Melville, Fife. *Died* at St Andrews, 14 May 1898.

BALFOUR-MELVILLE, JAMES HERIOT [15 October 1873]. Apprentice to, and eldest son of, James Balfour, W.S.—*Born* 8 July 1845. *Married* 21 November 1878, Mary Louisa (*died* 8 March 1930), elder daughter of Sir David Dundas of Beechwood and Dunira, Bart. *Died* at Comrie, 9 December 1913.

BALFOUR-MELVILLE, JOHN INGLIS [11 December 1906]. Apprentice to James Mylne and A. B. Campbell.—Second son of Leslie Melville Balfour-Melville, W.S. *Born* 16 April 1881. *Married* 26 June 1907, Emily Mary Frances (*died* 16 May 1958), youngest daughter of William Henry Haig of Cameron Bridge, Fife. *Died* 16 April 1963. *Firms*—Balfour & Scott and Hope, Todd & Kirk.

BALFOUR-MELVILLE, JOHN MACKINTOSH, of Pilrig and Strathkinnes [5 March 1835]. Apprentice to, and third son of, James Balfour of Pilrig.—*Born* 23 September 1811. *Married* 21 September 1841, Anne (*died* 17 December 1891), daughter of Harry Rainy, M.D., Professor of Forensic Medicine in the University of Glasgow. *Died* 23 September 1893.

BALFOUR-MELVILLE, LESLIE MELVILLE [17 July 1879]. Apprentice to James Mylne.—Sixth son of James Balfour-Melville, W.S. *Born* 9 March 1854. *Married* (1) 25 November 1879, Jeanie A. (*died* 15 December 1890), eldest daughter of William Wilson, M.D., and niece of the Right Hon. John Inglis, Lord Justice-General; (2) 7 July 1923, Harriet Maud, M.B.E. (*died* 9 April 1965), daughter of Malcolm Carey, Barnton. *Died* 16 July 1937.

BALLANTYNE, WILLIAM, OF SHIRVA [30 June 1801]. Apprentice to John Hunter.—Second son of James Ballantyne, Merchant in Glasgow. *Died* 1 May 1827.

BALLARD, ARCHIBALD ANDERSON [12 January 1891]. Apprentice to Frederick Pitman, John R. Anderson, W. H. Murray, and A. R. C. Pitman.—Eldest son of George Alexander Ballard of the Madras Civil Service. *Born* 17 November 1867. *Married* 24 October 1916, Kate Payne (*died* 24 December 1980), daughter of Mrs Payne, Fairlawn, Bromley, Kent. *Died* 29 January 1933.

BALLENDEN, JAMES. *See* BANNATYNE, JAMES, OF FORMANTHILLS AND KIRKTOUN OF NEWTYLE.

BALLINGALL, ANDREW HUNTER [6 June 1867]. Apprentice to John Dundas, William Wilson, and A. M. Bell.—Second son of William Ballingall, Factor, Sweetbank, Fife. *Born* 21 June 1841. *Married* 6 September 1876, Ellen (*died* 24 October 1936), elder daughter of Archibald Burns and Ellen Caroline Macpherson Macdonald of Glencoe. *Died* at Perth, 10 April 1901.

BALLINGALL, DAVID ANDREW FORRESTER, B.A.(OXON), LL.B. [24 December 1940]. Appprentice to William Henry Fraser and Others of Fraser, Stodart & Ballingall.—Son of David Ballingall, Estate Factor, Blair Drummond. *Born* 10 February 1916. Major, Intelligence Corps. Served U.K., North Africa, Italy and North West Europe 1940-45.

BALLINGALL, GEORGE DAVID [15 July 1886]. Apprentice to William Stuart Fraser.—Eldest son of David Ballingall, Factor, Blair-Drummond, Perthshire. *Born* 2 March 1852. *Married* 17 April 1888, Anne Niven M'Lean (*died* 7 July 1951) daughter of Robert Knox Masterson, Merchant, Hamilton, Canada (West). *Died* 6 October 1938. *Firm*—Fraser, Stodart, and Ballingall.

BANNATYNE, JAMES, OF FORMANTHILLS AND KIRKTOUN OF NEWTYLE [Before 1552].—Son of John Bannatyne, W.S. Also called James BALLENDEN. *Born* 3 May 1512. *Married* (1) Catherine Tailzefer; (2) Janet Cockburn. *Died* 1 January 1583-4.

BANNATYNE, JAMES [Before 1595].—Son of Thomas Bannatyne, one of the Senators of the College of Justice (Lord Auchinoul). *Born* 8 December 1546. *Married* —— Rutherford. Commissioner, 4 December 1595. Depute Clerk of Justiciary. *Died* 17 September 1597.

BANNATYNE, JOHN [Before 1527].—Son of John Bannatyne, Burgess of Edinburgh. Secretary to Archibald, 6th Earl of Angus. Justice-Clerk and Director of Chancery.

BANNATYNE, JOHN [Before 1611]. Signs of the Acts, 26 December 1627. *Married* Marion Wylie. Deputy Clerk Register.

BANNATYNE, OR BALLANTYNE, PATRICK [Before 1607]. Commissioner, 1 June 1607. *Married* 24 September 1595, Sara Johnston. *Died* October 1626.

BANNATYNE, THOMAS [Before 1530].

BANNERMAN, ALEXANDER [18 September 1714]. Apprentice to Andrew Haliburton.—*Died* about 1724.

BANNERMAN, CHARLES [5 July 1742]. Apprentice to George Chalmers.—Second son of Patrick Bannerman, Merchant and Lord Provost of Aberdeen. *Died* 6 February 1747, unmarried.

BANNERMAN, JAMES PATRICK [24 October 1879]. Apprentice to Hon. J. W. Moncrieff.—Second son of Rev. James Bannerman, D.D., Professor of Divinity, New College, Edinburgh. Born 8 August 1854. *Married* 20 July 1892, Amy Cecilia (*died* 24 October 1958), fourth daughter of Rev. A. B. Pringle, Vicar of Blakeney, Gloucestershire. *Died* 3 May 1905. *Firm*—Bell and Bannerman.

BARBER-FLEMING, VALERIE JANET, LL.B. [28 May 1979]. Apprentice to Ronald Kerr Will and Others of Dundas & Wilson *and* A. D. Stewart of Monrieff, Warren, Paterson & Co., Glasgow. Daughter of Charles Leonard, House Salesman, Edinburgh. *Born* 10 April 1955. *Married* 11 November 1978, Anthony John, son of Charles Elphinstone Barber-Fleming, Farmer, Balfron.

BARBOUR, PETER [29 July 1633]. Apprentice to Robert Wallace.—*Married* (contract, June 1634) Isabel, eldest daughter of Thomas Carmichael, Merchant Burgess, Edinburgh. Re-admitted, 21 November 1661. *Buried* 12 March 1663.

BARCLAY, ANTHONY [20 June 1769]. Apprentice to Alexander M'Millan.—Son of John Barclay, Writing-master in Dundee. *Married* 22 December 1801, Grace, eldest daughter of Rev. Patrick Grant, Minister of Cromdale. *Died* 27 September 1811.

BARCLAY, JAMES ROBERTSON, OF KEAVIL [25 February 1740]. Apprentice to Hew Crawford.—Son of George Robertson of Craigarnhall. *Married* 24 September 1744, Isobel, second daughter of Robert Wellwood, of Garvock, Fife. *Died* 8 July 1792.

BARCLAY, PETER GEORGE SWAN, LL.B. [8 December 1981*].—Son of Peter Barclay, Hotelier and Farmer, Hoswick, Sandwick, Shetland. *Born* 8 December 1956.

BARRETT, HILL HAMILTON [10 July 1893]. Apprentice to Francis J. Martin.—Son of Rev. Isaac Barrett, Minister of the Free Church of Scotland at Skirling, near Biggar. *Born* 31 July 1868. Director of Chamber of Commerce and other Institutions in Glasgow. *Died* at Kilmalcolm, 3 August 1934.

BARRY, GERALD WILLIAM STUART, B.A.(OXON), LL.B. [4 December 1967]. Apprentice to Michael Lorimer of Henderson & Jackson.—Son of Ivor William Gordon Barry, Barrister (Retired), Drymen. *Born* 18 December 1931. *Married* 10 September 1957, Elizabeth Ann, daughter of H. T. B. Morison, Company Director. *Firm*—W. & J. Burness.

BARRON, GEORGE [4 June 1829]. Apprentice to (1) Robert Burnett; and (2) Alexander Donald.—Son of John Barron, Aberdeen. *Married* 26 December 1837, Elizabeth (*died* 6 March 1892), second daughter of Alexander Adie, Optician, Edinburgh. *Died* 11 August 1851, aged 51.

BARTON, JOHN MACLEAN [2 May 1966]. Apprentice to Sir Ernest Wedderburn and Others of Shepherd & Wedderburn.—Son of Henry Barton, C.B.E., Solicitor of Inland Revenue for Scotland. *Born* 23 December 1936. *Married* 3 January 1970, Gertrude, daughter of Charles Duncan Cheyne. *Firms*—(1) Gordon Falconer & Fairweather (1963-66) and (2) Guild & Guild.

BAUCHOP, JAMES CALDER [10 December 1840]. Apprentice to Robert Rutherford.— Only son of Robert Bauchop, residing at Dens, near Bo'ness. *Born* 1814. *Died* 1852, unmarried.

BAXTER, ALAN GEORGE LAURIE, M.A.(CANTAB), LL.B. [26 November 1956]. Apprentice to Alexander Frederick Robertson and Another of J. & F. Anderson.—Son of Lieutenant Colonel Noel Edward Baxter, Leven, Fife. *Born* 5 June 1927. *Married* 6 September 1956, Elizabeth June, daughter of Vice-Admiral Sir Thomas Troubridge. *Firm*—Pagan, Osborne & Grace (formerly Pagan & Osborne), Cupar and St Andrews.

BAXTER, CHARLES [27 July 1871]. Apprentice to (1) Edmund Baxter; and (2) T. G. Murray and J. A. Jamieson.—Son of Edmund Baxter, W.S. *Born* 24 December 1848. *Married* (1) 24 July 1877, Grace Roberta Louisa (*died* 24 March 1893), youngest daughter of Major-General Robert Stewart, H.E.I.C.S.; and (2) 1 October 1895, Marie Louise (*died* 10 December 1956), fifth daughter of George Gaukroger, Southfield, Longniddry. *Died* at London, 29 April 1919. *Firm*—Mitchell and Baxter.

BAXTER, COLIN ANDREW, B.A.(CANTAB), LL.B. [17 November 1952]. Apprentice to John Richardson and Another of Scott Moncrieff & Trail.—Son of Andrew Paterson Baxter, East India Merchant. *Born* 6 March 1927. *Married* 11 May 1963, Ann Harriet, daughter of Hon. Patrick John Hepburne-Scott. *Firm*—W. & J. Burness.

BAXTER, EDMUND [11 July 1837]. Apprentice to Allan Macdougall.—Son of John Cockshot, Merchant, St Helens, Liverpool. *Born* 12 April 1813. Adopted by Charles Baxter, Writer, Edinburgh, and assumed the name of Baxter. *Married* 30 March 1847, Mary (*died* 11 August 1879), daughter of William Turnbull of Forthbank, Stirlingshire. Auditor of the Court of Session, 1866. *Died* 8 July 1894.

BAXTER, JAMES [5 December 1811]. Apprentice to John Dundas.—Son of Rev. Colin Baxter, Minister of Monzievaird. *Born* 1 March 1789. *Died* 18 May 1864, unmarried.

BAYLEY, GEORGE [18 June 1856]. Apprentice to Thomas Elder MacRitchie.—Eldest son of Isaac Bayley of Manuel, Stirlingshire, S.S.C. *Born* 12 October 1831. *Married* 24 March 1863, Helen Christian (*died* 26 May 1909), youngest daughter of William Hunt, of Navity, Fife, W.S. *Died* 3 April 1902. *Firm*—MacRitchie, Bayley, and Henderson.

BAYLEY, JAMES FRANCIS [10 July 1893]. Apprentice to, and son of, George Bayley, W.S.—*Born* 21 July 1869. *Died* 9 June 1950. *Firm*—MacRitchie, Bayley, and Henderson.

BAYNE, BRIAN JOHN ROBERT [15 December 1947]. Apprentice to J. Miller Thomson & Another of J. Miller Thomson & Co.—Son of John Sloane Bayne, W.S., Edinburgh. *Born* 10 May 1916. *Married* 3 August 1940, Margaret Lockie. Captain R.A.S.C. Served U.K., Egypt, Sicily, Italy and Germany 1939-45. Mentioned in Despatches Italy 1944. *Firm*—Boyd, Jameson & Young.

BAYNE, JOHN [1627]. Signs the Acts, 26 December 1627.

BAYNE, JOHN [25 February 1635]. Apprentice to Cuthbert Miller.—Second son of John Bayne, W.S. Name deleted from the Roll of the Society, 8 January 1666, after appointment as Sheriff-Clerk of Berwickshire.

BAYNE, JOHN, OF PITCAIRLY [9 January 1655]. Apprentice to John Semple.—Son of Donald Bayne, bower (bowmaker), Edinburgh, of the Tulloch family. *Married* 3 October 1643, Euphan Aikman, sister of Andrew Aikman, W.S. Re-admitted, 8 July 1661. Died 28 January 1681, aged 60. *Buried* in Greyfriars.

BAYNE, JOHN [9 June 1825]. Apprentice to John Mowbray.—Son of John Bayne, Schoolmaster in Leith. *Born* 1795. *Married* 20 July 1831, Jessie (*died* 15 August 1835), daughter of James Cassie, of Banff. Lecturer on Conveyancing to the Juridical Society. *Died* 10 May 1843.

BAYNE, JOHN SLOANE [26 March 1928]. Apprentice to James H. Jameson and Andrew St Clair Jameson.—Son of James Bayne, Artist, Edinburgh. *Born* 6 July 1875. *Married* 27 August 1907, Margaret (*died* 20 February 1955), daughter of John Robert M'Caw, Manufacturer, Ballykelly, Banbridge, County Down, Ireland. Author of *Back to Eden—the Secret of the Temple. Died* 21 June 1965. *Firm*—Boyd, Jameson, and Young.

BEATOUN, ALEXANDER, OF LANGHERMISTON [13 March 1650]. Apprentice to Alexander Douglas.—Second son of Alexander Beatoun, Skipper, Burgess of Anstruther. *Married* 27 February 1642, Marjorie, daughter of John Kennedy, Merchant and Vintner, Burgess of Edinburgh. Re-admitted, 21 November 1661. *Died* 9 November 1672, aged 57.

BEATSON, ALEXANDER [20 June 1793]. Apprentice to Alexander Mackenzie.—Son of Rev. David Beatson, Minister of Dunbarney. *Born* 25 April 1765. *Died* 10 October 1806.

BEATSON, ROBERT [13 May 1869]. Apprentice to Alexander Hamilton and George Thomas Kinnear.—Son of Robert Beatson, Writer in Edinburgh. *Born* 1 November 1833. *Married* 21 October 1879, Mary Editha (*died* 6 January 1928), second daughter of Robert Tod, M.D., Dysart. *Died* at Bournemouth, 3 April 1906.

BEGG, ANDREW VANNAN, B.L. [16 July 1889]. Apprentice to R. W. Wallace.—Son of John Begg, Ironmaster, Kinneil, Bo'ness, and great-grand-nephew of the Poet, Robert Burns. *Born* 15 April 1857. Special Constable in Great War period. *Died* 19 February 1935, unmarried. *Firm*—Wallace and Begg.

BEITH, DONALD [17 July 1862]. Apprentice to James Greig and Charles Morton.—Son of Gilbert Beith, residing in Lochgilphead. *Born* 25 November 1815. *Married* 16 November 1870, Mina Maria (*died* 23 February 1911), third daughter of James Balfour and widow of Andrew Murray, Jun., W.S. Admitted S.S.C., 1850. *Died* 9 October 1894.

BEITH, ROBERT DONALD [19 July 1872]. Apprentice to Andrew Murray, Jun., and Donald Beith, his uncle.—Son of Rev. Alexander Beith, D.D., Minister of the Free North Church, Stirling. *Born* 16 October 1844. *Died* at Dunoon, 23 December 1913.

BELL, ALAN RUTHERFORD, OF HILLOWTON [6 February 1888]. Apprentice to David Wardlaw.—Son of John Bell of Hillowton, Kirkcudbrightshire. *Born* 1 November 1862. *Died* at Norton, Malton, Yorks, 24 September 1903, unmarried.

BELL, ALEXANDER MONTGOMERIE [5 March 1835]. Apprentice to James Dundas.—Son of John Bell, Merchant in Paisley. *Born* 4 December 1809. *Married* 21 June 1836, Margaret (*died* 3 January 1885), eldest daughter of Hugh Colquhoun, Merchant in Glasgow. Professor of Conveyancing in the University of Edinburgh, 1856-66. Author of *Lectures on Conveyancing. Died* 19 January 1866.

BELL, ALEXANDER CLAUDE MONTGOMERIE [8 July 1901]. Apprentice to Charles Baxter and William Mitchell.—Son of John Montgomerie Ball, W.S. *Born* 4 March 1872. *Married* 29 July 1905, Robin Mary (*died* 7 December 1921), fourth daughter of John Bedwell Slater of Wetheral. *Died* 26 January 1924. *Firm*—Bell, Bannerman, and Findlay.

BELL, BENJAMIN [29 March 1898]. Apprentice to James Mylne.—Son of Robert Craigie Bell, W.S. *Born* 26 November 1872. *Married* 14 June 1913, Mary (*died* 19 February 1939), elder daughter of Rev. Alexander Paterson, M.A., formerly of Lilliesleaf. *Died* 8 December 1932.

BELL, BENJAMIN WILLIAM [13 June 1833]. Apprentice to, and son of, William Bell, W.S.—*Born* 23 July 1810. *Died* 22 August 1840, unmarried.

BELL, CARLYLE [6 March 1810]. Apprentice to Thomas Cranston.—Youngest son of Thomas Bell, Merchant in London. *Married* (1) 25 December 1806, Joan (*died* 6 January 1820), daughter of Rev. Robert Home, Minister of Polwarth; and (2) 13 July 1821, Jean Dickie (*died* 7 January 1885), eldest daughter of Charles Cuningham of Newholm, W.S. *Died* 27 August 1850, aged 71. *Firm*—Cuningham & Bell.

BELL, CHARLES, OF CRAIGFOODIE [19 August 1700]. Apprentice to William Dykes.—Son of Robert Bell, W.S. *Born* 14 June 1674. *Married* April 1706, Elizabeth, daughter of Rev. Andrew Ury, Minister of Muiravonside. *Died* May 1731.

BELL, CHARLES YOUNG BEATSON [13 November 1862]. Apprentice to, and son of, John Beatson Bell, W.S.—*Born* 9 June 1835. *Died* 26 April 1868, unmarried.

BELL, GIDEON WILLIAM, OF FOURTOUN [30 June 1831]. Apprentice to William Scott and Gilbert Laurie Finlay.—Second son of William Bell, Farmer, Swintonhill, Berwickshire. *Born* 14 August 1805. *Married* 10 October 1855, Barbara Leonora (*died* 3 September 1888), second daughter of General Alexander Dirom. *Died* 4 March 1887.

BELL, GRAHAM CLARK, B.L. [26 November 1962]. Apprentice to T. M. Jinkins and Others of Russell & Dunlop.—Son of John Clark Bell, W.S., Edinburgh. *Born* 29 May 1937. *Married* 20 July 1963, Marion, daughter of Henry Elder. *Firm*—Russell & Dunlop.

BELL, HAMILTON [8 August 1785]. Apprentice to Walter Ross.—Son of John Bell, stabler in Edinburgh. His mother kept a well-known tavern in Canongate. *Died* 6 May 1807. An interesting account appears in *Kay's Portraits*, CCLXIV, of how for a bet he carried a vintner's boy on his back from Edinburgh to Musselburgh.

BELL, JOHN [23 June 1757]. Apprentice to Hew Crawford.—Second son of John Bell of Alderston. *Married* 14 March 1774, Clementina (*died* 29 November 1811), daughter of John Blair of Dunskey, Wigtownshire. *Died* 12 July 1776.

BELL, JOHN, OF GREENHILL [24 November 1774]. Apprentice to John Bell.—Eldest son of Richard Bell of Between-the-Waters, Dumfriesshire. *Born* 12 September 1748. Drowned while bathing in the Kirtle, 9 September 1776.

BELL, JOHN, OF CRAIGEOCH [8 May 1798]. Apprentice to James Dundas.—Eldest son of John Bell. W.S. *Died* 15 November 1852, unmarried.

BELL, JOHN, OF CASTLECREAVIE [21 January 1874]. Apprentice to William Waddell.—Son of William Bell of Gribdae, Kirkcudbrightshire. *Born* 17 July 1848. *Married* 14 April 1879, Agnes (*died* 7 October 1910), eldest surviving daughter of James Newall of Goldielea, Kirkcudbrightshire. Deputy Keeper of the Great Seal, 1882. *Died* on or about 22 October 1894.

BELL, JOHN BEATSON, OF KILDUNCAN [28 February 1828]. Apprentice to Charles Nairne.—Eldest son of Rev. Andrew Bell of Kilduncan, Minister of Crail. *Born* 23 September 1802. *Married* 16 December 1830, Ann (*died* 23 June 1881), eldest daughter of Charles Young, Merchant in Leith. *Died* 15 May 1868.

BELL, JOHN CLARK [17 December 1934]. Apprentice to William Henry Fraser & Another of Fraser, Stodart & Ballingall.—Son of Thomas Bell, Civil Servant, Edinburgh. *Born* 17 May 1904. *Married* 11 August 1936, Christina Graham Campbell (*died* 14 January 1974). *Firm*—Russell & Dunlop.

BELL, JOHN MACKINTOSH, OF ROUNDSTONEFOOT [12 March 1894]. Apprentice to Sir John Gillespie and Thomas Paterson.—Son of Christopher Bell, Cashier of the Bank of Scotland, Edinburgh. *Born* 16 June 1871. *Married* 5 October 1925, Eliza Frances (*died* 10 April 1970), daughter of George Wright of Park Lane Hall, Doncaster. Transport Officer 3/5 K.O.S.B., 1915-19. *Died* 31 May 1951.

BELL, JOHN MONTGOMERIE [27 November 1862]. Apprentice to, and eldest son of, Alexander Montgomerie Bell, W.S.—*Born* 28 May 1837. *Married* 26 July 1870, Elizabeth Jane (*died* 11 December 1919), daughter of Henry Simpson, Selville, Portobello. *Died* 8 June 1910.

BELL, JOHN MONTGOMERIE [11 December 1911]. Apprentice to John Patrick Wright and Thomas M. Murray.—Only son of Matthew Montgomerie Bell, W.S. *Born* 30 June 1879. *Married* 16 April 1913, Jean (*died* 28 January 1972), youngest daughter of Lieut.-Colonel James Farquharson Macleod, C.M.G., Judge of the Supreme Court, North-West Territories, Canada. Served in France, Lieutenant 50th Canadian Infantry. Resident in Calgary, Alberta. *Died* 20 January 1946.

BELL, JOHN ROBIN SINCLAIR, B.A.(OXON), LL.B. [30 November 1959]. Apprentice to William Edgar Gray Muir and Others of Morton, Smart, Macdonald & Prosser.—Son of Ian Cardean Bell, O.B.E., M.C., Seed Merchant, Edinburgh. *Born* 28 February 1933. *Married* 27 April 1963, Patricia, daughter of Edward Upton of Martin-in-Cleveland, near Middlesbrough, Yorkshire. *Firm*—Tods, Murray & Jamieson.

BELL, KENNETH DRUMMOND, M.A.(CANTAB), LL.B. [27 March 1946]. Apprentice to R. Nevill Dundas and Others of Dundas & Wilson.—Son of H. J. Bell, Civil Engineer and Surveyor, Perth. *Born* 19 May 1915. *Married* (1) 13 September 1945, Joan Ellen Archer (divorced) and (2) 1 September 1964, Peggy Mary Lethbridge-Meyers (divorced 1971). Captain, Black Watch, Emergency Commission. Served Middle East, Palestine, Egypt, Aden, British Somaliland, Crete and Cyrenaica 1940-45. Political Officer in Aden and Gold Coast between 1945 and 1956. District Magistrate, Supreme Court, Ghana 1956-58.

BELL, KENNETH HAMILTON [19 November 1951]. *Born* 4 March 1911. Apprentice to T. J. Carlyle Gifford of Messrs. Baillie & Gifford. Present address unknown.

BELL, MATTHEW MONTGOMERIE [26 May 1864]. Apprentice to John Dundas, William Wilson, and Alexander Montgomerie Bell.—Second son of John Montgomerie Bell, Advocate, Sheriff of Kincardineshire. *Born* 5 March 1840. *Married* 4 April 1877, Jane Caroline (*died* 9 November 1877), second surviving daughter of James Cockburne, Rampore, Beauleah, Bengal. *Died* 7 February 1917.

BELL, MICHAEL JOHN, M.A., LL.B. [18 July 1966]. Apprentice to F. H. Simpson and Others of Fyfe Ireland & Co.—Son of L. J. A. Bell. *Born* 16 January 1941. *Married* (1) 2 October 1971, Hilary Anne, daughter of Dr Maurice O'Neill, and (2) 16 May 1980, Sarah Alison Goode. *Firm*—Drummond & Co.

BELL, RICHARD, OF CASTLE O'ER CRURIE [2 August 1859]. Apprentice to James Steuart.—Son of George Graham Bell of Crurie, Advocate. *Born* 12 September 1833. *Married* (1) 29 July 1864, Jane (*died* 6 June 1876), daughter of William Aitchison of Briery Hill; (2) 19 June 1878, Margaret Elizabeth (*died* 7 March 1879), daughter of Captain David Marshall, H.E.I.C.S.; and (3) 14 September 1880, Henrietta May (*died* 7 July 1926), second surviving daughter of S. H. May Somerville of Whitecroft. *Died* 25 May 1909.

BELL, ROBERT [29 November 1673]. Apprentice to Patrick Don.—*Married* March 1673, Margaret Lumsden (? daughter of Rev. Charles Lumsden, Minister of Duddingston). *Buried* 28 January 1685.

BELL, ROBERT [22 June 1784]. Apprentice to William Macdonald.—Eldest son of Rev. William Bell, one of the Ministers of Edinburgh. *Married* Mary Hamilton (*died* 9 January 1838), granddaughter of Claud Hamilton, Writer, Maybole. Admitted Advocate, 4 July 1812. Lecturer on Conveyancing. Author of *A Dictionary of the Law of Scotland*, and other legal works. *Died* 1 November 1816.

BELL, ROBERT [11 July 1938]. Apprentice to R. St. Clair Jameson and J. S. Bayne.—Son of William Bell, Ironmonger, Edinburgh. *Born* 22 April 1901. *Married* 11 September 1926, Elizabeth Ann, daughter of William Woodburn, Stonemason. Treasurer of the City of Edinburgh. *Died* at Naples, 12 October 1955. *Firm*—Boyd, Jameson & Young.

BELL, ROBERT CRAIGIE [26 May 1864]. Apprentice to John Ord Mackenzie and William Robert Baillie.—Second son of Benjamin Bell, Surgeon in Edinburgh. *Born* 13 September 1840. *Married* 20 July 1866, Isabella Moubray (*died* 21 June 1911), daughter of Rev. Lewis Hay Irving, Free Church Minister, Falkirk. *Died* 11 May 1912.

BELL, THOMAS CLARK, LL.B. [29 July 1968]. Apprentice to Ian R. Pitman & Others of J. & F. Anderson.—Son of John Clark Bell, W.S., Edinburgh. *Born* 7 April 1943. *Married* 15 May 1971, Catherine Marjorie, daughter of J. B. B. Lamb. *Firms*—(1) Russell & Dunlop; (2) Pairman Miller & Murray.

BELL, WILLIAM [16 June 1807]. Apprentice to Hugh Corrie.—Third son of Benjamin Bell of Hunthill, Surgeon in Edinburgh. *Born* 1783. *Married* 11 September 1809, Margaret Jane (*died* 31 August 1866), youngest daughter of John Craigie of Glendoick. Crown Agent, 1840-41. *Died* 19 June 1849.

BELL, WILLIAM BURT-MARSHALL, B.L. [20 July 1925]. Apprentice to George Dunlop, J. A. S. Millar, J. H. Guild, and J. S. L. Millar.—Son of John Bell of Castlecreavie, W.S. *Born* 7 November 1883. *Married* 10 July 1919, Ella Katherine Caroline, daughter of John Phillips of Earl's Hill House, Royston, Herts. Served with R.E. (Signals) Belgium and France, 1914-15; Egypt, Palestine, and Syria 1916-19; later became Major, Royal Corps of Signals. 1914 Star. *Died* 11 June 1943. *Firm*—Russell and Dunlop.

BELL-SCOTT, EUAN TODDY MORISON, LL.B. [11 December 1979].—Son of Thomas Brash Morison Bell-Scott, Shipping Manager, Edinburgh. *Born* 12 February 1954. *Married* 26 August 1978, Elizabeth Anne, daughter of Edward Hartley, Sales Manager, Perth. *Firm*—Russel & Aitken.

BEMBRIDGE, PETER CHRISTOPHER, LL.B. [4 December 1972]. Apprentice to (1) H. J. Haldane and Another of Haldanes, McLaren & Scott, and (2) C. A. Fraser of W. & J. Burness.—Son of Dr B. A. Bembridge, London. *Born* 11 August 1943. *Married* 31 July 1971, Alexandra Adriane, daughter of F. P. Küthe, Amsterdam.

BENNET, JAMES [11 December 1828]. Apprentice to Alexander Robertson.—Son of James Bennett, Merchant in Buckie. *Married* 25 April 1825, Margaret (*died* 1874), only daughter of William McKimmie, Elgin. *Died* 1859, aged 65.

BENNETT-CLARK, THOMAS WILFRID, LL.B. [13 December 1910]. Apprentice to William Campbell M'Ewen.—Son of George Bennet Clark, W.S. *Born* 12 November 1886. Mobilised as Lieutenant in 9th Batt. (Highlanders) The Royal Scots at outbreak of War and served in France and Flanders and Army of the Rhine, 1915-19. *Died* 11 November 1963. *Firm*—J. and A. F. Adam.

BENNETT, ALEXANDER [5 March 1835]. Apprentice to, and eldest son of, William Bennett, W.S. *Born* 25 September 1811. *Married* 8 March 1846, Isabella Nelson (*died* 1863). *Died* 17 February 1855.

BENNETT, DAVID ANDREW, M.A., LL.B. [26 November 1962]. Apprentice to Alastair Campbell Blair and Others of Davidson & Syme.—Son of Andrew Carmichael Bennett, Solicitor, Edinburgh. *Born* 27 March 1938. *Married* 6 October 1962, Marion Miller, daughter of William Park, Keeper of Manuscripts, National Library of Scotland, Edinburgh. Scottish Editor "Palmer's Company Law". *Firm*—A. C. Bennett & Fairweather (formerly A. C. Bennett & Son).

BENNETT, JAMES WILLIAM [29 March 1905]. Apprentice to Archibald S. Leslie.—Son of George William Bennett, Merchant and Member of Legislative Council, Antigua, Leeward Islands. *Born* 16 January 1879. *Married* 18 August 1920, Mary Arthur (*died* 6 June 1980), daughter of James Turnbull Richardson, M.D. Became a Tea-planter in Ceylon and a J.P. and unofficial Police Magistrate there. *Died* 9 July 1958.

BENNETT, WILLIAM [18 November 1817]. Apprentice to Thomas Scott.—Son of Andrew Bennett, Farmer at Brunstane, Mid-Lothian. *Married* —— (*died* 9 October 1857). *Died* 17 January 1843, aged 62.

BERRY, WILLIAM, OF TAYFIELD [16 January 1798]. Apprentice to (1) Lawrence Hill, and (2) Harry Davidson.—Son of John Berry of Bogie and Tayfield, Fife. *Born* 23 March 1774. *Married* 23 September 1823, Isabella (*died* January 1877), daughter of Sir Robert Bruce Henderson of Fordel, Bart. *Died* 9 December 1852.

BERRY, WILLIAM, M.A., LL.B. [3 December 1965]. Apprentice to Arthur Woodman Blair & Others of Strathern & Blair.—Son of John Berry of Tayfield, C.B.E., D.L., LL.D., Ph.D., Director of Nature Conservancy for Scotland (Retired), Newport-on-Tay, Fife. *Born* 26 September 1939. *Married* 15 December 1973, Elizabeth Margery, daughter of Sir Edward R. Warner, K.C.M.G., O.B.E. *Firm*—Murray, Beith & Murray.

BERTRAM, JOHN PRIMEROSE [11 June 1829]. Apprentice to James Nairne.—Eldest son of John Bertram, Corn Merchant in St Andrews. *Born* 1803. *Married* 1 October 1833, Georgina (*died* 12 February 1855), third daughter of James Turnbull. *Died* 16 October 1849. *Firm*—Nairne & Bertram.

BERTRAM, ROBERT DAVID DARNEY, M.A.(OXON), LL.B. [1 December 1969]. Apprentice to J. C. R. Inglis & Others of Dundas & Wilson.—Son of D. N. S. Bertram, Paper Merchant, Edinburgh. *Born* 6 October 1941. *Married* 23 September 1967, Patricia Joan, daughter of John Laithwaite, Engineer, St Helens, Lancashire. *Firm*—Dundas & Wilson (formerly Dundas & Wilson, Davidson & Syme).

BEVAN, JOHN STUART, M.A., LL.B. [11 December 1979]. Apprentice to Robert William Stewart Gray and Others of Ketchen & Stevens.—Son of John Campbell Bevan, Bank Manager, Kirkwall, Orkney. *Born* 10 July 1948. *Married* 16 September 1977, Anne Fiona, daughter of Sheriff Douglas Alexander Donald of Inverness. *Firm*—Ketchen & Stevens.

BEVERIDGE, JAMES [18 December 1826]. Apprentice to (1) Robert Graham, and (2) Adam M'Cheyne.—Son of William Beveridge, W.S. *Born* 1800. *Married* (1) Louisa Fuche; and (2) 4 September 1855, Matilda Wynne (*died* 1873). *Died* 16 August 1869.

BEVERIDGE, THOMAS KNOX [27 June 1833]. Apprentice to John Murray.—Son of Thomas Beveridge, Writer in Edinburgh. *Born* 1 August 1807. *Married* 22 April 1834, Ann (*died* 9 February 1879), youngest daughter of Dr Patrick Mushet of Birkhill, Stirlingshire. *Died* 11 April 1858.

BEVERIDGE, WILLIAM [8 August 1785]. Apprentice to James Thomson.—Second son of James Beveridge, Writer in Edinburgh. *Married* 22 November 1791, Barbara (*died* 16 June 1832), daughter of James May of Eddoch. *Died* 5 June 1807, aged 43.

BICKARTOUN, HARRY [Before 1586]. Commissioner, 16 December 1594. Fiscal, 1598-1601. *Married* Violet Tuedy (*died* 1625). *Died* 1601.

BIGGAR, JOHN MORRISON HAY, LL.B. [26 April 1976]. Apprentice to Kenneth Macrae and Others of Murray, Beith & Murray.—Son of Gordon Buchanan Biggar, Architect, Stirling. *Born* 21 January 1951. *Married* 29 March 1975, Annette Gillian, daughter of David Andrew Stuart Martin, Consultant Oral Surgeon, Perth. *Firm*—Murray, Beith & Murray.

BIGGART, THOMAS NORMAN, M.A., LL.B., O.St.J. [2 December 1974]. Apprentice to Thomas Patrick Spens of Maclay, Murray & Spens.—Son of Andrew Stevenson Biggart, Solicitor, Glasgow. *Born* 24 January 1930. *Married* 15 November 1956, Eileen Jean Anne, daughter of James Henderson Gemmell. *Firm*—Biggart, Baillie & Gifford (formerly Biggart, Lumsden & Co., Glasgow).

BILTON, LEWIS [16 November 1871]. Apprentice to John M. Lindsay and Alexander Howe.—Son of Captain Lewis Bilton, R.N. *Born* 16 October 1843. *Married* 11 June 1873, Hannah Marion (*died* 20 February 1929), youngest daughter of John Dorlin Grayson, Shipbuilder, Liverpool. *Died* 4 December 1924. *Firm*—L. and L. L. Bilton.

BILTON, LEWIS LEONARD, C.M.G. [12 December 1904]. Apprentice to William Augustus Hartley.—Son of Lewis Bilton, W.S. *Born* 4 October 1879. *Married* 30 November 1911, Helen Rachel (*died* 7 January 1965), eldest daughter of Neil Robson, Managing Director of Dixons Ltd., Ironmasters, Glasgow. Served abroad from August 1915 to June 1918. Second in command 17th Batt. The Royal Scots, afterwards Lieut.-Colonel commanding 2/8th Batt. The Worcestershire Regt. (T.). Twice mentioned in Despatches; awarded C.M.G. and Croix-de-Guerre Belgique. *Died* 2 December 1954. *Firm*—L. and L. L. Bilton.

BILTON, LEWIS NEIL [14 March 1938]. Apprentice to Lewis Leonard Bilton of L. & L. L. Bilton.—Son of Lewis Leonard Bilton, W.S., Edinburgh. *Born* 18 February 1914. Captain Royal Artillery. Served U.K. and Italy 1939-45. *Firm*—Kilgour, Macneill & Syme (formerly L. & L. L. Bilton and Macneill & Sime). (Retired.)

BINNIE, JOHN JAMES SIMPSON [20 March 1933]. Apprentice to Francis Chalmers and Patrick Turner Mackintosh.—Son of James Binnie, Solicitor, Grangemouth. *Born* 7 August 1909. *Married* 9 May 1955, Maude, daughter of John Maxwell, Grangemouth. Served 1942-45 in R.A. as Bombardier, U.K., Middle East and N.W. Europe. Provost of Grangemouth 1953-56. Joint Actuary Grangemouth Savings Bank. *Died* 2 June 1967. *Firm*—Binnie and Binnie, Grangemouth.

BINNING, ALEXANDER MONRO, OF AUCHENBOWIE [5 March 1829]. Apprentice to James Dundas.—Son of David Monro Binning of Softlaw. *Born* 28 May 1805. *Married* 4 August 1835, Harriet (*died* 7 March 1898), daughter of Dr Alexander Monro of Craiglockhart, Mid-Lothian. *Died* 12 December 1891.

BINNY, GRAHAM [12 November 1829]. Apprentice to James Laidlaw Mitchell.—Son of Andrew Binny, of the Excise, Dundee. *Born* 2 August 1800. *Married* 31 July 1826, Marianne (*died* 16 March 1891), daughter of Thomas Kyd, of the Exchequer, Edinburgh. *Died* 12 November 1882.

BINNY, JOHN [15 March 1861]. Apprentice to, and son of, Graham Binny, W.S.—*Born* 6 July 1837. *Married* 26 August 1869, Euphemia Bremner (*died* 14 September 1910), eldest daughter of David Crole, Solicitor to Inland Revenue, Edinburgh. *Died* 13 July 1873.

BIRRELL, ANDREW DAVID, LL.B. [9 December 1980]. Apprentice to George Lovat Fraser Henry and Others of Shepherd & Wedderburn.—Son of David Birrell, W.S., Edinburgh. *Born* 17 August 1956.

BIRRELL, DAVID, B.L. [20 March 1950]. Apprentice to The Hon. Adam George Watson and Others of Mackenzie Innes & Logan.—Son of William Birrell, Police Inspector, Edinburgh. *Born* 6 November 1924. *Married* 18 November 1955, Jean Pamella, daughter of Horace Sydney George Grant, London Port Authority Clerk. Flight Sergeant Royal Air Force Reserve Service 1944-48. *Firm*—Dundas & Wilson (formerly Davidson & Syme).

BIRRELL, GEORGE [1 July 1824]. Apprentice to (1) Henry Moncrieff; and (2) James Stuart.—Son of George Birrell, of Hon. East India Company's Service. *Born* 1800. *Married* 29 December 1832, Lucy (*died* 10 July 1885), eldest daughter of Hon. Charles Chipchase, Comptroller of the Customs, Island of St Lucia. Barrister of the Inner Temple, 9 December 1831, and Senior Member of Legislative Council of St Lucia. Attorney-General of Bahamas. *Died* 9 March 1837.

BIRRELL, JAMES GIBSON, B.A. [11 December 1979*]. Son of James Adamson Birrell, C.A., Carnoustie. *Born* 10 June 1948. *Married* 15 August 1970, Angela Hilary, daughter of Eric Soame, Personnel Officer, Abingdon, Oxfordshire. Qualified English Solicitor, 1972. New Inn Prize, 1972. *Firm*—Brodies.

BIRS, SAMUEL [Before 1606]. Signs Minute of 17 January 1606.—Son of Alexander Birs, Tailor Burgess of Edinburgh. *Married* (contract, 7 June 1601), Alison, daughter of Robert Glen of Inchkeire. *Died* 25 December 1616.

BISHOP, WILLIAM CLARK [18 January 1877]. Apprentice to John Dundas and William Wilson.—Son of John Baillie Bishop, Secretary of the Royal Bank of Scotland. *Born* 10 November 1849. *Married* (1) 14 October 1880, Mary (*died* 16 January 1900), daughter of John Jamieson of Kingask, Fife; and (2) 20 June 1914, Janet Mary (*died* 20 July 1969), daughter of James Johnstone, Dunelm, Lasswade. *Died* 22 April 1935.

BISSET, ALEXANDER JAMES RAMSAY, B.L. [15 March 1948]. Apprentice to T. J. Carlyle Gifford and Another of Baillie & Gifford.—Son of James Lamb Bisset, Builder, Musselburgh. *Born* 2 March 1914. *Married* 12 December 1945, Betty Anderson, daughter of James Colin Campbell Macarthur, Farmer, Elvanfoot, Lanarkshire. Captain Seaforth Highlanders, 51st Highland Division France 1939-40. Prisoner of war in Germany until 1945. *Firm*—Biggart, Baillie & Gifford (formerly Baillie & Gifford).

BISSET, HABAKKUK [Before 1586]. Reputed Author of *Ane short form of Process*, 1609. Clerk to Sir John Skene, Lord Clerk Register. Suspended for having no gown, 9 March 1610. Was one of the greatest oddities of his time. *Married* Agnes Wedderburn. His *Rolments of Courtis*, 3 vols., published by Scottish Text Society, 1919-25.

BISSET, ROBERT [Before 1609]. Mentioned 1609. *Died* before 1632.

BLACK, ALEXANDER DAVID MARTIN [29 November 1866]. Apprentice to (1) David M. Black; and (2) Colin Mackenzie.—Son of Rev. Patrick Black, residing at Worcester, Cape Colony. *Born* 24 September 1843. *Married* (1) 6 December 1866, Catherine Gibson Ramsay, only daughter of James Hackings, Inveresk; (2) 10 September 1872, his cousin, Mary Helen (*died* 23 March 1899), only daughter of Alexander Schulze, M.D., Victoria; and (3) 28 December 1899, Hannah (*died* 28 June 1923), eldest daughter of Rev. W. Lindsay Alexander, D.D., of Pinkieburn. *Died* 21 December 1911. *Firm*—Mackenzie and Black.

BLACK, ALEXANDER WILLIAM [19 October 1885]. Apprentice to John William Young and John Blair.—Third son of Rev. James Black, Minister of the Free Church at Dunnikier. *Born* 28 February 1859. *Married* 17 October 1888, Ellinor (*died* 14 June 1918), second daughter of Admiral Thomas Wilson, C.B., Edinburgh. M.P. for Banffshire, 1900-6. *Died* 29 December 1906—the result of a railway accident at Elliot Junction near Arbroath. *Firm*—Menzies, Coventry, and Black.

BLACK, CHARLES RITCHIE, M.A., LL.B. [12 July 1937]. Apprentice to John Richardson of Scott Moncrieff & Trail.—Son of The Rev. William R. Black, Edinburgh. *Born* 2 July 1908. *Married* 22 December 1937, Margery Anne, daughter of Alexander McKinna, C.B.E., Edinburgh. Major, R.A.S.C., in North Africa, Sicily, Italy and Orkneys. *Firm*—Warden, Bruce & Co.

BLACK, COLIN MACKENZIE, C.V.O. [24 March 1902]. Apprentice to, and son of, A. D. M. Black, W.S.—*Born* 7 October 1877. *Married* 8 July 1911, Rose Emily (*died* 3 October 1958), daughter of Rev. Canon Knox Little, and widow of Fred. Usher. Member of the King's Bodyguard for Scotland, Royal Company of Archers, 1902: Secretary later. Served in Great War with 60th Rifles (K.R.R.C.) and Staff in France. *Died* 5 October 1943. *Firm*—Mackenzie and Black.

BLACK, DAVID MARTIN [20 December 1821]. Apprentice to Alexander L. Ramage, John Blair, and William Bell.—Second son of Rev. Alexander Black, Minister of the Associate Burgher Congregation at Musselburgh. *Died* 5 April 1865, aged 68, unmarried.

BLACK, JAMES TODD, M.A., LL.B. [20 December 1948]. Apprentice to Thomas Rankin Wilson of Finlay & Wilson.—Son of John R. Black, Civil Servant, Edinburgh. *Born* 20 May 1922. *Married* 9 October 1953, Morag Jean, daughter of George Learmonth, Orkney. Flight Lieutenant R.A.F.; Served U.K., Italy and Kenya, 1941-46. *Firms*—(1) Drever & Heddle, Kirkwall 1953-58; (2) John Dickson & Son, Huntly.

BLACK, WILLIAM [13 July 1903]. Apprentice to James Mylne and Archibald Brown Campbell.—Son of Gavin Black of Wester Moffat, Coalmaster, Airdrie. *Born* 1 December 1878. *Married* 2 June 1904, Helen Mary Gray (*died* 18 December 1973), youngest daughter of John Campbell, S.S.C. Served in Salonica and France, Lieutenant R.A.S.C. (M.T.) *Died* 21 July 1966. *Firm*—Bruce and Black.

BLACKBURN, RICHARD FREDERICK [29 October 1880]. Apprentice to C. Mackenzie, A. D. M. Black, and J. M. Mackenzie.—Son of Robert Bogle Blackburn, Advocate, Sheriff of Stirling and Dumbarton. *Born* 17 July 1854. *Died* 18 September 1884, unmarried.

BLACKIE, DAVID [30 November 1819]. Apprentice to James Little.—Second son of Robert Blackie, Merchant in Kirkcudbright. *Born* 2 August 1825, Margaret (*died* 30 October 1884), only daughter of David Briggs of Strathairly, Fife. Editor, *Edinburgh Evening Post. Died* 2 September 1832.

BLACKWOOD, JAMES [21 December 1837]. Apprentice to Donald Horne.—Son of William Blackwood, Publisher in Edinburgh. *Born* 6 July 1814. *Died* 17 October 1871, unmarried.

BLACKWOOD, WILLIAM THORBURN, M.C., LL.B. [9 December 1907]. Apprentice to Frank Hunter.—Son of William Blackwood, Writer and County Clerk, Peebles. *Born* 10 April 1883. *Married* 8 July 1938 Catherine Edgar Glendinning (*died* 20 April 1968). Joint County Clerk of Peeblesshire, 1926. Clerk of the Peace for County of Peebles, 5 November 1928. Served in France with 8th Royal Scots, 1917-19; latterly Major commanding 51st Highland Divisional Reception Camp, France. *Died* 20 November 1957. *Firm*—Blackwood and Smith, Peebles.

BLAIR, ALAN HATCHARD, M.A., LL.B. [6 December 1971]. Apprentice to K. A. McLellan and Others of Dundas & Wilson.—Son of Sir Alastair C. Blair, K.V.C.O., W.S., Edinburgh. *Born* 26 March 1946. *Firm*—Dundas & Wilson (formerly Dundas & Wilson, Davidson & Syme) (resigned 1979).

BLAIR, Sir ALASTAIR CAMPBELL, K.C.V.O., B.A.(Cantab), LL.B. [19 December 1932]. Apprentice to William Henry Fraser & Others of Fraser Stodart & Ballingall.—Son of William Blair, W.S., Edinburgh. Born 16 January 1908. *Married* 30 March 1933, Catriona Hatchard, daughter of William Basil Orr, M.D. Major 94th Heavy AA Regiment R.A. Served in U.K., Middle East, Italy. Mentioned in Despatches, 30 June 1942. K.C.V.O. 1969. T.D. 1950. Secretary Queen's Bodyguard for Scotland, Royal Company of Archers 1946-59. Purse Bearer to Lord High Commissioner to the General Assembly of the Church of Scotland 1961-69. Retired 1977. *Firm*—Dundas & Wilson (formerly Davidson & Syme).

BLAIR, ALEXANDER [14 July 1628]. Apprentice to Robert Wynram.

BLAIR, ALEXANDER, of Dunrod [22 November 1790]. Apprentice to John Hunter.—Only son of Hugh Blair of Dunrod, Kirkcudbrightshire. *Born* 8 September 1766. *Married* 24 July 1800, Agnes (died 22 May 1809), second daughter of Sir David Maxwell of Cardoness, Bart. *Died* 24 June 1844.

BLAIR, ALEXANDER STEVENSON, C.M.G., C.B.E., T.D., D.L., B.A.(Oxon) [28 October 1889]. Apprentice to J. P. Wright and R. B. Blyth.—Eldest son of Patrick Blair, Advocate, Sheriff-Substitute of Inverness-shire, and grandson of Alexander Stevenson, W.S. *Born* 3 June 1865. *Married* 1 June 1892, Elinor Woodman (*died* 12 August 1949), second daughter of Arthur Woodman Dixon, Sunderland. C.M.G., 14 January 1916. T.D., 1918. Member of the King's Bodyguard for Scotland, Royal Company of Archers, 1920. Deputy-Lieutenant for County of City of Edinburgh, 1928. C.B.E., 1933. Fiscal, 1928-35. Lord Rector's Assessor on University Court, 1933. Lieut.-Colonel commanding 9th Batt. (Highlanders) The Royal Scots (T.F.), with British Expeditionary Force in France, 1915-17. Twice mentioned in Despatches. *Died* 10 September 1936. *Firm*—Strathern and Blair.

BLAIR, ARCHIBALD, B.A.(Cantab) [28 March 1904]. Apprentice to J. P. Wood, W. Babington, and Joseph Inglis.—Son of John Blair, W.S., Edinburgh. *Born* 10 February 1879. *Married* 26 July 1907, Mary Freer (*died* 25 November 1957), daughter of William Robert Ovens of The Peel, Selkirkshire. Lieutenant in the Royal Scots and Royal Air Force. Wounded, May 1915. *Died* 12 May 1955. *Firm*—Davidson and Syme.

BLAIR, ARTHUR WOODMAN, B.A.(OXON), LL.B. [20 July 1925]. Apprentice to Alexander Stevenson Blair and Another of Strathern & Blair.—Son of Alexander Stevenson Blair, W.S. *Born* 13 September 1901. *Married* 7 October 1926, Euphane Mary, daughter of Henry Edward Richardson, W.S. Major R.A., U.K. 1939-44. *Firm*—Strathern & Blair. (Consultant.)

BLAIR, GAVIN, OF BRAXFIELD. Apprentice to Robert Williamson.—Brother of Rev. James Blair, Minister of Port Montgomerie. M.P. for Lanark, 1617-21. Purchased lands of Braxfield, 1613. *Married* Janet Robertson. *Died* 1632.

BLAIR, GAVIN [9 June 1629]. Apprentice to Sir William Scott of Elie and Arthur Hamilton.—*Died* before 1652.

BLAIR, HUGH, OF AUCHENREOCH [22 November 1827]. Apprentice to, and son of, Alexander Blair, W.S.—*Born* 21 March 1806. *Married* 8 November 1833, Ann Gordon (*died* 20 June 1887), daughter of Patrick Sanderson of Sir William Forbes and Company, Bankers, Edinburgh. *Died* 5 January 1878.

BLAIR, JOHN [21 December 1809]. Apprentice to Robert Boswell.—Eldest son of John Blair of Garshake, Merchant in Glasgow. *Born* 1779. *Married* 24 December 1813, his cousin Margaret (*died* 19 February 1832), third daughter of Horatius Cannan, W.S. *Died* 21 April 1858.

BLAIR, JOHN [17 October 1878]. Apprentice to John William Young.—Second son of William Blair, Dalry, Ayrshire. *Born* 22 December 1839. *Married* 22 June 1869, Ann Miller (*died* 11 May 1896), youngest daughter of James Mather, Marionville, Trinity. *Died* 8 June 1903. *Firm*—Davidson and Syme.

BLAIR, JOHN WOODMAN, B.A.(OXON), LL.B. [27 April 1964]. Apprentice to John Herbert Richardson and Others of Dundas & Wilson.—Son of Arthur Woodman Blair, W.S. *Born* 25 January 1937. *Married* 2 April 1976, Claire Lucy, daughter of Sheriff Harold Ford. *Firm*—Strathern & Blair.

BLAIR, PATRICK [9 February 1860]. Apprentice to James Shepherd, T. M. Grant, and William Cuthbertson.—Second son of Hugh Blair, W.S. *Born* 4 October 1836. *Married* (1) 3 December 1873, Hon. Eleonora Jane Ross (*died* 25 April 1896), daughter of James, Lord Moncrieff of Tulliebole; and (2) 18 October 1899, Elizabeth Hunter (*died* 17 May 1917), daughter of William Thomas, Dundee, and widow of Archibald Anderson Watt of Denmylie, Fife. *Died* 10 November 1910.

BLAIR, ROBERT KERR [27 March 1899]. Apprentice to Patrick Blair.—Son of Alexander Blair, Sheriff of the Lothians and Peebles. *Born* 1 November 1876. *Married* 14 October 1902, May (*died* 20 October 1939), daughter of James Craik, W.S. *Died* 14 January 1942. *Firm*—Blair and Cadell.

BLAIR, ROBERT LEIGHTON ALEXANDER, LL.B. [11 December 1979*].—Son of Peter Chrystal Blair, Sales Manager, Edinburgh. *Born* 1 July 1951. *Married* 4 September 1976. Daphne Helena, daughter of William Marshall Hamilton Henderson, Farmer, Dunbar, *Firm*—Connell & Connell.

BLAIR, ROBIN ORR., M.A., LL.B. [3 December 1965]. Apprentice to The Hon. William Douglas Watson and Others of Fraser, Stodart & Ballingall.—Son of Sir Alastair C. Blair, K.C.V.O., W.S., Edinburgh. *Born* 1 January 1940. *Married* 20 May 1972, Elizabeth Caroline McCallum, daughter of Ian McCallum Webster. *Firm*—Dundas & Wilson (formerly Davidson & Syme).

BLAIR, THOMAS [Before 1586]. *Died* apparently before 1594.

BLAIR, WILLIAM [9 August 1782]. Apprentice to Isaac Grant.—Second son of William Blair of Thornhill. *Married* Ann Blair. *Died* 12 May 1800.

BLAIR, WILLIAM [14 December 1896]. Apprentice to, and son of, John Blair, W.S.—*Born* 5 April 1870. *Married* 27 June 1901, Emelia Mylne (*died* 3 July 1960), daughter of John Campbell, S.S.C. *Died* 5 January 1954. *Firm*—Davidson and Syme.

BLAKE, RICHARD PETER JAMIESON, LL.B. [13 May 1980*].—Son of Peter Douglas Jamieson Blake, Hotelier, Garvald. *Born* 21 October 1954. *Married* 4 September 1979, Mary Diana, daughter of Rev. William Glazebrook, Dollar.

BLANE, ANDREW, OF BLANEFIELD [24 November 1774]. Apprentice to Allan Clarke.— Eldest son of Gilbert Blane of Blanefield. *Born* 1744. Sheriff-Clerk of Ayrshire, 1815-21. *Died* 9 October 1839, unmarried.

BLYTH, ROBERT BRITTAIN [19 April 1876]. Apprentice to Alexander Hamilton, G. T. Kinnear, and Robert Beatson.—Second son of Benjamin Hall Blyth, Civil Engineer in Edinburgh. *Born* 13 December 1850. *Died* 8 September 1886, unmarried.

BOGLE, ANDREW [26 May 1842]. Apprentice to Harry Davidson.—Son of Andrew Bogle, Cashier of the Royal Bank of Scotland. *Born* 23 March 1811. *Married* 7 April 1863, Margaret Robertson (*died* 9 March 1889), daughter of John M'Kean, W.S. *Died* 4 October 1871.

BOGLE, DAVID BLYTH, C.B.E., M.A., LL.B. [19 December 1927]. Apprentice to John Alexander Stevenson Millar and Others of Russell & Dunlop.—Son of The Very Rev. Andrew Nisbet Bogle, D.D. *Born* 22 January 1903. *Married* 15 October 1955, Ruth Agnes, daughter of Charles Howard Nicolson. C.B.E. 1967. Major, Queen's Own Cameron Highlanders. Served U.K. and Middle East 1940-45. Member of Council on Tribunals 1958-70 (Chairman Scottish Committee 1952-70). Returned 1972. *Firm*— Lindsays, W.S. (formerly Lindsay Howe & Co.).

BOGLE, JOHN, OF BOGLESHOLE [22 September 1713]. Clerk, 21 January 1712. *Married* Isobel, daughter of Claud Henderson. *Died* September 1743.

BOGUE, JOHN, OF HALLYDOWN [21 June 1787]. Apprentice to Thomas Cockburn.—Son of John Bogue of Hallydown, Berwickshire. *Born* 1740. *Married* August 1767, Margaret, daughter of Henry Anderson, Farmer, Broughton, Edinburgh. *Died* 7 September 1818.

BOGUE, WILLIAM HUTCHISON, M.A., LL.B. [28 April 1958]. Apprentice to Simon Fraser and Another of Blair and Cadell.—Son of William Bogue, Farmer, Gourlaw, Rosewell. *Born* 16 February 1936. *Married* 9 December 1961, Helen Elizabeth, daughter of William Edmond, Master of Works, Midlothian County Council. *Firm*— Davidson & Shirley, Lanark.

BOLTON, ROBERT BUCHANAN ALEXANDER, LL.B. [1 December 1969]. Apprentice to (1) Patrick Arthur McLean and Another of Robson, McLean & Paterson, and (2) Robert Thomas Peden and Another of D. & J. H. Campbell.—Son of Thomas Bolton, Solicitor, Crieff. *Born* 19 September 1945. *Married* 1 April 1969, Margaret Elizabeth, daughter of F. F. Crichton. *Firm*—Graham & Finlayson, Crieff.

BONAR, HORATIUS, OF RANFURLY [22 January 1874]. Apprentice to Thomas Thomson and David Scot Dickson.—Fourth son of Rev. John James Bonar, D.D., Minister of St Andrew's Free Church, Greenock. *Born* 31 July 1843. *Married* 25 July 1883, Mary (*died* 18 December 1945), younger daughter of Thomas Thomson, W.S. *Died* 2 February 1917.

BONAR, JAMES [22 November 1827]. Apprentice to Charles Tawse.—Eldest son of James Bonar, Solicitor of Excise, Edinburgh. *Born* 20 June 1801. *Married* 7 December 1859, Caroline (*died* 1 October 1892), daughter of Alexander Glennie of Maybank, Aberdeenshire. *Died* 11 July 1867.

BONAR, JOHN JAMES [31 July 1922]. Apprentice to Adam W. Gifford and Colin M. Black.—Son of Horatius Bonar, W.S. *Born* 29 September 1893. Served in France; Captain 6th Royal Scots, and attached to Tank Corps. *Died* 18 December 1973. *Firm*—Bonar, Hunter, and Johnstone.

BOOG WATSON, WILLIAM NAIRN, T.D., B.L., B.Sc. [30 November 1959]. Apprentice to Robert Watson Martin and Others of Simpson, Kinmont & Maxwell.—Son of Dr W. N. Boog Watson, Edinburgh. *Born* 20 March 1931. *Firm*—Simpson Kinmont & Maxwell.

BOOTH, JOSEPH [9 December 1830]. Apprentice to James Shepherd.—Son of George Booth, Watchmaker, Springbank, near Aberdeen. *Died* 13 August 1871, aged 68, unmarried.

BORTHWICK, FRANCIS JOHN GORDON [10 July 1893]. Apprentice to John Ord Mackenzie (his grandfather), H. Cheyne, and J. Kermack.—Son of Francis Borthwick, residing in London. *Born* 15 January 1871. *Married* 6 August 1912, Eugenie Helen Francklyn (*died* 29 June 1977), daughter of Edmund Stow Thomson of Pelham House, Folkestone. *Died* 22 May 1948. *Firm*—Mackenzie and Kermack.

BORTHWICK, JAMES [Before 1586]. Commissioner, 16 December 1594. *Married* Marion Somerville. Rothesay Herald and Lyon Clerk. *Died* November 1605.

BORTHWICK, LOUIS [28 February 1828]. Apprentice to William Bell.—Third son of John Borthwick of Crookston, Mid-Lothian. *Born* 1801. *Married* 19 July 1844, Susan (*died* 15 January 1859), third daughter of John Westgarth, Surveyor of Customs. *Died* 22 September 1876.

BOSWALL, JAMES DONALDSON [29 October 1894]. Apprentice to R. Dundas, W. J. Dundas, and G. M. Paul.—Eldest son of Major-General James Roper Boswall of Wardie. *Born* 11 October 1870. *Married* 23 April 1908, Theresa (*died* 10 July 1938), eldest daughter of H. Rassam, First Assistant Political Resident at Aden and British Envoy to Theodore, King of Abyssinia. Captain 10th Batt. Seaforth Highlanders; afterwards attached to 1st Batt. The Essex Regiment. Served in Gallipoli, and fell in action 6 June 1915.

BOSWELL, ALEXANDER [8 December 1808]. Apprentice to, and second son of, Robert Boswell, W.S.—*Born* 1781. *Married* 30 August 1803, Mary (*died* 28 December 1865), daughter of John Sandeman, Perth. Lyon Clerk-Depute, 13 January 1801-4. Sheriff-Substitute of Berwickshire, 1836-50. *Died* 30 August 1850.

BOSWELL, JOHN DOUGLAS, of GARALLAN, T.D., LL.B. [27 March 1911]. Apprentice to William Gibson.—Only son of Patrick Charles Douglas Boswell of Garallan, Ayrshire. *Born* 16 February 1867. *Married* 1 August 1907, Janet Alice (*died* 4 October 1930), daughter of Robert Angus, of Ladykirk, Ayrshire. Deputy-Lieutenant Ayrshire, 1919. Served in South African War, with Imperial Yeomanry. Hon. Captain in Army. Served in Great War, 1914-18, in Gallipoli, Egypt, Palestine, France, and Flanders. Lieut.-Colonel commanding Ayrshire Yeomanry and 12th Batt. Royal Scots Fusiliers. Serbian White Eagle. Member of the King's Bodyguard for Scotland, Royal Company of Archers, 1921. *Died* 5 January 1948. *Firm*—Tait and Crichton.

BOSWELL, ROBERT, OF ST BOSWELLS [25 February 1773]. Apprentice to Thomas Tod.— Second son of Dr John Boswell, Physician in Edinburgh. *Born* 30 January 1746. *Married* June 1769, Sibella (*died* 25 December 1835), daughter of William Sandeman, Merchant, Perth. Lyon Depute and Clerk, 2 November 1770. *Died* 1 April 1804.

BOW, HENRY HARDIE [17 November 1825]. Apprentice to Alexander Douglas.— Second son of Robert Bow, Merchant in Edinburgh. *Died* 24 November 1826.

BOW, JOHN MACKENZIE [11 April 1887]. Apprentice to Patrick William Campbell.— Eldest son of Dr John Campbell Bow, Deputy Surgeon-General in the Bengal Army. *Born* 7 May 1863. Enlisted in Canadian forces. *Killed* in action, 16 August 1917.

BOWEN, STANLEY DOUGLAS, LL.B. [6 December 1976]. Apprentice to James John Lamb and Others of Stuart & Stuart, Cairns & Co.—Son of Stanley Bowen, Crown Agent for Scotland (Retired), Edinburgh. *Born* 29 July 1953. *Married* 15 October 1977, Susan Esther, daughter of Albert Thomson, Printer, Edinburgh. *Firm*—Stuart & Stuart, Cairns & Co.

BOWES, WILLIAM FORSYTH [4 December 1967]. Apprentice to Robert Francis Shepherd & Others of Shepherd & Wedderburn.—Son of William Bowes, Toolmaker, Edinburgh. *Born* 12 February 1923. *Married* 17 September 1945, Marion, daughter of John Broadhurst, Farmer. Sergeant Royal Signals, War Office Wireless Station 1942-1947. *Firm*—Shepherd & Wedderburn.

BOWIE, JAMES McEWEN, M.A., LL.B. [15 December 1930]. Apprentice to Donald McCallum Smith and Others of W. & J. Burness.— Son of John Lyall Bowie, Solicitor, Perth. *Born* 25 February 1906. *Married* 3 October 1934, Grace Mackenzie (*died* 12 January 1974) daughter of James Mudie, Company Secretary, Dundee. Flight Lieutenant R.A.F. Served U.K. and Gibraltar 1940-45. *Died* 1 March 1974. *Firms*—J. & J. W. Lyall Bowie, Perth and Coupar Angus, and Watson & Lyall Bowie, Coupar Angus.

BOWIE, JOHN, OF CAMSISCAN [7 July 1815]. Apprentice to Donald Maclean.—Son of William Bowie of Camsiscan, Ayr. *Married* 15 March 1813, Maxwell Margaret (*died* 1878), daughter of Captain Duncan Macdougall of Ardentrive, Argyllshire. Solicitor to Inland Revenue. *Died* 28 January 1862, aged 70.

BOWIE, ROBERT GIBSON [12 March 1893]. Apprentice to Somerville Greig.—Son of John Tweedie Bowie, C.A., Edinburgh. *Born* 2 April 1869. *Married* 24 March 1898, Mary Agnes Rist (*died* 10 May 1952), daughter of James Francis Gordon Shirrefs-Gordon of Craig Castle, Aberdeenshire. *Died* 21 November 1949.

BOWMAN, HUGH CRAIG, M.A., LL.B. [9 December 1980*].—Son of William Stevenson Bowman, Personnel Manager, Edinburgh. *Born* 17 January 1953. *Firm*—Morton, Fraser & Milligan.

BOYD, ALEXANDER [4 March 1826]. Apprentice to Francis Wilson.—Son of William Boyd, W.S. *Born* 1802. *Married* 23 September 1828, Lucy Frances (*died* 21 January 1838), only daughter of Major John Duddingston, 28th Regiment. *Died* 28 November 1840.

BOYD, GEORGE WILLIAM [12 December 1816]. Apprentice to Henry Jardine.—Son of William Boyd of Marchhill, Dumfriesshire. *Born* 1794. *Married* 14 May 1850, Mary Ann Bennet. *Died* November 1882.

BOYD, HUGH [28 March 1927]. Apprentice to Robert William Cockburn and Another of Guild & Shepherd.—Son of John William Parker Boyd, M.B., C.M., Liverpool. *Born* 27 November 1903. *Married* 2 September 1933, Catherine Johnston, daughter of Alexander Stewart, Perth. *Died* 17 April 1982. *Firm*—Shepherd & Wedderburn.

BOYD, IAN JAMES, B.A.(Oxon), LL.B. [30 April 1970]. Apprentice to William Nairn Boog Watson and Another of Simpson, Kinmont & Maxwell.—Son of J. L. M. Boyd, Company Director, East India, Merchant. *Born* 14 December 1938. *Firm*—Simpson, Kinmont & Maxwell.

BOYD, IAN STEWART, B.A.(Cantab), B.L. [21 July 1965]. Apprentice to D. C. McConnachie and Others of Davidson & Syme.—Son of Hugh Boyd, W.S., Edinburgh. *Born* 27 July 1939. *Married* 4 July 1969, Sylvia, daughter of Alexander Logan McClure, W.S., Edinburgh. *Firm*—Shepherd & Wedderburn.

BOYD, JAMES. *Married* (contract, 26 April 1620) Katherine, daughter of Robert Hamilton, Merchant Burgess of Lanark.

BOYD, MURDOCH [16 January 1888]. Apprentice to John Hope Finlay.—Son of John Boyd, Publisher, Edinburgh. *Born* 20 March 1865. *Died* 30 June 1894.

BOYD, ROBERT, younger of Drum [19 November 1801]. Apprentice to David Balfour.—Son of Robert Boyd of Drum. *Died* 10 December 1815.

BOYD, WILLIAM, of Hillhousefield [4 December 1794]. Apprentice to James Thomson.—Son of Archibald Boyd, of the Hon. East India Company's Service. *Married* 14 March 1798, Jessa (*died* November 1848), daughter of Alexander Brown, Merchant, Edinburgh. *Died* 21 June 1846, aged 74.

BOYD, WILLIAM [15 July 1886]. Apprentice to Robert Bruce Johnston.—Third son of Sir John Boyd of Maxpoffle, Roxburghshire, Lord Provost of the City of Edinburgh, and Isabella, daughter of John Lawson of Cairnmuir, Peeblesshire, W.S. *Born* 25 November 1861. *Married* 16 July 1890, Laura (*died* 5 September 1946), younger daughter of John Crerar, Halifax, Nova Scotia, Shipowner. Member of the King's Bodyguard for Scotland, Royal Company of Archers, 1905. *Died* 29 August 1945.

BOYD, WILLIAM MITCHELL [8 July 1828]. Apprentice to Alexander Monypenny.—Son of John Boyd of Broadmeadows, Selkirkshire. *Born* 29 August 1804. *Married* 4 August 1841, Anne, daughter of Dr James Hamilton, Professor of Midwifery, University of Edinburgh. *Died* at Madeira, 9 April 1894.

BOYES, THOMAS [15 September 1704]. Apprentice to David Balcanquall.—Son of Rev. John Boyes. *Married* 19 April 1708, Grizel, daughter of James Hay of Carriber, Linlithgowshire. Fiscal, 1710-16. *Died* April 1716.

BRAINE, HENRY MAURICE, M.A., LL.B. [16 December 1935]. Apprentice to James Falconer Fairweather and Another of Gordon, Falconer & Fairweather.—Son of H. A. Braine, Headmaster, Inverness. *Born* 10 May 1905. *Married* 12 November 1938, Violet, daughter of William Trench. Legal Member of Lands Tribunal for Scotland. *Firm*—Gordon, Falconer & Fairweather. (Retired.)

BRAND, JAMES GORDON [2 April 1906]. Apprentice to Henry Inglis Lindsay.—Son of James Brand, Kelvinside, Glasgow. *Born* 11 June 1872. *Married* (1) 11 August 1906, Elizabeth Mabel, younger daughter of Richard Thomas of Penarth, Glamorganshire; (2) 25 September 1922, Franziska Jessie (*died* 10 January 1955), younger daughter of Thomas Richard Bull, Taunton. Advocate and Sheriff-Substitute at Dumfries. *Died* 19 June 1933.

BRAND, WILLIAM [10 July 1834]. Apprentice to Scott, Finlay, and Balderston.—Son of Charles Brand, Farmer, in the Parish of Peterhead. *Born* 5 January 1807. *Married* 19 July 1848, Eleanor Bruce (*died* 24 December 1875), youngest daughter of Captain Bruce Mitchell, H.E.I.C.S. Secretary of Union Bank of Scotland. *Died* 18 October 1869.

BRAND, WILLIAM JOSEPH, T.D., B.L. [20 July 1950]. Apprentice to A. A. Innes Wedderburn and Another of Alex. Morison & Co.—Son of James Gordon Brand, W.S. *Born* 16 May 1925. *Married* 28 July 1951, Esme Grace, daughter of Thomas Ewart Perkins. A/B in Royal Navy, 1943-46.

BRASH, DONALD GRANGER, B.A.(CANTAB), LL.B. [11 December 1979]. Apprentice to Charles Snow Campbell and Others of Alex. Morison & Co.—Son of Richard James Brash, Company Director, Glasgow. *Born* 4 November 1950. *Married* 30 July 1977, Elizabeth Jane, daughter of Dr W. A. Ross, Laurencekirk. *Firm*—Alex. Morison & Co.

BREBNER, GRAEME DAVID ALBERT, LL.B. [6 December 1976]. Apprentice to Gerald William Stuart Barry and Others of W. & J. Burness.—Son of Albert Brebner, Consultant Designer, Edinburgh. *Born* 18 October 1952. *Married* 29 April 1978, Denise Elizabeth Prichard.

BREMNER, CHARLES [8 July 1790]. Apprentice to William Balderston.—Son of James Bremner, S.S.C., Edinburgh. *Born* 4 June 1768. *Married* 1834, Isabella (*died* 2 January 1844), daughter of Thomas Pender, Comptroller of Stamps and Taxes. *Died* 1 August 1857.

BREMNER, HUGH [7 June 1825]. Apprentice to Charles Bremner.—Son of Hugh Bremner, Accountant in Edinburgh. *Born* 1802. *Married* 11 June 1833, Catherine (*died* 7 January 1870), daughter of Robert Menzies of Trinity. *Died* 24 August 1869.

BRIDGES, DAVID JAMES [6 March 1845]. Apprentice to, and son of, James Bridges, W.S.—*Born* 26 August 1821. *Died* February 1852, unmarried.

BRIDGES, JAMES [22 June 1810]. Apprentice to James Hay.—Fourth son of David Bridges, Merchant in Edinburgh. *Married* (1) 18 August 1817, Jane (*died* 30 December 1829), youngest daughter of Lieut.-Colonel Macdonald, Royal Marines; and (2) 18 September 1838, Mrs Jane Mary M'Kerras Gracie (*died* 4 January 1887) of Williamscraig. Author of *View of the Political State of Scotland at Michaelmas 1811*. *Died* 6 May 1865, aged 80.

BRIDGES MACWHIRTER, MORAY ARCHIBALD, LL.B. [9 December 1980]. Apprentice to N. A. M. Mackay and Others of Biggart, Baillie & Gifford.—Son of Archibald Macwhirter, Sheriff and Commissary Clerk of Orkney and Kirkcaldy. *Born* 12 March 1945. *Married* 24 April 1976, Lesley Jane, daughter of Major Leslie Skinner, Royal Scots.

BRINGLOE, FRANCIS JOHN [29 June 1837]. Apprentice to John Bowie.—Son of Hugh Say Bringloe, Clerk of the Jury Court. *Born* 15 April 1814. *Married* 18 August 1842, Margaret (*died* 27 March 1891), daughter of Adam Thomson, Accountant in Edinburgh. *Died* 25 December 1858.

BRISBANE, JAMES [20 July 1695]. Apprentice to Robert Watson.—Second son of James Brisbane of Brisbane. *Married* (1) 10 July 1691, Anna (*died* October 1720), second daughter of John Cranston of Glen, Peeblesshire; and (2) December 1720, Ann, daughter of John Mitchell of Alderston.

BRODIE, FRANCIS [7 July 1803]. Apprentice to James Walker.—Second son of John Brodie, Tenant in Linplum. *Born* 1764. *Married* (1) 4 September 1795, Elizabeth (*died* 11 March 1805), daughter of Ellis Martin, Merchant in Leith; and (2) 31 December 1808, Margaret, second daughter of Gilbert Ker of Gateshaw, Roxburghshire. *Died* 23 October 1839.

BRODIE, GEORGE JAMES [28 October 1881]. Apprentice to John Clerk Brodie, his uncle.—Second son of Lieut.-Colonel Thomas Brodie, residing in Edinburgh. *Born* 20 February 1859. *Married* (1) 4 June 1890, Theresa Sophia Charlotte (*died* 21 December 1909), elder daughter of Lieut.-Colonel Wayne of Tickwood Hall, Shropshire; (2) 27 October 1914, Margaret Sarah Mary Josephine (*died* 28 February 1962), eldest daughter of W. J. S. Barber-Starkey, Aldenham Park, Bridgnorth, Shropshire, and of Knockshannoch, Glen Isla, Angus. *Died* 13 January 1936, at Wokingham, Berks.

BRODIE, JAMES GIBSON CRAIG [31 October 1879]. Apprentice to, and youngest son of, John Clerk Brodie, W.S.—*Born* 18 March 1855. *Married* 26 June 1878, Ellen Anne (*died* 20 June 1946), daughter of Edmund J. W. Wood of Henley Hall, Ludlow, Salop. *Died* 19 September 1884.

BRODIE, JOHN [4 July 1823]. Apprentice to James Jollie.—Eldest son of Francis Brodie, W.S. *Born* 1797. *Married* 3 March 1828, Margaret Amelia (*died* 16 May 1875), eldest daughter of Major-General Thomas William Kerr. *Died* 11 August 1865.

BRODIE, JOHN BUCHAN [16 November 1812]. Apprentice to Thomas Gordon.—Son of William Brodie, Writer in Edinburgh. *Married* Elizabeth Tucker (*died* 25 December 1848), daughter of David Shaw, sometime of Jamaica. *Died* 4 January 1866, aged 78.

BRODIE, JOHN CLERK, OF IDVIES, C.B., LL.B. [17 November 1836]. Apprentice to James Thomson Gibson-Craig.—Fourth son of Thomas Brodie, W.S. *Born* 20 May 1811. *Married* (1) 20 March 1832, Bathia Garden (*died* 25 September 1844), eldest daughter of Stewart Souter of Melrose, Banffshire; and (2) 16 November 1848, Penelope Marianne (*died* 2 July 1877), third daughter of Rev. John Sneyd, of Ashcombe, Staffordshire. Crown Agent, February 1847 to March 1852, and January 1853 to March 1858. Keeper of the Register of Sasines, 3 February 1858. Treasurer, 1870. Deputy Keeper of the Signet, 1882-87. *Died* 27 May 1888.

BRODIE, JOHN SNEYD [26 December 1873]. Apprentice to, and son of, John Clerk Brodie, W.S.—*Born* 23 October 1850. *Died* 1 June 1875, unmarried.

BRODIE, LUDOVICK, OF WHYTFIELD [11 July 1706]. Apprentice to John Campbell.—Son of Francis Brodie of Milnton, Elginshire. *Born* about 1681. *Married* 31 January 1706, Helen, daughter of John Grant, Writer, Edinburgh. Grandfather of Deacon Brodie. *Died* 16 June 1758.

BRODIE, THOMAS [18 June 1739]. Apprentice to John Macfarlane.—Second surviving son of Alexander Brodie of Lethen, Nairnshire. *Married*, proclaimed 2 March 1755, Phoebe (*died* 10 June 1787), daughter of Thomas Forbes of Thornton, Kincardineshire, and widow of John Scott of Hedderwick, Forfarshire. Commissary of Moray, 1753. Lyon Depute, 7 September 1754. *Died* 19 August 1770.

BRODIE, THOMAS [21 June 1787]. Apprentice to Samuel Mitchelson.—Second son of Thomas Brodie, W.S. *Born* 10 August 1760. *Married* Ann Taap (*died* 16 December 1847). Resigned his Commission, 18 February 1792. *Died* 14 September 1825.

BRODIE, Sir THOMAS DAWSON, of Idvies, Bart. [12 November 1857]. Apprentice to, and eldest son of, John Clerk Brodie, W.S. *Born* 26 December 1832. *Married* (1) 11 September 1861, Charlotte Frederika (*died* 27 May 1870), third daughter of Thomas John Furnell of Heathmount, County Limerick; and (2) 18 April 1876, Anne (*died* 18 February 1903), eldest daughter of William Dawson of Gairdoch, Stirlingshire. Deputy Keeper of the Privy Seal, 1869-74. Created a Baronet, 1 January 1892. *Died* at Idvies, 6 September 1896.

BROOK, ALEXANDER [13 July 1891]. Apprentice to Henry Tod.—Son of John Brook, Merchant, Haddington. *Born* 12 June 1865. Lieut-Colonel, 8th Royal Scots. Mentioned in Despatches. *Died* of wounds at Ypres, Belgium, 19 May 1915.

BROOKMAN, JAMES [29 October 1888]. Apprentice to Alexander Howe and William MacGillivray.—Son of Benjamin Brookman, Edinburgh. *Born* 7 June 1842. *Married* 19 December 1873, Annie (*died* 13 November 1932), second daughter of James Buchanan, Farmer, Ballafuil, Balquhidder. *Died* 24 October 1904.

BROTHERSTON, WILLIAM [12 December 1898]. Apprentice to John Macpherson, and thereafter to Robert Pringle.—Son of William Brotherston, Merchant, Edinburgh. *Born* 28 September 1875. *Married* 3 August 1910, Margaret Merry Smith, M.B., Ch.B., D.P.H. (*died* 17 October 1971), daughter of William Smith, Farmer. *Died* 12 January 1935.

BROUGHTON, CHARLES [1 March 1799]. Apprentice to Joseph Cauvin.—Third son of Edward Broughton, of the Excise. *Married* 5 June 1799, Helen (*died* 18 May 1822), daughter of John Peat, Writer in Edinburgh. *Died* 10 November 1823.

BROUN, ALEXANDER CARRUTHERS M'BRYDE [4 August 1880]. Apprentice to (1) Hector Monro; and (2) W. C. M'Ewen.—Son of Rev. Hugh M'Bryde Broun, Free Church Minister, Lochmaben. *Born* 5 June 1855. *Married* 6 September 1889, Jessie (*died* 23 August 1926), daughter of Robert Wanless, Edinburgh. *Died* 17 February 1892.

BROUN, HUGH, of Broadstone [15 July 1885]. Apprentice to Thomas Elliot Ogilvie Horne.—Eldest son of Hugh Broun of Broadstone, Ayrshire. *Born* 22 April 1861. *Died* 11 December 1939.

BROWN, ADAM [Before 1544]. *Died* 1552.

BROWN, ARCHIBALD CAMPBELL [30 March 1908]. Apprentice to D. Wardlaw and J. L. Mounsey.—Eldest son of A. G. Brown, W.S. *Born* 16 March 1884. Lieutenant R.F.A. *Killed* in action, 27 May 1918.

BROWN, ARCHIBALD GEORGE [13 January 1890]. Apprentice to Thomas D. Brodie.—*Born* 11 March 1850. Son of —— Brown, Music Seller, Elgin. *Married* 31 December 1874, Helen, only daughter of W. P. Faichney, Kinross. *Died* 1 September 1924.

BROWN, ARTHUR WALTER SHERRIFF [15 December 1930]. Apprentice to Euan Barclay Robertson and Hugh W. Eaton.—Son of John Hunter Brown, Insurance Clerk, Edinburgh. *Born* 15 May 1900. *Died* 9 November 1937.

BROWN, CHARLES [26 February 1753]. Apprentice to Robert Hepburn.—Son of Charles Brown of Coalstoun, East Lothian. *Died* at Bath, 25 April 1781.

BROWN, CHARLES MARSHALL, LL.B. [15 March 1920]. Apprentice to John L. Mounsey and A. G. Brown.—Son of A. G. Brown, W.S. *Born* 18 October 1889. Admitted Advocate, 14 July 1916. Resigned his Commission as such, 1919. *Married* 4 June 1921, Margaret (*died* 3 January 1936), daughter of Captain Wetherly, West Park, Cults, Aberdeenshire, and (2) Dorothy Barron Pentland Foswell or McArthur or Martindale (*died* 30 September 1976). Enlisted in Royal Fusiliers (Sportsman's Batt.); 2nd Lieutenant 3rd Gordons, November 1914; 1st Batt. in France, 1915; Lieutenant, July 1915; Captain, February 1917; wounded in September 1915 and September 1917. *Died* 21 June 1948. *Firm*—John Clerk Brodie and Sons.

BROWN, DAVID [11 July 1817]. Apprentice to Adam Rolland.—Son of James Brown, Bookseller in Edinburgh. *Died* 29 January 1836.

BROWN, DAVID [1 July 1825]. Apprentice to Alexander Douglas.—Eldest son of Rev. David Brown, Minister of Crailing. *Born* 1799. *Married* 8 April 1835, Mary Ann (*died* 24 May 1837), youngest daughter of James Taylor, of Lloyd's, London. Not known when he died.

BROWN, DAVID, YOUNGER OF PARK [12 November 1847]. Apprentice to John Scott and William C. Balderston.—Eldest son of Major David Brown of Park. *Born* 8 September 1822. *Married* 4 November 1856, Catherine (*died* 1874), daughter of Alexander Robertson, Edinburgh. *Died* 18 November 1861.

BROWN, FERGUS JOHN MACBRIDE, B.L. [23 April 1956]. Apprentice to William Watt and Others of Davidson & Syme.—Son of John MacBride Brown, Minister of Religion. *Born* 8 June 1929. *Married* (1) Joyce Marjory Riddoch Burwood (*died* 5 November 1966), and (2) 11 November 1967, Violet Evelyn, daughter of Albert J. Meek, Edinburgh. Procurator Fiscal, Peebles. *Firm*—Ferguson Reekie & Kilgour (1957-70).

BROWN, HENRY HILTON, B.L. [25 September 1939]. Apprentice to James L. Mounsey and Another of John C. Brodie & Sons.—Son of Dr H. Hilton Brown, Edinburgh. *Born* 16 October 1916. Major R.A. Served U.K. 1939-45 and France and Belgium 1939-40. *Died* 1 January 1948. *Firm*—John C. Brodie & Sons.

BROWN, JAMES [7 July 1824]. Apprentice to David Cleghorn.—Son of Thomas Brown, Builder at Uphall. *Born* 1800. *Died* 10 August 1845, unmarried.

BROWN, JOHN, OF PRATHOUSE [24 February 1809]. Apprentice to Thomas Scotland.—Son of John Brown, of Prathouse. *Died* 1 January 1819.

BROWN, JOHN [1 December 1825]. Apprentice to John Tweedie.—Eldest son of John Brown of Culter Mains, Lanarkshire. Author of a *Summary of the Turnpike Act. Died* 29 February 1872, aged 75, unmarried.

BROWN, JOHN OSBURN [2 December 1794]. Apprentice to James Thomson.—Son of Alexander Brown, Merchant in Edinburgh. *Born* 1771. *Married* (1) 14 July 1797, Agnes Campbell (*died* 12 October 1810), Lochdochart; and (2) 30 April 1812, Elizabeth Rae (*died* 22 January 1855), eldest daughter of John Campbell, Receiver-General of Customs. Second Clerk to Jury Court, 1815-30. *Died* 30 January 1838.

BROWN, JOSEPH LAMBERT [20 July 1925]. Apprentice to (1) George Murray Lawson; and (2) Robert Pringle and Arthur Walker Russell.—Son of Samuel Lambert Brown, Landowner in Norfolk. *Born* 21 January 1901. *Married* 25 March 1927, Gladys (*died* 26 February 1971), daughter of George Finlay, retired Examiner, Estate Duty Office, Edinburgh, *Died* 17 July 1957.

BROWN, NEIL JAMES BAXTER, LL.B. [11 December 1978]. Apprentice to (1) W. F. M. Whitelaw and Another of Beveridge & Kellas and (2) W. F. Bowes and Another of Shepherd & Wedderburn.—Son of Thomas Marshall Brown, Civil Servant, Edinburgh. *Born* 11 August 1953. *Married* 27 March 1980, Andrea Christine Davis, daughter of Andrew Tourney. Consultant Surgeon, Falkirk.

BROWN, ROBERT, OF KIRKLANDS [5 July 1782]. Apprentice to Thomas Tod.—Eldest son of Rev. James Brown, one of the Ministers of Edinburgh. *Born* 23 August 1758. *Married* 22 December 1782, Isabella (*died* 13 October 1832), eldest daughter of Alexander Adam, Architect and Slater, Edinburgh. *Died* 6 November 1812.

BROWN, ROBERT [16 June 1818]. Apprentice to William Molle.—Eldest son of Robert Brown, W.S. *Born* 1790. *Died* 15 May 1833, unmarried.

BROWN, ROBERT, OF WHITSOME NEWTON [16 July 1846]. Apprentice to John Scott and William C. Balderston.—Son of Robert Brown of Gilston. *Born* 26 October 1819. *Married* 3 July 1845, Sarah Ann, daughter of Alexander Hamilton, Mauchline. *Died* 28 December 1855.

BROWN, ROBERT JOHNSTON [14 November 1839]. Apprentice to Smith and Kinnear.—Son of William Henry Brown of Ratho Bank. *Born* 5 July 1816. *Married* 8 December 1855, Augusta Marcia (*died* 3 January 1891), daughter of Rev. Thomas Charles Brown, London. Cornet 14th King's Light Dragoons, 1842; Lieutenant, 1845; Captain, 1853; Major, 1864. *Died* 28 April 1876.

BROWN, WALTER, OF COLTON [6 July 1826]. Apprentice to John Russell.—Only son of Captain John Brown, of the ship *Wellington*, of Leith. *Born* 1802. *Married* 23 March 1840, Jane (*died* 1874), second daughter of James Spowart of Springbank. *Died* 4 July 1869.

BRUCE, ALEXANDER [Before 1583]. Natural son of Alexander Bruce, Burgess of Edinburgh.

BRUCE, ALEXANDER STEVENSON, T.D. [19 December 1932]. Apprentice to Thomas M. Murray and Another of Macandrew, Wright & Murray.—Son of Robert Alexander Bruce, W.S., Edinburgh. *Born* 19 August 1909. *Married* 3 June 1939, Jean Mary Barclay (*died* 12 February 1977). Major, R.A. Served U.K., France and Belgium 1939-45. *Died* 9 July 1959. *Firm*—Inglis, Orr & Bruce.

BRUCE, ARTHUR NICOL [8 July 1912]. Apprentice to W. J. Kirk and James Arthur Hope.—Son of Rev. William Straton Bruce, D.D., Minister of the Parish of Banff. *Born* 8 August 1887. *Married* 15 September 1915, Margaret Patrick (*died* 5 September 1952), daughter of Dr Alexander Stewart, of The Lindens, Uphall. Royal Italian Consul for Edinburgh and East of Scotland, 1927-33. Knight of the Crown of Italy. Lieutenant Royal Scots. During Great War served four years in France, N.W. Frontier, India, German East Africa, and in Italy. Major, Army Welfare Service. Served Home Forces 1939-43. *Died* 28 June 1943.

BRUCE, EDWARD [25 November 1780]. Apprentice to William Aytoun.—Eldest son of Captain James Bruce of the 26th Regiment. *Died* 27 February 1804.

BRUCE, GEORGE, OF WESTBROOK [17 April 1862]. Apprentice to Andrew Storie and W. R. Baillie.—Eldest son of Thomas Bruce of Langlee, W.S. *Born* 3 February 1829. *Died* 17 July 1892.

BRUCE, IAN WILLIAM BARCLAY, M.A., LL.B. [27 April 1953]. Apprentice to Robert Watson Martin and Others of Simpson, Kinmont & Maxwell.—Son of William D. Bruce, Master Painter, Brechin. *Born* 16 June 1927. *Married* 27 August 1954, Grace McQueen, daughter of William Hay, Butcher, Inverkeithing. *Firm*—Malcolm, Jack & Matheson, Dunfermline.

BRUCE, JAMES [25 June 1863]. Apprentice to Alexander Hamilton.—Son of James Bruce, of the Inland Revenue, residing in Edinburgh. *Born* 8 September 1838. *Married* 29 August 1871, Catherine, eldest daughter of John Russel, Dean of Guild, Edinburgh. *Died* 25 November 1915. *Firm*—Bruce and Kerr.

BRUCE, JAMES [12 December 1904]. Apprentice to W. J. Kirk and James Arthur Hope.— Son of James Bruce, W.S. *Born* 13 January 1880. *Married* 5 June 1912, Hannah Mary (*died* 2 May 1963), younger daughter of Lewis Bilton, W.S. Served Dardanelles, Egypt, and with Italian Expeditionary Force, 1914-18. Promoted Major and twice mentioned in Despatches. *Died* 14 December 1949. *Firm*—Bruce and Kerr.

BRUCE, JOHN, OF POWFOULIS [29 June 1843]. Apprentice to Walter Dickson and James Steuart.—Son of James Bruce of Powfoulis, Stirlingshire. *Born* 19 November 1815. *Married* 4 June 1857, Jessie (*died* 4 August 1875), third daughter of Robert Taylor of Broomland, Kirkcudbrightshire. *Died* at St Andrews, 8 January 1899.

BRUCE, ROBERT ALEXANDER [11 July 1898]. Apprentice to J. P. Wright.—Son of Edward Bruce, Builder and Contractor, Edinburgh. *Born* 28 September 1873. *Married* (1) 23 July 1903, Eliza (*died* 24 February 1905), younger daughter of Daniel McMillan, F.E.I.S., Glasgow; (2) 31 March 1908, Adelaide (*died* 28 July 1937) daughter of John Michael Pollock Stevenson, Writer, Glasgow, and (3) 15 October 1938, Isabella Catherine (*died* 3 January 1973), daughter of Thomas Brown, Edinburgh. *Died* 9 October 1940. *Firm*—Inglis, Orr, and Bruce.

BRUCE, RODERICK LAWRENCE, LL.B. [12 December 1977]. Apprentice to Ronald Kerr Will and Others of Dundas & Wilson.—Son of Thomas M. Bruce, Regional Ambulance Officer, S.E. Scotland, Edinburgh. *Born* 8 March 1948. *Married* 11 March 1972, Linda, daughter of John Johnstone, Personnel Manager, Parsons Peebles Ltd., Edinburgh. *Firm*—Dundas & Wilson.

BRUCE, THOMAS, OF LANGLEE [15 June 1810]. Apprentice to Archibald Tod.—Eldest son of George Bruce of Langlee, Roxburghshire, Depute Clerk of Session. *Born* 3 January 1785. *Married* 6 March 1828, Margaret (*died* 22 January 1902), daughter of Charles Steuart, W.S. Depute Clerk of Session, 14 January 1824 till death. *Died* 25 May 1850.

BRUCE, THOMAS [9 July 1819]. Apprentice to (1) John Dundas; (2) H. J. Rollo.—Son of James Bruce, Secretary to the Board of Excise. *Born* 1794. *Married* 13 January 1831, Matilda (*died* 17 August 1839), daughter of Thomas Gloag of Chapelton, W.S. *Died* 2 December 1837.

BRUCE-GARDYNE, CHARLES EVAN, B.A.(OXON), LL.B. [27 July 1953]. Apprentice to J. D. H. Dickson & Others of Tods, Murray & Jamieson.—Son of Captain E. Bruce-Gardyne, R.N., Middleton, Arbroath, Angus. *Born* 15 February 1927. *Married* 16 April 1966, Dorothy Margaret, daughter of Lieutenant Colonel H. A. C. Blair-Imrie. Members of Queen's Bodyguard for Scotland, Royal Company of Archers. *Firm*—Shiell & Small, Dundee.

BRUCE LOCKHART, KAREN, LL.B. [11 December 1979*].—Daughter of R. B. Bruce Lockhart, Public School Headmaster. *Born* 28 October 1942. *Firm*—Brodies.

BRUNTON, JAMES [27 November 1862]. Apprentice to James Mackenzie, J. B. Innes, and John Logan.—Son of William Brunton, Merchant in Edinburgh. *Born* 31 December 1838. *Married* 26 November 1868, Ellen Marion (*died* 3 October 1928), daughter of Montagu Gosset, London. Chamberlain to Duke of Roxburgh, 1865-1913. *Died* 7 November 1913.

BRYCE, GEORGE FERGUSON [21 July 1879]. Apprentice to John Cook.—Son of Archibald Hamilton Bryce, D.C.L., Edinburgh. *Born* 2 June 1855. *Firm*—J. A. Campbell and Lamond. *Died* 13 August 1941.

BRYCE, PETER ROSS, M.A., LL.B. [20 December 1948]. Apprentice to Robert Francis Shepherd and Others of Shepherd & Wedderburn.—Son of James Hutchison Bryce, Searcher of Records, Edinburgh. *Born* 16 July 1921. *Married* 23 April 1955, Janey Glover, daughter of John Gavin, W.S., Edinburgh. Major, Royal Scots, India. Partner of Messrs. Miller & Bryce, Searchers of Records, Edinburgh.

BRYDIE, DAVID WILSON, B.L. [10 July 1933]. Apprentice to James M. Cooper.—Son of James Brydie, Merchant, Dollar. *Born* 15 October 1899. *Married* 27 July 1927, Margaret Brown Hogg, daughter of John Brown Meikle, Headmaster, Carnock School, Dunfermline. Served with Seaforth Highlanders, 51st Division, and on Staff of 152nd Brigade H.Q., 1917-19. *Died* 27 October 1973. *Firms*—1946-59 Macpherson & Mackay; 1959-73 Shepherd & Wedderburn.

BRYDIE, JAMES WILSON, B.L. [13 May 1963]. Apprentice to George Lovat Fraser Henry and Others of Shepherd & Wedderburn.—Son of David Wilson Brydie, W.S., Edinburgh. *Born* 9 February 1932. *Married* 23 January 1971, Judith Margaret, daughter of John Carrie, Engineer. *Firm*—Shepherd & Wedderburn.

BRYSON, CATHERINE OGILVIE, LL.B. [12 May 1981*].—Daughter of A. G. S. Bryson, C.A., Edinburgh. Born 5 March 1957.

BUCHAN, JAMES [16 November 1781]. Apprentice to William Wilson, Sen.—Son of David Buchan, Bailie in Perth. *Died* 28 May 1814.

BUCHAN, JOHN [10 July 1770]. Apprentice to (1) George Turnbull; and (2) Charles Brown.—Third son of John Buchan of Letham. *Born* 6 October 1742. *Died* 17 August 1822.

BUCHAN, JOHN [19 November 1782]. Apprentice to Andrew Stuart, Jun.—Third son of Thomas Buchan of Auchmacoy, Aberdeenshire. *Died* in Jamaica, 1793.

BUCHAN, WILLIAM [19 November 1782]. Apprentice to John Buchan.—Eldest son of Hugh Buchan, Chamberlain of the City of Edinburgh. *Died* 26 April 1790.

BUCHANAN, CHARLES SNODGRASS, of Cunninghamhead [29 June 1838]. Apprentice to Cunningham and Bell.—Eldest son of David Snodgrass Buchanan of Cunninghamhead. *Born* 4 April 1813. *Died* 22 September 1849, unmarried.

BUCHANAN, ERIC DAVID, M.A., LL.B. [23 July 1956]. Apprentice to (1) Ralph Colley Smith and Others of Fraser, Stodart & Ballingall and (2) Andrew White Young and Another of J. & R. A. Robertson.—Son of Eric Paton Buchanan, S.S.C., Edinburgh. *Born* 2 July 1933. *Firm*—Steedman, Ramage & Co.

BUCHANAN, GEORGE GRAHAM, B.L. [30 April 1973]. (By Rule IX(a).)—Son of John Buchanan, Banker, Edinburgh. *Born* 4 October 1924. *Married* 1 August 1954, Anne Wallace (*died* 12 March 1970). Flying Officer, R.A.F. Pilot, 298 Squadron. Served South Africa, India and Burma. *Firm*—Peterkin & Kidd, Linlithgow.

BUCHANAN, GEORGE SMITH, M.A.(OXON), LL.B. [27 July 1953]. Apprentice to Ranald K. Cuthbertson and Others of Mackenzie, Innes & Logan.—Son of Rev. Joseph Buchanan. *Born* 10 April 1926. *Married* 28 April 1955, Ann Hughes Dickson (divorced).

BUCHANAN, HECTOR MACDONALD, OF DRUMNAKILN [8 March 1791]. Apprentice to William Macdonald.—Third son of Coll Macdonald of Boisdale, Inverness-shire. *Married* 13 July 1793, Jean (*died* 8 February 1852), daughter of Robert Buchanan of Drumnakiln and Ross Priory, whose name he assumed. Principal Clerk of Session, 17 May 1805 till death. Friend and fellow-clerk of Sir Walter Scott. *Died* 14 September 1828.

BUCHANAN, JOHN [Before 1594]. Signs Minute of 16 December 1594.—Brother to Patrick Buchanan of Treinanoche. *Married* 2 July 1600, Katherine Wallace. *Died* 23 October 1611.

BUCHANAN, JOHN, OF CATTER [13 December 1723]. Apprentice to Robert Campbell of Balvie.—Eldest son of James Buchanan of Middleton. *Married* (1) 31 January 1722, Ann (*died* 9 November 1722), second daughter of Andrew Paterson of Kirktown; (2) 26 December 1723, Mary (*died* 29 September 1727), daughter of Ronald Campbell of Balerno, W.S.; and (3) 24 August 1730, Janet (*died* 1 June 1784), daughter of Duncan Campbell, Merchant and Bailie of Edinburgh. *Died* before 4 March 1747.

BUCHANAN, MUNGO, OF AUCHENTORLIE [4 November 1695]. Apprentice to John Cuningham.—Third son of Mungo Buchanan of Tillichewan, Dumbartonshire. *Married* 22 January 1687, Anna Barclay. *Died* 3 April 1710.

BUCHANAN, NIGEL WALTER, T.D., B.A.(OXON), LL.B. [25 November 1963]. Apprentice to Hon. David Andrew Balfour and Others of Shepherd & Wedderburn.— Son of Colonel Edmund Pullar Buchanan, Touch, Stirling. *Born* 22 July 1933. *Firm*— J. & F. Anderson.

BUCHANAN, WILLIAM, OF ARDOCH [23 November 1802]. Apprentice to (1) George Johnston; and (2) Frederick Fotheringham.—Son of Thomas Buchanan of Ardoch, Hatter in Glasgow. *Born* 8 June 1777. *Married* 14 September 1803, Hon. Elizabeth Murray (*died* 17 May 1846), daughter of Alexander, seventh Lord Elibank. Art critic, and Author of *Memoirs of Painting. Died* 9 January 1864.

BUDGE, JAMES [7 June 1722].—Third son of Donald Budge of Toftingall, Caithness. *Died* before 1750.

BUDGE, JOSEPH, C.B.E., M.C. [24 March 1913]. Apprentice to (1) Thomas Rankin; and (2) Sir John Prosser, A. G. Muir, John Smart, and J. H. Macdonald.—Son of Joseph Budge, Managing Director, Wemyss Coal Co., Fife. *Born* 2 December 1887. *Married* 27 September 1916, Helen Stewart (*died* 20 July 1971), only daughter of Rev. Johnstone Walker, Minister of Langton, Berwickshire. County Councillor, Ross and Cromarty. Served 1916 to close of War. In Lovat Scouts, and as Lieutenant, Cameron Highlanders, afterwards attached to 1st Trench Mortar Battery. *Died* 18 February 1957.

BUDGE, WILLIAM, OF TOFTINGALL [21 August 1745]. Apprentice to James Budge, his uncle.—Son of David Budge, Tutor of Toftingall. *Married* Katherine (*died* 12 January 1789), third daughter of Alexander Sinclair of Olrig, Caithness. *Died* 28 September 1765.

BUIK, PATRICK REID [26 October 1888]. Apprentice to T. E. O. Horne, Thomas Horne, and David Lyell.—Third son of Major John Henry Buik of Pultneytown. *Born* 21 September 1863. *Died* at Perth, 12 March 1923.

BUIST, ALEXANDER ALLARDICE, B.A.(OXON) [20 March 1916]. Apprentice to J. R. M. Wedderburn, J. A. S. Carment, and Graham G. Watson.—Son of John Charles Buist, Jute Merchant, Balgillo, Broughty Ferry. *Born* 20 March 1888. *Married* 17 December 1914, Margaret Eileen, only daughter of Henry Deakin Ashton, Ollerslie, Darwen, Cotton Manufacturer. Served in War Office and India Office from 1914 to 1918. *Died* 19 January 1971.

BULLICK, PETER MAURICE, LL.B. [13 May 1980*]. Son of John Bullick, Bank Manager and Farmer, Stow, by Galashiels. *Born* 2 March 1940. *Married* 18 July 1964, Celina Elizabeth, daughter of Charles Augustus Lundy. *Firm*—James & David W. B. Tait, Kelso.

BURD, MELVILLE [28 February 1811]. Apprentice to John Campbell, *tertius*.—Son of Melville Burd, Farmer in Dalkeith. *Died* 5 September 1829, aged 45.

BURLEIGH, JOHN KARL, M.A., LL.B. [28 November 1955]. Apprentice to Edwin T. Stevens and Others of J. Miller Thomson & Co.—Son of The Very Rev. Professor Emeritus J. H. S. Burleigh, D.D., Edinburgh and Peebles. *Born* 14 January 1931. *Married* 10 April 1969, Ann, daughter of J. T. Currie. *Firm*—Drummond & Co. (formerly D. & J. H. Campbell).

BURN, GEORGE [17 March 1864]. Apprentice to Donald Horne.—Son of James Burn, W.S. *Born* 16 August 1828. *Died* 19 September 1878, unmarried.

BURN, HENRY JOHN [4 July 1823]. Apprentice to (1) John B. Brodie; and (2) Michael Linning.—Son of Robert Burn, Architect in Edinburgh. *Born* 7 April 1798. *Married* 10 June 1845, Charlotte Barbara (*died* 23 October 1892), youngest daughter of Sir Thomas Kirkpatrick of Closeburn, Bart. *Died* 10 January 1867.

BURN, JAMES [23 June 1817]. Apprentice to Robert Hill.—Son of George Burn, Factor to Henry Glassford, at Netherwood. *Married* 6 August 1827, Margaret (*died* 28 September 1850), daughter of John Heugh of Gartcows. *Died* 24 November 1863, aged 70.

BURN, ROBERT [29 May 1818]. Apprentice to James Forman.—Only son of David Burn, one of the Teachers at the Grammar School, Stirling. *Died* 17 January 1861, aged 71.

BURN-MURDOCH, ALEXANDER. *See* MURDOCH, ALEXANDER BURN-.

BURN-MURDOCH, ARCHIBALD. *See* MURDOCH, ARCHIBALD BURN-.

BURNESS, JAMES [11 July 1867]. Apprentice to Thomas G. Mackay and Alexander Howe.—Son of Robert Burness, Writer in Montrose. *Born* 2 November 1840. *Married* 26 April 1872, Henrietta (*died* 19 April 1919), daughter of William Ronaldson, Edinburgh. *Died* at St Leonard's-on-Sea, 7 September 1923.

BURNESS, RONALD [10 December 1900]. Apprentice to, and son of, James Burness, W.S.—*Born* 29 July 1875. *Married* 30 April 1919, Helena Victoria, daughter of Lieut.-Colonel John Campbell, Scottish Rifles, latterly Governor of H.M. Prisons at Perth and Edinburgh. Commission in Lovat Scouts, 1915. Served in Egypt, Salonica, and France, and retired with rank of Captain. *Died* 16 November 1935. *Firm*—W. and J. Burness.

BURNET, GAVIN [12 August 1633]. Apprentice to Andrew Hay.—Youngest son of William Burnet of Barns, Peeblesshire. *Married* Helen Ramsay (*died* 17 May 1664). *Died* October 1660.

BURNET, GEORGE WARDLAW, B.A.(Oxon), LL.B. [22 November 1954]. Apprentice to C. E. Stewart and Others of Murray, Beith & Murray.—Son of Sheriff J. R. Wardlaw Burnet, K.C., Sheriff Principal of Fife and Kinross. *Born* 26 December 1927. *Married* 26 July 1951, Jane Elena Moncrieff, daughter of M. M. Stuart, O.B.E. Member of Queen's Bodyguard for Scotland, Royal Company of Archers. (Secretary from 1968 to date). *Firm*—Murray, Beith & Murray.

BURNET, ROBERT [21 December 1671]. Apprentice to John Trotter.—Eldest son of Gavin Burnet, W.S. *Born* 13 July 1646. *Married* Elizabeth (*died* 29 March 1694), daughter of James Cockburn, Brewer, Yardheads, Leith. *Killed* in a duel with James Wishart of Logie, 16 July 1699.

BURNETT, ALEXANDER EDWIN [24 March 1873]. Apprentice to Archibald Watson Goldie.—Third son of Sir James Horn Burnett of Leys, Bart., W.S. *Born* 17 December 1842. *Died* 8 August 1895, unmarried.

BURNETT, ALISTAIR GEORGE MURRAY, LL.B. [4 December 1972]. Appentice to George Lovat Fraser Henry and Others of Shepherd & Wedderburn.—Son of George Murray Burnett, Principal, Heriot Watt University, Edinburgh. *Burn* 18 May 1950. *Married* 10 June 1972, Jennifer Edwards. *Firm*—Biggart, Baillie & Gifford (formerly Baillie & Gifford).

BURNETT, ANDREW, of Kirkhill [21 December 1730]. Youngest son of Thomas Burnett of Kirkhill, Advocate, Regent of Marischal College, Aberdeen. *Born* 1709. *Married* (1) —— (*died* 29 June 1766); (2) 26 April 1767, Ann Burnett of Burnetfield, daughter of Gilbert Burnett, Advocate, and widow of Colonel James Halliburton of Pitcur. *Died* 20 August 1776.

BURNETT, Sir JAMES HORN, of Leys, Bart. [9 July 1824]. Apprentice to John Morison.—Fifth son of Sir Robert Burnett of Leys, Bart. *Born* 21 June 1801. *Married* (1) 3 February 1831, Caroline Margaret (*died* 26 March 1836), daughter of Charles Spearmen of Thornley Hall, Durham; (2) 12 July 1837, his cousin, Lauderdale (*died* 5 November 1888), daughter of Sir Alexander Ramsay of Balmain, Bart., and widow of David Duncan of Rosemount, Forfarshire. *Died* 16 September 1876.

BURNETT, ROBERT [7 June 1821]. Apprentice to (1) James Gibson; (2) William Gardner.—Son of William Burnett, Factor at Crathes to Sir Robert Burnett of Leys. *Born* 1 August 1788. *Married* Amelia (*died* 23 June 1886), daughter of Rev. James Sherriffs, Minister of West Church, Aberdeen. *Died* 9 August 1828.

BURNETT, WILLIAM, of Barns [*c.* 1638].—Son of John Burnet and Margaret Scot, and nephew of Gavin Burnet, W.S. *Married* 1648, Christian, daughter of Dr Walter Whitford, Bishop of Brechin. Held several Offices of State under Charles I. *Died* 1675.

BURNETT-WHITE, JAMES [27 May 1941]. Apprentice to (1) John James Simpson Binnie of Binnie & Binnie, Grangemouth and (2) Gavin Black Louden Motherwell of Laing & Motherwell.—Son of James Burnett-White, Solicitor, Grangemouth. *Born* 28 December 1917. *Married* 11 September 1946, Sheena Wilson, daughter of Major Walter Robertson Dickens. Corporal Royal Air Force 1940-45; Served U.K. and Iceland. *Firm*—J. Burnett-White & Son, Grangemouth.

BURNS, ALEXANDER [9 March 1813]. Apprentice to Archibald Ferrier.—Seventh surviving son of John Burns, Surveyor of Customs at Bo'ness. *Died* 14 October 1832, aged 45, unmarried.

BURNS, DAVID MURRAY, M.A. [3 December 1965]. Apprentice to Sir Hugh Watson and Others of Dundas & Wilson.—Son of Alfred Morris Burns, Chartered Accountant, Dundee. *Born* 31 March 1931.

BURNS, JOHN, B.L., LL.D. [16 March 1891]. Apprentice to James Bruce and Thomas Kerr.—Son of Andrew Burns, Writer, Edinburgh. *Born* 5 November 1863. Author of several legal works. *Died* 7 September 1941. *Firm*—Burns and Waugh.

BURNS, MURRAY ALFRED AGNEW, LL.B. [25 April 1977]. Apprentice to (1) John Marr Davidson and Others of W. & J. Burness and (2) William Mark Kerr and Others of Bell & Scott, Bruce & Kerr.—Son of Ronald Kerr Murray Burns, Farmer, Glenisla, Angus. *Born* 25 May 1950. *Married* 22 March 1973, Sheila Marie, elder daughter of Robert Connelly. *Firm*—Bell & Scott, Bruce & Kerr.

BURNS, RICHARD MORRIS [29 March 1905]. Apprentice to Henry Cook and Charles Cook.—Son of James S. Burns, S.S.C., Edinburgh. *Born* 21 October 1881. In Royal Scots Fusiliers. *Killed* in action at Neuve Chapelle, 11 March 1915.

BURNS, RICHARD RONALD JAMES, B.A.(Oxon), LL.B. [24 April 1972]. Apprentice to Charles Annand Fraser and Others of W. & J. Burness.—Son of Ronald Kerr Murray Burns, Farmer, Glenisla, Angus. *Born* 5 May 1946. *Married* 6 September 1974, Catriona Douglas, daughter of William Walker, Dental Surgeon, Edinburgh.

BURNS, THOMAS, of Longcroft [22 February 1793]. Apprentice to Walter Scott.—Youngest son of James Burns of Glenfour. *Married* Anne Reoch. *Died* 18 December 1858, aged 88.

BURNS, THOMAS CHARLES [22 June 1837]. Apprentice to John Archibald Campbell.—Only son of Thomas Burns, W.S. *Born* 7 January 1814. *Married* 20 April 1837, Jane (*died* 1873), only daughter of John Livingston Campbell of Achalader, Argyllshire. *Died* 1848.

BURNS, WILLIAM [20 December 1920]. Apprentice to Keith Ramsay Maitland.—Son of Robert Burns, Auctioneer, Hawick. *Born* 3 November 1885. *Married* 29 March 1921, Agnes Margaret (Nancy) (*died* 15 November 1980), only daughter of Thomas Gaunt, Leith. *Died* 23 January 1951. *Firm*—John C. Brodie and Sons.

BURNSIDE, JAMES [22 November 1821]. Apprentice to William Drysdale.—Fifth son of John Burnside, Merchant in Glasgow. *Died* 12 August 1854, aged 60, unmarried.

BUTTER, JAMES [23 June 1817]. Apprentice to William Drysdale.—Son of Thomas Butter of Craigbea. *Died* 29 August 1824.

BUTTERS, HOWARD MacLAREN, B.A.(Cantab), LL.B. [15 December 1947]. Apprentice to Michael Lorimer of Henderson & Jackson.—Son of Howard Butters, Mechanical Engineer, New Zealand. *Born* 2 June 1908. *Married* 18 June 1936, Sylvia, daughter of Anthony Stoddard Murray, Solicitor, Glasgow. Major 131 Field Regiment Royal Artillery. *Died* 4 June 1967. *Firm*—Dundas & Wilson.

BUTTERS, JOHN ANTHONY HOWARD, B.A.(Cantab), LL.B. [25 November 1963]. Apprentice to Arthur Woodman Blair and Others of Strathern & Blair.—Son of Howard Maclaren Butters, W.S., Edinburgh. *Born* 27 January 1939. *Firm*—Dundas & Wilson.

CADDELL, WILLIAM, of Fossochie [22 September 1713]. Son of William Caddell, Merchant, Dunblane. *Married* Euphan Caddell. Clerk, 21 January 1711. *Died* 2 November 1724.

CADELL, HEW FRANCIS [13 July 1891]. Apprentice to John Cowan and James A. Dalmahoy.—Eldest son of Colonel Thomas Cadell, V.C., Chief Commissioner of the Andaman Islands. *Born* 10 April 1868. *Married* 9 October 1897, Fairley Charlotte (*died* 12 February 1935), eldest daughter of Alexander Blair, Sheriff of the Lothians. Major Lothians and Border Horse. Served in France and Egypt during Great War. *Died* 18 September 1947. *Firm*—Blair and Cadell.

CADELL, LEWIS IRVING, M.A. [16 July 1889]. Apprentice to J. O. Mackenzie, Harry Cheyne, and John Kermack.—Fourth son of Henry Cadell of Grange and Banton. *Born* 8 December 1865. *Married* 7 April 1897, Mary Louisa (*died* 12 November 1949), daughter of William Finlay, Actuary, Secretary of Scottish Equitable Life Assurance Society. Lieutenant R.A.S.C., M.T.(V). *Died* 24 August 1940. *Firm*—Cadell and Morton.

CADELL, WILLIAM, OF BANTON [6 June 1833]. Apprentice to Alexander Young.—Eldest son of James John Cadell of Grange, Linlithgowshire. *Born* 8 October 1810. *Married* 16 August 1847, Mary Robinson (*died* 1863), daughter of John Rodford, Edinburgh. *Died* 4 May 1862.

CAIRNS, ALEXANDER GORDON [10 December 1906]. Apprentice to Joseph R. M. Wedderburn and Graham Gilbert Watson.—Son of James Cairns, Manufacturer, Hamilton. *Born* 26 April 1878. Captain and Adjutant R.F.A., 32nd Brigade, France. Member of King's Bodyguard for Scotland, Royal Company of Archers, 1928. *Died* 8 April 1968. *Firms*—A. G. Cairns & Frazer 1947-52: A. G. Cairns & Simpson 1953-68.

CAIRNS, GEORGE MORTON [7 December 1908]. Apprentice to (1) William Blair and James Watt; and (2) William Morton.—Son of Henry Cairns, W.S. *Born* 1 September 1881. Lieutenant Black Watch (Royal Highlanders). *Killed* in action, 13 November 1916.

CAIRNS, HENRY [6 July 1854]. Apprentice to Walter Jollie.—Son of George Cairns, Solicitor at Law. *Born* 21 June 1831. *Married* 23 September 1879, Jane Stewart (*died* 23 January 1937) daughter of Alexander Morton, Banker, Edinburgh. *Died* 29 February 1908.

CAIRNS, JOHN BOYD [14 July 1853]. Apprentice to Donald Horne.—Eldest son of John Cairns, Writer in Edinburgh. *Born* 12 August 1827. Name deleted from list, 14 December 1911, he not having been heard of for upwards of fifty years.

CALDER, JAMES MORAY, M.A., LL.B. [20 December 1943]. Apprentice to Ian Coshieville Menzies & Another of Menzies & White.—Son of Alexander Squair Calder, Employers Federation Secretary, Edinburgh. *Born* 10 May 1918. *Married* 30 March 1954, Aileen Mary Alexander, daughter of Thomas Rankine, Hosiery Manufacturer. *Firm*—Menzies Dougal & Milligan (formerly Menzies & White).

CALLANDER, ALEXANDER DOUGAL, B.A.(OXON), [5 May 1953]. Apprentice to John Herbert Richardson and Others of Dundas & Wilson.—Son of Lawrence Dougal Callander, M.D. *Born* 10 March 1926. *Married* 25 April 1953, Mona Patricia Meldrum. Captain Queen's Own Cameron Highlanders. Served India, Japan and Malaya 1944-1947. Emergency Commission. *Firm*—Mathie, Macluckie & Lupton, Stirling.

CALLENDER, HERBERT STANLEY NEWTON [11 July 1892]. Apprentice to George Dunlop.—Son of John Archibald Callender, Edinburgh. *Born* 4 June 1868. *Married* 2 April 1897, Janet Gray (*died* 31 October 1953), third daughter of Alexander Lawson of Burnturk, Fife. *Died* 15 April 1918. *Firm*—J. and R. A. Robertson.

CALVERT, JOHN RUTHERFORD [4 June 1829]. Apprentice to Thomas Mackenzie.—Son of James Calvert, Teacher in the Academy of Montrose. *Died* 12 December 1854, aged 50, unmarried.

CAMERON, ALEXANDER [8 March 1838]. Apprentice to David Brown.—Son of Allan Cameron, Engraver in Edinburgh. *Born* 26 March 1803. *Married* Anne Watson (*died* 16 January 1839). *Died* at Melbourne, 31 March 1841.

CAMERON, SIR DUNCAN, OF FASSIFERN, BART. [12 August 1799]. Apprentice to James Fraser.—Second son of Sir Ewen Cameron of Fassifern, Argyllshire, Bart. *Born* 1770. Succeeded his father as second Baronet, October 1828. *Married* Mary Cameron of Strone. *Died* 15 January 1863.

CAMERON, EWAN KENNEDY, M.A., LL.B. [30 April 1962]. Apprentice to Alastair Campbell Blair and Others of Davidson & Syme.—Son of Alexander Cameron, Banker, Inverness. *Born* 10 May 1933. *Firm*—Dundas & Wilson (formerly Davidson & Syme).

CAMERON, HUGH FORBES, M.C., T.D., B.A.(CANTAB), LL.B. [12 July 1948]. Apprentice to (1) Euan Barclay Robertson and Others of J. & R. A. Robertson and (2) Sir John Ireland Falconer and Another of Fyfe, Ireland & Co.—Son of James Alexander Cameron, W.S., Edinburgh. *Born* 27 December 1917. *Married* 4 October 1941, Jean Robertson, daughter of William Robertson Kydd, C.A. Company Commander 5th Camerons, Brigade Major. D.S. Staff College. Served Africa, Italy, France and Germany. *Firm*—J. & R. A. Robertson. (Retired).

CAMERON, JAMES ALEXANDER, LL.B. [11 December 1911]. Apprentice to John Balfour Rainy.—Son of James Cameron, Schoolmaster, Stanley, Perthshire. *Born* 14 May 1881. *Married* 25 July 1914, Annie Clark (*died* 11 September 1931), daughter of Andrew Hutcheson of Beechwood, Perth. Lieutenant on General List during Great War. *Died* 7 December 1953. *Firm*—Fyfe, Ireland, and Co.

CAMERON, JAMES BLACK, LL.B., D.S.O., T.D., D.L. [1 April 1907]. Apprentice to (1) Ebenezer Denholm Young and James Findlay Roxburgh; and (2) Ebenezer Denholm Young.—Son of James Cameron, Keeper of H.M. Register of Deeds, Edinburgh. *Born* 9 June 1882. *Married* 4 June 1908, Helen Rhenius (*died* 1 August 1969), daughter of Frederick Rhenius Coles, F.S.A., Edinburgh. Chairman, City of Edinburgh Territorial Army Association. Deputy Lieutenant for the County of the City of Edinburgh. Commanded Lowland (City of Edinburgh) Heavy Battery, R.G.A., and served with it and in command of various Brigades of Heavy Artillery in France during Great War. Lieut.-Colonel; mentioned in Dispatches. *Died* 12 February 1946. *Firm*—Graham, Johnston, and Fleming.

CAMERON, JOHN RONALD, LL.B. [17 December 1934]. Apprentice to Donald M'Callum Smith, Ronald Burness, and Peter George Macdonald.—Son of John Forbes Cameron, M.A., Master of Gonville and Caius College, Cambridge. *Born* 8 March 1908. *Married* 23 April 1938, Adeline Mary, daughter of the late Robert Simson W.S. Lieutenant Argyll & Sutherland Highlanders. Prisoner of War 1940-41. *Died* at Posen, Germany (Poznan, Poland) 23 April 1941.

CAMERON, JOSEPH GORDON STUART, M.A., LL.B. [17 November 1952]. Apprentice to Gavin Leith Allardyce and Another of J. C. & A. Steuart.—Son of James Douglas Cameron, Solicitor, Edinburgh and West Linton. *Born* 4 February 1927. *Married* 24 July 1956, Celia Margaret, daughter of Hugh Alexander Russell Niven of Rugby and Galashiels. Lecturer in Conveyancing, University of Edinburgh 1955-67. Co-author with G. Campbell, H. Paton, Q.C., of *The Law of Landlord and Tenant in Scotland*, 1967. *Firm*—Stuart & Stuart, Cairns & Co. (formerly Stuart & Stuart).

CAMERON, RALPH COMPTON [13 July 1887]. Apprentice to David Wardlaw.—Son of Alexander Cameron of Mainhouse, Morayshire. *Born* 2 September 1861. *Married* 13 June 1895, Florence Mary (*died* 16 January 1951), only daughter of Alexander Grigor Allan of Blackfriars, Haugh, Elgin. *Died* 25 May 1904.

CAMERON, PETER ALFRED GRANT, B.L. [9 October 1972]. Apprentice to (1) Edmund Menzies and Others of Allan, Dawson, Simpson & Hampton and (2) A. J. Macdonald of W. B. Dickie & Son, Dundee.—Son of Dr. A. E. Cameron, Reader in Entomology, Edinburgh University. *Born* 15 November 1934. *Married* (1) 8 November 1961, Elizabeth Stewart, daughter of Frazer Munro, Pharmacist, and (2) 20 June 1970, Susan Rose, daughter of Frederick Gates, Engineer.

CAMPBELL, ALEXANDER [8 July 1796]. Apprentice to James Ferrier.—Second son of Sir Ilay Campbell of Succoth, Bart., Lord President of the Court of Session. *Died* 26 October 1799, unmarried.

CAMPBELL, ALISTAIR CARNEGIE. LL.B. [11 December 1979]. Apprentice to Alexander Mitchell Hodge and Others of Cowan & Stewart.—Son of Dr. Ian Dougald Campbell, Edinburgh. *Born* 14 February 1954.

CAMPBELL, ARCHIBALD [22 July 1720]. Apprentice to Ronald Campbell.—Eldest son of John Campbell, W.S. *Married* (1) April 1710, Jean, daughter of George Alexander of Peppermiln, Advocate; and (2) 6 August 1724, Helen (*died* 23 May 1748), daughter of John Ayton of Kinaldie. *Died* December 1727.

CAMPBELL, ARCHIBALD, OF SUCCOTH [5 February 1728]. Apprentice to Hew Crawford.—Second son of William Campbell of Succoth, Dunbartonshire. *Married* Helen (*died* 18 August 1767), daughter of John Wallace of Elderslie. Commissary of Glasgow, 20 August 1756. Deputy Keeper of the Great Seal, Principal Clerk of Session, 2 March 1770 to 4 March 1785. *Died* 28 July 1790.

CAMPBELL, ARCHIBALD [19 June 1812]. Apprentice to John Campbell, Jun.—Son of William Campbell of Duneaves, Perthshire. *Died* 28 January 1823.

CAMPBELL, ARCHIBALD, B.L. [28 March 1927]. Apprentice to Andrew Thomas Steele Scott and Another of Scott & Glover.—Son of Archibald Campbell, O.B.E., S.S.C. *Born* 17 April 1903. *Married* 5 April 1935, Cecile, only daughter of Right Hon. A. M. MacRobert, P.C., K.C., Edinburgh, sometime Lord Advocate for Scotland. Captain R.A.S.C. Served U.K. and North West Europe 1941-45. *Firm*—Archibald Campbell & Harley. (Retired).

CAMPBELL, ARCHIBALD BROWN, LL.B. [13 January 1890]. Apprentice to James Mylne.—Son of John Campbell, S.S.C. *Born* 23 September 1865. *Married* 19 June 1902, Charlotte Gray (*died* 11 May 1939), daughter of James Campbell, Writer, Saltcoats. Lieutenant and Assistant Adjutant 1st Batt. City of Edinburgh Volunteer Regiment during Great War. *Died* 1 March 1940. *Firm*—Mylne and Campbell.

CAMPBELL, ARTHUR, OF CATRINE [23 November 1813]. Apprentice to John Hunter.—Fourth son of Arthur Campbell of Auchmannoch, Ayrshire, *Born* 15 July 1788. *Married* 31 August 1825, Jane (*died* 15 January 1861), daughter of Thomas Barstow of Kelso. *Died* 3 March 1875.

CAMPBELL, ARTHUR, OF CATRINE [14 November 1850]. Apprentice to (1) W. C. Balderston, J. Scott, and W. Brand; and (2) John Scott.—Son of Arthur Campbell of Catrine, W.S. *Born* 27 December 1827. *Married* 26 December 1851, Cecilia (*died* 15 October 1906), third daughter of George Cleghorn of Weens, Roxburghshire, W.S. *Died* 8 July 1884.

CAMPBELL, BUCHANAN [12 December 1898]. Apprentice to J. C. Strettell Miller.—Son of Robert Campbell, Metal Merchant, Edinburgh. *Born* 14 January 1874. *Married* 15 October 1907, Jane Margaret (*died* 25 January 1948), eldest daughter of John Steele, Branxholm, near Hawick, Chamberlain to the Duke of Buccleuch there. *Died* 8 March 1958.

CAMPBELL, CHARLES SNOW, M.C., T.D., M.A., LL.B. [20 December 1937]. Apprentice to Euan Barclay Robertson and Others of J. & R. A. Robertson.—Son of Grigor William Boyd Campbell, S.S.C., Edinburgh. *Born* 9 April 1914. *Married* 26 June 1941, Jenny, daughter of George A. T. Walton. Major, R.A. Served U.K., France and North West Europe 1939-45. *Died* 20 January 1981. *Firm*—Alex. Morison & Co.

CAMPBELL, COLIN, OF CARWHIN [9 February 1686]. Apprentice to George Dallas.—Third son of Colin Campbell of Mochaster, Perthshire. *Born* 18 December 1652. *Married* 15 April 1677, Elizabeth, eldest daughter of Rev. Andrew Pringle, Minister of Castleton. Sheriff-Clerk of Caithness. *Died* 31 January 1715.

CAMPBELL, DAVID, OF BELMONT [1 December 1755]. Apprentice to Alexander Robertson.—Second son of John Campbell of Barcaldine, Argyllshire. *Married*, proclaimed 7 March 1756, Jean, daughter of Archibald Campbell, Edinburgh. Resigned his Commission, 14 March 1775 and went to New York. Alive in 1786.

CAMPBELL, DAVID [8 June 1826]. Apprentice to Craufurd Tait.—Third son of Archibald Campbell of Askomell, Argyllshire. *Married* 16 December 1819, Agnes (*died* 13 September 1850), youngest daughter of Alexander Pollock of Whitehill. Captain in 94th Regiment previous to admission. *Died* 24 December 1848, aged 58.

CAMPBELL, EDWARD MAITLAND, B.A.(CANTAB) [24 March 1924]. Apprentice to John Douglas Boswell Campbell.—Son of Patrick William Campbell, W.S. *Born* 14 May 1890. Served with 8th Royal Scots in Great War. *Firm*—Campbell and Don Wauchope. *Died* 17 December 1954.

CAMPBELL, GEORGE, OF ROMANNO AND CONDORRAT [18 January 1886]. Apprentice to (1) A. F. Adam and W. C. M'Ewen; (2) Arthur Campbell; and (3) A. H. Cooper.—Second son of Arthur Campbell of Catrine, W.S. *Born* 18 December 1862. *Married* 6 October 1892, Frances Caroline (*died* 14 October 1965), eldest daughter of Thomas Cuningham, Wine Merchant, Edinburgh, eldest son of Alexander Cuningham of Newholm, W.S. *Died* 25 February 1937. Firm—A. and A. Campbell.

CAMPBELL, GEORGE MUIR [16 January 1798]. Apprentice to (1) William Campbell; and (2) Hugh Corrie.—Third son of William Campbell of Crawfordton, W.S. *Born* 1773. *Married* Agnes (*died* 1 June 1819), daughter of —— Fergusson, Writer in Wigtown. *Died* 20 January 1836.

CAMPBELL, IAN MACLEOD, T.D., B.L. [15 December 1930]. Apprentice to (1) John Richardson of Scott Moncrieff & Trail and (2) Archibald Campbell of Archibald Campbell & Harley.—Son of Archibald Campbell, O.B.E., S.S.C. *Born* 13 March 1907. *Married* 2 December 1939, Jean Gordon, daughter of Lieutenant Gordon Sanderson, of the Gurkhas. Major, Special Air Service, Army Air Crew Corps. Served U.K. and North West Europe 1939-45. *Firm*—Archibald Campbell & Harley. (Retired).

CAMPBELL, JAMES, OF GARGUNNOCK AND PREVICK [3 March 1629]. Apprentice to William Cunningham.—Son of Hugh Campbell of Hullerhurst, Ayrshire. Re-admitted, 21 November 1661. *Married* 28 October 1630, Magdalen, daughter of Adam Cunningham, Advocate.

CAMPBELL, JAMES [14 June 1791]. Apprentice to John Campbell.—Second son of Farquhar Campbell of Lagganlochan, Writer in Islay. *Married*, proclaimed 20 February 1792, Jean (*died* 2 May 1846), daughter of John Moubray, Wright and Builder in Edinburgh. *Died* 6 December 1805.

CAMPBELL, JAMES, M.B.E., B.L. [20 March 1933]. Apprentice to Archibald Brown Campbell of Mylne and Campbell.—Son of James Campbell, Writer, Saltcoats. *Born* 5 February 1910. *Married* 28 July 1937, Ailsa, daughter of Quintin McClymont, Retired Rubber Planter. Lieutenant R.N.V.R. Honorary Sheriff Substitute of Ayr and Bute at Kilmarnock. *Firm*—Jas. Campbell & Co., Saltcoats.

CAMPBELL, JOHN, OF SUCCOTH [4 June 1674]. Apprentice to Richard Guthrie.—Son of William Campbell of Succoth, Dumbartonshire. *Married* (1) Janet (*died* 29 June 1675), daughter of John Hamilton of Woodhead, Merchant in Glasgow; and (2) Agnes, youngest daughter of William Stirling of Law, Dumbartonshire. M.P. for Argyllshire, 1681-2. *Buried* 14 June 1687.

CAMPBELL, JOHN [14 December 1691]. Apprentice to George Dallas.—Son of Captain John Campbell, natural son of Sir John Campbell of Calder. *Married* Elizabeth, daughter of John Campbell of Moy. *Buried* 14 April 1699.

CAMPBELL, JOHN, OF THE CITADEL, Leith [19 July 1779]. Apprentice to David Erskine.— Eldest son of John Campbell, first Cashier of the Royal Bank. *Born* 20 December 1753. *Married* (1) 18 November 1779, Helen (*died* 3 November 1783), daughter of John Callander of Craigforth, Stirlingshire; (2) 8 January 1787, Margaret, daughter of John Campbell of Clathick, Perthshire; and (3) 6 August 1801, Sophia (*died* 26 August 1868), daughter of Duncan Stewart of Ardshiel, Argyllshire. *Died* at Geneva, 11 August 1829.

CAMPBELL, JOHN, OF SMIDDYGREEN [24 November 1785]. Apprentice to Colquhoun Grant.—Second son of Dr Robert Campbell of Smiddygreen, Fife. *Married*, proclaimed 16 November 1778, Mary, daughter of Alexander Maclean, Minister of Kilninian. *Died* 14 February 1821.

CAMPBELL, JOHN, OF ANNFIELD [24 January 1792]. Apprentice to John Campbell.—Only son of John Campbell of Annfield and Shirgarton, Writer in Stirling. *Born* November 1770. *Married* 29 December 1794, Frances Allen (*died* 1847), youngest daughter of John Brown, Merchant, Glasgow. *Died* 9 January 1855.

CAMPBELL, JOHN ALEXANDER, LL.B. [9 December 1980]. Apprentice to James David Thornton and Another of Macrae, Flett & Rennie. Son of James Campbell, General Practitioner, Rosyth. *Born* 3 July 1956. *Married* 2 September 1978, Caroline Kathrin, daughter of Peter Siddons, Poultry Farmer.

CAMPBELL, JOHN ARCHIBALD [22 February 1813]. Apprentice to Alexander Duncan and John Campbell.—Eldest son of John Campbell of The Citadel, W.S. *Born* 1788. *Married* 10 October 1822, Emma (*died* 14 June 1855), daughter of Thomas Peter Legh of Lyme, Chester. Sheriff-Clerk of Mid-Lothian, 1843-60. *Died* 7 September 1866.

CAMPBELL, JOHN DOUGLAS BOSWELL [11 December 1911]. Apprentice to William Babington and Joseph Inglis.—Son of Patrick William Campbell, W.S. *Born* 29 April 1885. *Married* 6 November 1920, May Eudora, daughter of Henry Moncrieff Horsbrugh, C.A., and widow of Kenneth Mackenzie, W.S. Served in Remount Department and Royal Horse Artillery in the Great War. *Died* 11 September 1943. *Firm*—Campbell and Don Wauchope.

CAMPBELL, JOHN HOPE, LL.B. [13 July 1908]. Apprentice to John Little Mounsey.—Son of David Campbell, S.S.C., Edinburgh. *Born* 28 July 1885. *Married* 7 August 1915, Margaret Elizabeth (*died* 10 October 1955), third daughter of George Syme, Craigerne, Granby Road, Edinburgh. *Died* 16 November 1972 in Brazil. *Firm*—D. and J. H. Campbell.

CAMPBELL, JOHN HOPE, B.A.(CANTAB), LL.B. [20 November 1950]. Apprentice to James Little Mounsey and Others of John C. Brodie & Sons.—Son of John Hope Campbell, W.S., Edinburgh. *Born* 8 June 1923. *Married* (1) 8 September 1951, Ethel Margaret Joan, daughter of John Loudon, S.S.C. (marriage dissolved), and (2) Mary Patricia, daughter of Tom Redwood, Naval Officer. Captain, Gurkha Rifles. Served in India, Italy and Greece. *Firm*—D. & J. H. Campbell. (Retired).

CAMPBELL, JOHN KIRKPATRICK, OF GLENFEOCHAN [25 November 1796]. Apprentice to John Campbell, Jun.—Son of Archibald Campbell of Jura, Argyllshire. *Married* 29 July 1817, Mary Kirkpatrick (*died* 10 July 1836), only daughter of Alexander Campbell of the Island of Tobago. *Died* 28 April 1826.

CAMPBELL, JOHN TAIT, T.D., B.L. [6 July 1933]. Apprentice to A. B. Campbell of Mylne & Campbell.—Son of Robert Brown Campbell, M.D., F.R.C.P.E. *Born* 5 February 1907. *Married* (1) 6 August 1935, Edith Mary, elder daughter of W. E. G. Lawrie, Edinburgh, and (2) 24th July 1946, Helen Joan Freda, daughter of John Lapraik, O.B.E. Lieutenant Colonel, Royal Scots. Served U.K., France, Gibraltar and Italy 1939-45. Mentioned in Despatches. *Firm*—Mylne & Campbell. (Retired).

CAMPBELL, KENNETH MURRAY, M.A., LL.B. [22 July 1963]. Apprentice to Sir Charles G. Connell and Others of Connell & Connell.—Son of John Campbell, Inspector, Dumfries Gas Department, Dumfries. *Born* 20 October 1930. *Married* 31 March 1956, Madeleine Jean, daughter of Alexander Gillie, Police Sergeant, Edinburgh. Joint Editor with Sheriff C. H. Johnston, Q.C. of Sixth Edition of *Connell on the Agricultural Holdings (Scotland) Acts* (1970). *Firm*—Connell & Connell.

CAMPBELL, ORD GRAHAM [15 November 1838]. Apprentice to Andrew Tawse.—Youngest son of Archibald Graham Campbell of Shirvain, Argyllshire. *Born* 11 September 1816. *Married* 15 June 1858, Jeanette Ritchie (*died* 27 February 1891), daughter of William Wallace of Busby. *Died* 7 June 1890.

CAMPBELL, PATRICK, OF QUEENSHILL [8 March 1791]. Apprentice to William Campbell, his uncle.—Eldest son of William Campbell of Queenshill. *Born* 1764. *Married* 10 April 1800, Jane (*died* 1849), eldest surviving daughter of David Maitland of Barcaple, Kirkcudbrightshire. *Died* 11 December 1836.

CAMPBELL, PATRICK WILLIAM [20 October 1875]. Apprentice to (1) Robert Craigie Bell; and (2) James Mylne, Sen.—Eldest son of David Campbell, Mounthamilton, Manager of Royal Bank of Scotland, Ayr. *Born* 21 November 1850. *Married* 18 April 1883, Mary Walker (*died* 20 May 1927), eldest daughter of John Fergusson Cathcart, Merchant, Leith. Principal Clerk of Session in Second Division, 1893-1913. *Died* 28 February 1922.

CAMPBELL, RICHARD, OF HELENTONMAINS AND AUCHENBRECK [3 March 1818]. Apprentice to Robert Cathcart.—Fourth son of Richard Campbell of Helentonmains, Ayrshire. *Married* 8 August 1834, Ann Glass (*died* 1866), daughter of Archibald Douglas, Clangregor Castle. *Died* 27 July 1853, aged 59.

CAMPBELL, ROBERT, OF BALVIE [25 November 1701]. Apprentice to John Cuningham.—Son of Archibald Campell of Easter Torrie. *Married* (1) June 1702, Anna, daughter of John Campbell of Succoth; and (2) before 1713, Anna, second daughter of William Colquhoun of Craigton, Dumbartonshire. Fiscal, 1703-10. Agent for "the Good Town" of Edinburgh. *Died* February 1716.

CAMPBELL, ROBERT, OF SONACHAN [21 May 1805]. Apprentice to H. M. Buchanan,— Eldest son of Donald Campbell of Sonachan, Argyllshire. *Born* 29 December 1779. *Married* 16 June 1815, Susan (*died* 26 March 1854), only daughter of David Campbell of Combie, Argyllshire, *Died* 13 June 1877.

CAMPBELL, ROBERT GILLIES [16 January 1893]. Apprentice to Frederick Pitman and A. R. C. Pitman,—Youngest son of James Campbell, formerly Sheriff-Substitute of Edinburgh. *Born* 19 August 1868. *Married* 9 September 1914, Miriam Elizabeth (*died* 21 April 1958), youngest daughter of John Clemson of Leehurst, Wellington, Shropshire. Major 10th Service Batt. Seaforth Highlanders. *Died* at Cromarty, 12 February 1915.

CAMPBELL, RONALD, OF BALERNO [15 August 1695]. Apprentice to John Campbell of Succoth.—Son of Alexander Campbell of Kilcharmaig. *Married* (1) ——; and (2) 25 March 1697, Margaret (*died* 25 February 1761), daughter of James Hamilton of Hetherwick, East Lothian. Commissary of Argyll, 1694. Solicitor to "the Good Town" of Edinburgh. Deputy Keeper of the Signet, 1725–6. *Died* 30 August 1726.

CAMPBELL, THOMAS WEIR, B.L. [26 November 1962]. Apprentice to Arthur Woodman Blair and Others of Strathern & Blair.—Son of Robert Campbell, Osteopath, Edinburgh. *Born* 14 September 1934. *Married* (1) 22 September 1956, Ann Banks Whitton, daughter of James Currie, Engineer, Edinburgh, and (2) 1 August 1968, Flora McLeod, daughter of Walter Easton, Publisher, Jedburgh. *Firm*—Strathern & Blair.

CAMPBELL, WILLIAM, OF CRAWFORDTON AND CRAIGIEBURN [4 August 1777]. Apprentice to George Muir, his uncle.—Eldest son of Dr Patrick Campbell, Physician in Wigtown. *Married* (1) Miss M'Murdo; and (2) 14 May 1793, Lydia (*died* 1 December 1835), daughter of Rev. John Collow, Minister of Penpont. *Died* 6 May 1794.

CAMPBELL, WILLIAM [8 July 1800]. Apprentice to Archibald Gibson.—Second son of Sir James Campbell of Aberuchil, Bart. *Born* 14 May 1774. *Married* (1) 5 January 1804, Eliza (*died* 26 October 1818), daughter of William Hunter of Glenormiston; and (2) 25 October 1820, Jane (*died* 1863) second daughter of Hugh Cleghorn of Stravithie, Fife. *Died* 28 April 1849.

CAMPBELL, WILLIAM, OF QUEENSHILL [29 June 1826]. Apprentice to James Dundas.— Eldest son of Patrick Campbell of Queenshill, W.S. *Born* 15 February 1801. *Died* 8 October 1863, unmarried.

CAMPBELL, WILLIAM ANDREW [13 July 1936]. Apprentice to John A. S. Millar and Others of Russell & Dunlop.—Son of Rev. Andrew Campbell, Crieff. *Born* 11 March 1912. *Married* 15 April 1940, Jean Blair, daughter of John R. B. McGill. Captain, Royal Scots 1939–45. *Firm*—Macrae, Flett and Rennie. (Retired).

CAMPBELL, WILLIAM BOWIE STEWART, OF CLOICHFOLDICH [4 March 1826]. Apprentice to John Bowie.—Son of Major Alexander Campbell of Glenfalloch. *Born* 1803. *Married* (1) 16 March 1830, Sarah Priscilla (*died* 23 March 1834), only daughter of J. Fearnside, London; and (2) 5 April 1838, Janet W. Maxwell (*died* 25 April 1885), only child of Robert Stewart of Cloichfoldich, Perthshire. *Died* 11 June 1847.

CAMPBELL FRASER, PATRICK ALEXANDER, B.A.(OXON), LL.B. [27 November 1961]. Apprentice to Charles Edward Stewart and Others of Murray, Beith & Murray.—Son of Alexander Campbell Fraser, Land Agent, Borthwickshiels, Hawick. *Born* 12 October 1933. *Married* 14 October 1961, Kalitza Mary Stuart, daughter of Marcus Humphrey Ure Spurway, Midcalder.

CANNAN, HORATIUS, OF BARLAY [18 November 1784]. Apprentice to Robert Boswell.— Only son of John Cannan of Barlay, Kirkcudbrightshire. *Married* 18 November 1779, Catherine (*died* 6 July 1838), daughter of James Pyott, Bailie of Montrose. *Died* 17 April 1825, aged 68.

CANNAN, HORATIUS [17 November 1825]. Apprentice to, and third son of, Horatius Cannan, W.S. *Born* 1 August 1788. *Died* 18 February 1843, unmarried.

CANT, HARRY WALLACE, M.A., LL.B. [15 July 1949]. Apprentice to E. J. McCandlish and Others of Cowan & Dalmahoy.—Son of Henry Cant, S.S.C., Edinburgh. *Born* 5 July 1918. *Married* 14 February 1953, Mary Fleming, daughter of Dr. Henry F. Hamilton, F.R.C.S. Captain, R.A. 1939-46. Served in Western Desert, Sicily, North West Europe. Wounded in France 1944. *Firm*—J. & F. Anderson (formerly Menzies & Thomson).

CARGILL, JAMES [18 November 1784]. Apprentice to James Stewart.—Son of Walter Cargill, Merchant in Dunkeld. *Married*, proclaimed 30 June 1781, Marion, eldest daughter of William Jamieson, Architect and Contractor in Edinburgh. Resigned his Commission, 23 March 1795.

CARGILL, ROBERT [10 July 1812]. Apprentice to Hugh Watson.—Son of James Cargill, W.S. *Died* 21 February 1867.

CARLETON, ANDREW ALEXANDER ROSE, M.A., LL.B. [24 July 1967]. Apprentice to Charles David Pagan and Others of Pagan & Osborne, Cupar.—Son of Dr Sydney Alexander Carleton, Leicester. *Born* 28 July 1937. *Married* 14 October 1961, Aline Hart, daughter of James Borthwick Rae, Company Director. *Firm*—Pagan Osborne & Grace, Cupar and St Andrews. (Formerly Pagan & Osborne).

CARMENT, JOSEPH ALEXANDER STEWART [10 December 1906]. Apprentice to J. R. M. Wedderburn and G. G. Watson.—Son of Joseph Carment, C.E., of Coimbatoor, India. *Born* 30 October 1870. *Married* 30 June 1908, Matilda Katherine (*died* 14 March 1962), youngest daughter of Thomas Stevenson, 28 Lauder Road, Edinburgh. *Died* 21 February 1929.

CARMICHAEL, ALEXANDER [13 April 1650]. *Married* 1653, Judith Nairne (*died* 27 April 1667). *Buried* 24 June 1658.

CARMICHAEL, ARCHIBALD [23 December 1723]. Apprentice to William Kelso. *Married* 17 September 1719, Margaret, daughter of George Wallace of Moncastle. *Died* April 1743.

CARMICHAEL, IAN SCOTT, M.A., LL.B. [19 December 1949]. Apprentice to Thomas Young, of Gray, Muirhead & Carmichael.—Son of Robert Scott Carmichael, S.S.C. *Born* 2 October 1917. *Married* 10 April 1946, Mary Margaret, daughter of Robert Forbes, Banker. Major, Royal Scots. Served France, Africa and Burma 1939-45. *Died* 10 January 1982. *Firm*—Ian S. Carmichael & Co.

CARMICHAEL, JAMES, OF HAILES [30 June 1741]. Apprentice to Hugh Somerville.—Second son of the Hon. William Carmichael of Skirling, Advocate. *Married* 16 April 1750, Jenny (*died* 24 January 1784), youngest daughter of Sir John Clerk of Penicuik, Bart. Commissary of Lanark, 1743. *Died* 12 January 1781.

CARNEGIE, JAMES [16 August 1665]. Apprentice to James Allane.—Son of Robert Carnegie of Newgate, Angus.

CARNEGIE, JAMES, OF EDROM NEWTON [22 December 1825]. Apprentice to Francis Walker.—Son of John Carnegie, Tenant in Hailes. *Born* 1799. *Died* 23 April 1883, unmarried.

CARNEGIE, ROBERT [11 March 1670]. Apprentice to James Allane.—Fourth son of Sir Alexander Carnegie of Pitarrow, Bart. *Buried* 28 September 1670.

CARNEGY, JAMES. *See* GARDYNE, JAMES GARNEY.

CARRIE, GRANT, B.L. [22 March 1950]. Apprentice to W. A. Scott Douglas of Baillie & Gifford.—Son of William Carrie, Wholesale Grocer, Elgin. *Born* 19 September 1921. *Married* 4 May 1942, Alexandra, daughter of John Murray, Balloan, Dornoch. Major, Seaforth Highlanders; Served Middle East and North Africa, 1939-46.

CARRUTHERS, IAIN TAYLOR, LL.B. [11 December 1979]. Apprentice to Ronald Kenneth Watson and Others of Brodies.—Son of John Hornsby Hunter Carruthers, Company Director, Stirling. *Born* 23 June 1947. *Married* 4 September 1971, Alison Margaret, daughter of Roland Hill. *Firm*—Brodies.

CARRUTHERS, JAMES, OF PORTRACK, M.V.O., D.S.O. [27 March 1899]. Apprentice to J. O. Mackenzie, H. Cheyne, and J. Kermack.—Eldest son of Peter Carruthers of Portrack, Dumfriesshire. *Born* 17 July 1876. *Married* 11 February 1915, Violet Rosa (*died* 2 February 1959), younger daughter of Charles Markham of Tapton House, Chesterfield, Engineer. Joined Royal Artillery, 1900; retired with rank of Lieut.-Colonel, 1920. Served in Great War from August 1914. D.S.O., 1914. *Died* 27 June 1936.

CARSTAIRS, ROBERT, OF RADERNIE [9 December 1687]. Apprentice to William Hamilton.—Son of John Carstairs of Cassingray, Fife. *Born* 1645. *Married* 1679, Esther, daughter of Thomas Mills of Millhouse, Stafford. *Died* August 1705.

CASS, JOHN [22 December 1610]. Apprentice to Richard Cass.—*Married* 17 August 1603, Christain, daughter of William Kellie, W.S.

CASS, RICHARD, OF FORDELL [Before 1594].—Son of Robert Cass of Fordell, Mid-Lothian. Commissioner, 16 December 1594. *Died* 3 February 1632.

CASSELLS, ALEXANDER [10 June 1830]. Apprentice to James and Charles Nairne.—Fourth son of John Cassells of Arnprior, Perthshire. *Born* 1808. *Married* 25 October 1838, Catherine (*died* 21 November 1864), daughter of John Walker, Bellsbank, Dalmellington. *Died* 10 March 1875.

CATHCART, DANIEL [29 December 1658]. Apprentice to Robert Wallace, Richard ,Guthrie, and Hugh Paterson.—Son of William Cathcart of Waterheid, Ayrshire. Re-admitted, 13 January 1662. *Buried* 13 May 1686.

CATHCART, DAVID [16 May 1822]. Apprentice to George Russell.—Third son of David Cathcart of Auchendrane, Ayrshire, Lord Alloway, one of the Senators of the College of Justice. *Born* 2 December 1798. *Died* 1 January 1867, unmarried.

CATHCART, ROBERT, OF DRUM [25 November 1796]. Apprentice to (1) Andrew Mackenzie; and (2) Kenneth Mackenzie.—Younger son of Robert Cathcart of Genoch. *Born* 22 June 1773. *Married* 16 October 1797, Anne (*died* 11 May 1846), daughter of John Cadell of Cockenzie, East Lothian. Lockhart calls him a worthy and reliable man. Was partner of Archibald Constable. *Died* 18 November 1812.

CATHCART, ROBERT ALFRED [13 November 1849]. Apprentice to Thomas Macpherson Grant.—Eldest son of Elias Cathcart of Auchendrane. *Born* 3 February 1825. *Died* 15 February 1855, unmarried.

CAUVIN, JOSEPH [24 November 1785]. Apprentice to William Aytoun.—Eldest son of Louis Cauvin, Teacher of French in Edinburgh, and brother of Louis Cauvin, the Founder of Cauvin's Hospital. *Married* 20 April 1787, Esther (*died* 2 April 1813), only daughter of Dr Henry Cunningham. *Died* 23 November 1815.

CAY, JOHN [3 July 1851]. Apprentice to James Gillespie Davidson.—Eldest son of John Cay, Advocate. *Born* 13 July 1820. *Married* 21 July 1857, Geddes Elizabeth (*died* 15 December 1909), youngest daughter of Thomas Mackenzie of Applecross, Ross-shire, W.S. Solicitor to G.P.O. *Died* 28 May 1892.

CAY, ROBERT DUNDAS [7 March 1833]. Apprentice to David Welsh.—Youngest son of Robert Hodshon Cay of North Charlton, Judge of the High Court of Admiralty. *Born* 20 August 1807. *Married* 29 October 1835, Isabella (*died* 21 June 1852), fourth daughter of William Dyce of Cuttlehill, Aberdeenshire, M.D. Registrar of Supreme Court. Hong-Kong, 1844-55. *Died* 19 March 1888.

CHALMER, JOHN MUIR, OF GADGIRTH [7 January 1756]. Apprentice to John Macfarlane.—Son of John Muir of Ayr, and nephew of John Chalmer of Gadgirth. *Born* 24 July 1726. *Married* Elizabeth Farquhar, of Edinburgh (*died* 14 April 1804). Assumed name of Chalmer, 1764. *Died* 5 May 1774.

CHALMER, WILLIAM [3 December 1636]. Apprentice to Robert Pringle.—Son of George Chalmer of Auldquhat. *Married* (1) Margaret, daughter of Daniel Melville, W.S.; and (2) 13 May 1651, Isobell Garvie. Re-admitted, 21 November 1661. *Died* January 1668.

CHALMERS, ALEXANDER HENDERSON [6 July 1854]. Apprentice to James Mackenzie, J. B. Innes, and John Logan.—Son of Charles Chalmers of Monkshill, Advocate in Aberdeen. *Born* 20 September 1833. *Married* 27 October 1870, Meylia Jessie Marjory Williamson (*died* 1 April 1910), eldest daughter of Patrick Sinclair Laing, Deputy Inspector-General of Hospitals, Elgin. Commissary Clerk, Aberdeen. *Died* 3 November 1871.

CHALMERS, CHARLES, OF PORTLETHIN [20 October 1704]. Apprentice to William Thomson.—Second son of James Chalmers, Professor of Philosophy in the Marischal College of Aberdeen. *Married* (1) Jean, daughter of Alexander Boog of Burnhouses, Berwickshire; and (2) (contract, 23 September 1703), Helen, daughter of Alexander Young, Bishop of Edinburgh. Ensign, 24 February 1703, in the Scots Guards; afterwards Captain, but sold his Commission 1714. Killed fighting for King James at Sheriffmuir, 13 November 1715.

CHALMERS, FRANCIS [24 March 1913]. Apprentice to William Garson and James Garson.—Son of Andrew Bruce Chalmers, Schoolmaster, Kirkcaldy. *Born* 4 May 1869. *Married* 5 September 1898, Margaret Brown (*died* 23 April 1952), daughter of Thomas Crichton, Commission Agent. *Firm*—Skene, Edwards, and Garson. *Died* 27 September 1945.

CHALMERS, GEORGE [3 October 1723]. Apprentice to Thomas Gibson.—*Married* 6 October 1729, Elizabeth, daughter of Colin Arthur of Ballein. *Died* 9 December 1758.

CHALMERS, JAMES [25 June 1764]. Apprentice to (1) Alexander Tait; and (2) John Mackenzie.—Son of Andrew Chalmers, Writer in Edinburgh. *Married*, proclaimed 12 August 1780, Elizabeth (*died* 16 March 1833), daughter of Archibald Campbell, Collector of Customs, Prestonpans. *Died* at Westminster, 20 November 1830, aged 89.

CHALMERS, JAMES HAY [26 June 1856]. Apprentice to Archibald Watson Goldie.— Son of Rev. Peter Chalmers, Minister of the First Charge, Dunfermline. *Born* 7 January 1829. *Married* 23 August 1859, Marion Morrison (*died* 23 January 1898), elder daughter of Alexander Hay of Hardengreen, Mid-Lothian, W.S. *Died* 21 June 1860.

CHALMERS, JOHN [10 March 1813]. Apprentice to Bain Whyt.—Eldest son of Thomas Chalmers, Locksmith in Potterrow. *Born* 1784. *Died* 18 March 1833, unmarried.

CHALMERS, THOMAS [19 March 1888]. Apprentice to J. W. Young and John Blair.— Younger son of Thomas Chalmers of Longcroft, Linlithgowshire. *Born* 10 January 1863. Disappeared in Vienna on 29 April 1896. Presumed dead by Court as at 29 April 1903.

CHANCELLOR, EDWARD [26 June 1856]. Apprentice to John Dundas, William Wilson, and A. M. Bell.—Fifth son of Alexander Chancellor of Shieldhill, Lanarkshire. *Born* 22 September 1828. *Married* 17 April 1866, Ann Helen (*died* 13 April 1932), only daughter of John Robert Tod, W.S. *Died* 30 April 1907.

CHANCELLOR, GEORGE [17 July 1851]. Apprentice to Alexander Hamilton.—Third son of Alexander Chancellor of Shieldhill. *Born* 7 September 1825. *Married* 20 June 1861, Katherine Elizabeth (*died* 9 July 1930), youngest daughter of George Skene of Rubislaw. *Died* 4 April 1875.

CHAPLANE, ALEXANDER, OF COLLISTON [13 January 1673]. Apprentice to James Cheyne.—Eldest son of Robert Chaplane, Town Clerk Depute, Dundee. *Married* (1) Agnes (*died* 26 July 1674), daughter of James Smyth, Portioner of Nungate; and (2) 20 April 1676, Magdalene, daughter of Henry Killoch, Merchant Burgess, Edinburgh. Fiscal, 1683-4. *Buried* 15 April 1695.

CHAPMAN, JOHN, OF SCHELIS [Before 1532]. Nephew of Walter Chapman, W.S. *Married* Isobel Henderson.

CHAPMAN, WALTER, OF EWERLAND [Before 1494]. Was Scotland's first Printer in partnership with Andrew Millar. *Married* (1) Margaret Kirkettle; (2) Agnes Cockburn. *Died* 1538.

CHAPMAN, WILLIAM [Before 1541].

CHARTERIS, HENRY [29 July 1633]. Apprentice to James Stratoun.—Son of Henry Charteris, Primar of Edinburgh College. *Married* 14 November 1632, Mawsia Henrieson, niece of Charles Hamilton, Merchant Burgess of Edinburgh. *Died* 4 October 1641.

CHARTERIS, JAMES [5 September 1671]. Apprentice to John Alexander, elder.—Son of William Charteris of Auchinstrowan. *Married* Mary, daughter of Sir Francis Kinloch of Gilmerton, Bart., Lord Provost of Edinburgh. Commissary of Dumfries. *Buried* 30 January 1691.

CHARTERS, WILLIAM [23 November 1655]. Apprentice to Quintin Kennedy.—Son of William Charters of Auchinstrowan. *Married* 29 December 1653, Isobel, daughter of Quintin Kennedy, W.S. Re-admitted, 11 April 1661. *Buried* 15 March 1676.

CHESNUTT, ROBERT STUART [27 April 1959]. Apprentice to Alexander Harper and Others of Pearson, Robertson & Maconochie. Son of John Chesnutt, Master Tailor, Port Glasgow. *Born* 1 December 1912. *Married* 20 July 1940, Ernestina Francis, daughter of James Munro, Civil Servant. Captain, Royal Signals. Staff Officer, Directorate of Signals, War Office, and Major, Staff Officer, H.Q., Palestine. *Firm*—Pearson, Robertson & Maconochie. (Retired).

CHESSER, JOHN SIMM, LL.B. [14 July 1919]. Apprentice to Arthur H. M'Lean.—Son of John William Chesser, S.S.C., Lord Provost of Edinburgh. *Born* 12 February 1893. *Married* 19 June 1931, Kathleen Frances Haldane, only daughter of Frank H. Allan, Banker, Edinburgh. *Died* 9 November 1961.

CHEYNE, GEORGE DUGUID, M.A., LL.B., S.S.C. [28 July 1959] (by Rule IXa).—Son of Alexander Duguid Cheyne, Insurance Manager and Farmer. *Born* 20 March 1906. *Married* 23 May 1935, Nancy Fitzroy, daughter of Lewis Gordon Sandeman. Squadron Leader R.A.F.V.R., Flying Control Bomber Station. *Firm*—W. H. Mill, Macleod & Rose (latterly Scott, Moncrieff & Trail). (Now Consultant.)

CHEYNE, HARRY, OF GIRLSTA [19 March 1868]. Apprentice to, and son of, Henry Cheyne, W.S.—*Born* 2 March 1845. *Married* 20 July 1876, Dora (*died* 10 January 1937), daughter of George Todd Chiene, C.A., Edinburgh. *Died* 27 November 1915.

CHEYNE, HARRY [7 December 1908]. Apprentice to Harry Cheyne, F. J. G. Borthwick, G. Kermack, Ian MacIntyre, and J. G. Kirkpatrick.—Only son of Harry Cheyne, W.S. *Born* 8 December 1882. *Married* 3 February 1915, Anne Violet MacMillan (*died* 15 August 1969), eldest daughter of J. T. Salvesen, 6 Rothesay Terrace, Edinburgh. Major R.F.A. *Killed* in action in France, 10 July 1917.

CHEYNE, HENRY, OF TANGWICK [19 November 1829]. Apprentice to Joseph Gordon.—Eldest son of John Cheyne of Tangwick, Shetland. *Born* 24 August 1804. *Married* 7 May 1840, Barbara (*died* 1 August 1899), eldest daughter of William Hay of Laxfirth, Shetland. Clerk to the Admission of Notaries, 1855-68. *Died* 27 February 1868.

CHEYNE, JAMES [8 March 1642]. Apprentice to Robert Pringle.—Son of Walter Cheyne in Tillibin. Re-admitted, 21 November 1661.

CHEYNE, JAMES [12 September 1706]. Apprentice to William Thomson.—*Married* (1) September 1713, Elizabeth, daughter of Sir Charles Maitland of Pitrichie, Aberdeenshire; and (2) November 1724, Barbara (*died* 5 December 1750), daughter of Robert Ross of Achlossan, Aberdeenshire, and widow of Captain Francis Forbes. *Died* 8 April 1729.

CHEYNE, JAMES AUCHENLECK, OF OXENDEAN AND KILMARON [3 March 1818]. Apprentice to (1) Robert Cathcart; and (2) John Kermack.—Son of Ninian Richard Cheyne, Bookseller in Edinburgh. *Married* (1) 16 August 1821, Margaret Blair (*died* 31 May 1832), daughter of Andrew M'Kean, Edinburgh; and (2) 29 April 1834, Frances Charlton (*died* 1873), daughter of James Sprott, of Chittagong, Bengal. *Died* 21 June 1853, aged 58.

CHIENE, GEORGE TURCAN, D.S.O., M.C., T.D., B.L. [14 December 1931]. Apprentice to T. J. Carlyle Gifford and Another of Baillie & Gifford.—Son of George Lyall Chiene, F.R.C.S.E. *Born* 15 November 1907. *Married* 28 October 1939, Ada Mary, daughter of Charles Mackinlay, Whisky Merchant, Edinburgh. Major R.A. Served U.K. and France, North Africa and Italy 1939-45. *Firms*—(1) Cowan & Dalmahoy (1933-37); (2) Baillie Gifford & Co. (1937-72).

CHIENE, PETER, LL.B. [2 December 1974]. Apprentice to Patrick Watson Turcan and Others of Dundas & Wilson.—Son of George Turcan Chiene, W.S., Edinburgh. *Born* 13 July 1946.

CHIESLEY, JOHN [20 August 1697]. Apprentice to John Knox.—Grandson of Walter Chiesley of Dalry. *Married* Elizabeth Hislop. Deprived of his Commission, 24 December 1707, for repeated contraventions of the Acts.

CHIESLIE, WILLIAM, OF COCKBURN [4 August 1662]. Apprentice to John Semple.—Son of Rev. John Chieslie, Minister at Quodquen in the Sheriffdom of Lanark. *Married* before 1665, Agnes (*died* 29 July 1694), daughter of Samuel Rutherfurd, Principal of St Mary's College, St. Andrews. *Died* 13 February 1704, aged 70.

CHILD, WILLIAM ARUNDALE [18 November 1825]. Apprentice to (1) Archibald Crauford; and (2) James Dunlop.—Son of William Child of Glencorse, Merchant in Edinburgh. *Married* 21 February 1856, Amelia White (*died* 1865). Stipendiary Magistrate of Island of Tobago. *Died* at Tobago, 20 October 1861, aged 58.

CHILL, ROBERT DESMOND OLIPHANT, LL.B. [3 December 1973]. Apprentice to Sir Alastair C. Blair and Others of Dundas & Wilson, Davidson & Syme.—Son of Walter Henry Chill, Technical Consultant (Ferranti), Edinburgh. *Born* 22 October 1948. *Married* 13 July 1973, Margaret Ann, daughter of Wilfrid George Westlake, Senior Civil Servant. *Firm*—Kilgour, McNeill & Sime.

CHISHOLM, JAMES CROSBY, LL.B. [24 April 1972]. Apprentice to Henry Morris Braine and Others of Gordon, Falconer & Fairweather.—Son of Peter Chisholm, Haulage Contractor, Galashiels. *Born* 26 September 1945. *Married* 21 September 1973, Evelyn Agnes, daughter of Alexander Martin, Bank Manager, Edinburgh. *Firm*—Storie, Cruden & Simpson, Aberdeen.

CHRISTIAN, JAMES [12 February 1829]. Apprentice to George Hogarth.—Son of Peter Christian, Writer in Stonehaven. *Born* 1801. *Married* 8 July 1839, Robina (*died* 1 March 1885), youngest daughter of Robert Renton, Edinburgh. Sheriff-Clerk of Kincardineshire, 1861-76. *Died* 11 August 1876.

CHRISTIE, ALASTAIR KEITH, M.A., LL.B. [30 April 1970]. Apprentice to A. J. R. Bisset and Others of Baillie & Gifford.—Son of Dr Albert Christie, Consultant Anaesthetist, Clarkston, Renfrewshire. *Born* 18 July 1944. *Married* 11 September 1973, Bertha Miriam, daughter of Ernest Tinsley, Undertaker. *Firm*—Thorburn & Lyon, Peebles.

CHRISTIE, ANDREW, LL.B. [7 December 1970]. Apprentice to Kenneth Macrae and Others of Murray, Beith & Murray,—Son of Dr Albert Christie, Consultant Anaesthetist, Clarkston, Renfrewshire. *Born* 23 April 1947. *Married* 10 June 1976, Fanny Fung Yee. Partner with Deacons, Solicitors, Hong Kong.

CHRISTIE, JAMES, OF WHYTHOUSE [30 December 1647]. Apprentice to Robert Kirkwood.—Nephew of David Christie of Over Stenton. Re-admitted, 21 November 1661. *Married* 26 October 1648, Jean (*died* 27 October 1669), daughter of Archibald Primrose, Writer, Edinburgh. *Died* November 1670.

CHRISTIE, JOHN COCKBURN [8 February 1838]. Apprentice to George Turnbull.— Son of David Christie, Writer in Edinburgh. *Born* 29 April 1812. *Married* October 1842, his cousin, Helen (*died* 11 April 1889), daughter of Hector Christie of Lenton, Nottingham. Keeper of the Register of Deeds, etc., 1869-73. Deputy Keeper of the Records, 10 December 1873-80. *Died* 29 August 1880.

CHRISTIE, ROBERT LINDSAY BRUCE STARK [11 December 1856]. Apprentice to Charles Morton.—Second son of Robert Stark Christie of Teasses, Fife. *Born* 18 December 1832. *Married* 25 November 1868, Julianne Cockburn (*died* 17 February 1915), daughter of Captain Alexander Scott, 72nd Regiment. *Died* 27 December 1889.

CHRISTIE, WALTER CROSS BUCHANAN, OF BEDLAY AND PETERSHILL [15 July 1889]. Apprentice to Charles Morton and John Neilson.—Elder son of Thomas Craig Christie of Bedlay and Petershill, Lanarkshire. *Born* 5 December 1862. *Died* 28 January 1941.

CHRISTIE, WILLIAM LESLIE, T.D., LL.B., OF LOCHDOCHART [8 July 1907]. Apprentice to William Hugh Murray and Robert Octavius Pitman.—Son of William Christie of Lochdochart, Crianlarich. *Born* 20 March 1883. Served in France, 1915-19, with R.G.A. Promoted Major. *Died* 19 November 1950. *Firm*—Cairns, M'Intosh, and Morton.

CHRISTIE, WILLIAM MARTIN, M.A., LL.B. [27 April 1965]. Apprentice to Thomas Patrick Spens of Maclay, Murray & Spens.—Son of William Christie, H.M. Inspector for Schools (retired), Dundee. *Born* 18 March 1936. *Married* 30 October 1970, Shiela Graham, daughter of Captain Findlay Kerr, M.N. *Firm*—Mackenzie, Roberton & Co., Glasgow.

CHRISTISON, JOHN [25 November 1858]. Apprentice to James Hope, Robert Oliphant, and Robert Mackay.—Son of Sir Robert Christison, Bart., M.D. *Born* 14 October 1832. *Died* 12 November 1894, unmarried.

CHUTE, JOHN DESMOND FRANCIS, LL.B. [2 December 1974]. Apprentice to Ronald Kenneth Watson and Others of Brodies.—Son of Major D. C. F. Chute (retired), Malta. *Born* 18 September 1950.

CLAPPERTON, GEORGE [12 December 1793]. Apprentice to William Aytoun.—Son of William Clapperton, Merchant in Edinburgh. *Died* 1 August 1814.

CLAPPERTON, THOMAS [2 November 1881]. Apprentice to W. Traquair, W. T. Dickson, and T. S. MacLaren.—Son of John Clapperton, Merchant in Gorebridge. *Born* 15 September 1857. *Married* 17 December 1901, Jenata Jane Shines Bourman or Black, widow (*died* 21 August 1954). *Died* 20 August 1932.

CLARK, DANIEL SMITH [12 July 1897]. Apprentice to William Percival Lindsay.—Son of James Smith Clark, S.S.C., Edinburgh. *Born* 13 June 1875. *Died* 18 April 1920, unmarried.

CLARK, DUNCAN MALCOLM, M.A., LL.B. [11 December 1979]. Apprentice to E. G. Marquis and Another of J. & F. Anderson.—Son of Angus Clark, Company Director, Stirling. *Born* 17 May 1932. *Married* 24 May 1958, Rose Marion, daughter of Alexander Brown, Cupar. *Firm*—J. & F. Anderson.

CLARK, GEORGE BARRIE, LL.B. [11 December 1979*].—Son of George Hendrie Clark, Bank Manager, Thornhill. *Born* 22 February 1952. *Firm*—Morton, Fraser & Milligan.

CLARK, GEORGE BENNET [30 May 1878]. Apprentice to J. B. Innes and John and Charles B. Logan.—Son of William Bennet Clark, Advocate. Grandson of William Clark, W.S. (1803). *Born* 8 May 1853. *Married* 28 December 1882, Harriet Sophia (*died* 28 May 1939), daughter of Dr Martin, Edinburgh. *Died* 22 March 1929.

CLARK, JAMES GRAHAM, LL.B. [7 December 1970]. Apprentice to Ronald Kenneth Watson and Others of Brodie Cuthbertson & Watson. Son of John Melville Clark, W.S., Edinburgh. *Born* 14 July 1946. *Married* 3 July 1970, Teresa Mary, daughter of George Seed, F.R.C.S.E. *Firm*—Brodies (formerly Brodie, Cuthbertson & Watson).

CLARK, JOHN [29 July 1695]. Apprentice to Robert Bell.—*Married* Janet Paterson.

CLARK, JOHN MELVILLE, B.L. [15 March 1937]. Apprentice to Peter John Macdonald and Others of W. & J. Burness.—Son of Rev. James Graham Clark. *Born* 30 June 1908. *Married* (1) 29 August 1945, Isobel Katherine (*died* 2 October 1970), daughter of the Rev. William Weir Clark, and (2) 24 November 1978, Marjorie Anne Strang or Wilson. *Firm*—W. & J. Burness (retired).

CLARK, ROBERT GEORGE, B.L. [30 April 1962] (by Rule IXa).—Son of William Smith Clark, Solicitor, Edinburgh. *Born* 3 September 1928. *Married* 1 August 1959, Isobel May, daughter of J. Hamilton, Coldstream. *Firm*—J. Gibson Kerr & Co.

CLARK, THOMAS WILFRID BENNET. *See* BENNET-CLARK, THOMAS WILFRID.

CLARK, WILLIAM [7 July 1803]. Apprentice to Crauford Tait.—Eldest son of David Clark, Merchant in Edinburgh. *Married* 29 August 1814, Margaret (*died* 18 July 1830), daughter of Rev. William Bennet, Minister of Duddingston. Sheriff-Substitute of Clackmannanshire, 1832-52. *Died* 8 November 1863, aged 86.

CLARK, Sir WILLIAM MORTIMER [17 February 1859]. Apprentice to John Scott.— Son of John Clark, Manager of the Aberdeen Insurance Company. *Born* 24 May 1836. *Married* 22 November 1866, Helen, daughter of Gilbert Gordon, Peterborough. Called to Bar of Ontario, 1867. Chairman of Knox College and Member of Senate, University of Toronto. Q.C., 1890. Lieutenant-Governor of Ontario, 1903-8. Knighted, 1907. *Died* 12 August 1917.

CLARKE, ALLAN, OF WOODSIDE [29 June 1759]. Apprentice to Andrew Wallace.—Son of William Clarke, Merchant in Linlithgow. *Died* 8 January 1810.

CLARKE, GEORGE KENNETH VALENTINE, B.A.(CANTAB), LL.B. [20 November 1950]. Apprentice to Ranald Ker Cuthbertson and Others of Mackenzie, Innes & Logan.—Son of The Rev. Canon George Kirkcaldy Sturrock Clarke. *Born* 14 February 1923. *Married* 18 July 1953, Anne, daughter of Antony Johnstone. Captain, Lothian and Border Horse. Served France, Belgium, Holland and Germany 1944-45. *Firms*—(1) Mackenzie, Innes & Logan (after 1955, Cuthbertson & Watson; Brodie, Cuthbertson & Watson); (2) W. & J. Burness.

CLARKE, JOHN BERNARD, LL.B. [11 December 1979]. Apprentice to Ronald Kerr Will and Others of Dundas & Wilson.—Son of James Augustine Clarke, Retired Headmaster, Edinburgh. *Born* 8 April 1955.

CLASON, ANDREW, OF HALLYHARDS [5 December 1811]. Apprentice to Sir William Drysdale.—Son of Rev. Robert Clason, Minister of Logie. *Born* 26 April 1787. *Died* 23 September 1850, unmarried.

CLAY, ALEXANDER THOMSON [9 July 1894]. Apprentice to Robert Pringle.—Son of John Clay, Farmer, Kerchesters, Kelso. *Born* 27 September 1863. *Married* 24 September 1890, Jacobina Williamson (*died* 5 April 1927), daughter of John Turnbull Thomson, Surveyor-General, Dunedin, New Zealand. Auditor of the Court of Session, 18 March 1921. *Died* 29 November 1950. *Former firm*—Pringle and Clay.

CLEGHORN, DAVID [8 July 1800]. Apprentice to Charles Bremner.—Son of Thomas Cleghorn, Inspector-General of Imports and Exports for Scotland. *Born* 13 November 1775. Crown Agent, 1833-35 and 1837-40. *Died* 24 October 1840, unmarried.

CLEGHORN, GEORGE, OF WEENS [6 December 1804]. Apprentice to William Macdonald.—Second son of Thomas Cleghorn, Coach-maker in Edinburgh. *Born* 24 August 1781. *Married* 5 February 1822, Marion Catherine (*died* 1866), third daughter of Colonel John Dalton of Steningford Park, Yorks. Author of *Remarks on Ancient and Modern Art*, 1837. *Died* 7 July 1855.

CLEPHANE, HENRY [30 January 1798]. Apprentice to William Lumsdaine.—Fifth son of George Clephane of Carslogie, Fife. *Died* 18 October 1818.

CLERK, ALEXANDER [Before 1512].

CLERK, MALCOLM HENRY [20 April 1877]. Apprentice to J. M. Lindsay, Alexander Howe, and William MacGillivray.—Third son of John Clerk, Q.C. *Born* 14 May 1853. *Died* in Ceylon, 11 May 1890, unmarried.

COATES, DAVID EDWARD FERGUS, B.A.(CANTAB), LL.B. [14 December 1936]. Apprentice to A. P. Melville and Others of R. R. Simpson & Lawson.—Son of David Aitchison Coates, Solicitor, Perth. *Born* 10 January 1912. *Married* 23 September 1939, Wilma Brewster Imrie. Major, Black Watch (R.H.). Served U.K., France, North Africa and Italy 1939-44. *Killed in Action* at Cassino, 15 May 1944. *Firm*—J. & J. Miller, Perth.

COATES, MICHAEL FERGUS, B.A.(BELFAST), LL.B. [17 July 1972]. Apprentice to John S. Macfie and Others of Tods, Murray & Jamieson.—Son of David Edward Fergus Coates, W.S. Perth. *Born* 31 March 1941. *Married* 13 August 1966, Elizabeth Cecilia, daughter of Adrian Crestigny Furse-Roberts, Finance Director.

COCHRANE, JAMES DOUGLAS [15 December 1947]. Apprentice to F. J. G. Borthwick and Others of Mackenzie & Kermack.—Son of Alexander Fyvie Cochrane, Accountant, La Plata, Argentina. *Born* 7 July 1916. *Married* (1) 29 May 1940, Margaret Ferrier (*died* 1 August 1943), daughter of Doctor Archibald Milne, Director of Studies, and (2) 2 March 1946, Brenda Croshaw, daughter of John Croshaw Wilson, Manufacturer. Major, R.A.C. Served U.K. and North West Europe 1939-45. Wounded at Le Havre, September 1944. *Firm*—Alston, Nairn & Hogg.

COCHRANE, RANALD KER, B.L., C.St.J. [25 April 1955]. Apprentice to James L. Mounsey and Others of John C. Brodie & Sons.—Son of James Dean Cochrane, former General Manager of Standard Property Investment Co., Edinburgh. *Born* 8 December 1929. *Married* (1) 17 December 1955, Elizabeth Askew, daughter of Gregor Eadie, formerly Director of Scottish Brewers Ltd. Edinburgh, and (2) 16 May 1980, Gladys Eileen Shapiro or McArdle. *Firm*—MacRobert Son & Hutchison, Glasgow and Paisley.

COCKBURN, DAVID WILLIAM, LL.B. [25 April 1977] (by Rule IXa).—Son of William Cockburn. *Born* 4 February 1943. *Married* 7 October 1967, Evelyn, daughter of Thomas E. Wilmot. *Firm*—Archibald Campbell & Harley.

COCKBURN, GEORGE [8 December 1697]. Apprentice to Laurence Oliphant.—Son of James Cockburn, Provost of Haddington. *Married* Elizabeth Wallace.

COCKBURN, GEORGE RINTOUL, B.A.(Cantab), LL.B. [15 December 1947]. Apprentice to Robert Francis Shepherd and Others of Shepherd & Wedderburn.—Son of George Kerr Cockburn, Bank Manager, Dundee. *Born* 6 November 1916. *Married* 8 January 1944, Jean Margaret, daughter of Charles Edward Stuart McIntyre. Major, R.A.; Served U.K. and France, 1939-45. *Firm*—Shepherd & Wedderburn.

COCKBURN, NORMAN ARMITAGE, M.A., LL.B. [15 December 1947]. Apprentice to Robert Francis Shepherd and Others of Shepherd & Wedderburn.—Son of Norman Cockburn, Ironfounder, Edinburgh. *Born* 20 February 1914. *Married* 16 March 1946, Kathleen Mona, daughter of A. J. T. Taylor, Vancouver, Canada. Lieutenant R.A. and K.O.S.B. 1939-45. Served U.K. and North West Europe. Wounded in Belgium September 1944. *Firms*— Pringle & Clay; Blair, Cadell & Macmillan.

COCKBURN, ROBERT WILLIAM, LL.B. [28 March 1904]. Apprentice to James Mylne and A. B. Campbell.—Son of George Cockburn, Wine Merchant, Edinburgh. *Born* 17 May 1879. *Married* 4 December 1912, Margaret Strachan (*died* 28 September 1956), second daughter of Thomas Low, Distiller, Edinburgh. *Died* 31 May 1955. *Firm*— Shepherd and Wedderburn.

COCKBURN, THOMAS, OF ROWCHESTER [18 January 1749]. Apprentice to (1) James Home; and (2) Andrew Wallace.—Third son of David Cockburn, Bailie of Langton, Berwickshire. *Born* 1723. *Married* 3 December 1752, Agnes (*died* 1 February 1791), only child of John Scott of Belford. Deputy Keeper of the Great Seal. King's Writer, 1776. *Died* 13 July 1787.

COLDSTREAM, GEORGE ERNEST RAWSON, B.L. [11 December 1899]. Apprentice to Horatius Bonar and William Constable Hunter.—Son of John Phillips Coldstream, W.S. *Born* 10 February 1874. *Died* 2 July 1957. *Firm*—(sometime) Tawse and Bonar.

COLDSTREAM, JOHN PHILLIPS [14 November 1866]. Apprentice to (1) Robert Blair Maconochie and W. J. Menzies; and (2) R. B. Maconochie.—Second son of John Coldstream, M.D., Edinburgh. *Born* 6 June 1842. *Married* 25 April 1871, Emily (*died* 8 February 1914), second daughter of George Rawson, Lanesfield, Bristol, and widow of James Henderson, M.D., Shanghai. Assistant Clerk of Session, 1872-86. Author of *Procedure in the Court of Session*, 1878. *Died* at London, 25 December 1909.

COLQUHOUN, GEORGE, OF BALHARTIE [1 February 1664]. Apprentice to George Cruickshank.—*Married* (1) 5 December 1657, Christian Watson (*buried* 10 April 1666); and (2) 12 July 1667, Isobel Henderson. *Died* about 1691.

COLQUHOUN, JAMES [17 March 1797]. Apprentice to William Blair.—Son of Robert Colquhoun, Farmer at Touch. *Died* 29 June 1797.

COLQUHOUN, JOHN CARRUTH, LL.B. [6 December 1976]. Apprentice to Harry Wallace Cant and Others of J. & F. Anderson.—Son of Robert Hogarth Colquhoun, Publishers' Representative, Edinburgh. *Born* 2 June 1951. *Firm*—Stuart & Stuart, Cairns & Co.

COLQUHOUN, ROSEMARY HAIN MILLER, B.A.(CANTAB) [12 May 1981*].— Daughter of Robert Hogarth Colquhoun, Publishers' Representative, Edinburgh. *Born* 25 May 1948.

COLQUHOUN, WILLIAM DALZELL, OF GARSCADDEN [9 July 1789]. Apprentice to David Erskine.—Son of David Dalzell, Merchant in Glasgow. *Married* 16 December 1801, Elizabeth Glen (*died* 24 September 1853), youngest daughter of Sir Ilay Campbell of Succoth, Bart. Assumed name of Colquhoun, 1801. *Died* 28 January 1806.

COMBE, GEORGE [31 January 1812]. Apprentice to Alexander Dallas.—Third son of George Combe, Brewer in Edinburgh. *Born* 21 October 1788. *Married* 25 September 1833, Cecilia (*died* 19 February 1868), daughter of Mrs. Siddons, Tragedienne. Author of the *Constitution of Man*, and other works on phrenology. *Died* 14 August 1858.

COMRIE, PATRICK [8 March 1704]. Resigned his Commission, 27 June 1751.

CONACHER, JAMES PATRICK SINNOTT, B.L. [30 April 1962]. Apprentice to George Murray Lawson and Another of Murray, Lawson & Macdonald.—Son of Francis Conacher, Civil Servant, Edinburgh. *Born* 1 July 1913. Served Second World War as Craftsman (Telecommunication Mechanic), R.E.M.E., Military Government in Germany. *Died* 25 November 1979. *Firm*—Campbell Smith & Co. (formerly Campbell Smith, Mathison & Oliphant).

CONN, JAMES CAMERON, LL.B. [24 March 1930]. Apprentice to William Kerr Steedman.—Only son of James Conn, Solicitor and Bank Agent, Hawick. *Born* 18 May 1905. *Married* 16 June 1932, Florence Sim (*died* 8 June 1969), youngest daughter of William Lennox, S.S.C. *Died* 8 October 1957. *Firm*—Haddon and Turnbull, Hawick.

CONNEL, DAVID, LL.B. [11 December 1899]. Apprentice to James Bruce, Thomas Kerr, and John Burns.—Son of John Connel, Coalmaster, Burntisland. *Born* 8 August 1873. *Married* 20 June 1907, Christian Harcus (*died* 11 January 1958), eldest daughter of William Cuthbert, Burntisland. Depute Clerk of the Peace for Fife, 20 March 1907. *Died* 21 November 1941. *Firm*—Ross and Connell, Dunfermline.

CONNELL, ARCHIBALD [28 June 1821]. Apprentice to James Hope.—Second son of John Connell, Advocate. *Born* 1798. *Died* 14 March 1843, unmarried.

CONNELL, SIR CHARLES GIBSON, B.L., J.P., F.R.S.E. [19 March 1923]. Apprentice to John L. Mounsey and Another of John C. Brodie & Sons.—Son of Sir Isaac Connell, S.S.C., Edinburgh. *Born* 11 March 1899. *Married* 20 July 1927, Constance Margaret (*died* 11 March 1976), daughter of William Weir, Accountant. 2nd Lieutenant, Royal Field Artillery 1917-19. Served in Salonika. Edited 3rd, 4th and 5th Editions of *Connell on the Agricultural Holdings (Scotland) Acts*. *Firm*—Connell & Connell. (Consultant.)

CONNELL, DOUGLAS ANDREW, LL.B. [6 December 1976]. Apprentice to John Norris Fergusson and Others of Dundas & Wilson.—Son of Samuel Thomson Connell, Schoolmaster, Callander, Perthshire. *Born* 18 May 1954.

CONNELL, JAMES, OF CONHEATH [18 June 1829]. Apprentice to John and Walter Ferrier.—Only son of James Connell of Conheath, Dumfriesshire. *Born* 1805. *Married* (1) 20 April 1848, Isabella Lydia (*died* 6 June 1858), daughter of Thomas Corrie, W.S.; and (2) 28 April 1864, Matilda Hay, widow of Major-General Cox. *Died* 12 February 1876.

CONSIDINE, HUGH HERBERT, B.A.(CANTAB) [25 March 1912]. Apprentice to William Gibson.—Son of William Considine, S.S.C. *Born* 5 January 1887. *Married* 6 June 1914, Mary Gretchen (*died* 8 June 1961), daughter of Duncan MacLaren, S.S.C., Edinburgh. Served with 38th Heavy Battery, R.G.A. Lieutenant, 1917. Invalided home, September 1917. *Died* 20 August 1958. *Firm*—W. and H. Considine.

CONSTABLE, NELSON BRIGGS [28 January 1881]. Apprentice to (1) Henry Inglis; (2) R. W. Wallace; and (3) J. A. Trail.—Second son of William Briggs Constable of Benarty, Fife and Kinross. *Born* 24 June 1854. *Married* 4 October 1901, Margaret Wylie (*died* 1 October 1951), younger daughter of Andrew Constable. *Died* 28 August 1917.

COOK, ADRIAN HENRY, B.A.(OXON) [15 December 1919]. Apprentice to Keith R. Maitland.—Youngest son of Sir Henry Cook, W.S. *Born* 2 January 1889. *Married* 9 December 1920, Esme Noel (*died* 16 November 1972), daughter of Walter Millar Richard, Letterfounder, Edinburgh. Captain in A. and S. Highlanders. Served from 1914-19. Twice mentioned in Despatches. Member of King's Bodyguard for Scotland, Royal Company of Archers, 1927. *Died* 2 November 1938. *Firm*—W. and J. Cook.

COOK, CHARLES [3 August 1876]. Apprentice to, and son of, John Cook, W.S.—*Born* 18 August 1850. Collector of W.S. Widows' Fund, 1892-1922. *Died* 12 June 1922, unmarried.

COOK, SIR HENRY [30 November 1871]. Apprentice to, and son of, John Cook, W.S.—*Born* 28 July 1848. *Married* 17 June 1879, Margaret (*died* 28 September 1905), daughter of John Patten, W.S. Knighted, 1904. Secretary of the King's Bodyguard for Scotland, Royal Company of Archers. *Died* 9 March 1928.

COOK, HENRY JAMES DOUGLAS, B.A.(OXON), LL.B. [23 April 1956]. Apprentice to John Herbert Richardson & Others of Dundas & Wilson.—Son of Adrian Henry Cook, W.S. *Born* 26 December 1929. *Firm*—W. & J. Cook. (Retired.)

COOK, JOHN [Before 1620].—*Married* Isabella, daughter of Andrew Grant, Merchant Burgess of Perth. Commissary Depute of Dunkeld. *Died* 1640.

COOK, JOHN [10 March 1836]. Apprentice to, and eldest son of, Walter Cook, W.S. *Born* 21 May 1813. *Married* 12 October 1842, Margaret Sophia, daughter of Lieut.-General Sir John Hope, G.C.H. Collector of W.S. Widows' Fund, 1861-91. *Died* 4 December 1891.

COOK, JOHN, B.A.(OXON) [8 July 1907]. Apprentice to Sir Henry Cook and Charles Cook.—Eldest son of Sir Henry Cook, W.S. *Born* 26 May 1880. *Married* 6 December 1911, Frances Margaret Auldjo (*died* 20 April 1974), only daughter of Thomas Skene Esson, W.S. *Died* 18 December 1953. *Firm*—W. and J. Cook.

COOK, JOHN HOPE, B.A.(CANTAB), LL.B. [20 December 1948]. Apprentice to James Mounsey of John C. Brodie & Sons.—Son of John Cook, W.S., Edinburgh. *Born* 30 January 1918. Captain, Second Lothian and Border Horse. Served U.K., North Africa, Italy and Austria. Mentioned in Despatches. *Firm*—W. & J. Cook.

COOK, WALTER [18 May 1801]. Apprentice, 6 June 1792, to James Ferrier.—Son of Rev. John Cook of Newburn, Professor of Moral Philosophy in the University of St Andrews. *Born* 24 June 1776. *Married* (1) 12 October 1809, Johanna (*died* 24 October 1815), second daughter of John Moncreiffe of Sauchopwood; and (2) 12 June 120, Mary (*died* 22 December 1857), second daughter of Alexander Chrystie of Balchrystie. Collector of Widows' Fund, 1828-61. *Died* 17 February 1861.

COOPER, ALEXANDER HILL [20 April 1877]. Apprentice to Frederick Pitman.— Younger son of William Cooper of Failford, Ayrshire. *Born* 22 January 1852. *Married* 27 July 1881, Cecilia (*died* 18 November 1914), daughter of Henry Ritchie Cooper of Ballindalloch, Stirlingshire. *Died* 13 February 1938. *Firm*—Cooper and Brodie.

COOPER, GEORGE [25 June 1770]. Apprentice to Archibald Stuart.—Second son of Richard Cooper, Civil Engineer and Engraver in Edinburgh. *Died* 28 March 1777.

COOPER, JAMES MURRAY, LL.B. [14 July 1919]. Apprentice to Sir John Prosser and Andrew Gray Muir.—Son of John Cooper, C.E., Burgh Engineer, Edinburgh. *Born* 2 April 1895. Captain R.G.A., 1914-18. Mentioned in Despatches, July 1917. *Died* 9 November 1961. *Firm*—Macpherson and Mackay.

COOPER, WILLIAM, OF FAILFORD [22 November 1832]. Apprentice to Walter Dickson and James Steuart.—Second son of Samuel Cooper of Failford and Ballindalloch. *Born* 28 March 1808. *Married* (1) 30 July 1835, Isabella (*died* 14 May 1841), daughter of Robert Clark of Comrie Castle, Perthshire; (2) 17 October 1845, Margaret (*died* 26 March 1898), daughter of Rev. Alexander Hill, D.D., Professor of Divinity in the University of Glasgow. *Died* 31 December 1880.

CORMACK, DAVID [13 July 1908]. Apprentice to Sir Henry Cook and Charles Cook.— Son of John Ford Cormack, Solicitor, Lockerbie. *Born* 6 December 1883. *Married* 17 May 1918, Mary Trotter (*died* 13 October 1960), elder daughter of William Spence Fleming, Edinburgh. War Service from December 1915 to end of War. France and Flanders, 1917-18. Lieutenant R.F.A. *Died* 8 September 1971. *Firm*—Cormack and Byers, Lockerbie,

CORMACK, JOHN BELL [24 May 1827]. Apprentice to (1) James Saunders Robertson; and (2) James Arnott.—Son of Alexander Cormack, Merchant in Newfoundland. *Died* 1870.

CORMACK, WILLIAM FLEMING, M.A., LL.B. [20 December 1948]. Apprentice to Robert Francis Shepherd and Another of Shepherd & Wedderburn.—Son of David Cormack, W.S., Lockerbie. *Born* 26 August 1920. *Married* 5 October 1945, Sheila Dodds, daughter of Charles Braidwood. Captain, Argyll and Sutherland Highlanders, 1940-46. (Emergency Commission.) *Firm*—Cormack & Byers, Lockerbie.

CORNWALL, THOMAS [10 December 1829]. Apprentice to Donald Horne.—Son of James Cornwall, Commissioner of Excise, Linlithgow. *Born* 31 May 1806. *Died* 3 June 1833, unmarried.

CORRIE, HUGH, OF CULLOCH [3 July 1772]. Apprentice to John Davidson.—Second son of James Corrie of Speddoch, Dumfriesshire. *Married*, proclaimed 20 September 1772, Mary (*died* 2 August 1816), daughter of Rev. John Collow, Minister of Penpont. *Died* at Priestlands, Dumfries, 1 June 1805.

CORRIE, THOMAS, OF STEILSTON [3 March 1818]. Apprentice to James Gilchrist.—Only son of Hugh Corrie, W.S. *Married* 22 March 1814, Clementina Blair (*died* 1864), youngest daughter of Lieut.-Colonel Andrew Ross, 31st Regiment. Admitted Advocate, 14 December 1811. Manager of British Linen Company Bank, 1828-59. *Died* 15 April 1859.

COSENS, JOHN [14 November 1851]. Apprentice to James Shepherd and T. M. Grant.— Son of Rev. Peter Cosens, Minister of Lauder. *Born* 15 April 1827. *Died* 26 November 1857, unmarried.

COSENS, PETER HUNTER, M.B.E. [20 October 1890]. Apprentice to D. S. Moncrieff and J. A. Trail.—Son of Rev. Alexander Thomson Cosens, Minister of Broughton. *Born* 25 May 1864. *Died* 26 November 1931, unmarried.

COTTON, WILLIAM [12 April 1886]. Apprentice to George Robertson and J. H. Finlay.— Son of William Cotton, Tobacconist, Edinburgh. *Born* 22 August 1863. *Married* 15 April 1889, Alice Maud (*died* 19 January 1902), daughter of Thomas William Rose, Ealing. Middlesex. *Died* 23 April 1896.

COUPER, ADAM, OF GOGAR [1586].—Second son of James Couper, Merchant Burgess of Edinburgh. *Married* (1) (contract, 1 February 1592-3), Margaret (*died* July 1607), daughter of David Danielstoun, Goldsmith Burgess of Edinburgh; and (2) 19 November 1607, Elizabeth Home (*died* 3 December 1609). Fiscal, 1596-9. Principal Clerk of Session, 2 December 1597. *Died* 3 December 1608.

COUPER, ALEXANDER, OF FOULFOORD [Before 1625].—Third son of Adam Couper of Gogar, W.S. *Born* 15 November 1598. Commissioner, 24 January 1642. *Married* (1) Catherine Cochrane, of the family of Barbachlay; (2) Elizabeth Marjoribanks (*died* 22 September 1625); and (3) 24 August 1631, Isobel, eldest daughter of John Rae, Rector of the Grammar School, Edinburgh.

COUPER, ELIZABETH ANN, M.A., L.L.B. [28 May 1979]. (By Rule IX(a).)—Daughter of Joseph Lawson Couper, Schoolmaster, Balerno. *Born* 2 July 1941. *Firms*—(1) Robert White & Co. (2) Drummond & Co.

COUPER, SIR JOHN CHARLES, O.B.E., M.V.O. [16 January 1893]. Apprentice to A. D. M. Black and J. M. Mackenzie.—Eldest son of Charles Tennant Couper, Advocate, Principal Clerk of Session. *Born* 10 October 1867. *Married* 15 November 1899, Elsie Winifred (*died* 4 January 1954), only daughter of Benjamin Hall Blyth, C.E., Edinburgh. Purse Bearer and Deputy Purse Bearer to the Lord High Commissioner of the General Assembly of the Church of Scotland, 1900-31. Military Representative Recruiting Tribunals, and Chief Military Representative Edinburgh and National Service Department, 1914-18. O.B.E., 1918. M.V.O., 1929. Knight Bachelor, 1930. *Died* 29 June 1937.

COUPER, JOHN GIBSON [12 April 1886]. Apprentice to Robert Strathern.—Son of George Gordon Douglas Couper, residing in Edinburgh. *Born* 11 April 1861. *Died* 20 May 1915, unmarried.

COUPER, PETER [6 June 1803]. Apprentice to John Campbell *tertius.*—Son of Peter Couper, Shipmaster in Leith. *Married* 27 March 1809, Mary (*died* 17 December 1823), eldest daughter of Archibald Richardson, Merchant in Leith. Died 1854, aged 73.

COUSIN, JOHN DRYSDALE [22 March 1915]. Apprentice to J. E. Guild, Alfred Shepherd, and R. F. Shepherd.—Son of George Cousin, The Walk House, Alloa. *Born* 24 January 1890. *Married* 28 November 1917, Mabel Eugenie, youngest daughter of T. R. Burns, C.A., Ellenville House, Bangor, Co. Down. *Died* 18 January 1971.

COUTTS, DONALD CARGILL [21 March 1949]. Apprentice to Sir Ernest Wedderburn and Others of Shepherd & Wedderburn.—Son of James Coutts, Registrar, University of Glasgow. *Born* 6 June 1901. T.A.V.R. Royal Artillery. *Died* 20 January 1969. *Firm*— James Wright & Co., Bathgate (now Caesar & Howie).

COUTTS, THOMAS [1 July 1611]. Apprentice to Thomas Young.—*Married* Elizabeth Booge (*died* April 1626). *Died* 28 April 1627.

COVENTRY, HENRY JOHN [17 July 1862]. Apprentice to Thomas Graham Murray.— Third son of Rev. George Coventry of Shanwell, Kinross-shire. *Born* 5 June 1834. *Married* 19 September 1867, Mary Jane Douglas (*died* 26 July 1902), third daughter of Michael Thomson Carmichael of Eastend, Lanarkshire. *Died* 17 October 1910. *Firm*— Menzies, Coventry, and Black.

COWAN, ALAN ARCHIBALD, B.L. [16 February 1940]. Apprentice to William Cowan of Cowan & Stewart.—Son of William Cowan, W.S., Edinburgh. *Born* 1 June 1916. Captain R.A.: Served U.K., France, North Africa and Italy 1939-44. Joined 652 Air O.P. Squadron (1942), latterly Flight Commander. *Died* 17 June 1944, of wounds received in Italy.

COWAN, ALEXANDER [1 July 1828]. Apprentice to James and Charles Nairne.—Third son of Alexander Cowan, Papermaker at Valleyfield. *Born* 9 November 1804. *Married* 1 September 1829, Jane Annesley (*died* 8 February 1831), daughter of Thomas Thompson, M.P. for Evesham. *Died* at Bonn, 11 December 1831, aged 27.

COWAN, ARTHUR JAMES, M.A., LL.B. [21 March 1949]. Apprentice to Francis John Gordon Borthwick and Another of Mackenzie & Kermack.—Son of the Rev. Arthur Aitken Cowan, D.D., Edinburgh. *Born* 31 January 1913. *Married* 23 August 1940, Helen Agnes, daughter of Charles Calder Scott. Service with Royal Artillery in U.K., North Africa and Italy. *Firms*—(1) Mackenzie & Kermack (1948-59); (2) Morton Smart Macdonald & Prosser (then Morton Smart Macdonald & Milligan, now Morton Fraser & Milligan).

COWAN, GEORGE DEAS [10 July 1911]. Apprentice to John Cowan, J. A. Dalmahoy, and E. J. M'Candlish.—Son of Robert Cameron Cowan, C.A., Edinburgh. *Born* 3 November 1883. *Married* 5 November 1914, Marjorie Elizabeth (*died* 6 January 1967), elder daughter of Thomas Bennet Clark, C.A., Edinburgh. Major in Royal Scots. *Died* of wounds received in action, 22 April 1918. Mentioned in Despatches.

COWAN, HUGH [17 January 1822]. Apprentice to Alexander Hunter.—Son of William Cowan, Banker in Ayr. *Born* 1798. *Died* 9 January 1835, unmarried.

COWAN, JOHN [28 June 1860]. Apprentice to Patrick Dalmahoy.—Third son of John Cowan, Advocate, one of the Senators of the College of Justice (Lord Cowan). *Born* 14 December 1836. Commissioner of Lunacy for Scotland, 1881. Crown Agent, 1886 and 1892. Fiscal, 20 December 1887. Treasurer of W.S. Society, 13 June 1892. *Died* Father of the Society, 6 January 1927.

COWAN, RICHARD [6 December 1803]. Apprentice to Harry Davidson.—Son of Robert Cowan, Merchant in Glasgow. *Born* 9 December 1777. *Died* 20 May 1837, unmarried.

COWAN, ROBERT [14 November 1833]. Apprentice to Richard Cowan.—Son of Walter Cowan, Merchant in Leith. *Born* 1 March 1809. *Died* 4 May 1892, unmarried.

COWAN, ROBERT BRUCE [13 April 1885]. Apprentice to J. A. Jamieson, James Craik, and John Wharton Tod.—Son of John Cowan, Merchant, Stoneleigh, Greenock. *Born* 7 January 1861. Found *drowned* in Glasgow Canal, 30 March 1908, unmarried.

COWAN, WILLIAM [14 December 1896]. Apprentice to G. T. Balfour-Kinnear, Robert Beatson, James Balfour-Kinnear, and Ernest Hamilton.—Son of Archibald Cowan, Wine Merchant, Leith. *Born* 17 February 1873. *Married* 11 June 1913, Dorothy Isobel (*died* 8 May 1969), only daughter of Arthur Wemyss Horsbrugh, and granddaughter of James Wilkie, C.A., Edinburgh. War Service: Coast Defence and in France. Major R.G.A. *Died* 6 December 1950. *Firm*—Cowan and Stewart.

COWIE, HENRY [18 January 1749]. Apprentice to James Ramsay.—Eldest son of Archibald Cowie, Portioner of Pockneive, Stirlingshire, *Died* before 1754.

COWPER, CHARLES NEAVES [25 March 1901]. Apprentice to David Andrew Curror.—Son of Charles Neaves Cowper, S.S.C. *Born* 3 January 1878. *Married* 21 April 1917, Elizabeth Mary (*died* 9 April 1976), daughter of Joseph Leighton, Commercial and Law Printer, Edinburgh. During War period served with Volunteers, 1914-16; and R.G.A., 1916-19. *Died* 1 July 1944. *Firm*—C. N. Cowper and Co.

COX, CHARLES THOMAS [17 March 1890]. Apprentice to James H. Jameson. Son of George Addison Cox of Invertrossachs, Perthshire. *Born* 8 June 1865. *Married* 17 September 1891, Ellen Georgina (*died* 17 December 1940), only daughter of Charles Henry Blake of Glendelvine. Barrister of Inner Temple. In Great War, Lieutenant 4th Reserve Gordon Highlanders. *Died* 12 April 1948.

COX, ROBERT [11 July 1832]. Apprentice to George Combe.—Son of Robert Cox of Gorgie Mill, Mid-Lothian. *Born* 25 February 1810. Author of *Sabbath Laws and Sabbath Duties*, 1853, and other works. *Died* 3 February 1872, unmarried,

CRABBIE, WILLIAM GEORGE [17 November 1952]. Apprentice to (1) Charles Edward Stewart and Others of Murray Beith & Murray and (2) David Blyth Bogle and Others of Lindsay Howe & Co.—Son of George Ernest Crabbie, Company Director, Edinburgh. *Born* 15 October 1918. *Married* (1) 27 December 1940, Jane Evelyn Ravenscroft, daughter of W. W. Coe, U.S.A., and (2) 19 January 1973, Helen Steedman, daughter of Stephen James Mackie. Lieutenant Commander, R.N. (Regular). Served Atlantic, Mediterranean and Arctic. *Firm*—Lindsays (formerly Lindsay Howe & Co.).

CRAIG, HENRY VIVIAN GIBSON- [8 September 1870]. Apprentice to John and Henry Gordon Gibson.—Third son of Right Hon. Sir William Gibson-Craig of Riccarton, Bart. *Born* 25 September 1847. *Married* 27 June 1882, Emily Dulcibella (*died* 19 December 1943), daughter of Montagu Wilmot of Norton, Swansea. *Died* at Cheltenham, 19 May 1926.

CRAIG, JAMES, OF DALNAIR AND COSTERTON [13 May 1707]. Apprentice to William Forrester.—Son of Rev. James Craig, Minister of Killearn. *Married* February 1708, Magdalen, daughter of Alexander Chaplane of Colliston, Angus, W.S. *Died* 5 August 1743.

CRAIG, JAMES, O.B.E., M.A., LL.B. [17 November 1952]. Apprentice to Chilton Lind Addison-Smith of R. Addison-Smith & Co.—Son of James Craig, Coalowner, Ardrossan. *Born* 15 September 1914. *Married* 9 September 1942, Alice Norris, daughter of James McLennan, Leith. Lieutenant Commander R.N.V.R. Naval Legal Aid Officer (Scotland) 1946-47. *Firm*—R. Addison-Smith & Co.

CRAIG, SIR JAMES GIBSON-, OF RICCARTON, BART. [21 December 1786]. Apprentice to William Anderson.—Second son of William Gibson, Merchant in Edinburgh. *Born* 11 October 1765. *Married* 14 September 1796, Anne (*died* 24 May 1837), youngest daughter of James Thomson, Merchant in Edinburgh. Heritable Usher of The Court of Exchequer, *c.* 1810. Assumed the name of Craig by royal licence on 30 May 1823. Created a Baronet, 30 September 1831. *Died* 6 March 1850.

CRAIG, JAMES LEITH JOHNSTONE, M.A., LL.B. [2 December 1968]. Apprentice to Sir Peter George Macdonald and Others of W. & J. Burness.—Son of James Craig, W.S., Edinburgh. *Born* 23 May 1944. *Married* 10 May 1969, Susan Mary, daughter of Robert Reginald McDowell, *Firm*—R. Addison-Smith & Co.

CRAIG, JAMES THOMSON GIBSON- [25 June 1824]. Apprentice to, and second son of, Sir James Gibson-Craig, Bart. *Born* 12 March 1799. *Married* 23 November 1841, Jane (*died* 25 April 1863), daughter of Sir John Peter Grant of Rothiemurchus, and widow of Colonel Gervaise Pennington. *Died* 18 July 1886.

CRAIG, JOHN MOORE [18 December 1834]. Apprentice to Æneas Macbean.—Second son of John Craig of Prestonholme, Merchant in Leith. *Born* 11 October 1809. *Died* at the Cape of Good Hope, 10 February 1845, unmarried.

CRAIG, THOMAS HERBERT [13 December 1909]. Apprentice to David Shaw and Another of Thomson, Dickson & Shaw.—Son of Thomas Craig, S.S.C., Edinburgh. *Born* 30 November 1885. *Married* 6 July 1912, Nora Alexandra (*died* 4 March 1981), daughter of Ralph Tait Linton, Chemist. *Died* 13 September 1974. *Firm*—Cornillon, Craig & Thomas (now Cornillon Craig & Co.).

CRAIG, THOMAS HERBERT LINTON, T.D. [19 December 1938]. Apprentice to Mackenzie Smith Shaw of Thomson, Dickson & Shaw.—Son of Thomas Herbert Craig, W.S., Edinburgh. *Born* 30 June 1915. *Married* 23 April 1948, Margaret, daughter of John Howie, Farmer, Longniddry. Lieutenant Colonel R.A.: Served U.K., Italy and Austria 1939-45. Awaded the Italy Star. *Died* 5 January 1974. *Firm*—Cornillon, Craig & Thomas (now Cornillon Craig & Co.).

CRAIG, WILLIAM [7 March 1815]. Apprentice to James Little.—Eldest son of James Craig, Supervisor of Excise, Ayr, and afterwards at Haddington. *Married* 9 December 1818, Margaret Ann (*died* 3 August 1855), youngest daughter of Gillean Maclean of Scalasdale. *Died* 1826.

CRAIGIE, DAVID, OF DUNBARNEY [9 July 1756]. Apprentice to Laurence Craigie.—Third son of Robert Craigie of Glendoick, Perthshire, Lord President of the Court of Session. *Married*, proclaimed 15 October 1779, Dorothea, daughter of Sir George Clerk Maxwell of Penicuik, Bart. *Died* 17 August 1796.

CRAIGIE, HENRY [7 July 1829]. Apprentice to Roger Aytoun.—Fifth son of John Craigie of Quebec. *Born* 1807. *Married* 23 July 1839, Jessie (*died* 12 March 1875), daughter of Alexander Falconar of Falconhall, Edinburgh. *Died* 19 April 1867.

CRAIGIE, LAURENCE [6 February 1744]. Apprentice to Archibald Stuart.—Second son of Laurence Craigie of Kilgraston, Perthshire, Advocate. *Married*, proclaimed 25 August 1754, Elizabeth, daughter of Ensign Patrick Duncan of General Anstruther's Regiment. Resigned his Commission, 15 July 1780. *Died* 1781.

CRAIGIE, LAURENCE JOHN [8 July 1912]. Apprentice to James Burness, Donald M'Callum Smith, and Ronald Burness.—Son of David Craigie of The Yews, Balerno. *Born* 21 June 1887. *Married* 30 August 1913, Dorothy Ellis, younger daughter of John Marshall, LL.D., Rector of Royal High School, Edinburgh. Served with Royal Scots and Black Watch during Great War. *Died* 21 March 1961.

CRAIGIE, WILLIAM CHARLES [11 July 1771]. Apprentice to Samuel Mitchelson, Jun.—Second son of Thomas Craigie, Professor of Moral Philosophy in the University of Glasgow. *Married* Jane Guthrie, *Died* 29 May 1790.

CRAIK, JAMES [9 February 1871]. Apprentice to Thomas G. Murray and James A. Jamieson.—Son of Rev. James Craik, D.D., Glasgow. *Born* 13 March 1841. *Married* 12 November 1872, Gertrude Honora (*died* 4 August 1918), daughter of Joseph Bowstead of Hyde House, Gloucestershire. Deputy Keeper of the Privy Seal, 1874. *Died* 12 June 1899.

CRAIK, JAMES BOWSTEAD, B.A.(Oxon) [27 March 1899]. Apprentice to John Ord Mackenzie, H. Cheyne, John Kermack, George Kermack, and F. J. G. Borthwick.— Son of James Craik, W.S. *Born* 10 August 1874. *Married* 1 August 1912, Marie Sylvia (*died* 14 November 1955), younger daughter of William Robson of Grovehill, Kelso. Served in South African War with Imperial Yeomanry and in Great War with R.N.V.R. Auxiliary Patrol. *Died* 26 February 1957. *Firm*—Tods, Murray, and Jamieson.

CRANSTON, THOMAS, of Dewar [1 August 1786]. Apprentice to Samuel Mitchelson, Sen.—Eldest son of George Cranston of Dewar, Mid-Lothian. *Born* 1760. *Died* 21 October 1836, unmarried.

CRASSWELLER, PETER HOWARD, M.A.(Cantab), LL.B. [23 July 1951]. Apprentice to D. S. Macdonald of Scott & Glover.—Son of William Howard Crassweller, Bank Official, Salisbury, Wiltshire. *Born* 15 April 1916. *Married* 22 November 1941, Catherine Agatha Shiels, daughter of Thomas Mickel, Master Builder. Major R.A.S.C., B.E.F. 1939-40, North Africa and Italy 1943-45. *Firms*—Scott & Glover; Haldanes McLaren & Scott (after amalgamation).

CRAUFORD, ARCHIBALD [20 May 1794]. Apprentice to John Russell, Jun.—Son of James Crauford, Writer in Ayr. *Died* 28 September 1806.

CRAUFUIRD, ARCHIBALD, of Ardmillan [10 March 1803]. Apprentice to Alexander Young.—Eldest son of Archibald Craufuird of Ardmillan, Ayrshire. *Married* 4 November 1802, his cousin, Margaret d'Albœduf, daughter of Thomas Craufuird of Ardmillan. *Died* 16 May 1824.

CRAW, JOHN [7 July 1795]. Apprentice to John Taylor.—Son of John Craw, Writer in Haddington. *Married* Margaret, daughter of John Hardie, Brewer, St Anne's Yard, Edinburgh. Bailie of Holyrood. *Died* 23 March 1816, aged 44. Buried in Holyrood Abbey.

CRAW, WILLIAM ALDYN, T.D., M.A., LL.B. [16 December 1946]. Apprentice to Adam West Gifford and Others of Mackenzie & Black.—Son of James Hewat Craw, Farmer, West Foulden, Berwickshire. *Born* 23 November 1917. *Married* 13 March 1945, Lora Rennie (*died* 17 June 1974), daughter of John William Romanes, Chemical Engineer, Edinburgh. Major, Infantry. Served U.K., France, Madagascar, India, Persia, Iraq, Middle East, Italy and Germany 1939-45. Wounded April 1944 and April 1945. Mentioned in Despatches 1945. *Firm*—Bell & Scott, Bruce & Kerr (Bruce & Kerr prior to amalgamation).

CRAWFORD, ALEXANDER [16 December 1830]. Apprentice to William Patrick.—Son of William Crawford, Professor of Moral Philosophy in the University of St Andrews. *Born* 1801. *Married* 6 October 1834, Jane Brown (*died* 28 May 1855), daughter of Archibald Douglas, Advocate. *Died* 12 March 1838.

CRAWFORD, HEW, OF JORDANHILL [14 December 1716]. Apprentice to Robert Campbell,—Eldest son of James Crawford of Jordanhill, Sheriff-Depute of Renfrewshire. *Married* Mary (*died* 13 June 1767), daughter of James Greenshiels, Rector of Fiunough, Tipperary. Writer to the Prince of Wales. *Died* 21 February 1756.

CRAWFORD, JAMES [9 August 1770]. Apprentice to (1) Alexander Stevenson, of Montgreenan; and (2) William Fraser.—Second son of Hugh Crawford of Raisleygate. *Married*, proclaimed 24 December 1769, Catherine (*died* 21 August 1815), daughter of James Brown, Deacon of the Skinners, Edinburgh. *Died* 18 April 1783.

CRAWFORD, JAMES [10 March 1819]. Apprentice to John Mowbray.—Second son of Hugh Crawford of Brownmuir, Writer in Greenock. *Married* 22 July 1819, Eliza Harvey Bell (*died* 7 January 1839). *Died* 17 November 1868, aged 70.

CRAWFORD, JAMES [27 June 1833]. Apprentice to Walter Dickson and James Steuart.— Son of Alexander Crawford, Tenant in Rhodes, near North Berwick. *Born* 17 December 1808. *Married* (1) 25 August 1846, Euphemia (*died* 24 March 1849), daughter of Andrew Somerville, Luffness; and (2) 25 November 1856, Jane Watt (*died* 11 March 1890), daughter of Robert Davidson, H.E.I.C.S. *Died* 17 November 1863.

CRAWFORD, RONALD, OF RESTALRIG [7 March 1732]. Apprentice to (1) John Mein; and (2) James Armour.—Third son of Patrick Crawford of Auchenames, Ayrshire. *Married* August 1743, Katherine (*died* 12 August 1755), daughter of John Forbes of Newhall, Advocate. Commissary Clerk, Peebles, 1742. *Died* 11 July 1762.

CRAWFORD, THOMAS ALEXANDER, M.A., LL.B. [18 December 1950]. Apprentice to (1) Alan C. Frazer of Hagart & Burn-Murdoch and (2) Michael Lorimer of Henderson & Jackson.—Son of Thomas Crawford, Accountant & Hotelier. *Born* 14 July 1922. *Married* 26 June 1951, Martha Martin Broadfoot, daughter of Dr Robert McLean, Carluke. Flight Lieutenant R.A.F. 1940-46. *Firm*—Courtney, Crawford & Co. (formerly Pentland & Russell prior to amalgamation).

CRAWFORD, VICKI ANN MELVILLE, LL.B. [13 May 1980*].—Daughter of John Coulter, Insurance Manager, Ponteland, Northumbria. *Born* 24 August 1951. *Married* 27 September 1976, Hugh John Crawford, Solicitor, son of James Crawford, Solicitor, Gourock.

CRAWFURD, JAMES [29 June 1661]. Apprentice to James Campbell.—Second son of Patrick Crawfurd of Auchenames. *Married* Margaret Crawfurd (*died* 9 January 1662). *Died* before 1672.

CRAWFURD, JOHN [16 July 1661]. Apprentice to James Campbell.—Son of Hugh Crawfurd of Auchinwey. *Married* 4 October 1665, Christian, daughter of Laurence Scott, Merchant, Edinburgh. *Died* 1667.

CRAWFURD, ROBERT, OF CRAWFURDTOUN [8 March 1688]. Apprentice to Hugh Wallace of Inglistoun.—Son of Andrew Crawfurd of Drings. *Married* 29 April 1685, Margaret Cathcart.

CREASE, GEORGE [22 December 1836]. Apprentice to Alexander Stevenson.—Son of William Crease, Merchant in Edinburgh. *Born* 15 June 1810. *Died* 6 April 1838.

CRERAR, ALASTAIR HENRY [20 March 1922]. Apprentice to Sir R. R. Simpson and Others of R. R. Simpson & Lawson.—Son of Rev. Thomas Crerar of North Leith. *Born* 13 July 1896. *Married* 25 November 1933, Margaret (*died* 13 August 1975), elder daughter of James Peacock, Superintendent Engineer, Orient Line, London. Served First World War: Lieutenant, Royal Scots Fusiliers; Served in France. Severely wounded at the Somme 1916. Transferred to Royal Air Force 1918 as Fighter Pilot. Father of the Society. *Firm*—Campbell Smith Mathison & Oliphant (now Campbell Smith & Co.) (Retired 1964).

CRERAR, JAMES DRUMMOND, B.A.(CANTAB), LL.B. [30 November 1959]. Apprentice to (1) John James Bonar and Others of Bonar Hunter & Johnstone and (2) J. M. O. Mackenzie and Another of Mackenzie & Kermack.—Son of Alastair Henry Crerar, W.S., Edinburgh. *Born* 19 December 1934. *Married* 26 June 1965, Veronica Jean, daughter of William Gray, Bank Manager, Kilmarnock. Depute Sheriff Clerk of Chancery 1964-74. *Firms*—(1) Campbell Smith & Co. (formerly Campbell Smith Mathison & Oliphant); (2) Marshall, Henderson & Whyte; (3) Crerar & Co.

CRICHTON, DAVID [Before 1625]. Apprentice to Robert Williamson.—*Married* Marjory Hamilton. *Died* before 1638.

CRICHTON, HEW HAMILTON [14 June 1849]. Apprentice to James Campbell Tait.— Son of Hew Crichton, S.S.C., in Edinburgh. *Born* 7 September 1820. *Died* 21 April 1906, unmarried.

CRICHTON, NEIL JAMES, M.A., LL.B. [1 December 1969]. Apprentice to The Hon. W. D. Watson and Others of Fraser, Stodart & Ballingall.—Son of Francis Fairhead Crichton, Company Director, Banchory, Kincardineshire. *Born* 25 September 1943. *Married* (1) 3 September 1968, Theresa Celia Anne, daughter of Eric Francis, Oxford, and (2) 2 June 1979, Judith Lesley Milne Wilkinson. *Firm*—Courtney, Crawford & Co. (formerly Courtney & Co.).

CROMBIE, ALEXANDER, OF THORNTON [17 January 1861]. Apprentice to Thomas George Mackay and Alexander Howe.—Eldest son of Alexander Crombie of Thornton, Kincardineshire. *Born* 29 November 1836. *Married* (1) 7 September 1870, Elizabeth (*died* 6 October 1885), second daughter of Dr John Marshall, Chatton Park, Northumberland; and (2) 10 June 1901, Ellen Mary (*died* 2 October 1938), widow of Rev. Henry d'Arcy Simpson, Rector of St Laurence Church, Laurencekirk, and daughter of Joseph Cundall, Banker, Leith. *Died* 13 June 1914.

CROMBIE, ANDREW [27 February 1817]. Apprentice to William Balderston.—Son of John Crombie, Dyer in Edinburgh. *Born* 23 May 1793. *Married* 11 June 1834, Margaret (*died* 1867), daughter of —— Norgett, Hobart-Town, Tasmania. *Died* at Westbury, Tasmania, 20 July 1859.

CROMBIE, JOHN SOMERVILLE BRAND, B.L. [29 April 1968]. Apprentice to Charles Snow Campbell of Alex. Morison & Co.—Son of John Watson Brand Crombie, Civil Servant, Edinburgh. *Born* 10 August 1929. *Married* 15 August 1953, Isabella Rankin, daughter of William Cursiter, Engineer, Stromness, Orkney. *Firm*—Alex. Morison & Co.

CROMBIE, SIR THOMAS, OF KENMAY [3 March 1606].—*Married* 15 October 1606, Margaret, daughter of James Ker, Merchant Burgess of Edinburgh. M.P. Aberdeenshire, 1630-3, 1639, 1643. Sheriff of Aberdeen, 1633-5. *Died* 1644.

CROOKS, PETER [8 March 1821]. Apprentice to Alexander Dallas.—Son of Peter Crooks, Gardener at the Dean. *Born* 1799. *Married* 5 October 1824, Marion (*died* 17 April 1841), daughter of Peter Dods, Millfield, Haddington. Collector of Fee Fund, Court of Session, 1840-4. *Died* 4 March 1844.

CROWE, DAVID TERENCE, LL.B. [28 April 1969]. Apprentice to John Henry Constable Wishart and Others of Bonar Mackenzie & Kermack.—Son of Terence James Crowe, Industrial Chemist, Peebles. *Born* 9 August 1945. *Married* 30 November 1968, Catherine Margaret, daughter of The Rev. William Hurtley Clarke. *Firm*—Andrew Haddon & Crowe, Hawick (formerly Andrew Haddon & Co.).

CROWE, EVE COCHRANE, M.A., LL.B. [11 December 1978]. (By Rule IX(a).)—Daughter of James Crowe, M.M., Retired Police Superintendent. *Born* 26 March 1943. *Firm*—Alston, Nairn & Hogg (resigned 1979).

CRUICKSHANK, ALASTAIR HARVEY, LL.B. [28 November 1966]. Apprentice to Hon. David Andrew Balfour and Others of Shepherd & Wedderburn.—Son of Harvey Cruickshank, Solicitor, Perth. *Born* 10 August 1943. *Married* 12 October 1970, Moira Endacott, daughter of Richard Pollock, S.S.C., Edinburgh. *Firm*—Condie, Mackenzie & Co., Perth.

CRUICKSHANK, GEORGE [18 August 1652]. Apprentice to John Semple.—Eldest son of Gavin Cruickshank, in Ardiffrie. *Married* (1) 12 April 1649, Elizabeth (*died* 26 April 1660), daughter of Hugh Peebles, Writer; and (2) 5 December 1661, Elizabeth Gavin. Clerk, 1654-60. Re-admitted, 5 April 1661. *Buried* 19 February 1669.

CRUICKSHANK, JAMES ROBERT LESLIE, M.A., LL.B. [21 July 1937]. Apprentice to (1) James Watt of Davidson & Syme and (2) Ian Coshieville Menzies and Another of Menzies & White.—Son of George Leslie Cruickshank, Estate Factor, Fyvie, Aberdeenshire. *Born* 4 May 1903. *Married* 5 September 1936, Norah, daughter of Matthew James Burke. *Firm*—Menzies, Dougal & Milligan (formerly Menzies & White).

CRUICKSHANK, JAMES STANLEY ROWLAND, B.A.(CANTAB), LL.B. [19 December 1932]. Apprentice to Robert F. Shepherd and Others of Shepherd & Wedderburn. Advocate in Aberdeen.—Son of Alexander Thomas Cruickshank, Advocate in Aberdeen. *Born* 11 June 1906. *Married* 7 January 1935, Anne Grace, daughter of John Watt, Manager, Edinburgh. Lecturer in Constitutional Law and History, University of Aberdeen 1933-52. *Firm*—Brander & Cruickshank, Aberdeen.

CUBIE, ANDREW, LL.B. [29 April 1974]. Apprentice to James Thomson and Another of Fyfe Ireland & Co.—Son of Dr Alexander Cubie, Chest Consultant, Edinburgh. *Born* 24 August 1946. *Married* 29 August 1968, Heather Ann, daughter of William Mcdonald Muir, T.D., Hospital Administrator. *Firm*—Fyfe Ireland & Co.

CULLEN, JOHN [4 July 1828]. Apprentice to James Greig.—Fifth son of Thomas Cullen, Farmer, Dalmarnock. *Born* 1802. *Married* 9 August 1841, Catherine Ann (*died* 20 May 1898), daughter of William Buchanan, Advocate. *Died* 14 June 1863.

CULLEN, WILLIAM JAMES, LL.B. [15 July 1884]. Apprentice to James, J. H., and L. M. Balfour.—Son of Thomas Cullen, Inspector of Stamps and Taxes, Edinburgh. *Born* 9 September 1859. *Married* 4 July 1888, Grace Rutherford (*died* 20 March 1943), youngest daughter of William John Clark, Withington, Manchester. Resigned his Commission, 28 January 1890. Admitted Advocate, 19 March 1891. Sheriff of Fife, 1906-9. Appointed a Senator of the College of Justice (Lord Cullen), 20 July 1909. Resigned from the Bench, 31 December 1925. Died 19 June 1941.

CUMINE, FRANCIS GARDEN [16 February 1832]. Apprentice to George Robinson and Joseph Paterson.—Son of Archibald Cumine of Auchry, Aberdeenshire. *Born* 4 October 1803. *Died* 1843, unmarried.

CUMING, GEORGE, OF RELUGAS [3 July 1778]. Apprentice to (1) William Budge; and (2) John Mackenzie of Delvin.—Fourth son of Dr Patrick Cuming of Relugas, Minister at Edinburgh. *Born* 31 March 1746. *Married* 4 January 1783, Susanna Judith Craigie (*died* April 1829), daughter of Colonel Charles Halket of Halhill, Fife. *Died* 2 October 1804.

CUMMING, DONALD IAN, LL.B. [28 May 1979]. Apprentice to Ronald Kerr Will and Others of Dundas & Wilson.—Son of Rev. John William Cumming, Edinburgh. *Born* 3 October 1952. *Firm*—Dundas & Wilson.

CUMMING, GEORGE [5 December 1833]. Apprentice to Joseph Gordon.—Son of John Cumming, Banker in Forres. *Born* 16 October 1809. *Married* 5 October 1847, Jane Maria (*died* 26 May 1904), daughter of Robert Edmunds, London and widow of William Henry Burgess. *Died* 8 September 1883.

CUMMING, JAMES [12 January 1730]. Apprentice to Hugh Somerville.—*Married* (contract, 21 June 1725), Ann, daughter of William Alves, W.S. *Died* January 1735.

CUMMING, WILLIAM [2 April 1906]. Apprentice to William Stuart Fraser.—Son of Robert Cumming, S.S.C., Edinburgh. *Born* 3 September 1881. War Service: in R.G.A. *Died* 20 December 1962. *Firm*—Cumming and Duff.

CUMMING, WILLIAM [28 July 1952]. Apprentice to Peter George Macdonald and Another of W. & J. Burness.—Son of William Robert Duguid Cumming, Company Director. *Born* 28 July 1914. *Married* (1) 13 September 1939, Norah Estelle, (died 3 October 1972), daughter of Albert Adams Norris, Civil Servant, and (2) 23 February 1974, Patricia Wingate Thwaites or Hall, daughter of Harold Verdon Thwaites, Physician. Served in the ranks with Royal Artillery 1939-45. *Died* 5 July 1980. *Firm*—W. & J. Burness.

CUMYNG, MATHEW [Before 1623].—*Married* 7 August 1606, Mause Stenhope.

CUNINGHAM, ALEXANDER [30 January 1798]. Apprentice to Samuel Mitchelson, Jun.—Eldest son of Rev. Charles Cuningham, Minister of Tranent. *Born* 8 November 1745. *Married* April 1774. Fordyce (*died* 11 November 1840), one of the eight daughters of William Gray of Newholm, Lanarkshire, and sister of John Gray, W.S. *Died* 23 February 1827.

CUNINGHAM, ALEXANDER, OF NEWHOLM [13 December 1827]. Apprentice to Richard Mackenzie.—Son of Charles Cuningham of Newholm, W.S. *Born* 29 April 1805. *Married* 31 July 1834, Caroline (*died* 4 February 1886), daughter of Major-General Alured Dodsworth Fance, C.B. Secretary to Commissioners of Northern Lights, 1842-1874. *Died* 16 June 1883.

CUNINGHAM, CHARLES, OF NEWHOLM [19 February 1808]. Apprentice to Robert Dundas.—Eldest son of Alexander Cuningham, W.S. *Married* 5 June 1799, Elizabeth (*died* 11 March 1837), daughter of John Weir of Kerse. Town Clerk of Edinburgh, 4 February 1807 to 1851. *Died* 27 January 1856, aged 82.

CUNINGHAM, EDMUND CYPRIAN [24 January 1878]. Apprentice to R. L. Stuart and Harry Cheyne.—Son of Alexander Cuningham of Newholm, W.S. *Born* 7 March 1853. *Died* suddenly in All Saints' Church, Edinburgh, 26 October 1913.

CUNINGHAM, JOHN, OF BANDALLOCH [29 December 1684]. Apprentice to James Cunningham.—Son of William Cuningham of Drumbeg, Stirlingshire. *Married* 10 October 1678, Jean, daughter of William Weir of Blackwood, Lanarkshire. Fiscal, 1690-5. *Died* 24 February 1716.

CUNINGHAM, JOHN, OF BALBEGY [24 June 1713]. Apprentice to, and son of, John Cuningham of Bandalloch, W.S.—*Born* 10 May 1687. *Married* (1) Janet (*died* 18 March 1760), daughter of George Pitcairn of Balbougie; and (2) June 1760, Jean, daughter of Lawrence Binning of Wallyford. *Died* 10 September 1768.

CUNINGHAM, WILLIAM, OF BANDALLOCH [2 February 1713]. Apprentice to , and son of, John Cuningham of Bandalloch, W.S.—*Born* 30 September 1679. *Married* 27 April 1708, Martha, daughter of Sir George Suttie of Balgone, Bart. *Died* suddenly in Parliament House, 8 December 1743.

CUNINGHAM, WILLIAM GRAY [1 July 1824]. Apprentice to, and son of, Charles Cuningham of Newholm, W.S.—*Born* 6 December 1800. *Married* 21 June 1831, Janetta (*died* 1875), daughter of Captain Charles Grant of Greenpark, Linlithgowshire. *Died* 31 December 1838.

CUNNINGHAM, ALEXANDER. Deceased in 1628.

CUNNINGHAM, ALEXANDER, OF HARPERFIELD [13 February 1702].—*Married* (1) 11 November 1702, Katherine, daughter of Nicol Somerville, Writer; and (2) 16 October 1705, daughter of Alexander Stewart, D.C.S. *Died* 1708.

CUNNINGHAM, ALEXANDER, OF LATHRISK [4 July 1748]. Apprentice to Archibald Campbell.—Third son of Ninian Cunningham, Writer in Edinburgh. *Married* 12 February 1762, Jacobina (*died* 2 October 1782), only child of James Malcolm of Lathrisk. *Died* 17 August 1780.

CUNNINGHAM, HUGH, OF MONKREDDEN [12 July 1695]. Apprentice to John Cunningham of Enterkine.—*Married* Anne Brand. *Died* 22 May 1704.

CUNNINGHAM, OR CUNYNGHAME, JAMES [16 March 1670]. Apprentice to John Cunningham of Enterkine.—Son of James Cunynghame in Alloway. *Married* (contract, 9 November 1665), Isobell Graham. Author of *An Essay upon the Inscription of Macduff's Cross in Fife*, 1678. *Died* 1686.

CUNNINGHAM, JAMES [19 June 1823). Apprentice to James Gibson.—Second son of Alexander Cunningham, Baker, Edinburgh. *Born* 18 March 1800. *Married* (1) 26 April 1836, Margaret Sheaffe (*died* 2 May 1845), youngest daughter of Daniel Bagot, Dublin; and (2) 11 October 1846, Elizabeth Boyle (*died* 5 March 1890), youngest daughter of Alexander Dunlop of Keppoch. *Died* 6 November 1878.

CUNNINGHAM, JOHN, OF ENTERKINE [27 November 1660]. Apprentice to James Campbell.—Son of Adam Cunynghame of Previck, Ayrshire. *Born* 1633. *Married* (1) 23 January 1657, Elizabeth Paton (*died* 10 February 1676); and (2) 1 June 1677, Mary, daughter of John Murray of Polmaise. Ordinary Writer to the Treasury, 25 May 1661. *Died* May 1694.

CUNNINGHAM, JOHN [11 December 1828]. Apprentice to John Gibson, Jun.—Second son of John Cunningham of Balgounie, Perthshire. *Born* 1804. *Died* 6 April 1832, unmarried.

CUNNINGHAM, JOHN SMITH, OF CAPRINGTON [10 March 1803]. Apprentice to Archibald Tod.—Eldest son of Thomas Smith, Writer in Edinburgh, Principal Clerk of the Bills. *Born* 22 August 1780. *Married* 7 August 1812, Ann (*died* 1 March 1830), second daughter of Sir William Cunningham of Caprington, Ayrshire. Assumed name of Cunningham. *Died* 3 October 1855.

CUNNINGHAM, ROBERT JEFFREY, T.D., LL.B. [11 July 1892]. Apprentice to Robert Craigie Bell.—Son of Rev. John George Cunningham, D.D., St Luke's U.F. Church, Edinburgh. *Born* 24 June 1866. *Married* 8 August 1903, Mabel (*died* 9 September 1967), younger daughter of William Davidson, Merchant, San Francisco, California. War Service: in South Africa with Commission in Volunteer Company of K.O.S.B. Queen's S.A. medal and 3 clasps. In Great War commanded Depot 5th K.O.S.B. till return of Batt. from Germany, 1919. Practised in Annan 1894-1931. *Died* 23 July 1937.

CUNNINGHAM, SAMUEL [24 February 1809]. Apprentice to John Macnab.—Son of Patrick Cunningham, Writer in Edinburgh. *Born* 2 April 1775. *Married* 20 February 1807, Elizabeth (*died* 1833), daughter of John Milne, Ironmonger, Edinburgh. *Died* 10 July 1815.

CUNNINGHAM, WILLIAM, OF RATHILLET AND BROWNHILL [Before 1623].—Second son of James Cunningham of Ashinyards, Ayrshire. *Married* Rebecca Muirhead, daughter of the Laird of Linhouse. Depute Keeper of the Privy Seal. Usher to the Prince, 8 January to 20 February 1625. *Died* 6 August 1626.

CURLE, ALEXANDER ORMISTON, C.V.O., B.A.(CANTAB), LL.D. [14 March 1892]. Apprentice to John Philp Wood and William Babington.—Third son of Alexander Curle of Easter Morriston, Writer, Melrose. *Born* 3 May 1866. *Married* (1) 30 June 1898, Katherine Wray (*died* 5 June 1906), second daughter of George Tancred of Weens, Roxburghshire; and (2) 17 April 1909, Jocelyn Winifred (*died* 14 July 1925), only daughter of Henry Butler, Hans Court, London, W. Secretary Royal Commission on Ancient and Historical Monuments (Scotland), 1908; Director National Museum of Antiquities, 1913; Director Royal Scottish Museums, 1916-31; Member of Royal Commission on Ancient and Historical Monuments (Scotland), 1913. C.V.O., 1930. LL.D. (Glasgow) 1935. Author of *The Treasure of Traprain*. *Died* 7 January 1955.

CURLE, FREDERICK ROUS NEWLYN [8 December 1902]. Apprentice to Patrick Blair and Hew Francis Cadell.—Son of James Curle of Evelaw, Melrose, Solicitor. *Born* 16 March 1878. *Married* 9 June 1906, Sibella Helen (*died* 19 June 1977), second daughter of Major Alexander Towers-Clark, Middlesex Regiment. Provost of Melrose, 1922. War Service: with Lanarkshire Yeomanry, 1914-19. *Died* 11 May 1956. *Firm*—Curle and Erskine, Melrose.

CURLE, JAMES, of MORRISTON, LL.D. [13 April 1886]. Apprentice to William Stuart Fraser.—Eldest son of Alexander Curle of Morriston, Berwickshire, and Priorwood, Melrose. *Born* 27 March 1862. *Married* 17 September 1902, Alice Mary Blanchette (*died* 29 July 1940), only daughter of Colonel Herbert Augustus Tierney Nepean, of Midfield, Hawthornden. Member of King's Bodyguard for Scotland, Royal Company of Archers, 1897. *Died* 1 March 1944.

CURR, WILLIAM HENRY [26 October 1887]. Apprentice to Ralph and William John Dundas, and George M. Paul.—Son of Henry Curr, Pitkellony, Muthill, Perthshire. *Born* 14 April 1863. *Married* 7 July 1896, Annie Jane (*died* 26 January 1942), second daughter of James M'William, Writer, Glasgow. *Died* 25 June 1936. *Firm*—Nicolson, M'William & Co., Writers, Glasgow.

CURRIE, ALISTAIR DOWNIE, B.A., LL.B. [11 December 1979*].—Son of Ronald Campbell Burns Currie, Solicitor, Dunfermline. *Born* 1 January 1950. *Married* 31 July 1976, Helen, daughter of Brian Walker, Doncaster. *Firm*—Haddon & Turnbull, Hawick.

CURRIER, ANDREW [28 July 1715]. Apprentice to James Drummond.—*Married* (1) Helen, third daughter of Sir George Stirling of Glorat, Bart.; and (2) April 1723, Barbara (*died* 1741), daughter of George Alexander of Peffermiln, Mid-Lothian. *Died* August 1740.

CURROR, DAVID ANDREW [16 January 1887]. Apprentice to Thomas Watt Wallace.—Son of David Curror of Wester Craigduckie, Fife, S.S.C. *Born* 1 September 1861. *Died* 31 October 1929, unmarried.

CUTHBERTSON, BERTRAM HILL [28 March 1927]. Apprentice to George McIntosh and Another of Waddell, McIntosh & Peddie.—Son of Evan James Cuthbertson, W.S., Edinburgh. *Born* 24 April 1902. *Married* 12 September 1928, Shelagh Mary, daughter of William Hutchison, Tea Planter, Assam. *Firm*—Mackenzie, Innes & Logan (after 1955, Cuthbertson & Watson; Brodie, Cuthbertson & Watson; Brodies). (Retired.)

CUTHBERTSON, ERIC IAN [25 November 1963]. Apprentice to (1) Ranald Ker Cuthbertson and Others of Mackenzie, Innes & Logan, and (2) Ranald Ker Cuthbertson and Another of Cuthbertson Riddle and Graham.—Son of Ranald Ker Cuthbertson, W.S., Edinburgh. *Born* 17 November 1934. *Married* 17 November 1962, Shona Campbell Aitken, daughter of Francis Aitken Wright. *Firm*—Russel & Aitken (formerly Cuthbertson, Riddle & Graham).

CUTHBERTSON, EVAN JAMES [16 January 1893]. Apprentice to Charles B. Logan, Hon. James W. Moncrieff, and G. G. Soote.—Son of John Cuthbertson, Writer in Edinburgh. *Born* 30 January 1869. *Married* 5 July 1897, Mary (*died* 3 May 1933), youngest daughter of Nicol Cochrane, Edinburgh. *Died* 2 February 1941. *Firm*—Mackenzie, Innes, and Logan.

CUTHBERTSON, EVAN JAMES, M.A., LL.B. [25 November 1963]. Apprentice to David Blyth Bogle and Others of Lindsay Howe & Co.—Son of Bertram Hill Cuthbertson, W.S., Edinburgh. *Born* 15 September 1938. *Married* 5 October 1963, Judith Mary, daughter of Hugh Beveridge, Farmer. *Firm*—Brodies (formerly Brodie, Cuthbertson & Watson).

CUTHBERTSON, RANALD KER [23 March 1925]. Apprentice to The Hon. James W. Moncrieff and Others of Mackenzie, Innes & Logan.—Son of Evan James Cuthbertson, W.S., Edinburgh. *Born* 20 August 1899. *Married* (1) 7 January 1927, Agnes Thomson (*died* 19 January 1968), daughter of Henry Mitchell, Banker, Edinburgh, and (2) 22 October 1968, Mary Campbell, daughter of William Black, W.S. During First World War served with R.A.F. and R.G.A. (2nd Lieutenant). *Firms*—Mackenzie, Innes & Logan; Cuthbertson, Riddle & Graham; Russel & Aitken. (After amalgamation.)

CUTHBERTSON, WILLIAM [12 November 1847]. Apprentice to William Bell.—Son of Thomas Cuthbertson, Coachbuilder in Edinburgh. *Born* 1 February 1813. *Married* 9 July 1851, Jane Todd (*died* 15 March 1857). *Died* 2 January 1864.

DACKER, PHILIP ANDREW, LL.B. [12 December 1977]. Apprentice to Ronald Kerr Will and Others of Dundas & Wilson.—Son of Frederick A. Dacker, Shipping Agent, Edinburgh. *Born* 20 June 1949. *Married* 30 December 1972, Ellinor Lindsay, daughter of Dr Hugh Macdonald, Nairobi, Kenya. *Firm*—Dundas & Wilson.

DALE, BRIAN GRAEME, LL.B. [11 December 1979]. Apprentice to James John Lamb and Others of Stuart & Stuart, Cairns & Co.—Son of Reginald Cornelius Dale, Chartered Engineer, Bristol. *Born* 20 November 1946. *Married* 23 May 1970, Judith Gail de Beaufort, daughter of Rev. Preb. H. L. Franklin, Sub-Dean, Wells Cathedral, Wells. *Firm*—Stuart & Stuart, Cairns & Co.

DALGLEISH, ANDREW MARTIN CRICHTON, LL.B. [11 December 1979*].—Son of A. Martin Dalgleish, Architect, Edinburgh. *Born* 9 June 1951. *Married* 19 January 1974, Sheila Caroline Forsyth, daughter of John Black, Administration Manager, Life Association of Scotland, Edinburgh. *Firm*—Brodies.

DALGLEISH, JAMES, OF WEST GRANGE AND ARDNAMURCHAN [10 March 1825]. Apprentice to William Mackenzie and Alexander Monypenny.—Eldest surviving son of John Dalgleish of Dalbeath, Fife, Lieut.-Colonel 21st Foot. *Married* 30 June 1835, Elizabeth Christian (*died* 3 April 1892), second daughter of Laurence Johnston of Sands, Perthshire. *Died* 30 September 1870, aged 67.

DALL, CHARLES [18 June 1764]. Apprentice to Alexander Robertson.—Son of Robert Dall, Merchant in Arbroath. *Died* 26 March 1773.

DALLAS, ALASTAIR [12 December 1898]. Apprentice to Arthur Henry M'Lean.—Son of Duncan Forbes Dallas, S.S.C., Edinburgh. *Born* 2 May 1874. *Died* 2 January 1951. *Firm*—Forbes Dallas and Co.

DALLAS, ALEXANDER, OF RIDDOCHHILL [6 December 1803]. Apprentice to J. A. Higgins.—Son of Alexander Dallas, Tacksman of Standaline, Nairnshire. *Born* 27 November 1770. *Married* (1) Ann (*died* 25 January 1831), daughter of Dr Robert Forbes; and (2) 15 November 1831, Catherine (*died* 14 May 1881), daughter of Sir William Honyman of Armadale, Bart. *Died* 4 February 1834.

DALLAS, GEORGE, OF SAINT MARTINS [16 July 1661]. Apprentice to John Bayne.—Son of William Dallas of Budyett. *Born* 1636. *Married* 3 July 1660, Margaret (*died* 16 October 1697), daughter of James Abercromby of Pittencrieff. Fiscal, 1666-71. M.P. for Cromartyshire, 1665, 1667, 1669-74, 1678, 1681-82, 1685-86. Author of *A System of Stiles as now practicable within the Kingdom of Scotland*, 1697. *Died* April 1701.

DALLAS, GEORGE, OF PARKLEY [17 June 1723]. Apprentice to George Wilkie.—Son of George Dallas of Parkley, West Lothian. *Married* 24 December 1728, Susannah, daughter of James Mure of Earnshaw. *Died* 25 March 1779.

DALLAS, JAMES [3 July 1781]. Apprentice to Robert Boswell.—Eldest son of Thomas Dallas, Surgeon in Musselburgh. *Born* 21 January 1757. *Married* 17 April 1783, Nancy, daughter of John Milne of Stobcross. Resigned his Commission, 24 May 1792. *Died* 2 January 1802.

DALLAS, WILLIAM, OF BUDYETT [5 January 1687]. Apprentice to George Dallas of St Martins, his uncle.—Eldest son of Hugh Dallas of Budyett, Commissary Clerk of Ross. *Born* 10 April 1664. *Married* 10 February 1689, Henrietta, daughter of William Cockburn, Merchant, Edinburgh. Joint Fiscal, 1695 and 1697-1702. *Died* at Inverness, 23 April 1713.

DALLAS, WILLIAM [1 August 1788]. Apprentice to Samuel Mitchelson, Jun.—Fourth son of William Dallas, Wright in Edinburgh. *Baptized* 1 August 1759. *Married* 21 February 1797, Elizabeth (*died* 26 July 1838), youngest daughter of James Kerr, of the Island of Jamaica. *Died* 27 March 1852.

DALLAS, WILLIAM [21 December 1832]. Apprentice to, and son of, Alexander Dallas, W.S.—*Born* 25 December 1805. *Married* (1) 30 March 1832, Mary Ann, daughter of John Thomson of Northfield; and (2) 28 October 1845, Margaret (*died* 1872), daughter of Peter M'Ewen. *Died* 24 February 1851.

DALLMEYER, CHRISTOPHER JAMES YORK, D.S.O., T.D. [13 July 1931]. Apprentice to Keith R. Maitland and Others of John C. Brodie & Sons.—Son of R. O. J. Dallmeyer, Solicitor, London. *Born* 27 March 1907. *Married* 14 September 1939, Ursula Nina, daughter of Lord Kinross, Advocate and Sheriff Principal. Lieutenant Colonel, First Lothian and Border Yeomanry. Served France and North West Europe, 1940 and 1944-45. Awarded D.S.O. and Bar; Order of Leopold and Croix de Guerre (Belgium). *Firm*—Brodie, Cuthbertson & Watson. (Retired.)

DALMAHOY, JAMES ALEXANDER, M.V.O. [18 July 1877]. Apprentice to (1) Patrick Dalmahoy; and (2) John Cowan.—Son of Patrick Dalmahoy, W.S. *Born* 8 December 1853. *Married* 17 June 1895, Frances Marion (*died* 5 February 1958), daughter of Alexander Edward Henderson, Advocate, Sheriff-Substitute of Fife and afterwards of the Lothians. M.V.O., October 1905. *Died* 18 September 1911.

DALMAHOY, PATRICK, OF BOWERHOUSES [5 June 1823]. Apprentice to John Mowbray.—Son of Adam Dalmahoy, Glover in Edinburgh. *Born* 11 June 1798. *Married* 8 January 1833, Anna Catherine (*died* 16 February 1859), only daughter of Simon Sawers, of the Ceylon Civil Service. Fiscal, 1864-72. *Died* 5 September 1872.

DALMAHOY, PATRICK CARFRAE, D.S.O. [6 July 1896]. Apprentice to John Cowan and James A. Dalmahoy.—Son of Major-General Patrick Carfrae Dalmahoy, Bengal Staff Corps, and grandson of Patrick Dalmahoy, W.S. *Born* 31 October 1872. Second Lieutenant, Royal Scots, 4 August 1900. Served in South Africa. *Married* 25 October 1911, Mabel Houston (*died* 3 March 1963), daughter of W. H. Rogers, Johannesburg. Resident Magistrate, Renoni, S. Africa. *Died* 11 November 1928.

DALRYMPLE, HEW DRUMMOND KITSON, LL.B. [13 May 1980*].—Son of William Constable Dalrymple, Nursing Home Proprietor, Edinburgh. *Born* 12 November 1952. *Married* 3 September 1977, Deirdre Margaret, daughter M. Torquil Macneill, Procurator Fiscal, Aberdeen. *Firm*—Brodies.

DALRYMPLE, ROBERT, OF KILLOCH [28 March 1707]. Apprentice to John Cuningham.—Second son of Sir James Dalrymple of Borthwick, Bart. *Born* 25 July 1685. *Married* 5 September 1711, Elizabeth, daughter and co-heir of John Bowick, Merchant, Glasgow. *Died* 2 December 1765.

DALRYMPLE, ROBERT, OF DREGHORN AND PRESTWOODSIDE [10 December 1722]. Apprentice to Robert Dalrymple of Waterside, Dumfriesshire. *Died* 30 March 1765, aged 77.

DALRYMPLE, WILLIAM [31 March 1707].—Son of Robert Dalrymple, one of the Bailies of Ayr. *Married* Janet Menzies. Under Keeper of the Signet, 1707-8. *Died* 7 June 1732.

DALRYMPLE, WILLIAM [11 December 1828]. Apprentice to James Lang.—Son of James Dalrymple, Merchant in Edinburgh. *Born* 1795. *Married* 1833 —— (*died* 1874). *Died* 4 November 1834.

DALRYMPLE, WILLIAM [8 November 1849]. Apprentice to John Richardson.—Eldest son of William Dalrymple, S.S.C. *Born* 27 April 1821. *Married* Mary Agnes (*died* 3 November 1902), daughter of James Aitken, Writer, Edinburgh. *Died* 8 January 1886.

DALZELL, WILLIAM. *See* COLQUHOUN, WILLIAM DALZELL.

DALZIEL, GEORGE [24 June 1824]. Apprentice to John Buchan Brodie.—Son of John Dalziel, Writer in Earlston, Berwickshire. *Born* 14 January 1799. *Married* 23 October 1827, Charlotte (*died* 11 December 1884), second daughter of David Pearson, Edinburgh. Depute Keeper of the Privy Seal, 1853-69. *Died* 27 June 1869.

DALZIEL, GEORGE [14 November 1866]. Apprentice to, and son of, George Dalziel, W.S.—*Born* 13 July 1843. *Married* 29 September 1868, Mary (*died* 4 April 1923), eldest daughter of Charles Lyall, Farmer, Old Montrose. *Died* at North Berwick, 24 June 1926.

DALZIEL, GEORGE FRANCIS [28 March 1898]. Apprentice to J. P. Wright.—Son of George Dalziel, W.S. *Born* 18 February 1874. *Married* 23 July 1903, Eleanor Dennistoun (Norma) (*died* 29 July 1957), eldest daughter of Cecil Scott Arkcoll, Barrister, London. Member of the King's Bodyguard for Scotland, Royal Company of Archers, 1901. *Died* 6 August 1947. *Firm*—Tods, Murray, and Jamieson.

DALZIEL, JAMES SANDERSON [16 March 1896]. Apprentice to George Dalziel.—Son of John Dalziel, W.S. *Born* 14 November 1867. Joined 172nd Rocky Mountain Rangers, Canadian Expeditionary Force, in 1916. *Died* 15 November 1939.

DALZIEL, JOHN [15 November 1860]. Apprentice to, and eldest son of, George Dalziel, W.S.—*Born* 9 August 1838. *Married* 26 March 1863, Isabella Geddes (*died* 20 October 1897), eldest daughter of James Sanderson, Surgeon-Major, Madras Army. *Died* 24 April 1883.

DANIEL, PHINEAS [16 May 1822]. Apprentice to George Robinson.—Son of George Daniel, Writer in Fraserburgh. *Married* Clementina (*died* 25 October 1841), youngest daughter of William Shand, Craigellie, Aberdeenshire. Sheriff-Clerk of Dunbartonshire, 1834-67. *Died* 6 January 1867, aged 79.

DARLING, JAMES JOHNSTON [25 November 1824]. Apprentice to Robert Strachan.—Younger son of Paul Darling of Bogangreen. *Born* 1799. Author of the *Practice of the Court of Session*, 1833, and other legal works. *Died* 1 July 1842, unmarried.

DARLING, THOMAS [14 August 1633]. Apprentice to Robert Wallace.—*Married* 10 October 1633, Jean Herring.

DARLING, THOMAS [24 November 1831]. Apprentice to John Glassford Hopkirk.—Son of Thomas Darling, S.S.C. *Born* 16 October 1808. *Married* 13 March 1832, Charlotte, youngest daughter of Charles Hamilton of Fairholm, Lanarkshire. *Died* 13 June 1870.

DAVIDSON, ARTHUR LENNOX [18 October 1886]. Apprentice to Christopher Charles Nisbet.—Son of Major-General Davidson. *Born* 7 December 1862. *Died* 20 February 1929, unmarried.

DAVIDSON, CHARLES FORBES [27 May 1824]. Apprentice to (1) William Berry; and (2) Alexander Kettle.—Fifth son of Andrew Davidson, Advocate in Aberdeen. *Married* 9 June 1831, Eliza (*died* 24 August 1899), daughter of Charles Hill of Luthrie, Fife. *Died* 8 March 1853, aged 52.

DAVIDSON, GORDON CAMPBELL, M.A., LL.B. [20 December 1948]. Apprentice to Hon. Adam Watson and Others of Mackenzie, Innes & Logan.—Son of Sir Andrew Davidson, M.D., D.P.H., F.R.C.S.E., Stanley, Perthshire. *Born* 9 February 1923. *Married* 6 June 1969, Patricia Cecil, daughter of Cecil Grellier. Lieutenant, 2nd Battalion, Gordon Highlanders; Captain First Special Air Service.

DAVIDSON, HARRY, OF OLD BELSES [16 November 1781]. Apprentice to Robert Jamieson.—Second son of James Davidson, Merchant in Dysart. *Born* 10 April 1754. *Married* Ann (*died* 3 April 1814), daughter of Very Rev. James Gillespie, Principal of St Mary's College, St Andrews. Sheriff-Substitute of Mid-Lothian, 1791-1820. *Died* 11 February 1837. *Firm*—Davidson and Syme.

DAVIDSON, HUGH [2 October 1688]. Apprentice to Hugh Wallace of Inglistoun.—*Buried* 10 April 1695.

DAVIDSON, JAMES, OF BANKIER [29 June 1786]. Apprentice to James Ferrier.—Son of Rev. John Davidson, Minister of West Kilpatrick. *Born* 29 May 1763. *Married* (1) 8 August 1787, Mary (*died* 28 May 1788), daughter of Neil Buchanan of Auchintoshan, Dunbartonshire; (2) 15 April 1791, Elizabeth (*died* 11 December 1798), daughter of Rev. James Meek, D.D., Minister of Cambuslang; and (3) 9 March 1809, the widow (*died* 22 May 1816) of John Miller, of Jamaica. *Died* at Colzium, 18 June 1823.

DAVIDSON, JAMES GILBERT, M.A., LL.B. [13 May 1980*].—Son of George Thomson Davidson, Civil Servant, Edinburgh. *Born* 21 November 1938. *Married* 20 July 1965, Alison Rosemary, daughter of George Herbert Brown, Solicitor/Civil Servant, Edinburgh. *Firm*—Lindsay, Duncan & Black.

DAVIDSON, JAMES GILLESPIE [19 June 1812]. Apprentice to, and eldest son of, Harry Davidson, W.S.—*Born* 3 January 1789. *Married* 30 October 1828, Amelia Helen (*died* 22 March 1840), eldest daughter of Major-General John Lamont of Lamont, Argyllshire. *Died* 5 October 1843.

DAVIDSON, JOHN, OF WHITEHOUSE [20 December 1732]. Apprentice to Andrew Sutherland.—*Married* August 1740, Ann (*died* 2 November 1778), daughter of —— Fotheringham of Powrie. Principal Clerk of Justiciary. *Died* 7 April 1755.

DAVIDSON, JOHN, OF STEWARTFIELD AND HALTREE [3 April 1749]. Apprentice to George Balfour.—Son of James Davidson of Haltree, Bookseller in Edinburgh. *Married* Helen Gibson (*died* in February 1796). Author of a tract on the *Regiam Majestatem* and another on the *Black Acts*; also in 1771, *Accounts of the Chamberlain of Scotland, 1329-1331*. Crown Agent. Deputy Keeper of the Signet, 1778-97. See *Kay's Portraits*, XCIX. *Died* 29 November 1797.

DAVIDSON, JOHN JAMES [22 February 1821]. Apprentice to, and son of, James Davidson, W.S. *Born* 1797. *Married* ——. Teind Clerk, 1826-37. *Died* 20 May 1837.

DAVIDSON, JOHN MARR, M.A., LL.B. [27 July 1953]. Apprentice to Charles Alexander of Auld & Macdonald.—Son of John Marr Davidson, Solicitor, Lanark. *Born* 22 June 1923. *Married* 3 November 1945, Sylvia, daughter of William Russell, L.N.E.R. Engineer. High Constable of Holyrood. Captain, Cameronians (Scottish Rifles) 1942-1946. Served in Faroes, North Africa, Italy, Middle East, France and Germany. *Firms*—(1) Auld & Macdonald; (2) W. & J. Burness.

DAVIDSON, LAURENCE [18 November 1825]. Apprentice to (1) John Ferrier; and (2) Harry Davidson.—Fourth son of Harry Davidson, W.S. *Born* 31 October 1800. *Married* 6 December 1831, Emma (*died* 5 December 1868), youngest daughter of John Pryor, Halifax, Nova Scotia. *Died* 18 September 1868.

DAVIDSON, WILLIAM [23 March 1903]. Apprentice to Andrew Wishart and Kenneth Sanderson.—Son of Alexander Davidson, Auctioneer, Melrose. *Born* 9 February 1879. *Married* 9 June 1911. Anna Louisa (*died* 29 July 1963), eldest daughter of John Alexander Mackenzie, Ardlair, Spylaw Road, Edinburgh. *Died* at Perwick Bay, Isle of Man, 6 August 1933. *Firm*—Fraser, Davidson, and Whyte.

DAVIDSON, WILLIAM DUNKELD, M.C., M.A., LL.B. [15 July 1949]. Apprentice to George Alexander Roger of W. H. Mill, McLeod & Rose.—Son of William Davidson, Schoolmaster, Gateshead-on-Tyne. *Born* 10 December 1916. *Married* 12 September 1961, Jocelyn Marjorie, daughter of Captain Robert Mends, R.N. Major, 1st Battalion Queen's own Cameron Highlanders 1940-45. Served in India and Burma 1942-45. *Firm*—W. H. Mill, McLeod & Rose (now amalgamated with Scott, Moncrieff & Trail).

DAWLING, JAMES [4 June 1636]. Apprentice to Quinton Kennedy.—Son of John Dawling, Advocate. *Baptized* 17 March 1611.

DAWSON, JAMES, M.A., LL.B. [27 December 1939]. Apprentice to Sir John Prosser, and Others of Morton, Smart, Macdonald and Prosser.—Son of James Dawson, Woollen Manufacturers, Alva. *Born* 18 March 1915. *Married* 23 December 1939, Janet Margaret Chalmers, daughter of Dr J. S. Mitchell, F.R.C.S.E. Major, Black Watch 1939-46. Served U.K. and A.L.F.S.E.A. Emigrated to Rhodesia 1949.

DAWSON, PERCY FURNEAUX [13 July 1903]. Apprentice to James H. Jameson and James Young.—Son of Adam Dawson, Merchant, Leith. *Born* 25 May 1877. *Married* 1 March 1905, Christian Margaret (Daisy) (*died* 26 December 1963), elder daughter of Robert Menzies of Viewfield, Lanarkshire, S.S.C., Edinburgh. Served in Great War as Lieutenant R.G.A. *Died* 4 December 1956. *Firm*—Allan, Dawson, Simpson, and Hampton.

DEAR, ALASDAIR GEORGE WILBERT, M.A., LL.B. [4 December 1972]. (By Rule IX(a).)—Son of Sidney William Dear, Schoolmaster, Crathie, Aberdeenshire. *Born* 14 September 1935. *Married* 31 July 1965, Leslie Ann, daughter of Donald Robertson. *Firm*—Alasdair G. W. Dear & Co.

DEAS, DAVID WRIGHT [16 January 1894]. Apprentice to A. W. Black and Alan L. Menzies.—Son of Alexander Deas, Stationmaster, Cockburnspath. *Born* 12 December 1863. *Married* 31 May 1902, Isabella (*died* 18 November 1954), youngest daughter of John Snow, Rose Villa, Corstorphine. *Died* 9 April 1928.

DEAS, SYLVESTER FALCONER REID, OF HARTWOODHILL [17 December 1868]. Apprentice to James Duncan.—Younger son of Sir George Deas, Kt., one of the Senators of the College of Justice (Lord Deas). *Born* 3 February 1845. *Married* 7 October 1874, Alice (*died* 16 June 1896), second daughter of Michael Grayhurst Hewat, London. *Died* 6 January 1899.

DEMPSTER, ROBERT SCOTT. *See* Scott-Dempster.

DEMPSTER, THOMAS GREIG, T.D. [24 March 1930]. Apprentice to (1) David Mackenzie of Condie, Mackenzie & Co. Perth; and (2) William Babington and Others of Melville and Lindesay. Son of Thomas Dempster, Solicitor and Lord Provost of Perth. *Born* 29 June 1905. *Married* (1) 18 February 1932, Doris Henderson (*died* 3 July 1940), daughter of John Thomson Ramage, Marine Engineer, and (2) 7 March 1945, Barbara Elizabeth Mary, daughter of Robert Eric Hawkins, Insurance Manager. Member of Queen's Bodyguard for Scotland, Royal Company of Archers. Major R.A. (A.A.). Served U.K. and Europe 1939-45. *Firms*—(1) Cornillon Craig & Thomas (1930-1944); (2) Mackenzie & Black (1944-74); (3) Brodies (after amalgamation with Mackenzie & Black).

DENHOLM, HAROLD JOHN JOLLY, B.L. [28 November 1966]. Apprentice to Jack King Cyril Miller and Others of Simpson & Marwick.—Son of the Rev. Canon Robert Denholm. *Born* 23 March 1931. *Married* 14 November 1964, Marion, daughter of Sir Francis Gordon Bell, K.B.E., M.C., F.R.C.S., Dunedin, New Zealand. *Firm*—(1) Simpson & Marwick; (2) Balfour & Manson.

DENHOLM, PAUL, LL.B. [2 May 1966]. Apprentice to N. A. M. Mackay and Others of Baillie & Gifford.—Son of George L. Denholm, Shipbroker. *Born* 21 February 1941. *Married* 17 April 1965, Georgina Susanna Traill, daughter of Rev. James E. Lyon, Cellardyke, Fife. *Firm*—Drummond, Johnstone & Grosset, Cupar.

DENHOLM, ROBERT, M.A., LL.B. [20 July 1950]. Apprentice to Ralph Colley Smith and Others of Fraser, Stodart & Ballingall,—Son of Robert Denholm, Solicitor, Coatbridge. *Born* 6 July 1921. *Married* 24 September 1949, Elizabeth Ann, daughter of William King Clark, M.R.C.V.S., Edinburgh. Captain, R.A. Served U.K., France, Germany, Holland, Belgium, Egypt and Palestine, 1941-46. *Firms*—(1) Pagan and Osborne, Cupar; (2) W. & J. Ogilvy Shepherd, Leven; (3) Nicoll, Mackenzie & Denholm, Leven and St Andrews.

DENNISTON, ARCHIBALD [1 July 1837]. Apprentice to Walter Dickson and James Steuart.—Son of John Denniston, Merchant in Greenock. *Born* 14 March 1814. *Married* 7 September 1842, Janet (*died* 25 March 1899), third daughter of Allan Fullarton, Banker, Greenock. *Died* 23 June 1871.

DENNISTOUN, RICHARD [4 July 1829]. Apprentice to George Dunlop.—Son of Robert Dennistoun, Merchant in Glasgow. *Married* 11 March 1830, Hannah (*died* 1867), only daughter of John Meiklam of Carnbroe. *Died* 20 March 1848, aged 41.

DEWAR, ANDREW [24 October 1892]. Apprentice to George Dunlop.—Son of John Dewar of Lassodie, Fife. *Born* 20 May 1867. *Married* 12 June 1890, Annie Leslie (*died* 11 January 1919), youngest daughter of Angus Gregorson, Ardtornish. *Died* 7 March 1922.

DEWAR, ANDREW, B.L. [28 November 1966]. (By Rule IX(a).)—Son of David Dewar, Grainbroker, Dalkeith. *Born* 4 September 1919. Bombardier with 130 L.A.A. Regiment R.A., in A.A. Command (U.K.), 1939-45. *Firm*—Pearson, Robertson & Maconochie.

DEWAR, DAVID DEAS [15 March 1897]. Apprentice to F. J. Dewar.—Second son of Hugh Bruce Dewar, S.S.C., Edinburgh. *Born* 1 December 1868. *Married* 20 October 1898, Agnes Dickson (*died* 10 March 1934), younger daughter of John Hill, Carlowrie, Mid-Lothian. War Service: with 23rd (Sportsman's) Batt. The Royal Fusiliers, France and Overseas, 1914-16. *Died* 31 December 1942.

DEWAR, FRANCIS JAMES [5 May 1880]. Apprentice to (1) S. F. R. Deas; and (2) Hugh Hamilton Crichton.—Elder son of Hugh Bruce Dewar, S.S.C. *Born* 29 April 1855. *Married* 2 September 1896, Katherine Beatrice, second daughter of Arthur Wrigley, The Dale, Hoylake, Cheshire. *Died* 18 January 1921.

DI CIACCA, CESIDIO MARTIN, LL.B. [12 December 1977]. Apprentice to Ronald Kerr Will and Others of Dundas & Wilson.—Son of John Di Ciacca, Restaurateur, Cockenzie, East Lothian. *Born* 3 February 1954.

DEWAR, WILLIAM [20 June 1769]. Apprentice to Alexander Orr.—Second son of John Dewar of Cannan. *Born* May 1741. *Died* 1770.

DICK, ANDREW [11 January 1762]. Apprentice to (1) Robert Sym; and (2) Thomas Innes.—Son of John Dick of Compstoun. *Married* Ann Heugh. *Died* May 1778.

DICK, ELAINE BELL, LL.B. [11 December 1979*].—Daughter of Raymond Dick, Merchant Navy Engineer, Hamilton. *Born* 29 January 1955. *Firm*—Warden, Bruce & Co.

DICK, WALTER [Before 1598]—Son of Gilbert Dick, Burgess of Edinburgh.

DICK, WILLIAM [3 July 1772]. Apprentice to Leonard Urquhart.—Youngest son of Robert Dick, Writer in Edinburgh. *Died* August 1787.

DICK PEDDIE, JOHN ALEXANDER [24 March 1930]. Apprentice to Alexander Louis Dick Peddie of Waddell, McIntosh & Peddie.—Son of Coventry Dick Peddie, Advocate, Edinburgh. *Born* 30 July 1906. *Married* 10 April 1937, Helen Jean (*died* 20 February 1974), daughter of Senator Francis Charles Thompson, South Africa. *Firm*—Waddell, McIntosh & Peddie. (Retired.)

DICKIE, JOHN [3 August 1742]. Apprentice to Robert Hepburn.—Son of John Dickie of Corstorphine Hill, Merchant in Edinburgh. *Married* Ann (*died* 19 May 1791), daughter of Rev. George Fordyce, Minister of Corstorphine. *Died* 3 April 1755, aged 43.

DICKIE, JOHN [5 July 1814]. Apprentice to William Inglis.—Third son of William Dickie, Merchant in Dundee, afterwards in Edinburgh. *Born* 1783. *Died* 13 December 1839.

DICKSON, ALASTAIR RONALD, LL.B. [11 December 1979*].—Son of Sheriff Ian Dickson, W.S., Glasgow. *Born* 16 January 1951. *Married* 27 September 1974, Josephine Dolores, daughter of Robert Conlon. *Firm*—Dundas & Wilson.

DICKSON, ARTHUR HILL [14 January 1890]. Apprentice to Robert Strathern.—Youngest son of Alexander Dickson, Farmer, Hermiston, Mid-Lothian. *Born* 18 February 1867. *Married* 7 July 1896, Robina Christian (*died* 15 January 1960), daughter of John Scott Moncrieff, C.A., Edinburgh. *Died* 19 June 1935. *Firm*—Livingston and Dickson.

DICKSON, DAVID FRANCIS [14 March 1892]. Apprentice to D. S. Dickson and D. Shaw.—Son of David Scot Dickson, W.S. *Born* 23 June 1868. *Died* 3 September 1894, unmarried.

DICKSON, DAVID SCOT [26 June 1856]. Apprentice to Thomas George Mackay and Alexander Howe.—Eighth son of Walter Dickson of Monybuie, W.S. *Born* 23 September 1830. *Married* 19 September 1861, the Hon. Francis Sophia Addington (*died* 2 February 1934), daughter of William Leonard, second Viscount Sidmouth. *Died* 14 February 1900.

DICKSON, HENRY GORDON [27 February 1817]. Apprentice to William Handyside.—Son of Samuel Dickson, Builder in Edinburgh. *Married* 1 August 1817, Eliza, second daughter of William Gillespie, Merchant in Edinburgh. *Died* 30 September 1860, aged 74.

DICKSON, HENRY GORDON [16 March 1855]. Apprentice to, and eldest son of, Henry Gordon Dickson, W.S.—*Born* 11 March 1820. *Married* 16 September 1851, Jane Alder (*died* 28 January 1890), eldest daughter of Dr Adolphus Macdowall Ross, Edinburgh. *Died* 21 July 1889.

DICKSON, IAN ANDERSON [14 December 1931]. Apprentice to William Henry Fraser and Others of Fraser, Stodart & Ballingall.—Son of Robert Anderson Dickson, D.D.S., Scotstoun House, South Queensferry. *Born* 21 June 1905. *Married* 18 September 1943, Margaret Forbes, daughter of James John Ross, Stockbroker, Edinburgh. Sheriff of Lanarkshire at Hamilton 1961-77. *Died* 10 April 1982. *Firm*—John M. Alston & Son, Coatbridge. (Retired.)

DICKSON, JAMES LAWRENCE [16 January 1888]. Apprentice to David S. Dickson and David Shaw.—Son of James Gilchrist Dickson, Stockbroker, Edinburgh. *Born* 25 November 1861. *Died* at Sittingbourne, Kent, 19 January 1923.

DICKSON, JAMES MACBRIDE, LL.B. [21 July 1875]. Apprentice to Robert Burt Ranken.—Son of Andrew John Dickson, S.S.C. *Born* 7 January 1852. *Died* 2 January 1920.

DICKSON, JOHN, OF ROBBIEWHAT [30 June 1789]. Apprentice to Hugh Corrie.—Eldest son of David Dickson of Locharwoods, Dumfriesshire. *Born* 1759. *Married* 2 September 1790, Charlotte (*died* 20 July 1845), daughter of James Alison, Writer in Edinburgh. *Died* 23 November 1831.

DICKSON, JOHN [13 June 1806]. Apprentice to Archibald Gibson.—Son of Rev. David Dickson of Perisland, Minister of the New North Church, Edinburgh. *Born* 17 November 1781. *Died* at Kingston, Canada, 8 July 1823.

DICKSON, JOHN [29 June 1843]. Apprentice to, and eldest son of, Walter Dickson of Monybuie, W.S.—*Born* 30 October 1817. *Married* 29 June 1852, Eliza Jane (*died* 13 October 1890), daughter of Colonel Alexander Macleod, C.B. *Died* 6 December 1909.

DICKSON, JOHN DOUGLAS HAMILTON, O.B.E., Mus.Doc.(EDIN). [28 March 1910]. Apprentice to Sir John Prosser, Andrew Gray Muir, and John Smart.—Son of James Douglas Hamilton Dickson, Senior Fellow of St Peter's College, Cambridge. *Born* 18 October 1885. *Married* 5 June 1918, Marjorie Balfour, daughter of William Duncan Lowe, W.S., Edinburgh. War Service: Lieutenant, attached Royal Scots Fusiliers, 1917. Hon. Member of the Incorporated Society of Musicians (London) 1952. *Died* 5 December 1958. *Firm*—Tods, Murray, and Jameson.

DICKSON, JOHN GRAHAM, B.L. [30 April 1962]. Apprentice to D. C. McConnachie and Others of Davidson & Syme.—Son of Robert Dickson, Master Baker, Edinburgh. *Born* 8 October 1931. *Married* 15 September 1956, Jean Arthur, daughter of William Shirra. *Firm*—Dickson, Smith & Co. (incorporating H. & J. Smith, Forrester Cowie & Gray, and W. Gray Miller & Co.).

DICKSON, MAURICE RHYND, OF DEUCHAR, ANGUS, D.S.O., B.A.(OXON) [8 July 1907]. Apprentice to H. Cheyne, F. J. G. Borthwick, G. Kermack, Ian MacIntyre, and J. G. Kirkpatrick.—Son of Colonel John Farquhar Dickson, Panbride House, Carnoustie. *Born* 2 January 1882. *Married* 28 June 1910, Florence Elizabeth (*died* 26 September 1971), daughter of Sir Walter Thorburn of Glenbreck, Peeblesshire. War Service, 1914-1919. Lieut.-Colonel commanding 12th A. and S. Highlanders. Served in France and Balkans. D.S.O. Officer of the Legion of Honour (France). Twice mentioned in Despatches. *Died* 10 January 1940. *Firm*—J. and W. Macdonald, Arbroath.

DICKSON, ROBERT HAMISH, LL.B. [1 December 1969]. Apprentice to Hon. David Andrew Balfour and Others of Shepherd & Wedderburn.—Son of Ian Anderson Dickson, W.S., Glasgow. *Born* 19 October 1945. *Married* 12 August 1976, Janet Laird, daughter of A. Campbell, Port of Menteith. *Firm*—Brown, Mair, Gemmell & Hislop, Glasgow.

DICKSON, SAMUEL [16 March 1855]. Apprentice to, and third son of, Henry Gordon Dickson, W.S. *Born* 12 January 1826. *Married* 31 July 1860, Mary Campbell (*died* 7 September 1861), youngest daughter of David Johnstone of Overton, Stirlingshire. *Died* 22 February 1891.

DICKSON, THOMAS [18 May 1649]. Apprentice to Adam Watt.—*Married* (contract, 18 June 1647) Agnes, younger daughter of David Gardner, Skipper, Leith. Re-admitted, 21 November 1661. *Buried* 31 March 1668.

DICKSON, WALTER, OF MONYBUIE [20 May 1802]. Apprentice to Thomas Cranston.— Youngest son of John Dickson of Conheath, Provost of Dumfries. *Born* 5 November 1776. *Married* 2 December 1816, Margaret (*died* 1 September 1876), fourth daughter of Thomas Goldie of Craigmuie. *Died* 12 December 1855.

DICKSON, WALTER [30 January 1823]. Apprentice to William Renny.—Son of Archibald Dickson of Housebyres, Nursery- and Seedsman in Hawick. *Born* 1797. *Died* 9 July 1843, unmarried.

DICKSON, WILLIAM, B.A.(CANTAB) [13 July 1936]. Apprentice to Francis John Gordon Borthwick and Others of Mackenzie & Kermack.—Son of William Collins Dickson, Publisher, Dunblane, Perthshire. *Born* 28 December 1910.

DICKSON, WILLIAM TRAQUAIR, OF CORSTORPHINE [3 November 1870]. Apprentice to William Traquair, his uncle.—Son of John Dickson of Corstorphine. *Born* 7 June 1845. *Married* 27 June 1882, Elizabeth Madalene (*died* 15 June 1929), daughter of Rev. Archibald Stewart, D.D., Minister of Glasserton. *Died* 24 November 1926.

DIXON, ROBERT, OF LEVENGROVE [20 December 1827]. Apprentice to James Dundas.—Son of John Dixon, of the Dumbarton Glass Works Company. *Married* Louisa Lee (*died* 6 April 1857). *Died* 26 July 1833, aged 30.

DIXSON, JAMES HEGGIE [20 October 1875]. Apprentice to Robert and James Alexander Haldane.—Son of Robert Dixson, Edinburgh. *Born* 17 October 1852. *Married* 28 June 1881, Jane Callander Balloch (*died* 15 December 1945), daughter of Robert Honeyman, Merchant, Edinburgh. *Died* 6 April 1904.

DIXSON, ROBERT [7 December 1908]. Apprentice to Alexander Howe and Others of Lindsay, Howe & Co.—Son of James Heggie Dixson, W.S., Edinburgh. *Born* 26 July 1885. *Married* 24 July 1940, Mona Hortense Wyatt Mackenzie Kelly (*died* October 1945). Lieutenant, Recruiting Staff R.S.F. Depot, Ayr, First World War. *Died* 9 March 1978; Father of the Society on his death.

DOBIE, JAMES [16 July 1840]. Apprentice to (1) James Adam; (2) Roderick Mackenzie and Robert Macfarlane; and (3) Roderick Mackenzie.—Son of James Dobie, of Crummock, Writer in Beith, Ayrshire. *Born* 1819. *Died* 16 December 1840, unmarried.

DON, PATRICK [29 April 1662]. Apprentice to Robert Pringle, John Nicoll, elder, and Alexander Leslie.—Son of Alexander Don, Writer in Edinburgh. *Died* March 1672.

DONALD, ALEXANDER [6 July 1826]. Apprentice to William Inglis and Matthew Weir.—Eldest son of William Donald, Couliehare, Udny. *Born* 1796. *Married* 5 August 1830, Robina Mary (*died* 12 November 1892), youngest daughter of Alexander Millar, Montrose. *Died* 11 April 1846.

DONALD, DAVID MITCHELL COOKE, B.L. [20 November 1950]. Apprentice to R. M. Guild and Others of Shepherd & Wedderburn.—Son of J. J. Donald. *Born* 29 September 1914. *Married* 16 June 1941, Myra Catherine, daughter of J. G. Y. Lockie. Major, R.A., D.A.A.G. H.Q. 21 Army Group; Served France, Belgium and Germany. *Firm*—Shepherd & Wedderburn (1948-60).

DONALD, HUGH ROBERTSON, LL.B. [11 December 1979*].—Son of Robert Donald, Company Director, Edinburgh. *Born* 5 November 1951. *Married* 16 August 1975, Margaret Grace, daughter of James Wood, Agricultural Manager, Aberdeen. *Firm*—Shepherd & Wedderburn.

DONALD, JOHN, M.A., LL.B. [28 April 1975]. Apprentice to Hon. D. A. Balfour and Others of Shepherd & Wedderburn.—Son of James Donald, Bank Manager, Nairn. *Born* 5 January 1942. *Married* 18 September 1965, Jennifer Edith, daughter of Albert James Osmond Rask, Civil Servant. *Firm*—Shepherd & Wedderburn.

DONALDSON, GEORGE HAY [14 November 1833]. Apprentice to John Gibson, Jun.—Son of Stuart Donaldson, Merchant in London. *Born* 22 April 1810. *Married* 4 September 1844, Emma de Bois (*died* 17 December 1885), youngest daughter of James Russell, Entwood Court, Staffordshire. *Died* 1 May 1872.

DONALDSON, HAY [9 July 1802]. Apprentice to John Moir.—Third son of Hay Donaldson, Town Clerk of Haddington. *Married* Janet, daughter of George M'Call, Provost of Haddington. *Died* 30 September 1822.

DONALDSON, JOHN [Before 1514].

DONALDSON, JOHN, OF AUCHAIRNE [10 March 1808]. Apprentice to Vans Hathorn.—Only son of Rev. William Donaldson, Minister of Ballantrae. *Born* 16 October 1780. *Married* 29 March 1813, Margaret (*died* 8 April 1864), only daughter of John Ure, one of the Magistrates of Glasgow. *Died* 17 October 1849.

DONALDSON, ROBERT [26 June 1769]. Apprentice to Thomas Brodie.—Eldest son of George Donaldson, Sheriff-Clerk of Nairn. *Married* April 1767, Helen, only daughter of John Grant. W.S. Lyon Clerk Depute, 17 April 1755. Marchmont Herald, 11 October 1760-4. *Died* 27 August 1796.

DOUGAL, ALEXANDER, LL.B. [17 March 1919]. Apprentice to John Patrick Wright and Thomas Middleton Murray.—Son of David Dougal, W.S. *Born* 13 November 1892. *Married* 27 September 1918, Grace (*died* 12 March 1981), daughter of Alexander Kennedy Stewart, Chemist, Edinburgh. War Service: Lieutenant in R.G.A. *Died* 20 November 1973. *Firm*— J. L. Hill, Dougal, and Co.

DOUGAL, DAVID [16 January 1888]. Apprentice to William C. M'Ewen.—Son of Alexander Dougal, Linlithgow. *Born* 14 April 1864. *Married* 17 February 1892, Annie Hogarth (*died* 9 September 1936), daughter of Robert Miller, Merchant, Kilmarnock. *Died* 28 September 1934. *Firm*—J. L. Hill, Dougal, and Co.

DOUGAL, DAVID STEWART, B.L. [15 July 1949]. Apprentice to Alexander Dougal of J. L. Hill, Dougal & Co.—Son of Alexander Dougal, W.S., Edinburgh. *Born* 4 September 1920. *Married* 2 April 1958, Magaret Ethel, daughter of Robert Duncan. Major, Royal Signals 1940-46. Served in Burma. *Firms*—(1) J. L. Hill, Dougal & Co.; (2) Menzies Dougal & Milligan (after amalgamation).

DOUGLAS, ALEXANDER, OF BAITFORD [6 April 1630]. Apprentice to Robert Pringle.— Son of —— Douglas of Stobbs. *Married* (1) 30 June 1629, Agnes Pringle; (2) Agnes Lowrie (*died* 21 July 1695). *Died* before 1666.

DOUGLAS, ALEXANDER, OF CHESTERHOUSE [1 July 1808]. Apprentice to James Dundas.—Third son of Dr Christopher Douglas, Physician in Kelso. *Born* 19 June 1780. *Married* 20 March 1810. Janet Hardie (*died* 27 November 1856), second daughter of Robert Bow, Merchant in Edinburgh. Fiscal, 1844-51. His portrait by Sir John Watson Gordon, P.R.S.A., was bequeathed to the Society by his son Alexander Sholto Douglas, W.S. *Died* 1 July 1851.

DOUGLAS, ALEXANDER SHOLTO, OF GATESHAW [16 November 1854]. Apprentice to John Dundas, William Wilson, and Alexander M. Bell.—Son of Alexander Douglas, W.S. *Born* 27 November 1829. *Married* 16 December 1858, Helen M'Caul (*died* 16 November 1909), daughter of John Forrester, W.S. *Died* 4 August 1916.

DOUGLAS, CHRISTOPHER, OF CHESTERHOUSE [13 November 1834]. Apprentice to James and John Dundas.—Eldest son of Alexander Douglas, W.S. *Born* 13 February 1811. *Died* 11 November 1894, unmarried.

DOUGLAS, DAVID [15 December 1825]. Apprentice to Robert Rutherford.—Third son of James Douglas, Writer in Dunfermline. *Married* 26 December 1838, Margaret Lawson (*died* 4 August 1894), second daughter of Charles Hill of Luthrie, Fife. *Died* 6 September 1886.

DOUGLAS, DUNCAN SCOTT. *See* Scott Douglas.

DOUGLAS, HUGH SCOTT. *See* Scott Douglas.

DOUGLAS, JAMES [Before 1498].

DOUGLAS, JOHN [4 December 1794]. Apprentice to John Gordon.—Son of John Douglas of Burnhouse. *Born* 1768. *Died* 6 January 1854, unmarried.

DOUGLAS, JOHN BROWN [7 March 1833]. Apprentice to, and second son of, William Douglas, W.S. *Born* 25 August 1809. *Married* 22 January 1846, Mary Ann (*died* 28 April 1910), second daughter of John Turner of Turnerhall, Aberdeenshire. *Died* 28 April 1880.

DOUGLAS, JOHN BROWN [17 July 1879]. Apprentice to, and son of, John Brown Douglas, W.S.—*Born* 30 May 1852. *Married* 1 June 1882, Emma Jane (*died* 27 September 1938), daughter of Thomas Overy West, Seven-Score, Kent. *Died* 2 January 1908.

DOUGLAS, WALTER [8 January 1666]. Apprentice to, and son of, Alexander Douglas, W.S.—*Born* 31 December 1633. *Buried* 26 December 1666.

DOUGLAS, WILLIAM [23 November 1802]. Apprentice to Bain Whyt.—Son of Archibald Douglas, S.S.C., Edinburgh. *Born* 26 February 1781. *Married* 15 December 1806, Anna (*died* 28 April 1865), daughter of Captain John Brown of Broadchapel, Lochmaben. *Died* 16 July 1841.

DOUGLAS, WILLIAM ALEXANDER SCOTT. *See* Scott Douglas.

DOUGLAS, WILLIAM ROBIN, B.L. [25 April 1960]. Apprentice to Charles Stewart Henderson of Patrick & James.—Son of Archibald Douglas, Banker, Edinburgh. *Born* 17 October 1931. *Married* 18 October 1957, Margaret Amos, daughter of Laurence Littlejohn, Engineer. *Firm*—Patrick & James.

DOW, JOHN [7 July 1808]. Apprentice to James Hay.—Eldest son of Lieutenant Archibald Dow, Royal Navy. *Married* 11 July 1820, Margaret (*died* 24 March 1863), eldest daughter of William Russell, Glasgow. *Died* 5 October 1827, aged 43.

DOWIE, PETER [28 March 1898]. Apprentice to John Ross.—Son of Thomas Dowie, S.S.C., Leith. *Born* 9 April 1872. *Died* 9 May 1931, unmarried.

DREW, JAMES [12 December 1911]. Apprentice to H. Inglis Lindsay.—Son of John Drew, Coachbuilder, Edinburgh. *Born* 14 December 1867. *Died* 24 May 1917.

DRUMMOND, ALEXANDER [14 November 1684]. Apprentice to James Hay.—Son of Alexander Drummond, Bailie of Cockenzie. *Married* (contract, August 1690), Elizabeth, relict of David Balfour, Merchant, Cockenzie. *Died* December 1694.

DRUMMOND, CHARLES [10 December 1900]. Apprentice to John Blair.—Son of William Drummond, S.S.C., Edinburgh. *Born* 23 July 1877. *Married* 22 August 1904, Frances Marie Edgeworth (*died* 24 February 1957), elder daughter of Richard William Hunt, late of the Civil Service. *Died* at Burntisland, 6 August 1928.

DRUMMOND, SIR FRANCIS WALKER, OF HAWTHORNDEN, BART. [23 June 1807]. Apprentice to, and eldest son of, James Walker, W.S.—*Born* 9 June 1781. *Married* 4 January 1810, Margaret (*died* 14 May 1875), only daughter of Captain Sir John Forbes Drummond of Hawthornden, Bart., when he assumed her name and arms. Succeeded his father-in-law as second Baronet in terms of patent, 23 May 1829. *Died* 29 February 1844.

DRUMMOND, JAMES [8 October 1705]. Apprentice to Ronald Campbell.—*Married* July 1708, Violet, daughter of Thomas Bordlands of King's Stables. *Died* 1718.

DRUMMOND, JAMES, OF COMRIE [1 August 1788]. Apprentice to Thomas Tod.—Eldest son of Patrick Drummond of Comrie, Perthshire. *Married* 1 August 1792, Eliza, daughter of John Somners, Writer, Edinburgh. *Died* 1 February 1800.

DRUMMOND, JAMES [2 November 1881]. Apprentice to William Alexander Maclaren.—Son of Rev. James Drummond, Irvine. *Born* 9 April 1858. *Died* 9 August 1902, unmarried.

DRUMMOND, JOHN FORBES WALKER [16 November 1843]. Apprentice to, and third son of, Sir Francis Walker Drummond of Hawthornden, Bart., W.S. *Born* 19 January 1819. *Married* 11 September 1866, Emma Louisa (*died* 23 June 1920), youngest daughter of Butler Edmond Thornton of Skerton and Whittington, Lancashire. *Died* at Ednam House, Kelso, 4 June 1896.

DRUMMOND, PETER (FORMERLY PIERRE) WILLIAM [12 March 1893]. Apprentice to Thomas Dawson Brodie.—Son of Peter Robert Drummond, sometime Bookseller in Perth, thereafter Farmer at Balmblair, near Perth. *Born* 25 August 1857. *Married* 14 July 1897, Agnes Clark (*died* 29 September 1914), eldest daughter of James Thomson, Dundee. *Died* 18 February 1931.

DRUMMOND, WILLIAM OMAN, B.L. [11 July 1932]. Apprentice to William C. Hunter and Another of Bonar, Hunter & Johnstone.—Son of William Drummond, S.S.C., Edinburgh. *Born* 26 June 1907. *Married* 9 June 1938, Kathleen Elinor Mary (*died* 18 November 1981), daughter of Charles Shepley Kitching, Dominica, British West Indies. Major, Military Government. Served U.K. and N.W. Europe 1940-45. *Died* 25 February 1965. *Firm*—Drummond & Frazer.

DRYSDALE, NEIL, LL.B. [9 December 1980*].—Son of Stuart Drysdale, Solicitor, Crieff. *Born* 4 September 1955. *Married* 28 February 1980, Miriam, daughter of Rev. James Little, Dundee. *Firm*—Colville & Drysdale, Crieff.

DRYSDALE, THOMAS HENRY, LL.B. [30 April 1970]. Apprentice to James Stewart and Others of Shepherd & Wedderburn.—Son of Ian Drysdale, Chartered Engineer, Buchlyvie, Stirlingshire. *Born* 23 November 1942. *Married* 18 March 1967, Caroline, daughter of Dr Gavin Shaw, Glasgow. *Firm*—Shepherd & Wedderburn.

DRYSDALE, SIR WILLIAM, OF PITTEUCHAR [2 March 1804]. Apprentice to James Buchan.—Son of William Drysdale of Pitteuchar, Fife. *Born* 1776. *Married* (1) 30 October 1809, Jane (*died* 18 November 1812), only daughter of Rev. Alexander Fleming, D.D., Minister of Hamilton; (2) 7 September 1813, Jane (*died* 10 November 1818), only child of Thomas Cochrane of Burnside, M.D., Edinburgh; and (3) 7 November 1820, Elizabeth (*died* 5 April 1887), daughter of John Pew of Hillowtown, Kirkcudbright, and widow of William Copland of Colliston, Dumfriesshire. *Died* 4 June 1843.

DUCAT, JAMES STEWART [18 November 1830]. Apprentice to Warren Hastings Sands.—Son of Charles Ducat of Fullarton. *Married* 9 September 1834, Catherine (*died* 6 April 1887), daughter of James Steele, Surgeon, 52nd Regiment. *Died* 10 April 1853, aged 50.

DUDGEON, JOHN [28 May 1819]. Apprentice to (1) James Gilchrist; and (2) David Welsh.—Fourth son of John Dudgeon, Merchant in Leith. *Born* 11 August 1796. *Married* 22 October 1822, Isabella, daughter of John Falconer, Merchant in Glasgow. *Died* 30 August 1887.

DUDGEON, PATRICK, of East Craig [18 December 1823]. Apprentice to William Bell.—Eldest son of John Dudgeon of East Craig, East Lothian. *Born* 1798. *Married* 2 June 1822, Jane Alexandria (*died* 29 April 1868), eldest daughter of Lieut.-Colonel Alexander Duncan, H.E.I.C.S. *Died* 10 October 1846.

DUDGEON, WILLIAM CUNNINGHAM [12 January 1891]. Apprentice to George T. Balfour-Kinnear, R. Beatson, Ernest Hamilton, and James Balfour-Kinnear.—Son of Alexander Dudgeon, Farmer, Humbie, Kirkliston. *Born* 1 December 1866. Treasurer, John Watson's Institution. War Service: Major in the Royal Scots, 1914-18. *Died* 24 July 1935. *Firm*—Dudgeon and Farmer.

DUFF, ALEXANDER [30 January 1823]. Apprentice to Æneas Macbean.—Fourth son of Patrick Duff, Sheriff-Clerk of Elginshire. Author of a *Treatise on Feudal Conveyancing*, 1838, and other legal works. Admitted Advocate, 9 December 1848. Presenter of Signatures, 1847-54. *Died* 24 September 1854, aged 54, unmarried.

DUFF, JOHN DUNBAR [14 April 1884]. Apprentice to John Ross.—Son of Captain Sir Benjamin Duff, Glen-Arthur, Duddingston. *Born* 27 November 1854. Assistant Clerk and Extractor to the Signet, 1885-9. Clerk, Administrator of Justice, City Hall, Toronto. *Married* 26 February 1891, Margaret Graham (*died* 19 April 1934 at Toronto), youngest daughter of David Scott, Farmer, Meadowfield, Mid-Lothian. *Died* 28 November 1940.

DUFF, JOHN WHARTON WHARTON- [27 May 1869]. Apprentice to Thomas Graham Murray—Only son of John Robert Tod, W.S. *Born* 10 April 1845. *Married* 5 October 1869, Margaret Mary (*died* 10 February 1932), second daughter of John Ord Mackenzie of Dolphinton, W.S. Assumed the name of Wharton-Duff on succeeding, in 1904, to the Estate of Orton in the County of Elgin. Father of the Society on his death. *Died* 26 November 1935. He was a successful angler and landed salmon as late as October 1935, six months after his 90th birthday. *Firm*—Tods, Murray, and Jamieson.

DUFF, LACHLAN *See* Gordon, Lacahan Duff.

DUFF, PATRICK [23 July 1745]. Apprentice to Alexander Stevenson of Montgreenan.—Son of John Duff, Merchant in Elgin. *Married* Grizel, daughter of Sir Michael Balfour of Denmiln. *Died* 1765.

DUFF, RONALD ROXBURGH [13 May 1953]. Apprentice to David Blyth Bogle and Others of Lindsay, Howe & Co. *Born* 4 February 1931. *Firm*—A. & W. M. Urquhart.

DUFF, WILLIAM [12 August 1799]. Apprentice to Robert Donaldson.—Youngest son of Major Alexander Duff. *Died* 19 September 1809.

DUKE, GEORGE CARTNER, LL.B. [4 December 1967]. Apprentice to Professor A. J. McDonald of Dickie, Gray, McDonald & Fair, Dundee.—Son of Alexander R. Duke, Schoolmaster, Broughty Ferry, Dundee. *Born* 15 February 1944. *Married* 10 April 1970, Irene Susan Rolland, daughter of Robert W. Simpson.

DUKE, HAROLD LESLIE, M.A., LL.B. [19 December 1932]. Apprentice to James Little Mounsey and Another of John C. Brodie & Sons.—Son of Robert Whyte Duke, Linen Manufacturer, Brechin. Angus. *Born* 5 April 1907. *Married* 13 July 1940, Margaret Isobel, daughter of John Alexander Carnegie, Solicitor, Kirriemuir, Angus. *Firm*— Thomson & Baxter (formerly Mitchell & Baxter). (Retired 1974.)

DUMBRECK, JOHN [2 December 1824]. Apprentice to John Tweedie.—Eldest son of William Dumbreck, South Coates, Edinburgh. *Born* 1799. *Married* 10 November 1830, Euphemia, daughter of Charles Kinnear, Fingask. *Died* 3 November 1854.

DUN, ANDREW [31 May 1827]. Apprentice to (1) John Campbell and James Arnot; and (2) John Campbell, Jun.—Son of Andrew Dun, Rector of the Grammar School, Aberdeen. *Married* (1) Mary Ann Leslie (*died* 16 March 1839), daughter of John Rutherford of Hunthill; and (2) 26 July 1841, Mary Isabella (*died* 1871), daughter of Thomas Selby, Ipswich. *Died* 20 February 1854, aged 50.

DUNBAR, ALEXANDER [29 December 1682]. Apprentice to Alexander Home.—Son of Rev. James Dunbar, Minister of Abbey St Bathans. *Married* 13 December 1681, Catherine Hamilton.

DUNBAR, ARCHIBALD [25 November 1796]. Apprentice to John Innes.—Youngest son of William Dunbar of Netherbuckie. *Born* 24 July 1771. *Died* 19 June 1809.

DUNBAR, KEITH [19 December 1767]. Apprentice to Colquhoun Grant.—Second son of Sir William Dunbar of Durn, Banffshire. Depute Clerk of Session, 14 June 1780 till death. *Died* 1 April 1799, unmarried.

DUNBAR, KENNETH WATSON, LL.B. [12 December 1977]. Apprentice to Stephen Michael Seaman and Another of Archibald Campbell & Harley.—Son of Samuel Dunbar, Company Director, Greenock. *Born* 19 May 1947. *Married* 28 August 1974, Janet Torrance, daughter of William Wilson, Farmer, Gifford, East Lothian. *Firm*— Archibald Campbell & Harley.

DUNBAR, RONALD [27 January 1729]. Apprentice to Ronald Campbell,—*Married* December 1729, Margaret (*died* 25 February 1761), daughter of Ronald Campbell of Balerno, W.S. Appointed Clerk of the General Register of Hornings, 9 March 1728. Agent for City of Edinburgh. Fiscal, 1734-53. *Died* 23 December 1753.

DUNBAR, WILLIAM [4 July 1769]. Apprentice to Thomas Brodie.—Third son of Alexander Dunbar of Boath, Nairnshire. *Died* 18 February 1807, unmarried.

DUNCAN, ALEXANDER [25 November 1765]. Apprentice to James Graham.—Third son of Alexander Duncan, Clerk, of Dundee. *Married*, proclaimed 13 November 1768, Mary, daughter of John Simpson of Brunton, Fife. *Died* 10 November 1821.

DUNCAN, ANDREW GORDON MACAULAY, M.A., LL.B. [31 December 1941]. Apprentice to Charles Law Forbes of Aitken, Methuen & Aikman. *Born* 4 August 1914. *Firm*—Gordon Falconer & Fairweather (1947-62). Lecturer and latterly Senior Lecturer, Faculty of Law, University of Edinburgh, 1962-81.

DUNCAN, ANDREW JOHN [11 July 1837]. Apprentice to James Greig.—Youngest son of Andrew Duncan, Printer Glasgow. *Born* 24 June 1814. *Died* 7 June 1848, unmarried.

DUNCAN, GEORGE [19 November 1708]. Apprentice to Ronald Campbell.—Son of Alexander Duncan of Lundie. *Born* 21 March 1682. *Married* (1) 31 December 1708, Helen (*died* 1720), daughter of James Balfour, Merchant, Edinburgh; and (2) 10 March 1722, Jean Lidderdale. Town Clerk of Dundee. *Died* 1723.

DUNCAN, JAMES [17 February 1825]. Apprentice to William Bell.—Son of James Duncan, residing in Falkirk. *Born* 1797. *Married* 30 August 1842, Christina (*died* 7 January 1897), only daughter of John Duncan, Edinburgh. *Died* 27 September 1874.

DUNCAN, JAMES BARKER [14 November 1866]. Apprentice to, and eldest son of, James Duncan, W.S.—*Born* 25 May 1843. *Married* 3 April 1873, Louisa Janet (*died* 20 July 1920), fourth daughter of Alexander Brodie, Stirling. *Died* 30 January 1904. *Firm*—Duncan and Black.

DUNCAN, JOHN [27 June 1833]. Apprentice to James Farquhar Gordon.—Son of John Duncan, residing in Princes Street, Edinburgh. *Born* 23 November 1806. *Married* 17 September 1839, Janet, youngest daughter of Thomas Metcalf, Edinburgh. *Died* 21 June 1900.

DUNCAN, MALCOLM McGREGOR, M.A., LL.B. [21 March 1949]. Apprentice to Robert McCosh and Others of Gillespie & Paterson.—Son of the Rev. Reginald Duncan, Edinburgh. *Born* 23 January 1922. *Married* 24 July 1954, Winifred Petrie, daughter of Alexander Greenhorn. Flight Lieutenant R.A.F. 1942-46. Director of Administration, Edinburgh District Council.

DUNCAN, STUART, LL.B. [12 May 1980*].—Son of Charles Edward Duncan, Aberdeen. *Born* 22 July 1953. *Married* 4 November 1978, Avril Dorothy Munro, daughter of Colonel John Munro Wotherspoon, W.S., Inverness. *Firm*—A. C. Bennett & Fairweather.

DUNCAN, WILLIAM [8 July 1822]. Apprentice to Robert Cargill.—Son of John Duncan, Manufacturer in Kirkcaldy. *Born* 1794. *Married* Sylvester Ramsay (*died* 1862). *Died* 16 October 1837.

DUNCAN, WILLIAM THREIPLAND, OF DANEVALE PARK [16 July 1888]. Apprentice to (1) E. C. Cuningham; and (2) J. R. Anderson and W. H. Murray.—Eldest son of William Duncan of Danevale Park, Kirkcudbright, S.S.C. *Born* 1 December 1859. *Died* at Lerwick, 15 September 1898.

DUNDAS, DAVID ANDREW, M.A., LL.B. [14 September 1939]. Apprentice to J. Miller Thomson and Another of J. Miller Thomson & Co.—Son of George Dundas, Solicitor and Honorary Sheriff Substitute, Kirriemuir. *Born* 17 August 1915. Lieutenant Colonel, Army General List. Served U.K. and Middle East 1940-45. Mentioned in Despatches 1941. Thow Scholarship in Conveyancing (Edinburgh University), 1938. *Died* 9 July 1946. *Firm*—Wilkie & Dundas, Kirriemuir.

DUNDAS, JAMES HAMILTON [9 July 1829]. Apprentice to Walter Cook.—Second son of Gabriel Hamilton Dundas of Duddingston, Linlithgowshire. *Died* 7 October 1851, aged 45, unmarried.

DUNDAS, JAMES, OF OCHTERTYRE [28 November 1791]. Apprentice to James Robertson Barclay.—Fourth son of Ralph Dundas, Merchant in Edinburgh. *Born* 1752. *Married* 16 October 1794, Elizabeth, third daughter of William Graham of Airth. Depute Director in Chancery. *Died* 2 April 1831.

DUNDAS, JAMES KER, M.A., LL.B. [19 November 1951]. Apprentice to Robert Strathern Lindsay and Another of Lindsay, Duncan & Black.—Son of Adam Dundas, Shopkeeper. *Born* 1 January 1925. *Married* 15 September 1954, Mina Isabel, daughter of James Early. Served as Able Seaman R.N.V.R. 1943-46 in the Atlantic, Normandy, South East Asia and Australia. Called to Canadian Bar 1958. Q.C. 1973. Became a Canadian citizen 1968.

DUNDAS, JOHN [11 December 1769]. Apprentice to Charles Brown.—Son of James Dundas of Philipstoun, Linlithgowshire, Advocate. *Married* Katherine (*died* 3 December 1815), only daughter of Robert Smith, Surgeon, of Browsterlands family. Conjunct Town Clerk of Edinburgh, 13 January 1771. *Died* 4 May 1816.

DUNDAS, JOHN [29 June 1826]. Apprentice to Ralph James Dundas.—Fifth son of James Dundas, W.S. *Born* 19 December 1803. *Married* Jemima Christian (*died* 19 July 1863), fifth daughter of Day Hort Macdowall of Walkinshaw, Renfrewshire. *Died* 7 May 1873.

DUNDAS, JOHN, OF NEWHALLS [31 March 1712]. Apprentice to James Anderson.—Fifth son of John Dundas of Duddingston, West Lothian. *Married* 30 April 1711, Christian, daughter of Adam Mure of Blackhall. Presenter of Signatures, 1718. Fiscal, 1723-5. Lyon Depute from 1 February 1728 to 1744. *Died* 22 April 1769, aged 87.

DUNDAS, RALPH [19 March 1868]. Apprentice to, and son of, John Dundas, W.S. *Born* 22 October 1843. *Married* 30 March 1869, Emily Bridget (*died* 12 March 1934), elder daughter of Robert Robertson of Auchleeks, Perthshire. *Died* at Winton Castle, 8 October 1911. *Firm*—Dundas and Wilson.

DUNDAS, RALPH JAMES [25 June 1819]. Apprentice to William Wilson.—Eldest son of James Dundas, W.S. *Born* 21 August 1795. *Died* 26 April 1824.

DUNDAS, SIR ROBERT, OF BEECHWOOD, BART. [24 November 1785]. Apprentice to James Balfour.—Only son of Rev. Robert Dundas, Minister of Humbie. *Born* 30 June 1761. *Married* 20 July 1798, Matilda (*died* May 1842), daughter of Archibald Cockburn, Baron of Exchequer. Principal Clerk of Session, 14 June 1817 to 31 December 1830. Deputy Keeper of Sasines. Clerk of the Bills, 1820. Deputy to the Lord Privy Seal. Succeeded his uncle, General Sir David Dundas, Bart. *Died* 26 December 1835.

DUNDAS, ROBERT NEVILL, B.A.(OXON) [16 January 1893]. Apprentice to Ralph Dundas, W. J. Dundas, and G. M. Paul.—Son of Rev. Robert James Dundas, Clerk in Holy Orders, Albury Rectory, Guildford, and Honorary Canon of Winchester. *Born* 14 January 1867. *Married* 9 April 1896, Cecil Mary (*died* 23 May 1949), youngest daughter of Henry Hill Lancaster, Advocate, Edinburgh. Author of a *Memoir* of his only son, Captain Henry L. N. Dundas, M.C., Scots Guards. Member of the King's Bodyguard for Scotland, Royal Company of Archers, 1910. *Died* 27 August 1941. *Firm*—Dundas and Wilson.

DUNDAS, ROBERT WILLIAM, M.C. [7 December 1908]. Apprentice to Ralph Dundas, W. J. Dundas, G. M. Paul, and R. Nevill Dundas.—Son of Ralph Dundas, W.S. *Born* 10 June 1881. *Married* 16 January 1909, Mary (*died* 27 November 1955), daughter of Colonel Wardlaw Ramsay of Whitehill and Tillicoultry. During War held Commission in 8th Royal Scots (T.F.) and served on H.Q. Lines of Communication, France; D.A.Q.M.G., Headquarters, Tank Corps; promoted Major, awarded M.C., and mentioned in Despatches. *Died* 27 November 1928.

DUNDAS, WILLIAM JOHN [13 July 1871]. Apprentice to John Dundas and William Wilson.—Fourth son of George Dundas, Advocate, one of the Senators of the College of Justice (Lord Manor). *Born* 16 March 1849. Crown Agent, 1895-1905. *Died* 9 July 1921. *Firm*—Dundas and Wilson.

DUNLOP, ALEXANDER [1606]. Apprentice to John Wardlaw.—Signs the Acts 17 January 1606. *Married* (1) 4 May 1608, Elizabeth Seton (*died* 18 May 1612); (2) Marian, daughter of John Tweedie of Drumelzier. *Died* 8 July 1619.

DUNLOP, ANDREW, OF BARNHILL [19 November 1835]. Apprentice to Hugh Macqueen.—Son of Thomas Dunlop, residing at Barnhill, near Glasgow. *Born* 23 May 1809. *Married* 23 July 1839, Jane Marion (*died* 1894), only daughter of Archibald Ronaldson, Leith. *Died* 30 October 1857.

DUNLOP, GEORGE [23 June 1807]. Apprentice to David Balfour.—Second son of James Dunlop of Garnkirk, Lanarkshire. *Born* 6 February 1776. *Married* 2 September 1807, Isobel (*died* 27 April 1837), second daughter of William Simpson of Ogle, Angus. *Died* 6 December 1852.

DUNLOP, GEORGE [26 December 1873]. Apprentice to Anthony Murray.—Son of George Dunlop, and grandson of George Dunlop, W.S. *Born* 26 February 1849. *Married* 5 August 1875, Georgie Isabella (*died* 7 May 1923), eldest daughter of Robert Bogle Blackburn, Advocate, Sheriff of Stirlingshire. *Died* 23 June 1922.

DUNLOP, JAMES, OF MACNAIRSTON [9 March 1813]. Apprentice to John Ferrier.—Eldest son of George Dunlop of Macnairston, Ayrshire. *Died* 16 August 1847, aged 66, unmarried.

DUNLOP, ROBERT [5 July 1821]. Apprentice to William Patrick.—Son of Robert Dunlop, Merchant in Irvine. *Married* 4 March 1822, Helen Straton (*died* 1872), only child of Dr James Dunbar Mudie, Physician in Alford, Lincolnshire. *Died* 5 July 1847, aged 50.

DUNLOP, WILLIAM JOHN MERCER, LL.B., OF COTGREEN [27 March 1911]. Apprentice to J. R. M. Wedderburn, G. G. Watson, and J. A. S. Carment.—Son of Rev. Thomas Mercer Dunlop, Minister of U.P. Church, Pollokshaws. *Born* 8 July 1885. *Married* 29 July 1913, Olive Cameron (*died* 21 March 1963), youngest daughter of John M. Macpherson, W.S. *Died* at West Linton, 25 May 1920.

DUNNETT, ALAN LINKLATER, LL.B. [29 April 1974]. Apprentice to James Ian Hay Smith and Others of Bell & Scott, Bruce & Kerr.—Son of William Dunnett, W.S., Edinburgh. *Born* 24 July 1950. *Married* 1 August 1975, Linda Weir McColl. *Firm*— Lindsay, Duncan & Black.

DUNNETT, WILLIAM, A.F.C., B.L. [20 December 1937]. Apprentice to Kenneth MacEwan of W. H. Mill & Co.—Son of the Rev. William Alexander Dunnett, O.B.E., B.D., Dalkeith. *Born* 18 September 1912. *Married* (1) Constance Mary (divorced), daughter of Henry D. Fairbairn; (2) 26 July 1947, Enid Ethel Daphne, daughter of William George Stuart. Squadron Leader R.A.F. 1940-45. Awarded A.F.C. September 1945. *Firm*—Lindsay, Duncan & Black.

DUNSIRE, THOMAS, M.A., LL.B. [20 November 1950]. Apprentice to (1) J. D. S. Paterson and Another of Robson, McLean & Paterson, and (2) James Milligan and Another of J. & J. Milligan.—Son of Thomas Dunsire, Engineer, Highbridge, Somerset. *Born* 16 November 1926. *Married* 17 December 1966, Jean Mary, daughter of John Wright. Former Assistant Clerk and Extractor to W.S. Society. Ordinary Seaman Royal Navy, Second World War. *Firm*—J. & J. Milligan, thereafter amalgamated with Morton, Smart, McDonald & Milligan (now Morton, Fraser & Milligan).

DUNSMURE, JOHN [17 May 1832]. Apprentice to David Cleghorn.—Son of James Dunsmure, Secretary to the Commissioners of the British Fisheries. *Born* 16 September 1808. *Married* 3 July 1845, Jane Margaretta (*died* July 1877), daughter of Robert Bourne, Camdenville, New South Wales. Attorney, Sydney, New South Wales. *Died* 29 September 1864.

DURBIN, JOHN TERRENCE, M.B.E., LL.B. [11 December 1979]. Apprentice to Andrew Gray Muir of Alan R. Fairlie & Co.—Son of George William Durbin, Aberdeenshire and Edinburgh. *Born* 2 April 1928. *Married* 15 August 1962, Jean Duncan, daughter of Lieut.-Colonel H. B. Creighton, Singapore. *Firm*—Garden, Haig-Scott & Wallace.

DURLAC, MAURICE NICHOLSON, M.B.E., B.L. [19 March 1934]. Apprentice to P. Furneaux Dawson.—Son of Maurice William Durlac. *Born* 5 March 1910. Major R.A. Served U.K. and N.W. Europe 1940-45. *Died* 23 September 1970. *Firm*—Allan, Dawson, Simpson & Hampton.

DUTHIE, WALTER, OF BURNSIDE [10 March 1817]. Apprentice to William Handyside.—Son of Alexander Duthie, Advocate in Aberdeen. *Born* 1795. *Died* 30 September 1868.

DYCE, PETER [28 March 1927]. Apprentice to George P. Normand.—Son of Peter Dyce, Hotel Keeper, Corstorphine. *Born* 12 December 1902. Barrister and Solicitor in the Supreme Court of Nigeria, 1930. *Married* 14 September 1940, Edith Bottomley. *Died* 1 September 1941.

DYKES, WILLIAM [4 June 1690]. Apprentice to William Thomson, yr. *Married* (contract, 9 February 1692), Euphan Ramsay. *Died* before 1696.

DYKES, WILLIAM SHEDDEN, OF DARNACONNER [12 April 1886]. Apprentice to James Bruce and Thomas Kerr.—Son of the Rev. Thomas Dykes, D.D., Minister of Ayr. *Born* 18 June 1860. *Married* 30 July 1889, Flora (*died* 26 October 1934), youngest daughter of Alexander Maclean Hunter, sometime of Balla Balla, Cranbourne, Australia, and granddaughter of Alexander Hunter, W.S. *Died* 25 January 1907.

DYMOCK, JOHN [22 June 1826]. Apprentice to, and son of, William Dymock, W.S.—*Married* 14 July 1831, Margaret (*died* 1870), eldest daughter of John Waugh. *Died* 17 February 1841.

DYMOCK, WILLIAM [10 July 1811]. Apprentice to (1) Samuel MacKnight; and (2) Henry Moncreiff.—*Married* Helen (*died* 3 October 1852), daughter of William Maclean, Merchant, Edinburgh. *Died* 3 June 1826.

DYMOCK, WILLIAM M'LEAN [22 February 1838]. Apprentice to, and son of, William Dymock, W.S.—*Born* 27 March 1800. *Married* 12 June 1838, Margaret (*died* 29 December 1883), daughter of Charles Watson, Cabinetmaker, Edinburgh. *Died* 12 June 1848.

EASON, JOHN PATRICK, M.B.E., B.L. [19 March 1934]. Apprentice to William Babington and Others of Melville & Lindesay.—Son of Dr John Eason, Edinburgh. *Born* 8 September 1910. Lt. Col. Infantry. Served U.K., U.S.A., North Africa, India and Burma, 1939-44. Twice mentioned in Despatches. *Died* on active service in India 26 May 1944. *Firm*—Melville & Lindesay.

EASTERBROOK, SIDNEY ARTHUR FRANK, B.A.(CANTAB), LL.B. [16 March 1936]. Apprentice to A. S. Blair and Others of Strathern & Blair.—Son of Charles Cromhall Easterbrook, M.D., Dumfries. *Born* 13 August 1910. Captain R.A. (Heavy A.A.) Served U.K. and Middle East 1940-45. *Firm*—Baillie & Gifford (1946-58).

EASTON, HARRY MONTGOMERIE [27 March 1899]. Apprentice to R. B. Ranken.—Son of the Rev. James Cruickshank Easton, Minister of the Parish of Meldrum, Aberdeenshire. *Born* 31 August 1867. *Died* 28 March 1932.

EASTON, JAMES [6 June 1815]. Apprentice to James Horne.—Second son of Robert Easton of Strathmiln. *Died* 24 April 1820.

EASTON, JOHN, OF COUSTOUNE [Before 1594]. Commissioner, 1 June 1607. *Married* Margaret Cant. *Died* 25 January 1616.

EATON, HUGH WEMYSS [29 March 1926]. Apprentice to Euan B. Robertson.—Son of David Wemyss Eaton, Edinburgh. *Born* 23 January 1887. *Married* 31 August 1922, Jennie Margaret, daughter of Alex. Orr Symington, Civil Engineer. Lecturer on Evidence and Procedure, Edinburgh University, April 1930. War Service: Lieutenant Royal Scots, 1915-16; Staff-Captain R.F.C., 1917-19. Killed in a railway accident at Goswick, Northumberland, 26 October 1947, together with his wife. *Firm*—J. and R. A. Robertson.

ECCLES, ALEXANDER CHARLES WILLIAM ANDERSON, R.D., B.A.(CANTAB), LL.B. [30 November 1959]. Apprentice to James Robert Leslie Cruickshank and Another of Menzies & White.—Son of Herbert Anderson Eccles, Medical Practitioner, Philadelphia, Co. Durham. *Born* 8 January 1933. *Married* 17 June 1960, Judith Margaret, daughter of Gordon Patrick Hardy, M.P.S. *Firm*—J. L. Anderson, Gardner & Co., Cupar and Kinross.

EDGAR, JOHN, OF BRIDGELANDS [2 July 1771]. Apprentice to Charles Brown.—Eldest son of Peter Edgar of Bridgelands, Mid-Lothian. *Died* 8 July 1799, unmarried.

EDGAR, THOMAS [1627]. Signs the Acts, 28 December 1627. Clerk to the Incorporation of Chirurgeons, 1619. *Died* 1646.

EDGER, THOMAS. *Married* 11 November 1647, Bethea Maxwell. *Died* 1655.

EDMONSTOUN, WILLIAM, OF GLASS [14 July 1701]. Apprentice to Charles Row.— *Married* 3 August 1699, Isabella, daughter of John Nasmyth. *Died* 6 September 1722.

EDWARDS, JAMES RITCHIE PEACOCK [14 December 1896]. Apprentice to William Garson.—Son of William Peacock Edwards, S.S.C., Edinburgh. *Born* 18 April 1872. *Died* 12 October 1905, unmarried.

EDWARDS, ROBIN ANTHONY, C.B.E., M.A., LL.B. [30 November 1964]. Apprentice to Alastair Campbell Blair and Others of Davidson & Syme.—Son of Alfred Walton Edwards, Bank Accountant, Edinburgh. *Born* 7 April 1939. *Married* 31 August 1974, Elizabeth Alexander, daughter of David Mackay, Master Butcher, Annan. President of the Law Society of Scotland 1979-80. *Firm*—Dundas & Wilson (formerly Davidson & Syme).

ELDER, ARCHIBALD HENDERSON, M.A., LL.B. [16 March 1936]. Apprentice to Thomas Johnstone Carlyle Gifford and Another of Baillie & Gifford.—Son of William Elder, M.D., Leith. *Born* 5 June 1911. *Married* 22 December 1939, Helen Macdonald, daughter of John Maclennan. Captain K.O.S.B. Served U.K. and North West Europe 1939-45. Mentioned in Despatches for gallant and distinguished services in N.W. Europe, May 1945. Author of *Forms of Wills in accordance with the Law of Scotland*, 1947. *Firm*—Bell & Scott, Bruce & Kerr (formerly R.C. Bell & J. Scott). (Retired 1978.)

ELDER, JAMES [25 January 1855]. Apprentice to George Dalziel.—Third son of George Elder, Farmer, Grange, Banffshire. *Born* 29 July 1818. *Married* 24 June 1854, Susan Mary (*died* 19 June 1900), youngest daughter of Captain James Macdonald of Dalness, 61st Regiment. *Died* 1 April 1876.

ELDER, JOHN [8 February 1816]. Apprentice to Andrew Storie.—Eldest son of John Elder, Depute Clerk of Session. *Born* 3 April 1790. *Married* 10 October 1849, Jane Gibbs, only daughter of William Campbell, Merchant, Oporto. *Died* 9 February 1869.

ELDER, JOHN [28 June 1878]. Apprentice to W. J. Menzies and H. J. Coventry.—Son of John Elder, W.S. *Born* 28 July 1854. *Married* 24 February 1886, Mary Robertson (*died* 19 May 1949), daughter of Alexander Henderson, Montreal, Canada. *Died* 12 March 1895.

ELIES, THOMAS [19 September 1697]. Apprentice to James Anderson.—Son of James Elies of Southside, Mid-Lothian. *Married* (1) Janet, daughter of Francis Scott, Keeper of the Minute Book; and (2) Helen, daughter of John Hay, Under Clerk of Session. *Died* 8 March 1709.

ELLIOT, BARBARA RACHEL, LL.B. [11 December 1978]. Apprentice to Charles Kenneth Murray and Others of Gillespie, Macandrew & Co.—Daughter of Benjamin Aikman Elliot, Machine-room Overseer, Edinburgh Evening News and Dispatch, Edinburgh. *Born* 25 May 1952. *Firm*—Gillespie, Macandrew & Co.

ELLIOT, CORNELIUS, OF WOLFLEE [3 July 1758]. Apprentice to William Budge.—Eldest surviving son of William Elliot of Wolflee, Roxburghshire, Writer in Edinburgh. *Born* 13 April 1733. *Married* 8 August 1765, Margaret (*died* 7 October 1796), daughter of James Rannie, Wine Merchant, Leith. *Died* 9 February 1821.

ELLIOT, DONALD GEORGE, LL.B. [8 December 1975]. Apprentice to J. D. L. McIntosh and Others of Boyd, Jameson & Young.—Son of Andrew James Stenhouse Elliot, M.C., Company Director, Lasswade. *Born* 25 March 1951. *Married* 29 March 1978, Anne Marie McMorrow. *Firm*— Rollo, Steven & Bond, Dundee.

ELLIOT, JAMES, OF WOLFLEE [10 July 1798]. Apprentice to, and youngest son of, Cornelius Elliot, W.S. *Born* 29 February 1772. *Married* (1) 9 September 1799, Caroline (*died* 25 April 1824), daughter of Walter Hunter of Polmood, Peeblesshire; and (2) 17 January 1827, Margaret (*died* 6 August 1856), daughter of Robert Davidson of Pinnacle Hill, Roxburghshire. *Died* 2 February 1855.

ELLIOT, JOHN [14 April 1694]. Apprentice to Andrew Baillie.—Son of Rev. Robert Elliot. *Married* November 1691, Elizabeth, daughter of Rev. James Fithie. Granted £100 Scots on 7 August 1699 to take him to the Scots Colony of Darien. *Died* abroad, October 1699.

ELLIOT, ROBERT JOHN, LL.B. [6 December 1971]. Apprentice to Paul Nicholas Robert Harding-Edgar and Another of Lindsays.—Son of R. T. Elliot, Farmer, Kelso. *Born* 18 January 1947. *Married* 25 March 1971, Christine Ann, daughter of William Rae Glencross, Paper Converter, Glasgow. *Firm*—Lindsays.

ELLIOT, WILLIAM SCOTT, OF ARKLETON [13 June 1833]. Apprentice to (1) George Lyon; and (2) William Bell.—Son of Adam Scott of Arkleton, Dumfriesshire, Merchant in Leith. *Born* 22 March 1811. *Married* 6 March 1848, Margaret (*died* 16 March 1911), daughter of Lewis A. Wallace, Architect, Edinburgh. *Died* 20 May 1901.

ELLIOT-BATES, REV. JOHN ELPHINSTONE, OF MILLBOURNE [11 July 1833]. Apprentice to William Bell.—Fourth son of James Elliot of Wolflee, W.S. *Born* 27 May 1810. *Married* 8 March 1843, Georgina (*died* 7 November 1891), third daughter of Colonel Ralph Bates, whose name he assumed. Rector of Whalton, Northumberland. *Died* 1 January 1890.

ELLIOTT, ANDREW KIRKWOOD McCOSH, B.A.(CANTAB), LL.B. [17 November 1952]. Apprentice to Robert Francis Shepherd and Others of Shepherd & Wedderburn.—Son of Professor Thomas Renton Elliott, C.B.E., D.S.O., F.R.S. *Born* 9 November 1924. Served with Scots Guards (3rd Battalion) 1943-47 in Germany. *Firm*— Gillespie, McAndrew & Co. (formerly Gillespie & Paterson and Hope, Todd & Kirk).

ELLIS, ADAM GIB [9 December 1817]. Apprentice to William Dymock.—Son of William Ellis, S.S.C. *Born* 1794. *Married* 8 August 1823, Catherine (*died* 3 February 1853), third daughter of Major David Robertson, Assistant Barrack-Master-General, Edinburgh. Fiscal, 1851-64. *Died* 13 May 1864.

ELLIS, ROBERT [29 May 1828]. Apprentice to Adam Gib Ellis, his brother.—Son of William Ellis, S.S.C., Edinburgh. *Married* 16 July 1829, Margaret Gillespie (*died* 11 January 1851), eldest daughter of Rev. Dr Mitchell, Newtonhill. *Died* 18 July 1868, aged 72.

ELLIS, WILLIAM [15 November 1860]. Apprentice to, and son of, Robert Ellis, W.S.—*Born* 22 July 1830. *Died* in Switzerland, 8 September 1893, unmarried.

ELPHINSTONE, Sir JAMES, of Logie, Bart. [16 August 1671]. Apprentice to Archibald Nisbet.—Son of William Elphinstone of Ressaviot. *Married* 2 September 1673, Cecilia (*died* 10 November 1706), daughter of John Denholm of Muirhouse. Created a Baronet, 2 December 1701, "for his pure zeall to King William's Government." Commissary of Edinburgh, November 1679. Keeper of the Signet, 1691-6. M.P. Aberdeenshire, 1693-1702. *Died* 10 March 1722, aged 78.

ERSKINE, DAVID [18 June 1764]. Apprentice to (1) Hew Crawford; and (2) James Robertson Barclay.—Fourth son of John Erskine of Carnock and Cardross, Advocate. *Married* 29th April 1781, Ann (*died* 10 March 1836), daughter of William Graham of Airth, Stirlingshire. *Died* at Naples, 5 April 1791.

ERSKINE, DAVID, of Cardross [8 July 1796]. Apprentice to David Erskine and James Dundas.—Fourth son of James Erskine of Cardross, Perthshire. *Born* 10 January 1772. *Married* 5 September 1803, Hon. Keith Elphinstone (*died* 4 August 1841), fourth daughter of John, eleventh Lord Elphinstone. *Died* 28 November 1847.

ERSKINE, NORMAN ALEXANDER, LL.B. [11 December 1979*].—Son of William Erskine, Railwayman, Dunfermline. Born 2 December 1944. *Married* 18 December 1965, Sheena Christine, daughter of William Yule, Miner.

ERSKINE, ROBERT [16 August 1700]. Apprentice to Robert Watson.—*Died* before 1715.

ERSKINE, STUART, M.A., LL.B. [15 March 1937]. Apprentice to J. Miller Thomson and Another of J. Miller Thomson & Co.—Son of William Erskine, Draper, Dunfermline. *Born* 18 January 1906. Flight Lieutenant R.A.F. Served U.K. 1942-45. *Died* 10 October 1959. *Firms*—(1) Shield & Purvis; (2) Chalmers & Hore.

ESSERY, MICHAEL JOHN, LL.B. [17 July 1972]. Apprentice to Edward Graham Marquis and Others of J. & F. Anderson.—Son of Lawrence Harry Essery, Shipwright. *Born* 22 November 1940. *Married* 15 April 1968, Rhoda Janet Margaret, daughter of J. D. M. Hardie, O.B.E. *Firm*—J. & F. Anderson.

ESSON, GEORGE AULDJO [24 March 1873]. Apprentice to T. G. Murray and J. A. Jamieson.—Eldest surviving son of George Auldjo Esson, C.A. *Born* 25 January 1849. Became a Stockbroker. *Died* October 1922.

ESSON, THOMAS SKENE [27 January 1882]. Apprentice to Frederick Pitman.—Second surviving son of George Auldjo Esson, C.A. *Born* 29 January 1858. *Married* 12 September 1889, Elizabeth Reid (*died* 9 May 1938), youngest daughter of James Simpson Fleming, Cashier, Royal Bank of Scotland. Member of the King's Bodyguard for Scotland, Royal Company of Archers, 1903. *Died* 27 April 1947. *Firm*—Tods, Murray, and Jamieson.

EWART, JOHN [20 October 1884]. Apprentice to John Turnbull.—Eldest son of James Ewart of Southland, New Zealand. *Born* 8 September 1852. *Married* 10 January 1899, Catherine Helen (*died* 21 February 1958), eldest daughter of Lieut.-Colonel Charles May Allan Morant, late 4th Madras Cavalry, and granddaughter of Mrs Telfer Smollett of Bonhill. *Died* 28 May 1930.

EWART, THEODOSIUS FORREST [16 November 1837]. Apprentice to William Grierson.—Son of David Ewart, Depute Clerk of Chancery. *Born* 30 September 1813. Assistant Clerk of Chancery, 1837-48. *Died* 16 April 1848, unmarried.

EWART, THOMAS [21 November 1815]. Apprentice to Sir Henry Jardine.—Son of David Ewart, Depute Clerk of Chancery. *Born* 1791. *Married* 16 September 1828, Alicia (*died* 1882), daughter of Thomas Yorstoun, Chamberlain to the Duke of Queensberry. Struck off Roll, 15 February 1830, on conviction for embezzlement, etc., and sentence of outlawry. *Died* at Charleston, 6 March 1831.

EWEN, IAN DUGUID, B.L., B.Com. [29 April 1968]. (By Rule IX(a).)—Son of Victor Ewen, Insurance Inspector, Aberdeen. *Born* 20 November 1925. *Married* 15 August 1950, Isobel, daughter of John Cassie Ballantyne, Ironmonger. Served R.A.F. 1943-47. *Firm*— W. & J. Burness.

EWING, JOHN, of CRAIGTOUN [21 July 1704]. Apprentice to John Cunningham of Enterkine.—Son of Walter Ewing, W.S. *Born* 11 December 1659. *Married* 25 August 1698, Margaret, daughter of John Rowan of Bedland. *Died* 31 October 1733.

EWING, ROBERT JAMES ORR. *See* ORR EWING.

EWING, WALTER [16 October 1658]. Apprentice to John Semple.—Son of Thomas Ewing of Keppoch, Dunbartonshire. *Married* (1) Susanne (*died* 6 December 1662), daughter of Thomas Forrester, W.S.; and (2) 1 December 1665, Mary, eldest daughter of —— Bryson of Craigtoun. Re-admitted, 11 July 1661. *Buried* 6 December 1670.

FAIR, JAMES STEWART, M.A., LL.B. [28 November 1966]. Apprentice to Professor A. J. McDonald of W. B. Dickie & Sons, Dundee.—Son of James Stewart Fair. *Born* 30 September 1930. *Married* 13 July 1968, Anne Lesley, daughter of the Rev. Neil Cameron, Monifieth. *Firm*—Thorntons & Dickie (formerly Dickie, Gray, McDonald & Fair), Dundee.

FAIRLIE, ALAN ROBERT, B.L. [25 November 1963]. Apprentice to Charles Alexander of Auld & Macdonald.—Son of Robert Fairlie, Company Director, Nairn. *Born* 13 April 1928. *Married* 2 July 1953, Bobbette Beryl Ruby, daughter of Stanley Leslie Hills. *Firms*—(1) Auld & Macdonald; (2) Alan R. Fairlie & Co; (3) Duncan, Walker & Fairlie. (Retired from practice.)

FAIRWEATHER, JAMES FALCONER [8 December 1902]. Apprentice to T. J. Gordon and James Falconer.—Son of David Fairweather, Manufacturer, sometime residing in Dundee, afterwards at Ashbank, Monifieth. *Born* 23 January 1869. *Married* 17 December 1902, Helen Kydd (*died* 17 August 1948), daughter of Rev. David Whitton, Principal of Hislop College, Nagpur, C.P., India. S.S.C., 1895. Fiscal, 1935. *Died* 9 February 1963. *Firm*—Gordon, Falconer, and Fairweather.

FAIRWEATHER, STANLEY WHITTON, B.A.(OXON) [20 March 1933]. Apprentice to Robert Nevill Dundas and Others of Dundas & Wilson.—Son of James Falconer Fairweather, W.S., Edinburgh. *Born* 13 December 1906. *Married* 8 April 1937, Faith Torrance, daughter of Harry Torrance Thomson, M.D. Flight Lieutenant R.A.F.V.R. Served U.K. and India and Burma 1940-45. *Firm*—Gordon, Falconer & Fairweather. (Retired.)

FALCONER, JAMES [14 April 1884]. Apprentice to Thomas Jarron Gordon.—Son of Donald Falconer residing at Carmyllie, Angus. *Born* 9 June 1856. *Married* 12 September 1906, Ada Angelique (*died* 5 January 1937), daughter of Robert Kennedy, C.E., Madras, and widow of William Lang Todd, Advocate, Edinburgh. M.P. for Forfarshire, 1909-18. *Died* at London, 21 April 1931. *Firm*—Gordon, Falconer & Fairweather.

FALCONER, Sir JOHN IRELAND, M.A., LL.B., LL.D. [19 July 1920]. Apprentice to Neil Macvicar.—Son of Rev. Charles Falconer, Free Church, Fortrose. *Born* 30 November 1879. *Married* 16 October 1913, Catherine Louise Mary (*died* 12 August 1935), daughter of John Norman Robinson of Bunkers Hill, Carlisle and Croftheads, Moffat. War Service from 1 October 1914 to January 1919. Major 9th Batt. The Royal Scots. Knight Bachelor 1946; Lord Provost of Edinburgh 1944-47. Partly instrumental in the foundation of the Edinburgh International Festival 1947. *Died* 6 April 1954. *Firm*—Fyfe, Ireland and Co.

FALCONER, JOHN LESLIE, T.D., M.A., LL.B. [28 June 1941]. Apprentice to Sir William C. Johnston and Others of Murray, Beith & Murray.—Son of Sir John Ireland Falconer, LL.D., W.S., Edinburgh. *Born* 27 February 1916. *Married* 28 January 1948, Anne, daughter of Captain J. Porter, R.N. Staff Captain, R.A. Served U.K., North Africa and Central Mediterranean, 1939-45. *Firm*—Fyfe, Ireland & Co.

FALL, GEORGE [24 December 1708]. Apprentice to Thomas Pringle.—Under Keeper of the Signet, 2 January 1710. Town Clerk of Dunbar. *Married* 30 April 1713, Margaret, daughter of David Reid, Provost of Sanquhar. *Died* 25 November 1742.

FARQUHAR, ARTHUR, of Elsick [1 July 1837]. Apprentice to John Donaldson and William Campbell of Queenshill.—Son of James Farquhar, Surgeon in the Royal Navy. *Born* 15 March 1813. *Died* 13 September 1887, unmarried.

FARQUHAR, JOHN GRAY, of Gilmillscroft [2 March 1826]. Apprentice to (1) John Bowie; and (2) George Dunlop.—Son of Lieut.-Colonel James Gray Farquhar of Gilmillscroft, Ayrshire. *Born* 1803. *Died* 5 July 1836, unmarried.

FARQUHARSON, ALEXANDER [26 July 1703]. Apprentice to Alexander Alisone.—Son of Rev. Robert Farquharson, Minister of Kennethmont. *Married* Helen, sister of George Marshall, Painter, Edinburgh. *Died* 16 April 1735.

FARQUHARSON, CHARLES, of Inverey and Achlossan [8 November 1708]. Apprentice to Sir James Elphinstone.—Son of John Farquharson of Inverey, Aberdeenshire. *Died* 1747, unmarried.

FARQUHARSON, GEORGE [2 March 1826]. Apprentice to Vans Hathorn.—Only son of Thomas Farquharson of Howden. *Died* 13 July 1844, aged 50, unmarried.

FARQUHARSON, JAMES, of Whitehouse. Apprentice to Thomas Crombie.—Signs the Acts, 26 December 1627. Second son of Donald Farquharson of Castleton of Braemar. Re-admitted, 15 February 1661. *Married* (1) Marion Hay, whose father was a lawyer in Edinburgh; and (2) (contract, 9 February 1648) Ann, daughter of Colonel Thomas Gardyne, of the Russian Service. *Died* 1666.

FASSON, FRANCIS HAMILTON [11 July 1904]. Apprentice to J. P. Wright and T. M. Murray.—Son of Deputy Surgeon-General Charles Hamilton Fasson, R.N. *Born* 21 September 1877. *Married* 8 October 1908, Lilias Clara Bruce (*died* 28 August 1966), youngest daughter of James Blair of Dalshian, Pitlochry. During Great War, served in Gallipoli, Egypt, and Salonica. Captain 2nd Scottish Horse. Twice mentioned in Despatches. *Died* 23 October 1955.

FELLOWES, CHARLES LOUIS [19 October 1891]. Apprentice to J. A. Jamieson, George Dalziel, J. Craik, and J. W. Tod.—Son of Vice-Admiral Charles Fellowes, C.B. *Born* 4 April 1868. *Died* 16 January 1893, unmarried.

FENTON, WILLIAM BUCHAN JAPP [15 January 1894]. Apprentice to William Grant Lumsden Winchester.—Son of William Japp of Broomhall, Solicitor, Alyth. *Born* 13 June 1868. Assumed his mother's name of Fenton in July 1919. *Died* 17 July 1925.

FERGUS, JAMES [4 July 1769]. Apprentice to William Fraser.—Son of John Fergus, Merchant in Edinburgh, killed by the falling of the North Bridge, 3 August 1769. *Married*, proclaimed 7 February 1768, Susan (*died* 6 June 1810), daughter of James Freebairn, Collector of Excise, Perth.

FERGUSON, SIR ADAM [23 November 1795]. Apprentice to (1) Lawrence Hill; and (2) Harry Davidson.—Son of Adam Ferguson, Professor of Moral Philosophy in the University of Edinburgh. *Born* 21st December 1770. *Married* 16 April 1821, Margaret (*died* 4 December 1857), daughter of John Stewart of Stenton and widow of George Lyon of Bucklersberry. Collector of Widows' Fund, 1803-5. Captain 101st Foot, February 1808; served during Peninsular War. Knighted, 1822. *Died* 25 December 1854.

FERGUSON, ALISTAIR JAMES REX, LL.B. [3 December 1973]. Apprentice to David Campbell Macpherson of Wallace & Guthrie.—Son of Alexander James Ferguson, Bank Manager, Edinburgh. *Born* 14 May 1943. *Married* 3 October 1968, Marjory Anne, daughter of John Calder Fowler. *Firm*—(1) Wallace & Guthrie; (2) Skene, Edwards & Garson (after amalgamation, 1979).

FERGUSON, DAVID NEIL, LL.B. [11 December 1979*].—Son of William Ferguson, Administration Officer, Galashiels. *Born* 29 August 1947. *Married* 4 October 1979, Christine Anne, daughter of Andrew Strachan. *Firm*—Keir, Moodie & Co.

FERGUSON, HARRY SCOTT [13 July 1914]. Apprentice to (1) Patrick Reid Buik; and (2) William Blair and James Watt.—Son of William Scott Ferguson, Farmer, Pictstonhill, Perth. *Born* 25 February 1887. *Married* 13 February 1915, Lilian Ethel (*died* 22 June 1965), daughter of J. J. Cridlan of Maisemore Park, Gloucester. War Service: Captain in Black Watch. *Died* 25 September 1953. *Firm*—Ferguson and Shepherd, Alyth.

FERGUSON, IAN MAXWELL, M.C., B.L. [15 July 1949]. Apprentice to Charles Maxwell Young of Young & Cruickshank.—Son of William Hood Ferguson, Keg and Drum Manufacturer, Brechin. *Born* 15 July 1918. *Married* 26 March 1954, Sheila Swanston, daughter of Craig Mitchell, C.B., formerly Deputy Secretary of Department of Health for Scotland. Captain Royal Artillery. Served in France and Belgium 1940, Madagascar 1942, Assam and Burma 1943-45. *Firms*—(1) Young & Cruickshank (1948-59); (2) Maxwell Ferguson & Co. (1959-66); (3) Patrick & James (now Consultant).

FERGUSON, JOHN [28 January 1836]. Apprentice to David Welsh.—Son of James Ferguson, residing in Bonnington. *Born* 24 March 1814. *Died* 8 November 1865, unmarried.

FERGUSON, JOHN [16 January 1893]. Apprentice to Hugh Auld and James Macdonald.—Son of Robert M'Nair Ferguson, D.Ph., 12 Moray Place, Edinburgh. *Born* 15 August 1869. *Married* 17 August 1909, Grace Maria (*died* 12 July 1972), daughter of Edward M'Cabe, Gwelo, Rhodesia, South Africa. *Died* 24 May 1939.

FERGUSON, SHEONA ANNE, LL.B. [9 December 1980]. Apprentice to Ronald Kerr Will and Others of Dundas & Wilson. Daughter of Ian Maxwell Ferguson, W.S., Edinburgh. *Born* 1 May 1957.

FERGUSON, THOMAS [16 June 1807]. Apprentice to James Thomson.—Second son of James Ferguson of Kinmundy, Aberdeenshire. *Born* 17 April 1768. *Married* 9 September 1802, Catherine (*died* 18 February 1810), second daughter of James Cumine of Kininmonth. *Died* 28 May 1828.

FERGUSON, THOMAS [22 June 1819]. Apprentice to Thomas Ferguson, his uncle.— Third son of James Ferguson of Kinmundy. *Born* 21 July 1794. *Married* 6 October 1828, Barbara (*died* 31 July 1831), second daughter of James Hutchison, Merchant, Peterhead. *Died* 30 January 1831.

FERGUSON, WELLWOOD ROBERTSON, O.B.E. [16 July 1888]. Apprentice to William Ferguson and J. C. Junner.—Son of William Ferguson, W.S. *Born* 25 April 1865. *Married* 30 January 1895, Ethel Murray (*died* 6 December 1952), youngest daughter of John Hutchinson Robertson, M.D., J.P., of Singapore, S.S. *Died* 3 March 1949.

FERGUSON, WILLIAM [11 March 1818]. Apprentice to William Gracie.—Only son of Walter Ferguson, Candlemaker in Edinburgh. *Born* 2 September 1786. *Married* 18 August 1815, Margaret (*died* 13 December 1849), daughter of William Auchie, Edinburgh. *Died* 15 March 1849.

FERGUSON, WILLIAM [17 July 1851]. Apprentice to Smith and Kinnear.—Son of William Ferguson, W.S. *Born* 25 January 1829. *Married* 21 August 1855, Elizabeth Robertson (*died* 14 January 1900), daughter of Rev. William Glendonwyn Crosbie, Minister of Parton, Kirkcudbrightshire. *Died* 24 January 1887.

FERGUSSON, HENRY DUNCAN [15 February 1844]. Apprentice to Walker, Richardson, and Melvill.—Sixth son of Sir James Fergusson of Kilkerran, Bart. *Born* 30 September 1817. *Married* 16 June 1846, Anna (*died* 31 August 1910), daughter of Robert Nasmyth, F.R.C.S., Edinburgh. *Died* 22 October 1866.

FERGUSSON, JAMES [7 June 1797]. Apprentice to Alexander Keith.—Son of John Fergusson, Coppersmith in Edinburgh. *Married* 12 January 1800, Isabella (*died* 24 March 1805), daughter of John Anderson, Canongate. *Died* 26 May 1811.

FERGUSSON, JAMES [24 May 1814]. Apprentice to Joseph Cauvin.—Third son of Neil Fergusson of Woodhill, Perthshire, Advocate. *Born* 1793. *Died* 19 May 1850, unmarried.

FERGUSSON, JOHN [6 June 1707]. *Died* 1726.

FERGUSSON, JOHN NORRIS, B.L. [23 November 1953]. Apprentice to John Herbert Richardson and Others of Dundas & Wilson.—Son of Ian V. L. Fergusson, Company Director, Leamington Spa, Warwickshire. *Born* 26 August 1928. *Married* 14 July 1956, Elizabeth Marigold, daughter of Major Hugh King, M.C. *Firm*—Dundas & Wilson (formerly Dundas & Wilson, Davidson & Syme).

FERGUSSON, JOSEPH GILLON, OF ISLE [16 November 1871]. Apprentice to Alexander Maconochie Hare.—Only son of Robert Don Gillon Fergusson of Isle, Dumfriesshire. *Born* 14 January 1848. *Married* (1) 24 January 1882, Edith Mary Scott (*died* 7 May 1890), daughter of James Scott Elliot of Blackwood, Dumfriesshire; and (2) 27 December 1899, Evelyn Romanes Newlyn (*died* 26 November 1957), third daughter of James Curle, Solicitor, Melrose. *Died* 30 November 1908.

FERGUSSON, SAMUEL ROBERT, OF MIDDLEHAUGH [24 June 1835]. Apprentice to James Hope.—Son of James Fergusson of Middlehaugh, Perthshire. *Born* 29 May 1812. *Married* 21 April 1852, Janet (*died* 23 May 1913), second daughter of Hugh Watson, Keillor, Angus. *Died* 26 September 1890.

FERRIE, THOMAS BROWN [25 November 1824]. Apprentice to Robert Strachan.—Son of Alexander Ferrie, Writer in Edinburgh. *Married* Jessie, daughter of John Dickson, Mason, Edinburgh. *Died* 10 February 1860, aged 58.

FERRIER, ARCHIBALD CAMPBELL [8 July 1796]. Apprentice to (1) David Erskine; and (2) James Dundas.—Second son of James Ferrier, W.S. *Born* 15 August 1773. *Married* 20 January 1800, Catherine (*died* 13 January 1826), eldest daughter of Francis Garden, Merchant, Greenock. *Died* 25 December 1814.

FERRIER, JAMES [3 July 1770]. Apprentice to Archibald Campbell of Succoth.—Third son of John Ferrier of Kirkland, Renfrewshire, and his wife Grizel, daughter and heiress of Sir William Sandilands Hamilton, Bart., of Westport and Belsyde, Linlithgowshire. *Born* 1744. *Married* February 1767, Helen (*died* 20 February 1797), daughter of Robert Coutts, Montrose. Principal Clerk of Session, 25 May 1802 to 22 June 1826. Commissioner for the Duke of Argyll. Father of Susan Edmonstone Ferrier, Novelist. *Died* 18 January 1829.

FERRIER, JOHN [24 February 1794]. Apprentice to, and eldest son of, James Ferrier, W.S.—*Born* 25 October 1771. *Married* 4 May 1804, Margaret (*died* 5 January 1833), daughter of John Wilson, Merchant in Paisley. Deputy Keeper of the Great Seal. *Died* 23 November 1852.

FERRIER, JOHN WILSON [21 November 1833]. Apprentice to, and son of, John Ferrier, W.S.—*Born* 8 September 1810. *Died* 13 December 1845, unmarried.

FERRIER, THOMAS HENRY [13 July 1848]. Apprentice to John Mackenzie Lindsay.—Son of Walter Ferrier, W.S. *Born* 20 July 1822. *Married* 28 March 1871, Elizabeth (*died* 15 November 1922), daughter of Rev. Samuel Key of Fulford Hall, Patron and Vicar of the Parish of Fulford, Yorkshire. *Died* 24 March 1887.

FERRIER, WALTER, OF TORAVON [15 November 1811]. Apprentice to John Ferrier, his brother.—Sixth and youngest son of James Ferrier, W.S. *Born* 24 March 1784. *Married* 15 December 1818, Henrietta (*died* 20 November 1882), only daughter of Thomas Gordon of Clouden Bank, Dumfries. *Died* 13 August 1856.

FIELD, HENRY [14 March 1872]. Apprentice to James Steuart.—Youngest son of Rev. Edward Burch Field of Moreland, Kinross-shire. *Born* 28 May 1847. *Married* 24 October 1878, Joan Grassie (*died* 18 January 1934), daughter of William Lawson, Halifax, Nova Scotia. *Died* at Middle Bluff, Manitoba, 4 January 1894.

FIELD, JAMES HAMILTON [13 May 1869]. Apprentice to John Brown Innes.—Eldest surviving son of Rev. Edward Burch Field of Moreland, Kinross-shire. *Born* 15 November 1843. *Died* 9 January 1879, unmarried.

FIFE, ROBERT DONALD MATHIESON, LL.B [11 December 1978]. Apprentice to George Stuart Russell and Others of Strathern & Blair.—Son of Robert Fife, Seedsman, Edinburgh. *Born* 2 September 1955. *Married* 8 November 1975, Jean Elizabeth, daughter of Edward McVitie, Head Forester, Dalmeny.

FINDLATER, HENRY JAMES, B.A.(CANTAB) [12 December 1898]. Apprentice to R. C. Bell and J. Scott.—Son of John Findlater, Manager of the Town and County Bank, Aberdeen. *Born* 4 February 1873. *Died* 28 April 1936. *Firm*—Macqueen and Findlater, Aberdeen.

FINDLAY, CHARLES ALASTAIR, T.D. [14 July 1947]. Apprentice to John Carr Gillespie Lees and Others of Gillespie & Paterson.—Son of Major Charles W. Findlay, Kippen, Stirlingshire. *Born* 2 September 1914. *Married* (1) 18 August 1943, Evelyn Carr Harris (*died* 1963); and (2) 18 April 1964, Esme Breda Langa Adie or Bennett. Captain Royal Scots. Served U.K., France and N.W. Europe 1940-45. *Firm*—Thomson & Baxter (formerly Thomson, Dickson & Shaw and Mitchell & Baxter).

FINLAY, CHARLES PATRICK [18 November 1858]. Apprentice to John Scott and Sir John Gillespie.—Fourth son of Gilbert Laurie Finlay, W.S. *Born* 15 September 1833. *Married* 15 January 1861, Anne Arabella (*died* 14 February 1878), eldest daughter of Major-General Robert Stewart, H.E.I.C.S. *Died* 19 March 1905.

FINLAY, GILBERT LAURIE [8 February 1816]. Apprentice to William Balderston.— Son of Rev. William Finlay, Minister of Polmont. *Born* 29 September 1792. *Married* 6 May 1822, Grace Hunter (*died* 1 February 1868), daughter of George Charles, M.D., Ayr. Manager of the Edinburgh Life Assurance Society. *Died* 1 April 1872.

FINLAY, JOHN HOPE [21 November 1867]. Apprentice to Alexander Forsyth Adam and John Kirk.—Son of Charles Finlay, Assistant Clerk of Session. *Born* 13 January 1839. *Married* (1) 13 June 1878, Jane Bertram (*died* 17 April 1879), daughter of Alexander Ronaldson, Glasgow; and (2) 13 September 1883, Jane Ferguson (*died* 20 March 1929), youngest daughter of Alexander Annandale of Westbarns and widow of Alexander Duncan. Keeper of the Register of Sasines, 1888-1907. *Died* 11 January 1907.

FINLAY, MUIR PRINGLE, M.B.E., LL.B. [14 December 1936]. Apprentice to Walter Finlay of W. & W. Finlay.—Son of Walter Finlay, W.S., Edinburgh. *Born* 17 May 1911. *Married* 30 August 1941, Florence Elizabeth, daughter of Hugh Maclean, Joppa. Solicitor in Scotland to the Ministry of Works. *Died* 10 January 1960. *Firm*—Hamilton, Kinnear & Beatson.

FINLAY, NINIAN JAMIESON [25 May 1883]. Apprentice to John Cowan and James A. Dalmahoy.—Son of William Finlay, M.D., Trinity. *Born* 31 January 1858. *Married* 30 June 1894, Fordyce Aimee (*died* 11 June 1948), third daughter of William Warden, Glasgow. *Died* 7 March 1936. *Firm*—Bell, Bannerman, and Finlay.

FINLAY, ROBERT, OF WALLYFORD [8 July 1796]. Apprentice to (1) Samuel Mitchelson; and (2) John Tait.—Eldest son of James Finlay of Wallyford. *Died* 11 April 1808.

FINLAY, THOMAS, OF BALCHRYSTIE [24 May 1720]. Apprentice to John Macfarlane.— Son of James Finlay of Balchrystie, Fife. Attorney-at-Law, Barbadoes. *Died* June 1760.

FINLAY, WALTER, O.B.E. [27 March 1899]. Apprentice to Charles Baxter and William Mitchell.—Son of William Finlay, S.S.C., Edinburgh. *Born* 3 December 1876. *Married* 13 July 1908, Ethel Mary Bruce (*died* 7 December 1931), third daughter of Hugh White, Grain Merchant, Leith. Solicitor in Scotland to H.M. Office of Works. Served with Volunteers during Great War. *Died* 15 March 1953. *Firm*—W. and W. Finlay.

FINLAY, WILLIAM FRANCIS [14 March 1892]. Apprentice to D. S. Moncrieff and J. A. Trail.—Son of William Finlay, F.F.A., Edinburgh. *Born* 17 May 1868. *Married* 15 September 1915, Christian Reid (*died* 3 September 1977), younger daughter of David G. Maule, Norwich. Member of the King's Bodyguard for Scotland, Royal Company of Archers, 1911. *Died* 20 July 1937.

FINLAYSON, ALBERT HAROLD CHARLES, LL.B. [4 December 1972]. Apprentice to Alexander Jackson Ambrose and Others of Macandrew, Wright & Murray.—Son of William Finlayson, Inverness. *Born* 11 January 1942. *Married* 3 September 1966, Julia Mary, daughter of John Bousfield, Shrewsbury. *Firm*—Gillespie, Macandrew & Co. (formerly Macandrew, Wright & Murray).

FINLAYSON, JOHN KENNETH, M.A., LL.B. [29 April 1968]. (By Rule IX (a).)—Son of Alexander Finlayson, Designer, Kirkcaldy. *Born* 21 May 1931. *Married* 7 September 1963, Patricia Anne, daughter of David James Lumsden, Bank Manager. *Firm*—Bonar Mackenzie (formerly Bonar, Mackenzie & Kermack).

FINLAYSON, WALTER [10 March 1813]. Apprentice to Charles Bremner.—Son of William Finlayson, Depute Clerk of the Bills. Stipendiary Magistrate for district of Montego Bay, Jamaica. *Died* at Jamaica, 21 December 1841, aged 60, unmarried.

FISHER, JOHN [22 February 1838]. Apprentice to Walker, Richardson, and Melville.—Eldest son of Daniel Fisher, S.S.C. *Born* 17 July 1814. *Died* 30 July 1899, unmarried.

FLEEMING, ROBERT [5 May 1796]. Apprentice to Francis Strachan.—Son of Robert Fleeming, Printer in Edinburgh. *Died* 26 July 1847, aged 76, unmarried.

FLEMING, ALEXANDER [13 November 1816]. Apprentice to Sir William Drysdale.—Son of the Rev. Alexander Fleming, D.D., Minister of Hamilton. *Born* 26 October 1792. *Married* 14 March 1850, Euphemia (*died* 13 April 1897), daughter of David Scott, Farmer, Northfield, Mid-Lothian. *Died* 27 July 1879.

FLEMING, ALEXANDER BUIST [6 July 1896]. Apprentice to David Shaw.—Son of Alexander Fleming, S.S.C., Edinburgh. *Born* 2 February 1874. *Died* 23 February 1933, unmarried.

FLEMING, HEW, OF POLCALK [8 March 1726]. Apprentice to Robert Hepburn.—Son of John Fleming, Advocate. *Baptized* 29 August 1700. *Died* March 1737.

FLETCHER, ANGUS [4 July 1822]. Apprentice to John Archibald Campbell.—Second son of Archibald Fletcher, Advocate. Relinquished the legal profession and became a Sculptor in London. *Died* 6 March 1862, aged 63, unmarried.

FLETCHER, ARCHIBALD, OF PARKHILL [4 July 1783]. Apprentice to William Wilson.—Son of Angus Fletcher, Poobale, Glen Lyon, brother of Archibald Fletcher of Dunans. *Born* 1745. *Married* 16 July 1791, Eliza (aged 17, *died* 5 February 1858), daughter of Miles Dawson, Tadcastle. Having been admitted Advocate in 1791, name removed from Roll of Society. Author of several pamphlets and papers for the times, he was known as "The Father of Burgh Reform." Also see *Kay's Portraits*, ii. 445-7; Cockburn's *Life of Jeffrey*, i. 89-91; *Dict. of Nat. Biog.*, xix. 298; Ferguson's *Henry Erskine*; etc. *Died* 20 December 1828.

FLETCHER (OR FLESHEOUR), DAVID [1594]. Servant to John Skene, Advocate.—Brother of Robert Fletcher, Merchant Burgess, Dundee. *Married* 7 July 1596, Marion Wylie. *Died* 11 November 1616.

FLETCHER, WILLIAM [11 April 1887]. Apprentice to Robert Burt Ranken.—Fourth son of William Fletcher, Merchant in Elgin. *Born* 12 June 1861. *Married* 12 October 1907, Cecilia Frances (*died* 31 March 1915), third daughter of John Thomson, J.P., St Laurence, Polwarth Terrace, Edinburgh. *Died* 7 November 1907.

FLETT, IAIN JAMES ROSS, LL.B. [6 December 1971]. Apprentice to P. J. Oliphant and Others of Pearson, Robertson & Maconochie.—Son of J. Flett, Company Director, Linlithgow. *Born* 23 May 1947. *Married* 3 October 1974, Rachel Mary, daughter of W. L. Smith, Blairgowrie.

FLETT, ROBERT JAMES ROBERTSON [12 July 1897]. Apprentice to Colin G. Macrae.—Son of David Flett, Writer and N.P., Edinburgh. *Born* 11 May 1868. *Married* 15 February 1917, Maude Jean Gladstone (*died* 12 February 1953), only daughter of George R. Glendinning, Hattonmains, Kirknewton. *Died* 5 January 1943.

FOGGO, THOMAS CLARK, LL.B. [3 December 1973]. Apprentice to James MacLean of Skene, Edwards & Garson.—Son of Thomas Clark Foggo, Monumental Mason, Cowdenbeath. *Born* 26 July 1943. *Married* 13 November 1968, Carol Anne, daughter of Alexander Kennedy Kinghorn, Mill Worker, Selkirk. *Firm*—Skene, Edwards & Garson.

FORBES, ALEXANDER, OF FYNNERSCIES [25 March 1635]. Apprentice to John Baird.—Son of Robert Forbes, Portioner of Fynnerscies. *Married* 7 April 1668, Janet, daughter of William Simpson, Merchant Burgess, Edinburgh.

FORBES, ALEXANDER [6 December 1773]. Apprentice to John Watson.—Son of James Forbes of Balfour. *Died* 1799.

FORBES, ALEXANDER [20 July 1841]. Apprentice to James Shepherd.—Son of Rev. George Forbes of Bleloch and Inverernan, Aberdeenshire. *Born* 6 October 1819. *Died* 27 June 1849, unmarried.

FORBES, ANDREW [3 July 1792]. Apprentice to John Russell, Jun.—Son of George Forbes of Upper Boyndlie, Aberdeenshire. *Died* 5 May 1795.

FORBES, ARTHUR, OF SCHIVES [1 March 1697]. Apprentice to Sir James Elphinstone of Logie.—Fourth son of Sir John Forbes, second Baronet of Craigievar. *Born* 1669. *Married* Margaret Fraser, sister to Brodland and relict of Alexander Fraser of Innerallochie. *Died* 1726.

FORBES, ARTHUR. *See* GORDON, ARTHUR FORBES.

FORBES, CHARLES LAW, LL.B. [14 July 1930]. Apprentice to James Methuen.—Son of Rev. William Forbes, Cairneyhill Manse, Dunfermline. *Born* 28 July 1902. *Married* 23 January 1965, Mrs Jean T. B. Muir, daughter of Dr W. S. Wood, Edinburgh. Major, R.A. Served U.K. and N.W. Europe 1940-45. *Died* 24 March 1966. *Firm*—Aitken, Methuen, and Aikman.

FORBES, WILLIAM [19 August 1720]. Apprentice to John Stewart.—Second son of Sir David Forbes of Newhall, Mid-Lothian. *Married* 3 August 1722, Ann (*died* July 1740), daughter of James Nairn, one of the bailies of Edinburgh. Fiscal, 8 November 1725. *Died* 29 April 1771.

FORBES, WILLIAM, OF CASTLETON [17 November 1825]. Apprentice to James Thomas.—Son of Robert Forbes of Castleton, Kincardineshire. *Born* 1799. *Married* 28 August 1849, Jane Duff Grant (*died* 3 August 1891), eldest daughter of Robert Watson, Banker, Forres. *Died* 7 August 1872.

FORD, PATRICK JOHN, M.A.(Cantab), LL.B. [28 May 1979]. Apprentice to Francis Hugh Simpson and Others of Fyfe, Ireland & Co.—Son of Sheriff Harold Frank Ford, Perth. *Born* 14 September 1952.

FORMAN, ALEXANDER GEORGE [2 July 1868]. Apprentice to (1) Edmund Baxter; and (2) John Nairne Forman, his father.—*Born* 17 April 1845. *Died* 25 January 1925, unmarried.

FORMAN, JAMES [16 November 1784]. Apprentice to Alexander Abercromby.—Son of James Forman, Tenant in Blackdub, Stirling. *Married* ——. *Died* 12 March 1824.

FORMAN, JOHN, of Staffa [9 July 1801]. Apprentice to James Forman, his uncle.—Eldest son of John Forman, Baker, Stirling. *Born* 26 September 1775. *Married* 29 May 1805, Hannah (*died* 19 October 1849), daughter of Rev. James Nairne, of Claremont, D.D., Minister of Pittenweem. *Died* 4 December 1841.

FORMAN, JOHN [30 November 1819]. Apprentice to, and son of, James Forman, W.S.—*Died* 12 September 1821.

FORMAN, JOHN [13 November 1862]. Apprentice to, and son of, John Nairne Forman, W.S.—*Born* 4 January 1838. *Married* 23 April 1872, Catherine (*died* 27 November 1910), second surviving daughter of Bernard Gilpin Cooper of Hazel Grove, Cheshire. *Died* 18 February 1882.

FORMAN, JOHN NAIRNE, of Staffa [22 November 1827]. Apprentice to, and eldest son of, John Forman of Staffa, W.S.—*Born* 6 April 1806. *Married* 16 October 1835, Jane (*died* 10 November 1881), only daughter of Robert Mitchell of Airth, Stirlingshire. *Died* 30 January 1884.

FORMAN, ROBERT CRAWFORD BANKS, LL.B., LL.M. [25 April 1977]. Apprentice to (1) A. E. Leslie of Shiels & Macintosh and (2) M. M. Duncan of Edinburgh District Council.—Son of Robert Banks Forman, University Lecturer. *Born* 30 March 1948. *Married* 2 April 1971, Aileen, daughter of E. McNab, Insurance Manager. *Firm*—Dan McKay & Norwell.

FORREST, CHRISTOPHER JAMES, LL.B. [3 December 1973]. Apprentice to Neil Alexander Milne and Others of Miller Thomson & Robertson.—Son of William Dick Forrest, C.A., Edinburgh. *Born* 4 April 1949. *Married* 19 January 1974, Shona Catherine, daughter of George Kay, Bank Manager. *Firm*—T. & T. Gibson & Kennedy, Falkirk.

FORREST, JAMES [25 June 1770]. Apprentice to John Bell.—Third son of John Forrest, Merchant in Edinburgh. *Born* 1744. *Married* 10 December 1776, Catherine (*died* 30 August 1781), only daughter of James Forrest of Comiston, Mid-Lothian. *Died* 1 July 1820.

FORREST, JOHN ARTHUR [15 July 1884]. Apprentice to John William Young and John Blair.—Third son of Lieut.-Colonel Sir William Forrest of Comiston, Bart. *Born* 10 January 1860. *Died* on the Links, North Berwick, 24 March 1923.

FORREST, THOMAS, of Kirkton [23 November 1631]. Apprentice to John Ker.—*Married* (1) Janet Hay (*died* February 1635); (2) Grizel Lockhart. *Died* 2 January 1652.

FORRESTER, ANDREW [14 November 1872]. Apprentice to (1) J. C. Tait and H. H. Crichton; and (2) Donald Beith.—Son of William Forrester of Glenmiln, Stirlingshire. *Born* 22 July 1839. *Married* 1 September 1870, Margaret Crighton (*died* 9 April 1891), eldest daughter of Andrew Carmichael Haddow of Little Galla, Lanarkshire. *Died* 30 July 1915.

FORRESTER, ANDREW LUDOVIC [10 July 1899]. Apprentice to J. H. Dixson.—Youngest son of William Forrester of Arngibbon and Blaiket, Stirlingshire. *Born* 15 July 1874. *Died* 28 August 1910, unmarried.

FORRESTER, JOHN, OF BARNS [12 June 1823]. Apprentice to Alexander Goldie.—Son of Rev. Alexander Forrester, Minister of West Linton. *Born* 3 March 1799. *Married* 8 September 1829, Lilias (*died* 26 August 1880), daughter of Robert Cowan, Surgeon, Glasgow. *Died* 11 September 1882.

FORRESTER, WILLIAM [22 July 1682]. Apprentice to Andrew Young.—Son of Mr Alexander Forrester, one of the Ministers of the City of Edinburgh, who was thrust out when Episcopacy came in, and was imprisoned on the Bass and in the Tolbooth. *Married* 20 April 1686, Rachel (*died* December 1720), daughter of Sir David Balfour of Forret, one of the Senators of the College of Justice (Lord Forret). *Died* 1 October 1701.

FORSYTH, HENRY [18 May 1837]. Apprentice to (1) James Swan; and (2) Donald Horne.—Son of Robert Forsyth of Redhouse, West Lothian, Advocate. *Born* 29 June 1814. *Married* 9 October 1846, Janet Spottiswoode (*died* 16 May 1899), daughter of John Sawers of Bell's Mills, Edinburgh. Procurator-Fiscal at Forfar, 1847-64. *Died* 6 March 1891.

FORSYTH, JAMES SOMERLED [11 July 1904]. Apprentice to William Campbell M'Ewen.—Son of James Noel Müller Forsyth of Quinish, Isle of Mull. *Born* 3 December 1874. During War served in Canadian Infantry, 1915-18; wounded at Somme; prisoner in Germany. Resident in Canada. *Died* at Vancouver 1 January 1941.

FORSYTH, JOHN [Before 1576]. *Married* Margaret Cant. *Died* October 1581.

FORTOUN, ROBERT [1606]. Signs the Acts 17 January 1606. *Married* 16 July 1607, Helen, daughter of James Winram, W.S.

FOTHERINGHAM, ALEXANDER CAMPBELL, M.A., LL.B. [13 December 1960]. Apprentice to William Lindsay of Ketchen & Stevens.—Son of Alexander Campbell Fotheringham, Seedsman, Duns, Berwickshire. *Born* 25 November 1927. *Married* 14 August 1963, Agnes Stewart, daughter of Robert Burns, Clerk. *Firm*—Ketchen & Stevens. (Retired.)

FOTHERINGHAM, FREDERICK [6 December 1791]. Apprentice to Thomas Innes.—Son of Dr Robert Fotheringham, Physician in Dundee. *Married* —— (*died* 1834). *Died* 16 December 1824.

FOTHERINGHAM, FREDERICK [17 November 1814]. Apprentice to Alexander Pearson.—Fifth son of Alexander Ogilvy Fotheringham of Powrie, Forfarshire. *Born* 1792. *Died* 15 January 1877, unmarried.

FOTHERINGHAM, HENRY [23 November 1827]. Apprentice to (1) William Berry; (2) Alexander Kettle; and (3) John Forman.—Eldest son of Henry Fotheringham, residing at the Inch, near Kincardine. *Died* 17 March 1842, aged 43, unmarried.

FOTHERINGHAM, WILLIAM KENNEDY, B.A.(OXON), LL.B. [28 April 1952]. Apprentice to Alexander Macfie and Another of Scott & Glover.—Son of William Fotheringham, Timber Merchant, Glasgow. *Born* 1 December 1917. *Married* 1 June 1955, Eileen McInroy, daughter of Alfred Scott, Captain, Merchant Navy. Captain, R.A. Served West Africa Command (Sierra Leone, Nigeria); India and Burma Command 14th Armies, 1939-45. Awarded Burma Star. *Firms*—(1) Pitcairn & Mathers; (2) Inglis, Orr & Bruce; (3) Macrae, Flett & Rennie; (after amalgamation with former firm) (Consultant).

FOX, ALASTAIR GORDON, LL.B. [1 December 1969]. Apprentice to (1) Arthur Woodman Blair and Others of Strathern & Blair and (2) Charles David Pagan of Pagan, Osborne & Grace, Cupar.—Son of Major P. A. H. Fox, D.S.O., Thornhill, Dumfriesshire. *Born* 1 January 1946. *Married* 3 June 1978, Caroline Helen Catherine Mann. *Firm*—J. & F. Anderson.

FRANK, JOHN, OF BUGHTRIG [2 January 1682]. *Married* (1) 23 August 1674, Elizabeth Grier (*died* 14 April 1689); and (2) 26 July 1690, Agnes (*died* 1704), daughter of William Syme, Advocate. Fiscal, 1684-6. Treasurer, 1686-91. Advocate, 16 June 1691. *Buried* 25 February 1700.

FRASER, ALEXANDER [23 November 1795]. Apprentice to, and second son of, James Fraser, W.S.—*Born* 24 August 1773. *Married* Jane Henderson (*died* 24 February 1848). *Died* at Berbice, 9 September 1816.

FRASER, ALEXANDER DAVID [10 March 1820]. Apprentice to Charles Tawse.— Youngest son of Simon Fraser of Farraline, Inverness-shire. *Born* 1795. *Died* 6 October 1839, unmarried.

FRASER, ANDREW [22 November 1832]. Apprentice to Robert Roy.—Son of Angus Fraser, residing in Dornoch. *Born* 31 May 1805. *Married* 23 June 1841, Janet (*died* 5 August 1897), youngest daughter of Robert Brown of Gilston. Sheriff-Substitute at Fort-William, 1838-73. *Died* 15 June 1873.

FRASER, CHARLES ANNAND, M.V.O., LL.B. [30 November 1959]. Apprentice to Sir Peter George Macdonald and Others of W. & J. Burness.—Son of The Very Rev. John Annand Fraser, M.B.E., D.D., Moderator of the General Assembly of the Church of Scotland. *Born* 16 October 1928. *Married* 7 September 1957, Ann, daughter of William Francis Scott-Kerr of Sunlaws and Chatto. Purse Bearer to successive Lords High Commissioner to the General Assembly of the Church of Scotland. *Firm*—W. & J. Burness.

FRASER, DONALD [12 December 1796]. Apprentice to James Ferrier.—Son of Rev. Paul Fraser, Minister of Craigneuk. *Died* 1802.

FRASER, HUGH, OF STRUY [7 February 1822]. Apprentice to James Robertson.—Second son of Hugh Fraser of Struy, Inverness-shire. *Died* 2 December 1866, unmarried.

FRASER, IAIN GORDON, B.A.(CANTAB), LL.B. [1 December 1969]. Apprentice to Sir Ernest Maclagan Wedderburn and Others of Shepherd & Wedderburn.—Son of Dr Donald Alexander Fraser, Inverness. *Born* 28 April 1932. *Married* 21 March 1970, Rachel, daughter of Brigadier Sir George Harvie-Watt, Q.C. *Firms*—(1) Pitcairn & Mathers; (2) J. C. & A. Steuart.

FRASER, JAMES, OF GORTULLEG [29 July 1762]. Apprentice to William Fraser of Balnain.—Son of Thomas Fraser, younger of Gortulleg, Inverness-shire. *Born* 1729. *Married* 19 January 1769, Jean (*died* 29 August 1824), eldest daughter of Alexander Spalding of Holm, Kirkcudbrightshire. *Died* at Tyndrum, 30 November 1805, from injuries received by his carriage being upset.

FRASER, JAMES JOHN [29 November 1821]. Apprentice to Robert Hill.—Son of Charles Fraser of Williamston, Aberdeenshire. *Born* 1801. *Died* 3 June 1839, unmarried.

FRASER, JOHN, OF BORLUM [29 June 1752]. Apprentice to William Fraser.—Son of John Fraser, Merchant in Inverness. *Married* (contract dated 30 October 1744) Jean (*died* 15 May 1799), eldest daughter of David Brown of Golf Hall, Edinburgh. *Died* 17 August 1795, aged 84.

FRASER, PATRICK ALEXANDER CAMPBELL. *See* CAMPBELL FRASER.

FRASER, SIMON, OF FORD [19 December 1767]. Apprentice to, and eldest son of, William Fraser of Ford, W.S.—*Born* October 1741. *Married* 2 March 1784, Janet Cruickshank (*died* 6 July 1829), daughter of Captain Charles Douglas of Clifton Hall, Philadelphia. *Died* 25 September 1819.

FRASER, SIMON, M.C. [17 December 1923]. Apprentice to R. K. Blair and H. F. Cadell.—Son of Simon Fraser, Wool Merchant, Edinburgh. *Born* 30 June 1883. *Married* 6 December 1915, Christina Millicent (*died* 8 August 1974), daughter of Henry Ferguson, Household Controller. Commission in 9th Royal Scots; served in France; wounded 1916. Chevalier of the Legion of Honour (France); mentioned in Despatches, and retired as Brevet-Major. *Died* 26 May 1966. *Firm*—Blair and Cadell.

FRASER, WILLIAM, OF BALNAIN [2 February 1736]. Apprentice to (1) Hercules Scott; and (2) Harry Maule.—Second son of Alexander Fraser of Balnain. *Born* 14 November 1703. *Married* November 1748, Jane (*died* 7 August 1783), daughter of Archibald Macaulay of Ardencaple, Lord Provost of Edinburgh. *Died* 10 December 1775.

FRASER, WILLIAM, OF FORD [11 March 1740]. Apprentice to James Budge.—Son of William Fraser of Ballifurth. *Married* May 1738, Julian (*died* 19 January 1772), daughter of John Campbell of Lochdochart. *Died* 3 March 1767.

FRASER, WILLIAM, OF GLENMADE [21 June 1813]. Apprentice to Craufurd Tait.—Son of Luke Fraser of Glenmade, one of the Masters of the High School of Edinburgh. *Born* 1786. *Married* 30 April 1823, Bethia (*died* 19 September 1883), daughter of Francis Taylor, Edinburgh. *Died* 26 September 1862.

FRASER, WILLIAM, YOUNGER OF CULBOCKIE [10 February 1825]. Apprentice to James Mackenzie and William Innes.—Eldest son of William Fraser of Culbockie. *Married* 25 July 1826, Margaret (*died* 14 March 1838), eldest daughter of David George Sandeman of Springland, Perthshire. *Died* 6 January 1829.

FRASER, WILLIAM, *tertius* [20 November 1828]. Apprentice to Francis Wilson.—Son of William Fraser, Edinburgh. *Born* 27 November 1805. *Married* 17 July 1833, Margaret (*died* 23 January 1872), youngest daughter of John Torrance, Writer in Hamilton. Town Clerk of the Canongate. *Died* 8 April 1874.

FRASER, WILLIAM HENRY [9 July 1900]. Apprentice to John Cowan and James A. Dalmahoy.—Eldest son of William Stuart Fraser, W.S. *Born* 2 March 1876. *Married* 17 December 1903, Katharine Margaret (*died* 4 February 1965), daughter of John James Cowan of Bavelaw. *Died* 26 June 1966. *Firm*—Fraser, Stodart, and Ballingall.

FRASER, WILLIAM STUART [30 May 1861]. Apprentice to, and son of, William Fraser, *tertius*, W.S. *Born* 3 October 1836. *Married* 14 April 1875, Annabella (*died* 15 October 1903), youngest surviving daughter of George Brooke Nelson, Solicitor, Leeds. Fiscal, 23 November 1899. *Died* 6 June 1918.

FRAZER, ALLAN CAMERON, M.A., LL.B. [15 March 1948]. Apprentice to A. G. Cairns of A. G. Cairns & Frazer.—Son of the Rev. Alexander Frazer. *Born* 16 September 1911. *Married* 21 April 1943, Charlotte Ella, daughter of David Cumming Edwards, Marine Engineer. Sergeant 155 Field Ambulance R.A.M.C. (France 1940); Lieutenant R.A.O.C. in U.K. Chevalier of Orange Order of Nassau. Netherlands Consul in Edinburgh. *Firms*—(1) A. G. Cairns & Frazer; (2) Hagart & Burn-Murdoch.

FREER, ALLAN ORMISTON [23 March 1903]. Apprentice to J. P. Wright and T. M. Murray.—Eldest son of John Freer, Solicitor, Melrose. *Born*—16 July 1879. *Married*—8 December 1904, Elizabeth Montgomery (divorced 4 October 1910), elder daughter of William Crozier Smith of Whitehill, St Boswells. *Died* 12 February 1957.

FREER, DAVID [12 March 1788]. Apprentice to Alexander Duncan.—Second son of David Freer of Innernethy. *Born* 1761. *Died* 22 January 1837, unmarried.

FRENCH, JOHN [9 July 1829]. Apprentice to James Swan.—Youngest son of James French, Burnhouse, Lanarkshire. *Born* 9 May 1801. *Married* 30 January 1841, Christian (*died* 23 November 1845), daughter of John Cameron, Woodville, Murrayfield. *Died* 16 September 1869.

FRENCH, JOHN, LL.B. [13 April 1886]. Apprentice to George Robertson and John Hope Finlay.—Son of John French, Merchant, Leith. *Born* 6 December 1859. *Died* 1 July 1939.

FREW, MICHAEL GRAEME, M.A., LL.B. [2 December 1974]. Apprentice to Hon. D. A. Balfour and Others of Shepherd & Wedderburn.—Son of Dr James S. Frew, Consultant Physician, Dundee. *Born* 11 March 1944. *Married* 4 September 1971, Caroline, daughter of James Boyes, Managing Director, York.

FRIER, ALEXANDER. *Married* before 1603, Jean Hamilton, widow of Archibald Rintoul, Saddler Burgess, Edinburgh.

FRIER, GEORGE [Before 1552]. *Died* November 1571.

FULLARTON, ADAM, OF BARTONHOLM [24 November 1686]. Apprentice to John Muir.—Son of James Fullarton of Bartonholm, Ayrshire. *Married* 14 February 1695, Agnes, daughter of Laurence Scott of Bavelaw. *Died* 1709.

FULLARTON, ROBERT, OF BARTONHOLM [10 August 1705]. Apprentice to Adam Fullarton.—Second son of George Fullarton of Fullarton and Dreghorn, Ayrshire. *Married* 15 March 1716, Grizel, daughter of John Stuart of Ascog, Bute. *Died* 15 September 1754.

FULLARTON, ROBERT, OF CRAIGHALL [18 September 1714]. Apprentice to Adam Fullarton.—Eldest son of Robert Fullarton of Craighall, Ayrshire. *Born* 1687. *Married* September 1713, Margaret (*died* 10 October 1748), daughter of John Wallace, Merchant, Edinburgh. Comptroller of the Customs at Leith. *Died* 23 March 1757.

FULTON, DAVID CAIRNS, M.C., B.L. [16 December 1946]. Apprentice to Joseph Ellis Inglis and Another of Melville & Lindesay.—Son of John Wilson Fulton, Civil Servant. *Born* 3 October 1922. *Married* 19 February 1947, Anna Christian, daughter of George Lionel Orchard. Lieutenant 2nd Lothian & Border Horse. Served U.K. and C.M.E. 1941-44. Wounded August 1944. Appointed Fiscal to the Society 1980. *Firm*—Tods, Murray & Jamieson.

FULTON, JOHN DAVID ORCHARD, LL.B. [11 December 1978]. Apprentice to (1) Ronald Kerr Will and Others of Dundas & Wilson and (2) William Milne Richardson of Tods, Murray & Jamieson.—Son of David Cairns Fulton, W.S., Edinburgh. *Born* 16 November 1953.

FYFE, ALEXANDER [20 August 1697]. Apprentice to Colin Campbell of Carwhin.—*Married* 17 March 1696, Catherine Forbes, relict of George Watt, Writer, Edinburgh. Author of *The Royal Martyr, King Charles I.: an Opera*, 1705. *Died* 3 April 1718.

FYFE, DAVID GORDON, LL.B. [4 December 1967]. Apprentice to D. C. Scott-Moncrieff and Others of Tods, Murray & Jamieson.—Son of James Gordon Fyfe, W.S., Peebles. *Born* 28 March 1943. *Married* 8 April 1976, Susan Benn. *Firm*—Blackwood & Smith, Peebles.

FYFE, JAMES GORDON, T.D., D.L., M.A., LL.B. [28 July 1952]. Apprentice to William Thorburn Blackwood of Blackwood & Smith, Peebles.—Son of Alexander Fyfe, Solicitor, Peebles. *Born* 5 May 1918. *Married* (1) 28 March 1942, Phyllis Una (*died* 1956), daughter of Major J. W. Goodford of Chilton Cantelo, Somerset, and (2) 15 July 1958, Kathleen Jean Wolfe Murray, daughter of Captain George Wolfe Murray, Meldonfoot, Peebles. Major R.A. Served U.K. and France and Germany 1939-45. *Firm*—Blackwood & Smith, Peebles.

GAIRDNER, ROBERT [1594]. Signs Minutes of 16 December 1594. Suspended from membership 14 November 1595—20 January 1596 for signing precepts which had not been written by him or his clerks.

GAIRDNER, THOMAS, OF CRAIGEND, STIRLING [17 June 1816]. Apprentice to (1) Robert Cathcart; and (2) John Kermack.—Son of Captain Robert Gairdner of Mountcharles. *Born* 22 October 1791. *Married* 16 August 1831, Marion Dalrymple (*died* 1876), daughter of John Montgomery. *Died* 2 March 1860.

GALBRAITH, DAVID STEUART, OF MACHRICHANISH [27 May 1824]. Apprentice to Norman Lockhart.—Second son of Daniel Galbraith, Farmer in Dunaltach. *Born* 9 October 1782. *Married* (1) 9 June 1812, Elizabeth (*died* 1 May 1853), only daughter of James Fraser, R.N., Plymouth; (2) 12 May 1863, Elizabeth Alger (*died* 1870). *Died* 27 December 1863.

GALBRAITH, JAMES FRASER [23 February 1844]. Apprentice to James Stewart Ducat.—Eldest son of David Steuart Galbraith of Machrichanish, Argyllshire. W.S. *Born* 22 August 1813. *Married* 1845, Cecilia Sarah De Lisle (*died* 26 September 1879). *Died* 27 March 1858.

GALBRAITH, PETER [Before 1550]. *Married* Agnes Wardlaw. *Died* April 1571.

GALBRAITH, WILLIAM, LL.B. [16 January 1888]. Apprentice to William Stuart Fraser.—Son of Thomas Littlejohn Galbraith, Sheriff-Clerk of Stirlingshire and Town Clerk, Stirling. *Born* 22 October 1861. *Married* 31 July 1894, Mary Emily (*died* 20 December 1943), third daughter of William Henry Morris of Moorburn, Largs. *Died* 11 April 1953. *Firm*—Fraser, Stodart, and Ballingall.

GARDEN, ARTHUR WILLIAM [11 July 1910]. Apprentice to J. R. M. Wedderburn and G. G. Watson.—Son of William Garden, Paper Manufacturer, Penicuik. *Born* 1 June 1883. Lieutenant in R.A.S.C., and saw service during Great War in Salonica. *Died* 1 March 1934.

GARDINER, JAMES, OF HAUGHHEAD [22 January 1835]. Apprentice to Alexander Dallas and Thomas Innes.—Son of Rev. Matthew Gardiner, D.D., Minister of Bothwell. *Born* 18 May 1811. *Married* 16 October 1855, Charlotte (*died* 17 September 1903), daughter of Louis Henry Ferrier of Belsyde, West Lothian, and widow of Sir John Eyton Campbell of Auchenbreck, Bart. Sheriff-Substitute at Campbeltown, 1848-79. *Died* 8 December 1879.

GARDINER, JOHN RONALD, B.L. [30 November 1964]. Apprentice to Norman Smith and Another of Brodie, Cuthbertson & Watson.—Son of John Ritchie Gardiner, O.B.E., G.M., West Kilbride, Ayrshire. *Born* 25 October 1938. *Married* 4 December 1965, Aileen Mary, daughter of William Montgomery, Kirkcudbright. *Firm*—Brodies (formerly Brodie, Cuthbertson & Watson).

GARDNER, ALEXANDER [30 June 1789]. Apprentice to Alexander Duncan.—Eldest son of Alexander Gardner, Farmer at Reddoch, Stirlingshire. *Married*, proclaimed 27 March 1788, Agnes, daughter of John Loch, Jamaica. *Died* 1816.

GARDNER, CHARLES WILLIAM, B.L. [21 March 1932]. Apprentice to William J. Guild and Others of Guild & Guild.—Son of Henry J. Gardner, Solicitor, Edinburgh. *Born* 30 May 1905. *Married* 23 December 1933, Margaret Mary Blair (*died* 14 January 1981), daughter of Captain James Younger, Rangoon. *Died* 24 November 1979. *Firm*— Ferguson, Wallace & Gardner (latterly Cornillon, Craig & Thomas).

GARDNER, HAMILTON GRAY [22 June 1837]. Apprentice to John Hunter, Jun.— Eldest son of Gilbert Ogilvy Gardner, residing in Edinburgh. *Born* 26 May 1814. *Died* 25 February 1863, unmarried.

GARDNER, HENRY ROBINSON WILSON, B.L. [3 June 1946]. Apprentice to T. J. Carlyle Gifford and Others of Baillie & Gifford.—Son of Henry John Gardner, Solicitor, Edinburgh. *Born* 10 December 1915. *Married* (1) 12 March 1944, Catherine Smith (*died* 18 December 1973), daughter of George Baxter, Stamper and Teller, Inland Revenue, Edinburgh, and (2) 12 June 1974, Margaret Scott or McGill. Lieutenant Queen's Own Cameron Highlanders. Served U.K., India 1940-43. Discharged after contracting poliomyelitis in India. *Firms*—(1) Cuthbert & Gardner, Kinross; (2) J. L. Anderson, Gardner & Co., Kinross and Cupar.

GARDNER, JAMES, LL.B. [2 December 1968]. Apprentice to Charles Maxwell Ogilvie and Another of Gray, Muirhead & Carmichael.—Son of Robert Gardner, Ironfounder, Falkirk. *Born* 4 January 1946. *Firm*—Gray, Muirhead & Carmichael.

GARDNER, JOHN [21 December 1786]. Apprentice to Isaac Grant.—Eldest son of Alexander Gardner, Jeweller in Edinburgh. Attorney-at-Law, Jamaica. *Died* 1794.

GARDNER, PETER [28 December 1868]. Apprentice to Thomas G. Mackay and Alexander Howe.—Son of James Gardner, Orchardbank, near Perth. *Born* 14 November 1835. *Married* 13 April 1881, Georgiana Christian (*died* 27 October 1917), daughter of James Swanston, Marshall Meadows, Berwick. *Died* 14 August 1899.

GARDNER, WILLIAM [22 February 1813]. Apprentice to Sir James Gibson-Craig.— Second son of Alexander Gardner, Writer in Edinburgh. *Born* 1784. *Died* 11 June 1836, unmarried.

GARDYNE, JAMES CARNEGY, OF FINHAVEN [11 December 1810]. Apprentice to George Russell.—Second son of Thomas Carnegy of Craigo, Angus. *Born* 3 November 1785. *Died* 6 June 1864, unmarried.

GARRETT, GEORGE ALAN, B.L. [15 May 1942]. Apprentice to John Roger Orr and Another of Simpson & Marwick.—Son of William Garrett, Advocate, Edinburgh. *Born* 29 June 1916. *Married* 23 July 1945, Anny, daughter of Dr Panagiotis Tzouliadhis. R.A. Served U.K. and Egypt, also Italy and Greece 1940-45. *Died* 9 May 1977. *Firm*— Mitchell & Baxter (latterly Thomson & Baxter).

GARSON, JAMES [28 March 1898]. Apprentice to William Garson, his brother.—Son of George Garson, Stromness. *Born* 14 March 1865. *Married* 29 September 1909, Wilhelmina (*died* 23 November 1935), younger daughter of Thomas Bonnar, House Painter, Edinburgh. *Died* 21 January 1927.

GARSON, WILLIAM [18 March 1889]. Apprentice to W. F. Skene and Lewis Bilton.—Son of George Garson, Stromness. *Born* 20 December 1855. *Married* 5 February 1898, Agnes Cathie (*died* 4 May 1942), second daughter of Robert Scarth of Binscarth, and widow of John Macrae, Procurator-Fiscal of Orkney. *Died* 6 July 1915.

GARTSHORE, JAMES, OF ALDERSTON [6 October 1729]. Apprentice to Alexander Hamilton of Pencaitland.—Son of Mr James Gartshore, Minister of Carmichael. *Married* (1) Jean (*died* 12 Aug. 1750), daughter of Sir Patrick Scott of Ancrum, and widow of David Muirhead of Linhouse; and (2) June 1756, Helen (*died* 1788), daughter of John Spottiswoode, Advocate. *Died* 23 January 1774.

GASCOIGNE, MICHAEL NEIL CLIFTON, LL.B. [19 December 1973]. Apprentice to William Leslie and Others of Brodies.—Son of C. A. H. Gascoigne, Chartered Land Agent, Aberdeen. *Born* 1 February 1949. *Married* 20 September 1975, Anna Jennifer Milne. *Firm*—Brodies.

GAVIN, JOHN, O.B.E., LL.B. [18 July 1921]. Apprentice to W. H. Fraser, G. D. Ballingall, and W. Galbraith.—Son of John Gavin, Shipbroker, Royal Terrace, Edinburgh. *Born* 26 December 1894. *Married* 2 June 1923, Jean Mary, daughter of Lieutenant Reginald Abercromby Willis, R.N., Tunbridge Wells. Enlisted in 9th Royal Scots 1915, but later transferred to 469th Home Service Employment Company. Instrumental in the formation of the Scottish Home for the War Blinded at Linburn. Chairman, Royal Blind Asylum Board, 1944-61. *Died* 25 March 1961.

GAY, WILLIAM JAMES, M.A., LL.B. [13 May 1963]. Apprentice to Robert Scott and Another of Hagart & Burn-Murdoch.—Son of William Gay, Engineer, Avonbridge. *Born* 14 August 1931. *Married* 2 June 1964, Norma, daughter of Robert Patterson Inglis. *Firm*—Hagart & Burn-Murdoch.

GENTLE, JAMES [8 July 1823]. Apprentice to James Greig.—Son of James Gentle, S.S.C. *Born* 5 January 1799. *Died* 5 October 1890, unmarried.

GEORGE, EDWARD HARRY, O.B.E. [17 December 1928]. Apprentice to John J. Herdman.—Son of Charles George, S.S.C. *Born* 3 May 1904. *Married* 4 November 1929, Rosa Mary, daughter of George Grossmith, Actor Manager, of Spanish Place, London. Colonel, General Staff. Served U.K. and N.W. Europe 1940-45. *Died* 30 November 1957.

GIBB, JOHN STIRLING, B.L. [26 November 1956]. Apprentice to (1) Harold Leslie Duke and Another of Mitchell & Baxter and (2) Ronald Macduff Urquhart of A. & W. M. Urquhart.—Son of Robert Gibb, W.S., Edinburgh. *Born* 8 January 1930. *Married* 8 June 1957, Shiela Mary Rose, daughter of Edgar Dobson, Canon of Inverness Cathedral. *Firms*—(1) Pitcairn & Mathers and (2) Robson, McLean & Paterson.

GIBB, ROBERT [8 July 1907]. Apprentice to Arthur Henry M'Lean.—Son of John Stirling Gibb, Commission Agent, 31 East Claremont Street, Edinburgh. *Born* 16 March 1884. *Married* 24 April 1920, Claire Gladys, elder daughter of John Sturrock, Merchant, Edinburgh. During Great War served as Gunner R.F.A., 1917-19; and afterwards held commission in R.A.S.C. *Died* 27 May 1941.

GIBSON, SIR ALEXANDER, OF DURIE [Before 1631].—Son of Sir Alexander Gibson of Durie, one of the Senators of the College of Justice (Lord Durie). *Married* (1) Margaret Hamilton; and (2) 1625, Cecilia, daughter of Thomas Fotheringham of Powrie. Commissioner, 18 October 1631. Clerk of Council and Session, 25 July 1632. Knighted, 15 March 1641. Lord Clerk Register, 13 November 1641. Raised to the Bench, 2 July 1646; deprived, 13 February 1649. *Died* June 1656.

GIBSON, ARCHIBALD [4 January 1630]. Apprentice to William Cunningham.—*Married* Rebecca Logan. *Died* 1660.

GIBSON, ARCHIBALD [29 June 1661]. Apprentice to John Rowan.—Fourth son of Andrew Gibson, Burgess of Edinburgh, and brother to Alexander Gibson, Dean of Bower. *Born* 1634. *Died* September 1666.

GIBSON, ARCHIBALD, OF LADHOPE [3 July 1782]. Apprentice to Thomas Cockburn.— Only son of Rev. John Gibson, Minister of St Cuthbert's, Edinburgh. *Born* 8 August 1760. *Married* (1) 22 September 1785, Grace. daughter of Thomas Hogg, Merchant in Edinburgh; and (2) May 1817, Helen Blackie (*died* 25 September 1855). *Died* 9 April 1845.

GIBSON, GEORGE [Before 1550].

GIBSON, HENRY GORDON [29 May 1851]. Apprentice to, and second son of, John Gibson, Jun., W.S. *Born* 20 March 1827. *Married* 21 June 1860, Elizabeth Murray (*died* 29 December 1917), eldest daughter of Major J. M. Home, 36th Regiment. *Died* 8 February 1869.

GIBSON, JAMES *See* CRAIG, SIR JAMES GIBSON-

GIBSON, JAMES THOMAS, LL.B. [13 April 1885]. Apprentice to Francis James Dewar.—Son of Robert Gibson, Merchant, Edinburgh. *Born* 3 February 1859. Resident in Australia. *Died* there, 10 July 1935.

GIBSON, JOHN [19 November 1805]. Apprentice to John Hunter.—Son of Alexander Gibson, Town Clerk of Paisley. *Married* 4 December 1806, Agnes Mitchell (*died* 26 Feb. 1872), daughter of Ebenezer Mason, Merchant, Edinburgh. Resigned his Commission, 1822.

GIBSON, JOHN [12 June 1818]. Apprentice to, and eldest son of, Archibald Gibson, W.S. *Born* 1 February 1789. *Married* (1) 21 July 1818, his cousin, Catherine (*died* 27 August 1842), third daughter of John Dickson of Kilbucho, Peeblesshire, Advocate; and (2) 10 April 1849, Mary Ann Mazyck (*died* 9 March 1889), second daughter of Paul Weston, Physician, Charleston, U.S.A. *Died* 31 January 1879.

GIBSON, JOHN, *tertius*, OTHERWISE KNOWN AS JUNIOR [16 July 1819]. Apprentice to James Nairne.—Son of George Gibson, Merchant in Leith. *Born* 15 January 1796. *Married* 14 September 1824, Charlotte Ellen, eldest daughter of John Gordon, Edinburgh. Deputy Keeper of the Great Seal, 1853-58. Treasurer, 1862-70. Agent of Sir Walter Scott and Trustee for his creditors. Author of "Reminiscences of Sir Walter Scott" (1871). *Died* 14 September 1877.

GIBSON, JOHN HENRY [16 January 1888]. Apprentice to Robert Strathern.—Son of Henry Gordon Gibson, W.S. *Born* 1 August 1862. *Married* 19 February 1894, Catherine Mary Sear (*died* 8 March 1926). *Died* 5 April 1898.

GIBSON, THOMAS [26 August 1718]. Apprentice to Hugh Somerville.—Son of Alexander Gibson of Durie, Fife. *Married* Jean (*died* 2 January 1786), daughter of Colonel Thomas Dalyell of the Scots Guards. Principal Clerk of Session, 29 July 1726 till death. *Died* 6 April 1779.

GIBSON, THOMAS [13 January 1891]. Apprentice to George M'Intosh.—Son of John Gibson, Bank Teller in Edinburgh. *Born* 17 January 1866. *Married* 14 April 1898, Elizabeth Ann (*died* 27 May 1948), daughter of James Ross of Arnotdale, Falkirk. *Died* 8 June 1944. *Firm*—T. & T. Gibson & Kennedy, Falkirk.

GIBSON, WILLIAM [29 May 1878]. Apprentice to James Campbell Tait.—Son of Andrew Gibson, Builder, Auchinleck, Ayrshire. *Born* 27 July 1851. *Married* 31 March 1886, Jane Leyden (*died* 28 August 1944), eldest daughter of George M'Intosh, S.S.C., Edinburgh. *Died* 14 July 1923. *Firm*—Tait & Crichton.

GIFFORD, ADAM WEST [13 April 1885]. Apprentice to Colin Mackenzie, A. D. M. Black, and J. M. Mackenzie.—Son of John Gifford, Edinburgh. *Born* 12 January 1862. *Married* 15 July 1891, Charlotte Jean (*died* 19 May 1929), eldest daughter of James M'Laren, East India Merchant, Hampstead, London. *Died* 22 September 1945. *Firm*—Mackenzie and Black.

GIFFORD, DAVID ALAN, M.A., LL.B. [8 December 1975]. Apprentice to David Ronald Reid and Others of W. & J. Burness.—Son of William Cordiner Gifford, Civil Servant, Rosyth. *Born* 22 August 1946. *Married* 30 September 1972, Aileen Guthrie, daughter of James Guthrie Valentine, Kinghorn. *Firm*—W. & J. Burness.

GIFFORD, JOHN RENSHAW, B.A.(CANTAB) [13 December 1926]. Apprentice to Wm. A. MacGillivray and John P. Watson.—Son of Adam West Gifford, W.S. *Born* 23 September 1901. Lieut. R.N.V.R. H.M.S. *Repulse*. Believed *died* of wounds received at sinking of *Repulse* off coast of Malaya, 10 December 1941. *Firm*—Mackenzie and Black.

GIFFORD, THOMAS JOHNSTONE CARLYLE, LL.D., M.A., LL.B. [29 March 1905]. Apprentice to Henry Cook and Another of W. & J. Cook.—Son of Patrick Gifford, Farmer, Twynholm, Kirkcudbrightshire. *Born* 14 January 1881. *Married* (1) 11 June 1907, Maude Oriel Reata (data 3 August 1958), daughter of the Hon. Charles Henry Pearson, LL.D., Fellow of Oriel College, Oxford; and (2) 4 May 1960, Sophia Mary Wharton, daughter of John Hepburn Millar, Advocate. Employed by British Government during Second World War on realisation of British Securities on the American market. *Died* 24 January 1975. *Firm*—Baillie & Gifford (now Biggart, Baillie & Gifford).

GILBERT, ROBERT HENRY, B.L. [15 July 1949]. Apprentice to T. J. Carlyle Gifford and Others of Baillie & Gifford.—Son of Robert Gilbert, Solicitor, Inverness. *Born* 30 October 1924. *Married* 15 April 1951, Margaret Isabella, daughter of Dr David Garden. *Firm*—Anderson, Shaw & Gilbert, Inverness. (1950-56.)

GILCHRIST, DUGALD, YOUNGER OF OSPISDALE [23 June 1829]. Apprentice to Adam Gib Ellis.—Eldest son of Dugald Gilchrist of Ospisdale, Sutherland. *Born* 1804. *Died* 1 December 1834, unmarried.

GILCHRIST, JAMES [28 November 1791]. Apprentice to Hugh Corrie.—Eldest son of James Gilchrist, Merchant in Dumfries. *Born* 1765. *Married* 2 August 1802, Jessie (*died* 1834), daughter of Hugh Corrie of Calloch, W.S. Director, British Linen Company, 1795-1816. *Died* 28 August 1816.

GILCHRIST, JAMES GORDON [14 July 1947]. Apprentice to John Douglas Boswell and Others of Tait & Crichton.—Son of Sir James A. Gilchrist, Q.C., Sheriff Principal of Lothians and Peebles, Edinburgh. *Born* 4 September 1915. *Married* 7 October 1950, Joan Margaret Thomson. Lance Corporal R.A.S.C. Served U.K., India, Assam and Burma 1939-45. *Firms*—Haddon & Turnbull, Hawick, and Stevenson & Johnston, Langholm.

GILKERSONE, JAMES [27 November 1655].

GILL, JAMES [18 December 1922]. Apprentice to David Maxwell.—Son of William Gill, Merchant, Edinburgh. *Born* 15 November 1885. *Married* (1) 27 April 1932, Hannah (*died* 17 August 1934), daughter of John Russell, J.P., Trinity, Chamberlain of Leith, and (2): 10 December 1935, Elizabeth Geddes. During Great War was Captain R.G.A., and served in France. *Died* 9 May 1951. *Firm*—Maxwell, Gill, and Pringle.

GILLANDERS, GEORGE [17 December 1829]. Apprentice to Richard Mackenzie and William Sharpe.—Second son of John Gillanders of Highfield, Ross-shire. *Born* 1805. *Died* in India 12 October 1846, unmarried.

GILLESPIE, Sir JOHN [18 July 1844]. Apprentice to J. O. Mackenzie and William Sharpe.—Second son of George Gillespie of Biggar Park. *Born* 3 May 1822. *Married* 18 March 1847, Margaret Ross (*died* 11 February 1899), daughter of George Robertson, one of the Deputy Keepers of the Records. Secretary to the King's Bodyguard for Scotland, Royal Company of Archers. Knighted 1883. *Died* 2 January 1901.

GILLESPIE, JOHN HAMILTON [21 April 1875]. Apprentice to, and second son of, Sir John Gillespie, Kt., W.S.—*Born* 14 October 1852. *Married* (1) 17 September 1880, Mary Ann McIvor (*died* 23 November 1904); and (2) 23 May 1905, Blanche (*died* 31 December 1957), daughter of Richard P. McDaniel, Sarasota, Florida, U.S.A. Mayor of Sarasota, 1903-8. *Died* at Sarasota, Florida, 7 September 1923.

GILLESPIE, MICHAEL RUTHERFORD CLARK, B.A.(Cantab), LL.B. [12 July 1948]. Apprentice to James Harrower Guild of Russell & Dunlop.—Son of Rutherford Clark Gillespie, W.S., Castle Douglas, Kirkcudbrightshire. *Born* 2 March 1918. *Married* 12 April 1950, Janet Isabelle, daughter of George Melrose, Hallett, South Australia. Major K.O.S.B. Served India and Burma 1939-45. Honorary Sheriff Substitute, District of Stewartry, at Kirkcudbright. *Firm*—Lidderdale & Gillespie, Castle Douglas.

GILLESPIE, RUTHERFURD CLARK [10 December 1906]. Apprentice to W. J. Kirk and J. A. Hope.—Son of William Gillespie of Hillowton, Solicitor, Castle-Douglas. *Born* 26 September 1882. *Married* 30 October 1911, Helen Marjorie (*died* 11 January 1970), youngest daughter of William Tod, 3 Belgrave Place, Edinburgh. Captain on general list during Great War. Attached H.Q. Scottish Command. *Died* 6 May 1954. *Firm*—Lidderdale and Gillespie, Castle-Douglas.

GILLESPIE, THOMAS [2 April 1906]. Apprentice to Robert Strathern.—Son of James Gillespie, Architect, St Andrews. *Born* 5 July 1879. *Married* 24 November 1920, Carlotta, younger daughter of S. A. Macdonnell, Sydney. Latterly resident in British Columbia, Canada. *Died* 22 March 1958.

GILMOUR, JOHN [6 May 1598]. Apprentice to Robert Stewart.—Son of John Gilmour in Auchtermuchty. *Married* (1) Margaret (*died* August 1609), daughter of James Wintoun, Portioner of Newburgh; and (2) Elizabeth Edmond. Father of Sir John Gilmour of Craigmillar, Lord President, 1661. *Died* before 1638.

GILMOUR, ROBERT [12 July 1638].—Son of John Gilmour, W.S. *Born* 4 January 1601. *Married* Elizabeth, daughter of Thomas Sydserff. *Died* 25 September 1647.

GILMOUR, ROBERT LITTLE [4 March 1790]. Apprentice to Robert Sym.—Son of William Charles Little Gilmour of Liberton, Mid-Lothian. *Died* 29 March 1820.

GILROY, ALEXANDER [26 December 1933]. Apprentice to A. W. Gifford, C. M. Black and J. R. Gifford.—Son of Harold Bowman Gilroy, Fingask, Errol. *Born* 19 March 1906. *Married* 27 August 1931, Thelma McClymont Tubbs (*died* 23 May 1980). Served in Scottish Horse, Second World War. *Died* 22 March 1953.

GILROY, HAROLD DANVERS [20 December 1937]. Apprentice to Sir William Haldane and Another of W. & F. Haldane.—Son of Harold Oman Gilroy, Fingask, Errol, Perthshire. *Born* 6 November 1901. Served in Black Watch, R.H.R. Killed in action, Middle East, September 1941.

GIRDWOOD, RICHARD STUART HAXTON, LL.B. [30 April 1973]. Apprentice to Alan Forrest Stark and Others of Morton, Fraser & Milligan.—Son of Ronald Haxton Girdwood, Professor of Therapeutics, Edinburgh. *Born* 3 May 1947. *Married* 10 August 1974, Roberta Anne, daughter of William Hamilton Egan, Mount Egerton, Victoria, British Columbia. Barrister and Solicitor of Supreme Court of Victoria, 1974.

GIRVAN, DOUGLAS WILLIAM, M.A., LL.B. [13 November 1953]. Apprentice to Robert Francis Shepherd and Others of Shepherd & Wedderburn.—Son of Andrew Douglas Girvan, Company Director, Edinburgh. *Born* 25 December 1929. *Married* 31 March 1956, Sylvia Isobel, daughter of Samuel Sidney Dowds, Optician, Londonderry, N. Ireland.

GLASS, ALEXANDER [4 February 1695]. Apprentice to Robert Watson.—Son of Alexander Glass of Sauchie, Stirlingshire. *Married* Jean, daughter of Robert Blackwood, Dean of Guild, Edinburgh. Joint Fiscal, 1699-1702. Treasurer of the Society, 1714-22. *Died* 8 February 1733.

GLASS, WILLIAM [18 November 1830]. Apprentice to Walter Jollie.—Son of David Glass of Smiddygreen, Fife. *Died* 6 February 1857, aged 51, unmarried.

GLEGG, ANDREW HOGG [14 March 1892]. Apprentice to J. W. Young and John Blair.—Son of Robert Glegg of H.M. Exchequer. *Born* 2 September 1859. *Married* 6 June 1895, Jessie Chirnside, only daughter of John Francis Pillans, of Maines and Sunnyside, Berwickshire, and of 9 Craigmillar Park, Edinburgh. *Died* 2 February 1945.

GLEN, ALEXANDER [8 June 1804]. Apprentice to James Home of Linhouse.—Third son of Rev. Alexander Glen, Minister of Dirleton. *Born* 20 November 1777. *Died* 1841, unmarried.

GLOAG, THOMAS, OF CHAPELTON [28 June 1793]. Apprentice to George Cuming.—Eldest son of John Gloag, Merchant in Edinburgh. *Married* 21 September 1801, Elizabeth (*died* 28 June 1810), daughter of Captain John M'Intosh of Harwood. *Died* 4 January 1810.

GLOVER, JOHN [16 July 1889]. Apprentice to (1) John Bruce; and (2) A. T. S. Scott.—Son of Henry Douglas Glover, Solicitor, Gatehouse-of-Fleet. *Born* 19 August 1865. *Married* 2 September 1896, Alexina Maggie M'Clellan Casement (*died* 17 June 1948). *Died* 30 June 1927. *Firm*—Scott & Glover.

GLOVER, WILLIAM [12 June 1823]. Apprentice to Peter Couper.—Son of John Glover, Wright in Leith. *Married* 22 September 1823, Jane, daughter of James Cumming, Shipmaster in Leith. *Died* 17 February 1864, aged 66.

GOLDIE, ALEXANDER, OF RYES [25 January 1742]. Apprentice to, and son of, Thomas Goldie, W.S.—*Married* May 1747, Elizabeth (*died* 28 November 1789), daughter of Patrick Heron, younger of Heron, Galloway. *Died* 1782.

GOLDIE, ALEXANDER, OF BROOMLEE [17 October 1798]. Apprentice to Hugh Corrie.— Fourth son of James Goldie of Stenhouse. *Married* 16 September 1799, Miss Corsan, Baldoon (*died* 23 December 1843). *Died* 26 December 1850, aged 80.

GOLDIE, ARCHIBALD WATSON [5 March 1818]. Apprentice to James Gilchrist.— Second son of Archibald Goldie in Shaws of Tinwald. *Born* 21 January 1793. *Married* (1) 14 March 1833, Frances (*died* 18 May 1835), daughter of Darcy Lever of Arklington Hall, Yorks; and (2) 25 October 1860, Henrietta Townsend (*died* 16 February 1904), daughter of Rev. George Vaughan Hart, younger of Glen Alla, Donegal. Law Agent and Director of National Bank of Scotland. *Died* 19 November 1872.

GOLDIE, JAMES [17 February 1825]. Apprentice to, and son of, Alexander Goldie, W.S.—*Born* 1801. *Died* 10 March 1834, unmarried.

GOLDIE, THOMAS [26 March 1723]. Apprentice to William Alves. *Born* 1685.—Son of Thomas Goldie of Muirbank, Kirkcudbright, and Stenhouse, Dumfries. *Married* (1) Margaret Irving; and (2) Henrietta Sharp. Writer to the Privy Seal, 14 June 1733. *Died* 14 December 1741.

GOLDIE, WILLIAM, OF BROOMLEE [24 June 1835]. Apprentice to, and son of, Alexander Goldie, W.S. *Born* 9 August 1803. *Married* 28 May 1839, Mary (*died* 28 February 1887), eldest daughter of Captain Charles Hope Reid of Grangehill, Ayrshire. *Died* 7 August 1868.

GOODBURN, WILLIAM MILNE, M.A., LL.B. [26 November 1962]. Apprentice to David Fulton and Another of Tods, Murray & Jamieson.—Son of Robert Weir Goodburn, Solicitor, Peebles. *Born* 21 January 1939. *Married* 18 December 1961, Edith Ann Luke, daughter of George Morrison, Solicitor, Duns. *Firm*—Blackwood & Smith, Peebles.

GOODE (OTHERWISE GUDE), GEORGE [Before 1508].

GORDON, ADAM, OF ARRADOUL AND CAIRNFIELD [16 June 1796]. Apprentice to Craufurd Tait.—Second son of John Gordon of Cairnfield, Banffshire. *Born* 13 February 1773. *Married* 4 March 1799, Elizabeth (*died* 29 January 1847), daughter of Patrick Cruickshank of Stracathro, Forfarshire. *Died* 17 March 1847.

GORDON, ADAM HAY, OF AVOCHIE [15 November 1827]. Apprentice to John Gordon.— Second son of Major Adam Hay of the 35th Regiment. *Born* 18 September 1803. *Married* 13 April 1841, Anne M'Kerrel (*died* 3 September 1897), eldest daughter of James Brown, C.A., Edinburgh. Assumed name of Gordon, 1857. *Died* 8 April 1872.

GORDON, ALASTAIR JAMES, M.A., LL.B. [29 April 1968]. Apprentice to Charles G. Reid and Others of Thomson, Dickson & Shaw. *Born* 2 June 1941. *Firm*—W. & J. Burness.

GORDON, ALEXANDER, OF CAIRNFIELD [25 November 1723]. Apprentice to George Kennedy.—Son of Robert Gordon of Lunan. *Born* 17 November 1687. *Married* (1) Elizabeth (*died* 25 January 1735), daughter of —— Gordon of Cairnfield; and (2) Jane (*died* 11 September 1774), daughter of Sir John Gordon of Park, Bart., and of Shillagreens. *Died* 21 February 1775.

GORDON, ALEXANDER SHAND [17 March 1890]. Apprentice to Henry Tod.—Eldest son of Alexander Gordon, S.S.C., Edinburgh. *Born* 17 July 1867. *Married* 17 November 1909, Elizabeth Catherine (*died* 27 March 1947), elder daughter of Robert Logan Logan, Tea-planter, Assam, India. *Died* 5 February 1938. *Firm*—A. and A. S. Gordon.

GORDON, ARTHUR FORBES [9 December 1830]. Apprentice to John Gordon, Jun.— Son of Colonel Arthur Forbes of the 32nd Regiment. *Born* 2 June 1806. *Married* 20 April 1843, Charlotte (*died* 16 April 1890), eldest daughter of Colonel William Balfour of Trenaby, Orkney. Assumed name of Gordon. *Died* 27 August 1873.

GORDON, CHARLES, OF CLUNY [15 July 1763]. Apprentice to William Fraser of Ford.— Second son of John Gordon of Cluny, Aberdeenshire. *Married* 8 November 1775, Joanna (*died* 7 September 1798), daughter of Thomas Trotter of Mortonhall, Mid-Lothian. *Died* 8 May 1814.

GORDON, CHARLES [7 July 1824]. Apprentice to John Ker.—Son of Charles Gordon, Advocate in Aberdeen. *Died* 12 October 1848, aged 47, unmarried.

GORDON, CHARLES AUGUSTINE, OF DRIMNIN [10 December 1906]. Apprentice to Robert Strathern.—Son of Joseph Clement Gordon of Drimnin, Morven, Argyllshire. *Born* 8 January 1882. Assistant Public Trustee, Zanzibar, 1925-29. Public Trustee, Nigeria, 1929-32. Served in France and Flanders, 1915-19. Lieutenant in the Royal Scots. *Died* 9 August 1954.

GORDON, DAVID HUTCHISON, OF LARGLANGLEE [15 June 1837]. Apprentice to Andrew Storie.—Fourth son of Robert Gordon, Writer in Kirkcudbright. *Born* 10 August 1813. Procurator-Fiscal of Kirkcudbright, 1839-78. *Died* 16 March 1878, unmarried.

GORDON, DONALD NEIL, M.A., LL.B. [8 December 1975]. Apprentice to William Dunnett of Lindsay, Duncan & Black.—Son of Ian Gordon, Consultant Physician, Aberdeen. *Born* 30 March 1951. *Married* 14 September 1973, Alison Mary, daughter of William B. Whyte, Durness. *Firm*—Carlton & Reid, Dundee.

GORDON, GEORGE [15 March 1720]. Apprentice to Ronald Campbell.—*Married* 2 August 1727, Katherine, daughter of James Cleland, Merchant, Edinburgh. *Died* 21 March 1747.

GORDON, GEORGE [January 1740]. Apprentice to James Craig.—Eldest son of George Gordon, Writer in Edinburgh. *Born* 1715. *Married* February 1747, Joan Mary, daughter of Captain James Muirhead of Lauchope, Lanarkshire. *Died* 16 October 1783.

GORDON, GEORGE MORE, OF CHARLETON [29 June 1838]. Apprentice to Adam Gib and Robert Ellis.—Eldest son of John Shank More, Advocate. *Born* 21 March 1816. *Married* 10 August 1848, Janet, eldest daughter of Harry Gordon, Liverpool. *Died* 6 November 1899.

GORDON, GORDON CLUNES [19 July 1842]. Apprentice to, and second son of, Joseph Gordon, W.S.—*Born* 29 May 1811. Served eight years in Indian Navy before apprenticeship. *Died* 25 November 1843, unmarried.

GORDON, REV. HENRY [1 July 1825]. Apprentice to, and eldest son of, Thomas Gordon, W.S.—Ordained Minister of Newmarket and King, Ontario, 1834. Called to Presbyterian Church, Gananoque, Canada, 1837. Moderator of Presbyterian Church of Canada, 1854. *Died* 13 December 1880, unmarried.

GORDON, HUNTER [3 June 1824]. Apprentice to, and eldest son of, James Farquhar Gordon, W.S.—Latterly a Barrister in London. *Died* 1855, aged 54, unmarried.

GORDON, JAMES [Before 1631]. Deputy Keeper of the Signet, 1631. *Married* (1) Janet Kirk (*buried* March 1631), relict of William Keith of Beyton; (2) Margaret Alexander.

GORDON, JAMES [12 November 1829]. Apprentice to James Mackenzie and William Innes.—Son of William Gordon of Hallmyre, Peeblesshire. *Married* 18 July 1844, Harriet (*died* 28 February 1877), eldest daughter of J. Davies, Seatown. *Died* 11 March 1870.

GORDON, JAMES [20 November 1845]. Apprentice to Andrew Storie and William R. Baillie.—Eldest son of Rev. Robert Gordon, D.D., one of the Ministers of Edinburgh. *Born* 24 July 1821. *Married* 18 June 1852, Agnes Webster (*died* 2 November 1898), second daughter of J. Hepburn Millar, Merchant, Glasgow. Sheriff-Substitute at Banff, 1853-77. Author of works on family history, etc. *Died* Father of the Society, 23 May 1914.

GORDON, JAMES FARQUHAR, OF BALMOOR [19 December 1794]. Apprentice to (1) John Gordon; and (2) Adam Rolland.—Eldest son of John Gordon of Balmoor, W.S. *Married* (1) 13 November 1797, Lilias, daughter of Charles Hunter of Burnside, Angus; and (2) 1805, Margaret (*died* 29 September 1849), only child of Robert Haldane of Airthrey and Auchengray, Stirlingshire. *Died* at Avranches, Normandy, 23 December 1843.

GORDON, JAMES FRASER [15 July 1852]. Apprentice to Robert Mackay.—Son of William Gordon, residing at Minmore, Banffshire. *Born* 7 September 1816. *Married* 27 July 1851, Eleanor Sinclair (*died* 1863), daughter of Archibald Leslie of Balnageith, Elginshire. *Died* 24 April 1861.

GORDON, JAMES EDWARD [14 March 1892]. Apprentice to James Barker Duncan.—Second son of Alexander Gordon, S.S.C., Edinburgh. *Born* 11 September 1869. *Died* 14 March 1933, unmarried.

GORDON, JOHN, OF BALMOOR [8 July 1763]. Apprentice to Leonard Urquhart.—Son of Alexander Gordon of Auchenlachries, Aberdeenshire. *Married* 16 October 1770, Margaret (*died* 13 December 1829), daughter of James Stuart of Binend, Lord Provost of Edinburgh. *Died* 24 October 1789.

GORDON, JOHN [24 June 1774]. Apprentice to James Gartshore.—Eldest son of Thomas Gordon, Surgeon in Dumfries. *Born* 1748. *Married* 21 July 1786, Jane (*died* 25 July 1831), eldest daughter of Thomas Shairp of Houstoun, Linlithgowshire. *Died* 27 October 1832.

GORDON, JOHN, OF CARLETON [26 June 1789]. Apprentice to John Tait.—Son of Alexander Gordon of Carleton, Ayrshire. *Married* 24 June 1793, Margaret, only daughter of Dr Jasper Tough of Hillhead, Kirkcudbright. *Died* 13 March 1817.

GORDON, JOHN, OF AVOCHIE [19 December 1794]. Apprentice to Andrew Steuart, Jun.—Eldest son of John Gordon of Avochie. *Born* 1771. Deputy Receiver-General. *Died* 11 July 1842, unmarried.

GORDON, JOHN TAYLOR, OF NETHERMUIR [18 November 1825]. Apprentice to James Heriot.—Second son of Maxwell Gordon, W.S. *Born* 1801. *Married* December 1855, Margaret Grant (*died* 28 June 1916), daughter of Robert Watson. *Died* 24 June 1884.

GORDON, JOSEPH, OF CARROLL [16 February 1804]. Apprentice to Charles M'Intosh.—Eldest son of Captain John Gordon of Carroll, Sutherland. *Born* 1777. *Married* 30 July 1808, Ann (*died* 1882), youngest daughter of Gordon Clunes of Crakaig, Sutherland. Clerk to Admission of Notaries Public, 1839-55. *Died* 7 March 1855.

GORDON, LACHLAN DUFF, OF PARK [26 June 1769]. Apprentice to Alexander Stuart.—Fourth son of John Duff of Culbin, Morayshire. *Married* 14 September 1781, Rachel, second daughter of Roger Hog of Newliston, West Lothian. *Died* 14 May 1808.

GORDON, MAXWELL, OF NETHERMUIR [28 June 1793]. Apprentice to (1) Colquhoun Grant; and (2) John Taylor.—Son of William Gordon of Nethermuir. *Married* 30 March 1799, Jane (*died* 3 August 1848), daughter of John Taylor of Blackhouse, Ayrshire, W.S. *Died* 24 December 1809.

GORDON, ROBERT [18 August 1731]. Apprentice to James Budge.—*Died* June 1740.

GORDON, ROBERT, OF EDINTORE [17 August 1798]. Apprentice to John Innes.—Eldest son of John Gordon of Grieshop and Edintore, Elginshire. *Born* 6 May 1775. *Married* 30 August 1806, —— Wilkie (*died* 1863), widow of Archibald Burnett, Bengal. *Died* 1 August 1815.

GORDON, ROBERT, OF BARDARROCH [18 November 1830]. Apprentice to Alexander Blair.—Son of William Gordon, Sen., Writer in Dumfries. *Born* 1807. *Married* 23 April 1840, Sarah, second daughter of Wilson Fisher, Whitehaven. *Died* 2 December 1883.

GORDON, THOMAS, OF BUTHLAW [24 July 1672]. Apprentice to Alexander Hamilton.—Eldest son of James Gordon of Buthlaw, Aberdeenshire. *Married* 9 September 1673, Janet (*died* 4 May 1693), daughter of David Fletcher, Bishop of Argyll. Clerk of Justiciary, 6 November 1682. *Buried* 12 May 1690.

GORDON, THOMAS, OF WHITBURN [5 July 1782]. Apprentice to Andrew Stuart.—Only son of Rev. Thomas Gordon, Minister of Speymouth. *Born* 16 June 1755. *Married* 6 April 1785, Letitia (*died* 14 January 1814), daughter of Hugh M'Veagh, Manufacturer in Huntly. *Died* 6 March 1845.

GORDON, THOMAS [12 November 1840]. Apprentice to James Macallan.—Fourth son of William Gordon of Campbelton, Kirkcudbright. *Born* 14 February 1817. *Married* 6 July 1847, Eliza Cecilia (*died* 25 January 1890), third daughter of George Shaw Brooke, Jaffna, Ceylon. *Died* 9 October 1876.

GORDON, THOMAS JARRON [22 July 1868]. Apprentice to James Hope and Robert Mackay.—Son of James Gordon, Merchant in Forfar. *Born* 15 October 1837. *Married* 22 August 1871, Caroline Elizabeth (*died* 10 January 1937), only daughter of Henry Churton of West Mount, Cheshire. *Died* 26 April 1925.

GORDON, WILLIAM [14 November 1664]. Apprentice to John Bayne.—Son of James Gordon, W.S. *Married* 25 January 1666, Helen Anderson. *Died* March 1680.

GORDON, WILLIAM, OF GREENLAW AND CULVENNAN [25 January 1742]. Apprentice to Thomas Goldie.—Only son of second marriage of Sir Alexander Gordon of Earlstoun, Bart. *Born* 1706. *Married* 1740, Isabella (*died* October 1802), daughter of John M'Culloch of Barholm and Jean Gordon of Culvennan, his wife. *Died* 28 October 1757.

GORDON, WILLIAM, OF HARPERFIELD [5 July 1742]. Apprentice to (1) Hugh Somerville; and (2) Archibald Stuart.—Son of Dr John Gordon, Physician in Aberdeen. Latterly a Solicitor in London. *Died* 22 August 1787.

GORDON, WILLIAM, OF ROTHNEY [9 July 1789]. Apprentice to Samuel Mitchelson.—Only son of George Gordon of Rothney, Aberdeenshire. *Died* at Rothney, 10 February 1824.

GORDON, WILLIAM, OF CULVENNAN [12 February 1824]. Apprentice to Alexander Blair.—Eldest son of David Gordon, Captain in the Dumfriesshire Militia. *Born* 17 August 1800. *Married* 17 August 1825, Agnes Marian (*died* 23 May 1853), third daughter of John Hyslop of Lochend. *Died* 27 January 1858.

GORDON, WILLIAM JOHN, OF WINDHOUSE [27 October 1882]. Apprentice to Robert Strathern.—Son of John Gordon, Merchant in Dundee. *Born* 2 December 1857. Lieutenant R.N.V.R. Commanded patrols in Shetland waters. *Died* at sea, 4 January 1923.

GOUDY, ROBERT GEORGE, M.A., LL.B. [28 July 1952]. Apprentice to Arthur Woodman Blair and Another of Strathern & Blair.—Son of Patrick Goudy, Captain and Quartermaster the Black Watch, Port Patrick, Wigtownshire. *Born* 2 November 1917. *Married* 8 July 1944, Marcia Helen, daughter of John Ernest Moss, Building Contractor, Liverpool. Lieutenant, R.N.V.R. Served Home Fleet, Mediterranean Fleet and Western Approaches 1940-46. *Firm*—Strathern & Blair.

GOULD, FRANCIS ROBERTSON, B.L. [12 July 1948]. Apprentice to Euan Barclay Robertson and Others of J. & R. A. Robertson.—Son of William Gould, Fitter, Edinburgh. *Born* 21 October 1908. *Married* 4 August 1939, Margaret Henderson Black (*died* 10 January 1973), daughter of Thomas Todd, Gardener. Flight Lieutenant, R.A.F. Served Middle East, Second World War. *Firm*—J. & R. A. Robertson.

GOVAN, JOHN, OF BLALOWAN [13 June 1806]. Apprentice to David Balfour.—Son of Dr John Govan, Physician in Cupar. *Died* 22 October 1861, aged 79, unmarried.

GRACE, CHARLES DAVID BAIRNSFATHER, B.L. [19 December 1949]. Apprentice to Arthur H. C. Hope and Others of Hope, Todd & Kirk.—Son of Charles Lindesay Playfair Grace, W.S., St Andrews, Fife. *Born* 16 May 1922. *Married* 30 November 1946, Winifred Mary, daughter of G. Richardson, Bank Manager, South Shields. 2nd Lieutenant Coastal Defence, transferred (Captain) Argyll & Sutherland Highlanders (attached to Green Howards), Second World War. *Died* 28 October 1967. *Firm*—C. S. & C. L. P. Grace (1919-65) (latterly Pagan, Osborne & Grace, Cupar).

GRACE, CHARLES LINDESAY PLAYFAIR [15 December 1919]. Apprentice to Harry Cheyne, F. J. G. Borthwick, J. G. Kirkpatrick, Ian MacIntyre, and Harry Cheyne, Jun.—Son of Charles Stuart Grace, W.S., St Andrews. *Born* 1 October 1892. *Married* 7 September 1920, Nancy Beatrice, daughter of Lieut.-Colonel P. R. Bairnsfather, 14th Bengal Lancers. Clerk to Income Tax Commissioners of St Andrews District. Captain Highland Cyclist Batt. during Great War. *Died* 3 February 1959. *Firm*—C. S. and C. L. P. Grace, St Andrews.

GRACE, CHARLES STUART [28 April 1882] Apprentice to Sir John Gillespie and Thomas Paterson.—Son of Stuart Grace, Town Clerk of St Andrews. *Born* 6 April 1859. *Married* (1) 17 February 1885, Ella Mary (*died* 1 January 1926), eldest daughter of William Francis Lindesay of Fairieland, Ceylon; (2) 10 November 1926, Frances Mary, youngest daughter of Professor Hebblethwaite, Liverpool. *Died* 30 January 1936.

GRACIE, JOHN BLACK [29 November 1821]. Apprentice to Charles Oliphant.—Seventh son of John Gracie, Merchant in Wanlockhead. *Married* 1822, Jane Mitchell Leburn (*died* 11 September 1848). Principal Clerk of Commissary Court. *Died* 10 May 1847, aged 48.

GRACIE, WILLIAM [4 March 1805]. Apprentice to Alexander Young.—Eldest son of James Gracie, Accountant in Dumfries. *Married* 24 January 1806, Elizabeth Emily (*died* 1844), eldest daughter of Thomas James of Helsingham Hall, Cumberland. *Died* 24 March 1813.

GRAEME, JAMES, OF GARVOCK [8 March 1827]. Apprentice to Roger Aytoun.—Eldest son of Robert Graeme of Garvock. *Born* 23 July 1803. *Married* 26 June 1837, Helenade, only surviving daughter of Charles De Jersey, Attorney-General at Guernsey. *Died* 12 December 1859.

GRAEME, JOHN, OF ESKBANK [10 July 1770]. Apprentice to James Smyth.—Youngest son of Robert Graeme of Camno, brother to John Graeme of Balgowan, Perthshire. *Married* 29 June 1781, Mary Scott of Usan, Angus (*died* 18 April 1849). *Died* 19 September 1814.

GRAEME, ROBERT, OF WELL HALL [14 May 1835]. Apprentice to Roger Aytoun.—Son of Robert Graeme of Garvock. *Born* 12 June 1811. *Married* 28 April 1843, Anne (*died* April 1888), third daughter of Patrick Baron Seton of Preston, Linlithgowshire. *Died* 13 October 1870.

GRAHAM, ALEXANDER SPEARS [1 July 1830]. Apprentice to Tod and Hill.—Second son of Thomas Graham, residing in Leopold Place, Edinburgh. *Born* 1807. *Married* 1837, Eliza (*died* 18 March 1884 at Perth), second daughter of Colonel Robert Stirling, of H.E.I.C.S. *Died* June 1849.

GRAHAM, DOUGLAS FINLAY ROSS, M.A., LL.B. [7 September 1948]. Apprentice to George Purvis-Russell-Balfour-Kinnear and Others of Hamilton, Kinnear & Beatson.—Son of Donald Ross Graham, Accountant, Edinburgh. *Born* 11 May 1919. *Married* 21 March 1945, Winifred Hunter, daughter of Andrew Riddell, Solicitor. Gunner, R.A. Served U.K. 1939-40. *Firm*—Russel & Aitken (now amalgamated with Cuthbertson, Riddell & Graham).

GRAHAM, DOUGLAS RIDDELL ROSS, LL.B. [28 April 1975]. Apprentice to J. Leslie Falconer and Another of Fyfe, Ireland & Co.—Son of Douglas Finlay Ross Graham, W.S., Edinburgh. *Born* 14 June 1952. *Married* 14 September 1979, Caroline Janet Mitchell.

GRAHAM, HARRY [20 November 1671]. Apprentice to William Thomson.—Son of Robert Graham of Rothiesholme. *Married* 30 March 1676, Marion, daughter of James Hamilton, Merchant, Edinburgh. *Died* 23 May 1699.

GRAHAM, HENRY CUNNINGHAM [13 November 1834]. Apprentice to John Home.—Son of John Graham, Jeweller in Edinburgh. *Born* 1 January 1806. *Married* 14 April 1835, Jane Forrester (*died* 11 December 1839), eldest daughter of Rev. Archibald Maconochie, Minister of Bonkle. *Died* 11 April 1858.

GRAHAM, HUMPHREY [10 March 1813]. Apprentice to David Thomson.—Eldest son of Lieut.-Colonel Humphrey Graham, Chamberlain to the Duke of Argyll. *Born* 28 January 1789. *Married* 18 September 1826, Joanna, youngest daughter of Adam Wilson, D.C.S. *Died* 28 November 1868.

GRAHAM JAMES, OF DAMSIDE [14 November 1726]. Apprentice to John Lumsdaine.—Son of Robert Graham of Kirkland, Town Clerk of Perth. *Born* 28 July 1694. *Married* (1) 30 April 1728, Christian, daughter of George Balfour of Balbirnie, Fife; and (2) April 1740, Bethia (*died* 5 June 1776), daughter of James Deans of Woodhouselee, Mid-Lothian. *Died* 16 November 1763.

GRAHAM, REV. JAMES [11 December 1788]. Apprentice to Lawrence Hill.—Son of Thomas Graham, Writer in Glasgow. *Born* 22 April 1765. *Married* 17 March 1802, Janet (*died* 31 August 1815), daughter of Thomas Graham of Blatwood. Admitted Advocate, 17 March 1795. Ordained 28 May 1809. Curate of Shipton, Gloucester, and of Sedgfield, Durham. Author of *The Sabbath* and other poems. *Died* 14 September 1811.

GRAHAM, JAMES HOPE STEWART, OF DUNABBIE [2 November 1881]. Apprentice to William Stuart Fraser.—Son of James Graham of Dunabbie, Dumfriesshire. *Born* 16 April 1856. *Married* 13 October 1888, Isabel (*died* 20 July 1915), daughter of Robert Carlyle, Waterbeck, Dumfriesshire. *Died* at Waterbeck, 17 October 1922.

GRAHAM, JOHN [Before 1636].

GRAHAM, JOHN [20 May 1800]. Apprentice to John Morison.—Son of John Graham, Farmer at Colleum. *Died* 1831.

GRAHAM, KEITH HUNTER ROSS, LL.B. [7 December 1970]. Apprentice to Sir Alastair Campbell Blair and Others of Davidson & Syme.—Son of Douglas Finlay Ross Graham, W.S., Edinburgh. *Born* 29 May 1947. *Married* 1 September 1973, Patricia, daughter of Crofton Logan, Building Estimator, Edinburgh.

GRAHAM, PATRICK, OF ROBSHILL [25 November 1824]. Apprentice to John Tweedie.— Only son of John Graham of Robshill, Renfrewshire. *Born* 1799. *Married* 4 October 1831, Janet (*died* 11 March 1842), daughter of Allan Pollock of Faside, Renfrewshire. *Died* 15 November 1867.

GRAHAM, ROBERT [17 March 1797]. Apprentice to John Campbell.—Second son of James Graham of Duchraw, Stirlingshire. *Died* 27 August 1818.

GRAHAM, THOMAS [5 July 1821]. Apprentice to John Campbell.—Eldest son of Archibald Graham of Drumquhassle, Stirlingshire, Cashier to the Thistle Bank, Glasgow. *Born* December 1793. *Married* 14 March 1822, Agnes, daughter of Robert Veitch of Hawthornbank. Joint Keeper of the Register of Sasines for Renfrew. *Died* 29 June 1881.

GRAHAM, THOMAS EDWARD [19 March 1888]. Apprentice to John Clerk Brodie.— Elder son of James Graham, C.A., Glasgow, and grandson of Thomas Graham, W.S. *Born* 5 June 1863. *Died* 16 November 1896, unmarried.

GRAHAM, WILLIAM STIRLING. *See* STIRLING, WILLIAM.

GRANGER, JOHN [1 July 1790]. Apprentice to (1) William Wilson, Jun.; and (2) Walter Scott.—Only son of David Granger of Brokencross. *Died* 3 December 1828.

GRANT, ALEXANDER [28 June 1787]. Apprentice to Isaac Grant.—Son of Patrick Grant of Nevie. *Married* —— (*died* 2 April 1819). *Died* 4 July 1808.

GRANT, COLIN CAMPBELL [15 November 1860]. Apprentice to Allan Menzies and Robert Blair Maconochie.—Second son of Rev. James Grant, D.D., D.C.L., Edinburgh. *Born* 13 June 1830. Resigned his Commission, 9 November 1865. Called to the English Bar, 17 November 1868. *Died* 27 April 1902.

GRANT, COLQUHOUN, OF BURNSIDE [29 June 1759]. Apprentice to Alexander Steuart.— Third son of John Grant of Burnside. *Born* 14 February 1721. *Married* Christian, daughter of George Paton of Grandholm. Served during the '45 in Prince Charles' Life Guards. Fought at Culloden. *Died* 2 December 1792.

GRANT, DUNCAN, OF BUCHT [24 February 1825]. Apprentice to Kenneth and Thomas Mackenzie.—Son of James Grant of Bucht, Inverness-shire. *Born* 29 October 1801. *Married* 21 December 1847, Catherine Monro (*died* 24 March 1891), daughter of Alexander Warrand, M.D., H.E.I.C.S. *Died* 9 December 1873.

GRANT, SIR FRANCIS JAMES, K.C.V.O., LL.D. [10 January 1887]. Apprentice to (1) William Reid; and (2) Alexander Paterson Purves.—Second son of John Grant, Marchmont Herald, Edinburgh, and nephew of James Grant, Novelist. *Born* 4 August 1863. *Married* (1) 27 April 1899, Anne Irvine Cruickshank (*died* 1 April 1918), eldest daughter of David Charles Edmondston of Buness, Shetland, and (2) 30 October 1935, Violet Madeleine Bourne (*died* 16 April 1977), elder daughter of Rev. Joseph Murphy, Chaplain to the Forces. Carrick Pursuivant of Arms, 17 May 1886. Rothesay Herald, 8 September 1898. Lyon Clerk, 3 October 1898. Lord Lyon King of Arms, and Secretary of the Order of the Thistle, 10 May 1929. C.V.O., 1931. K.C.V.O., 1935. LL.D., 1931. Author of *Zetland Family Histories* and many other works on heraldry and genealogy. Joint Editor of *Fasti Ecclesiae Scoticanae*. *Died* 17 February 1953.

GRANT, FREDERICK BURNS, B.L. [13 May 1963]. Apprentice to Patrick C. Smythe and Others of J. & F. Anderson.—Son of Frederick Burns Grant. *Born* 5 October 1916. *Married* 19 September 1947, Dorothy (*died* 1957), daughter of Joseph Nicol. Lieut. R.N.V.R. Officer in Charge of Assault Craft Flotilla. Served in North African, Sicilian and Italian landings and "D Day" Invasion 1942-44. *Firm*—Gillespie, Macandrew & Co. (after amalgamation with Macandrew, Wright & Murray).

GRANT, ISAAC, OF HILTON [1 July 1763]. Apprentice to James Gartshore.—Son of John Grant in Belnatomb. Clerk to the Commissioners of Teinds. *Died* 27 December 1794, aged 70, unmarried. His tombstone in Greyfriars bears that "in him the poor lost a friend, the rich, a cheerful facetious companion, and the world an honest man."

GRANT, JAMES, OF BURNHALL [6 February 1792]. Apprentice to John Gordon.—Second son of Patrick Grant of Glenmoriston, Inverness-shire. *Born* 1768. *Married* 27 July 1803, Helen (*died* 27 February 1864), daughter of Charles Shearer of Knowhead. *Died* 6 June 1834.

GRANT, JAMES [19 June 1818]. Apprentice to John Tweedie.—Eldest son of Nathaniel Grant, S.S.C. *Born* 1790. *Died* March 1844, unmarried.

GRANT, SIR JAMES MONTEITH, K.C.V.O., M.A., LL.B. [18 July 1927]. Apprentice to James Watt and Another of Davidson & Syme.—Elder son of James Ricketts Grant, S.S.C., Edinburgh. *Born* 19 October 1903. *Married* (1) 29 June 1935, Frieda (*died* 10 August 1955), daughter of Stuart Lorimer, Edinburgh; and (2) 24 April 1958, Yvonne Margaret, daughter of Geoffrey Legh Wilkinson, Barrister at Law, Dental Surgeon in Leeds. Lord Lyon King of Arms 1969-81; K.C.V.O., 1969; Secretary to the Order of the Thistle since 1971; K.St.J. 1970; Carrick Pursuivant 1946; Marchmont Herald 1957. *Died* 1 December 1981. *Firms*—M. McGregor & Co. and W. B. Rankin & Nimmo (both now amalgamated with Hagart & Burn-Murdoch).

GRANT, JOHN [3 December 1729]. Apprentice to Robert Hepburn. *Married* 4 March 1726, Catherine, daughter of James Baird of Chesterhall, W.S. *Died* 26 May 1759.

GRANT, JOHN PETER [8 July 1822]. Apprentice to John Kermack.—Son of Rev. James Grant, Minister of Laggan, and his wife Ann MacVicar, the distinguished authoress of *Letters from the Mountains*, etc. *Born* 1 June 1799. *Married* (1) 16 March 1833, Margaret (*died* 17 April 1837), youngest daughter of Moses Steven, of Polmadie, Renfrewshire; (2) 22 October 1840, Robina (*died* 11 September 1850), daughter of Robert Grant of Kincorth, Morayshire; and (3) 17 November 1852, Jane Adinston (*died* 20 May 1892), daughter of Walter Graham, M.D., Dalkeith. *Died* 15 December 1870.

GRANT, JOSEPH [7 March 1815]. Apprentice to John Renton.—Only son of Allan Grant, Messenger-at-Arms, Edinburgh. *Born* 1793. *Died* 24 February 1873, unmarried.

GRANT, PATRICK [8 December 1825]. Apprentice to Harry Davidson.—Eldest son of James Grant, W.S. *Born* 2 June 1804. *Married* 6 August 1838, Emilia (*died* 16 March 1909), daughter of Evan Baillie of Dochfour, Inverness-shire. Sheriff-Clerk of Inverness-shire, 1831-70. *Died* 18 April 1870.

GRANT, ROBERT, OF RUTHRIE [8 March 1734]. Apprentice to Andrew Hay of Montblairie.—Eldest son of John Grant of Ruthrie. *Married* Catherine, daughter of William Cumming of Craigmill. *Died* 11 July 1783.

GRANT, ROBERT SIMPSON [16 July 1889]. Apprentice to John Cowan and James A. Dalmahoy.—Second son of William James Grant of Beldornie, Banffshire. *Born* 16 August 1865. *Married* 29 August 1895, Katherine Ann, daughter of Andrew Gauld, Seed Merchant. *Died* 3 March 1942.

GRANT, THOMAS MACPHERSON, OF CRAIGO [23 November 1837]. Apprentice to James Shepherd.—Son of Sir George Macpherson of Ballindalloch, Bart. Assumed name of Grant. *Born* 30 June 1815. *Died* 23 September 1881, unmarried.

GRAY, ALASTAIR DONALD, LL.B. [11 December 1979*].—Son of Robert William Stewart Gray, W.S., Edinburgh. *Born* 13 June 1947. *Married* 29 September 1970, Catherine Margaret, daughter of Bradford Falconer, Company Director, Edinburgh. *Firm*—Snell & Co.

GRAY, ALEXANDER [30 June 1760]. Apprentice to John Syme.—Son of John Gray, Writer in Fochabers. *Married* (1) Margaret Alves (*died* 23 July 1773); and (2) October 1773, Ellen, daughter of Archibald Stewart, Merchant, Edinburgh. Substitute Keeper, 16 November 1762. *Died* 14 January 1780.

GRAY, ALEXANDER STEWART [10 January 1887]. Apprentice to (1) James Gibson Craig Brodie; and (2) John Little Mounsey.—Son of William Gray, residing at Brownrigg, North Berwick. *Born* 17 May 1862. *Married* 10 April 1894, Aida Mary (*died* 11 October 1942), second daughter of James Alexander Forbes, Kilmeny, Merchiston, Edinburgh. *Divorce*, 19 March 1912. Achieved some notoriety as leader of the London "hunger marchers" in 1908. *Died* 13 April 1937.

GRAY, ANDREW [23 May 1820]. Apprentice to Thomas Cranston.—Eldest son of David Gray of Snipe, Tacksman of Dalhousie Mains, Mid-Lothian. Collector of Fee Fund, Court of Session, 1844-5. *Died* 28 July 1846, aged 54, unmarried.

GRAY, ARCHIBALD SCOTT, LL.B., C.A. [29 July 1968]. Apprentice to James Stewart and Others of Shepherd & Wedderburn.—Son of John Gray, Solicitor, Dundee. *Born* 15 January 1945.

GRAY, GEORGE [27 June 1839]. Apprentice to William Bell.—Son of George Gray, Surgeon in Edinburgh. *Born* 3 December 1808. *Married* (1) 1839, Martha Moses (*died* 28 November 1886); and (2) 22 February 1887, Helen (*died* 9 September 1892), daughter of William Wright, M.D., Edinburgh, and widow of John Wright, M.D., Lochgilphead. *Died* 19 April 1891.

GRAY, GEORGE ADINSTON [18 December 1826]. Apprentice to (1) Walter Dickson of Monybuie; and (2) George Dunlop.—Son of David Gray of Snipe, Mid-Lothian. *Died* 29 June 1851, aged 51, unmarried.

GRAY, JAMES [16 February 1710]. Apprentice to John Montgomerie.—*Married* Isobel White. *Died* November 1733.

GRAY, JOHN [1 July 1763]. Apprentice to John Dickie.—Eldest son of William Gray of Newholm. Town Clerk of Edinburgh, 1786-1811. *Died* 15 February 1811, unmarried.

GRAY, JOHN [24 June 1824]. Apprentice to Francis Brodie and George Imlach.—Third son of John Gray, Solicitor-at-Law. *Married* 17 April 1837, his cousin Harriet Louisa (*died* 28 June 1870), daughter of Andrew Gray of Craigo, Dumfriesshire. *Died* 16 October 1868, agd 70.

GRAY, JOHN PATERSON, M.A., LL.B. [4 December 1972]. Apprentice to (1) Ronald Kerr Will and Others of Davidson & Syme and (2) Professor A. J. McDonald and Others of Dickie, Gray, McDonald & Fair, Dundee.—Son of John Gray, Solicitor, Dundee. *Born* 23 September 1947. *Married* 21 March 1975, Alice Mary Philip. *Firm*— A. & R. Robertson & Black, Blairgowrie.

GRAY, KENNETH MORTON CROFT, B.A.(Oxon), LL.B. [14 December 1936]. Apprentice to J. Miller Thomson and Another of J. Miller Thomson & Co.—Son of William Croft Gray, S.S.C., Edinburgh. *Born* 5 January 1911. *Married* 19 February 1942, Eleanor Agnes Orford, daughter of John Eason, M.D., F.R.C.P.E. Captain Royal Scots. Served U.K. and N.W. Europe 1941-45. Solicitor to the Post Office in Scotland from 1962. *Firm*—Scott Moncrieff & Trail (formerly Croft Gray & Son and J. & J. W. Mackenzie prior to amalgamation in 1946). (Retired 1978.)

GRAY, ROBERT WILLIAM STEWART, M.A., LL.B. [18 March 1935]. Apprentice to J. Miller Thomson and Another of J. Miller Thomson & Co.—Son of Robert Gray, S.S.C., Edinburgh. *Born* 21 October 1911. *Married* 2 April 1942, Isabella Nairne, daughter of Archibald Stewart of the Chartered Bank. Bombardier, R.A. Served U.K. 1939-45. *Firm*—Ketchen & Stevens (prior to amalgamation, Campbell, Gray & Maitland).

GREEN, ALEXANDER DAVID MACKENZIE, M.A., LL.B. [11 December 1979*].— Son of Alexander Green, Auctioner and Valuator, Cupar. *Born* 31 December 1949. *Married* 1 March 1975, Sheila, daughter of James Finlay. *Firm*—Pagan, Osborne & Grace, Cupar.

GREEN, HENRY ARCHIBALD VAUGHAN [10 July 1911]. Apprentice to H. S. N. Callander of J. & R. A. Robertson.—Son of Harry Vaughan Green, Artist. *Born* 2 January 1888. *Married* (1) 3 September 1914, Katharine Mary Frances (*died* 22 May 1955), daughter of Dr Josiah George Blackman, Landport, Hants; and (2) 20 September 1963, Fiona, daughter of William James McLaren, Q.C. (Canada). Special Counsel, Law Department, Canadian Pacific Railway. *Died* 6 June 1979.

GREENLAW, GEORGE [30 January 1797]. Apprentice to Sir Robert Dundas of Beechwood.—Son of Rev. Michael Greenlaw, D.D., Minister of Creich. *Born* 7 May 1769. *Married* 15 July 1808, Katherine (*died* November 1833), daughter of George Makgill of Kemback, Fife. *Died* 12 December 1834.

GREGORSON, ANGUS MACLAINE [16 January 1893]. Apprentice to P. W. Campbell and James Mylne.—Son of Angus Gregorson, Sheep Farmer, Australia (of the Ardtornish family). *Born* 5 July 1868. *Married* 11 October 1902, Beatrice Margaret Roper (*died* 20 March 1926), eldest daughter of the late James Roper Boswall of Wardie, Major-General, H.M. Indian Army (late Madras Staff Corps). Captain 9th Royal Scots, 1914. *Died* 13 February 1944.

GREIG, ALEXANDER, OF HALLGREIG [5 March 1801]. Apprentice to (1) William Campbell of Crawfordton; and (2) James Horne.—Eldest son of David Greig of Hallgreig. *Born* 1776. *Married* 8 January 1810, Jane (*died* 22 March 1862), daughter of John Whittet of Potterhill, Perth. Solicitor to Admiralty, 1807. *Died* 29 March 1857.

GREIG, DAVID [6 March 1817]. Apprentice to James Greig.—Son of Rev. David Greig, Minister of the Associate Burgher Congregation of Lochgelly. *Married* 12 July 1824, Catherine (*died* 1866), daughter of Joseph Maxton, Edinburgh. *Died* 26 January 1825.

GREIG, GEORGE, OF ECCLES [13 July 1848]. Apprentice to, and eldest son of, James Greig of Eccles, W.S.—*Born* 12 March 1823. *Married* 24 July 1866, Isabella (*died* 13 December 1914), younger daughter of William Richardson Dickson of Alton, Roxburghshire. *Died* 19 June 1869.

GREIG, JAMES, OF ECCLES [4 March 1805]. Apprentice to Robert Hill.—Son of George Greig of Bridgend, near Kinross. *Born* 10 March 1782. *Married* 10 October 1820, Agnes (*died* 30 March 1867), second daughter of John Borthwick of Crookston, Mid-Lothian. *Died* 10 December 1859.

GREIG, JAMES, OF WEST CAMBUS [11 December 1823]. Apprentice to James F. Gordon.— Son of John Greig, Ironmonger in Edinburgh. *Born* 19 April 1798. *Married* 11 September 1827, Agnes Helen (*died* 26 May 1877), daughter of Peter Macfarlane, of West Cambus, Clackmannanshire. *Died* 25 December 1850.

GREIG, JOHN BORTHWICK [7 June 1859]. Apprentice to, and son of, James Greig of Eccles, Berwickshire, W.S.—*Born* 2 May 1824. *Married* 12 August 1857, Mary Jane (*died* 28 April 1902), eldest daughter of William Grant of Funchal, Madeira. Parliamentary Solicitor to Society. *Died* 16 August 1903.

GREIG, SOMMERVILLE [15 March 1861]. Apprentice to John Auld.—Son of James Greig of West Cambus, W.S. *Born* 6 November 1835. *Died* 2 October 1919, unmarried.

GRETTON, GEORGE LIDDERDALE, B.A.(DURHAM), LL.B. [9 December 1980]. Apprentice to Robert William Stewart Gray and Another of Ketchen & Stevens.—Son of David Foster Gretton, B.B.C. Programme Director, Birmingham. *Born* 10 November 1950. *Married* 27 July 1976, Helen Jessica, daughter of Gareth Morgan, Professor of Greek, University of Texas, Austin, U.S.A.

GREY, MICHAEL FRANCIS, B.A.(OXON), LL.B. [4 December 1967]. Apprentice to A. J. R. Bisset and Others of Baillie & Gifford.—Son of Major Frederick George Margaritus Grey, Regular Soldier, H.L.I. *Born* 16 April 1941. *Married* 6 August 1966, Mary Eileen, daughter of John Hunter Paterson. *Firm*—Gillespie, Macandrew & Co. (formerly Gillespie & Paterson and Hope, Todd & Kirk).

GRIERSON, ANDREW [1 March 1832]. Apprentice to Andrew Tawse.—Son of Andrew Grierson, Clothier in Edinburgh. *Born* 1 January 1808. *Died* 9 October 1876, unmarried.

GRIERSON, HENRY JAMES, B.A.(CANTAB) [6 July 1896]. Apprentice to A. T. S. Scott.—Son of Henry Grierson, of Milton Park, Kirkcudbrightshire, J.P., D.L. Born 17 June 1868. *Married* 19 April 1898, Flora, younger daughter of Major Herbert Buchanan of Arden, Dunbartonshire. During War was Adjutant 2/6th Black Watch, 1915-16; France, 1916; A.P.M., Dover Garrison, 1917-19. Major. *Died* 17 January 1961.

GRIERSON, JAMES GILBERT HAMILTON [11 December 1911]. Apprentice to William Stuart Fraser and W. H. Fraser.—Son of Sir Philip J. Hamilton Grierson, Advocate, Solicitor of Inland Revenue, Edinburgh. *Born* 1 May 1887. 2nd Lieutenant Royal Scots Fusiliers. *Killed* in action at the Dardanelles on 12 July 1915. He bequeathed his collection of English Literature to the Library.

GRIERSON, THOMAS [30 June 1789]. Apprentice to Andrew Blane.—Son of David Grierson, Farmer, Cubbox, Kirkcudbright. *Died* 5 September 1826.

GRIERSON, WILLIAM. *See* YORSTOUN, WILLIAM GRIERSON.

GRIEVE, ANDREW [24 May 1821]. Apprentice to John Ross.—Son of John Grieve, Civil Engineer in Edinburgh. *Married* 1843, Louisa Jane (*died* 30 March 1897), daughter of Captain Salmond, H.E.I.C.S. *Died* 6 May 1870, aged 73.

GRIEVE, JOHN [12 December 1904]. Apprentice to James Burness.—Son of Charles Cassells Grieve of Bank Park, Tranent. *Born* 19 October 1881. *Married* 2 July 1918, Helen Maude Renee (*died* 8 November 1949), daughter of John Ogilvy Macrae, of Antwerp, Belgium. Major R.A.S.C., and served during Great War in Egypt, Macedonia, Serbia, and Palestine. *Died* at Fort-William, 14 July 1926.

GRIFFITHS, JOHN ROBERT, B.A.(OXON), LL.B. [6 December 1971]. Apprentice to (1) William Denys Cathcart Andrews and Others of Shepherd & Wedderburn and (2) A. J. Ambrose and Others of Macandrew, Wright & Murray.—Son of Dr H. W. C. Griffiths, Consultant Anaesthetist, Edinburgh. *Born* 16 September 1944. *Married* 28 June 1969, Diana Jane, daughter of C. G. Wallace, Milton Bridge, Midlothian.

GRIMSTON, KENNETH ROBERT, M.A., LL.B. [4 December 1967]. Apprentice to Frederick J. L. Main of Bonar, Hunter & Johnstone.—Son of Edward Robert Tymon Grimston, Headmaster, Edinburgh. *Born* 4 July 1934. *Married* 13 September 1958, Josephine Kay, daughter of Robert Burton Crook, Standish, Lancashire. *Firm*—J. & F. Anderson.

GROTE, GILBERT [Before 1552]. Clerk of the Diocese of Caithness. His Protocol Book was published by the Scottish Record Society, 1914.

GRUBER, HARRY, B.L. [26 November 1962]. (By Rule IX(a).)—Son of Frederick Harry Gruber. *Born* 26 August 1927. *Married* 8 March 1954, Doris Sophia, daughter of Frederick Egner. *Firm*—Haldanes, McLaren & Scott (formerly Haldanes & McLaren).

GUEST, The Hon. SIMON EDWARD GRAHAM, LL.B. [8 July 1974]. Apprentice to Sir Alastair Blair and Others of Davidson & Syme.—Son of Rt. Hon. Lord Guest of Graden, P.C., Senator of the College of Justice and Lord of Appeal in Ordinary. *Born* 22 April 1949. *Married* 3 September 1977, Fiona Boyd, daughter of R. W. T. Lamont, Draper, Kilmarnock. *Firm*—Bell & Scott, Bruce & Kerr.

GUILD, ALEXANDER [26 March 1900]. Apprentice to James Reid.—Son of David Guild, Burnside, Forfar. *Born* 6 August 1852. *Married* 26 September 1883, Margaret Arnot (*died* 20 March 1921), second daughter of William Macmeikan, Writer, Edinburgh. *Died* 10 December 1925. *Firm*—Reid & Guild, then Guild & Guild.

GUILD, DAVID JAMES, B.L. [28 November 1955]. Apprentice to W. J. Guild of Guild & Guild.—Son of William John Guild, W.S., Edinburgh. *Born* 28 May 1929. *Married* 12 April 1971, Brigid Elizabeth, daughter of Kenneth Nigel Mackenzie, Canon in the Scottish Episcopal Church. *Firm*—Guild & Guild.

GUILD, IVOR REGINALD, M.A.(Oxon), LL.B. [19 December 1949]. Apprentice to Robert Francis Shepherd and Others of Shepherd & Wedderburn.—Son of Arthur Marjoribanks Guild, Stockbroker, Dundee. *Born* 2 April 1924. Procurator Fiscal to the Lyon Court; Clerk to the Court of Holyroodhouse. *Firm*—Shepherd & Wedderburn.

GUILD, JAMES HARROWER [9 July 1900]. Apprentice to George Dunlop and J. A. S. Millar.—Son of William Guild, Mugdrum, Newburgh, Fife. *Born* 11 December 1872. *Married* 5 April 1906, Marion Lyon (*died* 31 July 1967), daughter of James Lyon Guild, Inverness. *Died* 8 March 1951. *Firm*—Russell and Dunlop.

GUILD, JOHN ERSKINE [15 July 1886]. Apprentice to J. O. Mackenzie, Harry Cheyne, and John Kermack.—Son of John Guild, Merchant, Dundee. *Born* 23 June 1860. *Married* 22 January 1898, Florence Martha (*died* 30 November 1951), second daughter of David Turnbull, W.S. *Died* 10 April 1914.

GUILD, REGINALD MACKENZIE [7 July 1913]. Apprentice to J. E. Guild, A. Shepherd and R. F. Shepherd.—Son of Alexander Mackenzie Guild, Stockbroker, Dundee. *Born* 1 March 1888. *Married* 27 January 1930, Mary Wilson, daughter of John Wilson Brodie, C.A., Edinburgh. During Great War, Sergeant 1st Vol. Batt. The Royal Scots (Lothian Regt.). Member of the King's Bodyguard for Scotland, Royal Company of Archers. *Died* 17 December 1957. *Firm*—Shepherd and Wedderburn.

GUILD, STUART ALEXANDER, T.D., B.L. [20 November 1950]. Apprentice to William John Guild and Another of Guild & Guild.—Son of William John Guild, W.S., Edinburgh. *Born* 25 January 1924. *Married* 21 November 1950, Fiona Catherine, daughter of Andrew Francis MacCulloch, Analytical Chemist, Edinburgh. Captain R.A. Served in India, Burma, French Indo-China and Malaya 1942-47. *Firm*—Guild & Guild.

GUILD, WILLIAM JOHN [8 December 1913]. Apprentice to, and son of, Alexander Guild, W.S.—*Born* 1 February 1889. *Married* 12 April 1923, Mary Margaret Morton (*died* 4 May 1967), elder daughter of J. A. Stuart, S.S.C., Edinburgh. During War served with R.F.A. in France, 1915-16. Appointed Acting Captain. Scottish Amateur Golf Champion 1926. *Died* 8 December 1958. *Firm*—Guild & Guild.

GULLAND, WILLIAM [18 June 1856]. Apprentice to Thomas Gray Scott.—Eldest son of Charles Gulland, Writer in Falkland. *Born* 19 December 1828. *Died* 30 January 1898, unmarried.

GUMLEY, CHARLES STEWART [21 March 1932]. Apprentice to Andrew Wishart and Others of Wishart & Sanderson.—Son of Sir Louis Stewart Gumley, LL.D., D.L., Lord Provost of Edinburgh (1935-38). *Born* 28 May 1908. *Married* 5 April 1938, Frances, daughter of Captain John Arthur Fearnside, M.C. *Died* 24 November 1977. *Firm*—Connell & Connell.

GUNN, HAMISH IAIN TURNER, M.A., LL.B. [15 July 1949]. Apprentice to T. J. Carlyle Gifford and Another of Baillie & Gifford.—Son of James Turner Gunn, M.B., Ch.B., F.R.C.S.E., Auchterarder, Perthshire. *Born* 28 May 1915. *Married* 26 October 1961, Blanche Elizabeth, daughter of Kenneth Noel Young, Attorney, Durban, South Africa. Lieutenant (A/Captain) Royal Scots, 1939-46. *Firm*—J. C. & A. Steuart.

GUTHRIE, ALEXANDER [Before 1550].

GUTHRIE, ALEXANDER [4 January 1698]. Apprentice to James Winraham.—Son of Thomas Guthrie, Dyer Burgess of Linlithgow. *Married* (1) (contract, 25 July 1695) Matilda Pearson; and (2) 11 September 1700, Jean, daughter of James Menteith of Auldcathie, West Lothian. *Died* 30 September 1729.

GUTHRIE, CHARLES [7 December 1903]. Aprentice to (1) L. A. Guthrie; and (2) J. P. Wood, W. Babington, and J. Inglis.—Son of Charles John Guthrie, K.C., LL.D., one of the Senators of the College of Justice (Lord Guthrie). *Born* 9 September 1879. *Married* (1) 12 June 1907, Janie Alice Christian (*died* 1 October 1928), only daughter of John Lornie Sievwright, Stockbroker, Dundee, and Craiglea, Newport, Fife; and (2) 18 October 1930, Louisa Emily (*died* 31 March 1957), daughter of John Crommelin Brown, I.C.S., and widow of W. A. Mackay, M.D., F.R.C.S., Huelva, Spain. Director of Edinburgh Legal Dispensary. War Service: Lieutenant and Equipment Officer 5th Brigade, R.A.F. *Died* 9 November 1962. *Firm*—Wallace & Guthrie.

GUTHRIE, JAMES [Before 1627]—Son of Rev. Henry Guthrie, Minister of Bendochy. *Married* (contract, 30 October 1633), Margaret, sister to William Halyday of Tullibole. *Died* before 1649.

GUTHRIE, JAMES [25 February 1720]. Apprentice to, and son of, Alexander Guthrie, W.S.—*Married* Jean, daughter of John Dickson, Merchant, and Accountant to the City of Edinburgh. Author of *An Introduction to the Knowledge of Decimal Arithmetic*, 1731. *Died* March 1737.

GUTHRIE, JOHN [20 April 1688]. Apprentice to William Guthrie.—*Married* (contract, 4 December 1692), Euphan (*died* May 1745), daughter of John Butler of Kerland. *Died* before 1704.

GUTHRIE, JOHN GRAEME ROBERTSON, T.D. [16 March 1936]. Apprentice to William Babington and Others of Melville & Lindesay.—Son of Charles Guthrie, W.S., Edinburgh. *Born* 17 May 1911. *Married* 24 June 1936, Margaret Monica Grosvenor, daughter of John Grosvenor Stewart, Carpet Manufacturer, Lasswade. Major, R.A.C., 2nd Lothian and Border Horse. Served U.K. 1939-45. *Died* at Malta, 8 January 1953. *Firm*—Wallace & Guthrie.

GUTHRIE, LAURENCE ANDERSON [15 July 1886]. Apprentice to Patrick William Campbell.—Son of Patrick Guthrie, Merchant in Edinburgh, and grandson of Rev. Thomas Guthrie, D.D. *Born* 16 June 1863. *Married* 30 July 1890, Helena Elizabeth Mary (*died* 11 September 1928), only daughter of James Muirhead, Advocate, Professor of Civil Law in Edinburgh University. *Died* 7 August 1933. *Firm*—Wallace and Guthrie.

GUTHRIE, RICHARD [1612]. Signs the Acts of 7 December 1612. *Died* before 1633.

GUTHRIE, RICHARD [14 December 1627]. Servitor to John Shairp of Houston, Advocate. Re-admitted, 21 November 1661. Resigned his Commission, and *died* January 1664.

GUTHRIE, WILLIAM [7 March 1664]. Apprentice to Richard Guthrie.—*Married* 22 October 1663, Mary, daughter of Richard Guthrie, W.S., and widow of John Lockhart of Heids, Advocate. *Buried* 16 January 1673.

HAGART, JAMES VALENTINE [12 November 1868]. Apprentice to Archibald Burn Murdoch.—Son of James Valentine Hagart of Glendelvine, Perthshire, S.S.C. *Born* 1845. *Died* 22 September 1900, unmarried.

HAIG, JAMES, OF BEMERSYDE [15 November 1827]. Apprentice to Hugh Watson.—Eldest son of James Haig of Bemersyde, Berwickshire. *Born* 4 October 1795. *Died* 14 January 1854, unmarried.

HAIG, JOHN BALFOUR [11 January 1892]. Apprentice to John Cowan and J. A. Dalmahoy.—Son of William James Haig of Dollarfield, Dollar. *Born* 19 September 1868. *Married* 28 June 1900, Edith Robson (*died* 5 April 1955), daughter of Charles William Wilson, Shipowner and Timber Merchant, Quebec, Canada. Procurator-Fiscal of Clackmannanshire, 1897. Clerk to Commissioners of Income Tax, 1897. Clerk of Lieutenancy, 1930. *Died* 17 October 1938. *Firm*—MacWatt and Haig, Alloa.

HALDANE, ARCHIBALD RICHARD BURDON, C.B.E., D.Litt., B.A.(OXON), LL.B. [13 December 1926]. Apprentice to George David Ballingall and Others of Fraser, Stodart & Ballingall.—Son of Sir William Stowell Haldane, W.S. *Born* 18 November 1900. *Married* 12 December 1941, Janet Macrae, daughter of Thomas Henry Simpson-Smith. Author of several books on Scottish subjects. (Retired.) *Firms*—(1) W. & F. Haldane and, after amalgamations, (2) Haldane & McLaren and Haldanes, McLaren & Scott.

HALDANE, FRANCIS GROVE [16 July 1889]. Apprentice to W. J. Dundas.—Son of James Haldane, C.A., Edinburgh. *Born* 30 November 1866. *Married* 12 June 1893, Gertrude Hilda Taylor (*died* 14 October 1940), stepdaughter of Peter M'Lagan of Pumpherston. *Died* 7 February 1932. *Firm*—W. and F. Haldane.

HALDANE, GEORGE [25 May 1635]. Apprentice to Harry Osburn.—Son of George Haldane and grandson of George Haldane of that Ilk. *Married* Isabel, daughter of Dundas of Newliston. *Buried* 4 January 1663.

HALDANE, HERBERT JOHN, B.A.(OXON), LL.B. [14 December 1936]. Apprentice to Robert Nevill Dundas and Others of Dundas & Wilson.—Son of Herbert William Haldane, C.A., Edinburgh. *Born* 19 March 1912. Captain R.A. Served U.K. and North West Europe 1939-45. *Firm*—Haldanes, McLaren & Scott (formerly W. & F. Haldane and Haldanes & McLaren). (Retired 1978.)

HALDANE, JAMES ALEXANDER [12 December 1867]. Apprentice to, and eldest son of, Robert Haldane, W.S. *Born* 11 December 1844. *Married* 22 July 1868, Sarah Jean (*died* 3 August 1933), only child of John Reid of Bellevliet, Cape Town. *Died* at Forres, 23 August 1901.

HALDANE, ROBERT, OF CLOANDEN [5 March 1829]. Apprentice to John Yule.—Third son of Captain James Alexander Haldane, H.E.I.C.S. *Born* 27 January 1805. *Married* (1) 20 July 1841, Jane (*died* 24 February 1851), daughter of John Makgill of Kemback, Fife; and (2) 27 July 1853, Mary Elizabeth (*died* 20 May 1925), second daughter of Richard Burdon Sanderson of West Jesmond, Northumberland. *Died* 12 June 1877.

HALDANE, ROBERT MUNGO JOHN [12 December 1977]. Apprentice to J. C. R. Inglis and Others of Dundas & Wilson.—Son of James Haldane, C.A., Edinburgh. *Born* 21 June 1952.

HALDANE, WILLIAM CUNINGHAME [16 December 1824]. Apprentice to Robert Fleming.—Second son of John Haldane, Writer in Edinburgh. *Married* 22 August 1833, Catherine Ann (*died* 29 April 1897), fifth daughter of Alexander Miller of Monkcastle. *Died* at Wollongong, N.S.W., 4 July 1844, aged 43.

HALDANE, Sir WILLIAM STOWELL, B.L., of CLOAN AND FOSWELL [19 March 1888]. Apprentice to Alexander Howe and William MacGillivray.—Youngest son of Robert Haldane, W.S. *Born* 19 August 1864. *Married* 29 June 1892, Margaret Edith Stuart (*died* 13 November 1943), elder daughter of Thomas Nelson, Printer, Edinburgh. Crown Agent, 1905. Knighted, 1912. *Died* 7 November 1951. *Firm*—W. and F. Haldane.

HALIBURTON, ANDREW [26 August 1699]. Apprentice to David Haliburton.—Second son of John Haliburton of Newmains, Berwickshire. *Born* 9 March 1673. *Married* 18 April 1700, Marion, second daughter of Robert Elliot of Middlemiln, Roxburghshire. *Died* 20 February 1738.

HALIBURTON, ANDREW [1 July 1763]. Apprentice to Hew Crawford.—Son of James Haliburton, W.S. Resigned his Commission, 8 August 1785, and *died* 26 January 1794, unmarried.

HALIBURTON, DAVID [4 December 1693]. Apprentice to James Peter.—Son of Thomas Haliburton of Newmains, Berwickshire. *Died* 29 April 1697, aged 58, unmarried.

HALIBURTON, JAMES [8 March 1726]. Apprentice to Alexander Hamilton of Dechmont.—*Married* 6 April 1726, Euphan, daughter of Andrew Dunnet, Merchant, Edinburgh. *Died* 25 November 1773.

HALIBURTON, WILLIAM [Before 1508].

HALL, ALASTAIR DAVID ARMSTRONG, LL.B. [11 December 1979]. Apprentice to Duncan Campbell McConnachie and Others of Dundas & Wilson.—Son of David Armstrong Hall, Landowner and Company Director, Eaglesham, Renfrewshire. *Born* 1 October 1956.

HALL, JOHN SHARP [9 July 1821]. Apprentice to Craufurd Tait.—Son of Rev. James Hall, Minister of Lesmahagow. *Born* 7 February 1798. *Married* Margaret Fleming (*died* 24 January 1840). *Died* at Bedford, Province of Quebec, 30 September 1885.

HALL, ROBERT [8 July 1828]. Apprentice to John Forman.—Son of Robert Hall, one of the Magistrates of Edinburgh. *Born* 1804. *Died* 12 July 1840, unmarried.

HALL, SAMUEL JAMES, B.L. [28 November 1955]. Apprentice to Arthur Henry McLean and Others of Robson, McLean & Paterson.—Son of Samuel James Hall, Company Director, Edinburgh. *Born* 29 May 1930. *Married* 26 July 1957, Olive Douglas, daughter of David Kerr. *Firm*—Robson, McLean & Paterson.

HALYBURTONE, GEORGE. Reponed, 30 May 1636. *Died* before 1646.

HALYDAY, JOHN, of TULLIBOLE [Before 1555].—Son of John Halyday of Dumfries. *Married* (1) Marion Cuke; and (2) Elizabeth Hay. Admitted Advocate, 17 March 1584. *Died* 19 September 1606.

HAMILTON, ALEXANDER, of HILL [16 July 1642]. Apprentice to James Kirkwood.—Eldest son of James Hamilton of Hill, Lanarkshire. *Married* (contract, 2 August 1637) Marion (*died* 13 March 1685), daughter of Patrick Ellis, Merchant Burgess of Edinburgh. Depute Justice-Clerk, 1642. *Died* March 1672.

HAMILTON, Sir ALEXANDER, of HAGGS, BART. [15 July 1700]. Apprentice to William Forrester.—Son of Sir Alexander Hamilton, first Baronet of Haggs. *Died* about 1710.

HAMILTON, ALEXANDER, OF DECHMONT AND PENCAITLAND [6 November 1711]. Apprentice to Hugh Somerville.—Second son of James Hamilton of Pencaitland, East Lothian, W.S., who became a Senator of the College of Justice, with the title of Lord Pencaitland. *Married* Mary, eldest daughter of Sir Francis Kinloch of Gilmerton, Bart. *Died* 21 March 1758.

HAMILTON, ALEXANDER [31 May 1827]. Apprentice to James Hamilton of Kames.— Eldest son of Charles Hamilton, Merchant in Glasgow. *Born* 1797. *Married* (1) 3 November 1836, Margaret Chisholm (*died* 13 January 1841), only daughter of Richard Landreth of Island of Grenada; and (2) 15 July 1845, Mary Chisholm (*died* 3 November 1894), eldest daughter of Charles Robertson of Kindeace, Ross-shire. *Died* 1 January 1884.

HAMILTON, ANDREW, OF SPITTALHAUGH [3 July 1781]. Apprentice to John Russell.— Son of Charles Hamilton of Spittalhaugh, Peeblesshire. *Died* 3 May 1807.

HAMILTON, ARTHUR [Before 1594]. *Died* about 1629.

HAMILTON, DANIEL, OF GILKERSCLEUGH [29 June 1786]. Apprentice to David Erskine.—Third son of Alexander Hamilton of Gilkerscleugh, Lanarkshire. *Born* 1760. *Married* 20 December 1793, Harriet, second daughter of Walter Campbell of Shawfield, Lanarkshire. *Died* 30 June 1823.

HAMILTON, ERNEST [27 October 1882]. Apprentice to Alexander Hamilton, George Thomas Kinnear, and Robert Beatson.—Son of Alexander Hamilton, W.S. *Born* 23 March 1859. *Died* 13 June 1927, unmarried.

HAMILTON, FRANCIS [11 December 1828]. Apprentice to James Bridges.—Son of William Hamilton, Writer in Hamilton. *Married* 2 November 1829, Mary Stevenson, eldest daughter of Captain D. Mackintosh, Royal Highlanders. *Died* at Hamilton, 17 December 1858, aged 54.

HAMILTON, JAMES, OF PENCAITLAND [19 February 1683]. Apprentice to Sir James Elphinstone.—Second son of Robert Hamilton of Presmennan. *Born* 28 August 1659. *Married* Catherine, daughter of —— Denholm of Westshiells. Town Clerk of Edinburgh, 1683. Clerk Register, 27 February 1697. Clerk of Parliament. Principal Clerk of Session, 2 June 1697. Elevated to the Bench, 8 November 1712, when he assumed the title of Lord Pencaitland. Resigned, 1726. *Died* 30 May 1729.

HAMILTON, JAMES, OF KAMES [5 March 1801]. Apprentice to Daniel Hamilton, his brother.—Youngest son of Alexander Hamilton of Gilkerscleugh. *Married* 12 December 1808, Harriet Frances (*died* 12 December 1860), daughter of Richard Wynne of Folkingham, Lincolnshire. *Died* 5 January 1849, aged 72.

HAMILTON, JOHN [15 March 1644]. Apprentice to John Mudie.—Re-admitted, 21 November 1660.

HAMILTON, JOHN [24 October 1678]. Apprentice to William Charteris.—Son of Major Robert Hamilton. *Married* 19 October 1677, Rachel, daughter of Robert Sandilands, elder, Merchant Burgess of Edinburgh.

HAMILTON, JOHN [2 January 1682]. Apprentice to Robert Hamilton of Presmennan, his uncle.—Elder son of Mr James Hamilton, Minister of Eaglesham. *Married* 4 April 1684, Agnes (*died* 19 December 1742), daughter of William Law of Lauriston, Goldsmith, Edinburgh, and sister of the financier.

HAMILTON, JOHN, OF NEWTON [3 March 1707]. Apprentice to John Cuningham.—
Eighth son of William Hamilton of Wishaw. *Born* 30 November 168. *Married* Jean (*died* 25 February 1745), daughter of —— Gartshore of that Ilk. *Died* 25 January 1757.

HAMILTON, JOHN [30 July 1716]. Apprentice to John Loutfoot.—Fiscal, 1726-8. Resigned his Commission, 27 June 1748.

HAMILTON, JOHN [2 March 1826]. Apprentice to Walter Dickson.—Second son of Captain John Hamilton of 73rd Regiment. Substitute Keeper of the Signet, 1831-67. Admitted Advocate, 8 July 1815. *Died* 25 January 1870, aged 77, unmarried.

HAMILTON, PATRICK [Before 1612]. Signs the Acts, 26 December 1627. *Married* 16 April 1612, Marjorie, daughter of James Hamilton of Haggs, and widow of James Crawford, Portioner of Broughton.

HAMILTON, ROBERT, OF PRESMENNAN [24 March 1648]. Apprentice to Thomas Forrest.—Son of James Hamilton of Barncleugh, Lanarkshire. *Married* 17 March 1653, Marion, eldest daughter of John Denholm of Muirhouse. Re-admitted, 21 November 1661. Principal Clerk of Session, 5 June 1661. Resigned his Commission, 3 February 1668. Admitted Advocate, 13 June 1677. Elevated to the Bench, 1 November 1689, when he assumed the title of Lord Presmennan. *Died* 10 November 1695, aged 73.

HAMILTON, ROBERT [12 April 1648]. Apprentice to John Mudie.—*Married* 10 January 1656, Elizabeth Wellwood (*died* 26 March 1689). Clerk to Society, 1660-81. Re-admitted, 21 November 1661. *Buried* 19 April 1687.

HAMILTON, ROBERT [12 March 1736]. Apprentice to James Baillie.—*Died* November 1742.

HAMILTON, ROBERT [24 June 1830]. Apprentice to John Bowie.—Son of John Hamilton, Receiver-General of Customs. *Born* 1806. *Married* 13 July 1840, Christina Crawford (*died* 18 January 1890), daughter of Rev. Thomas MacKnight, D.D., Edinburgh. *Died* 21 June 1872.

HAMILTON, ROBERT PETER CRAIGEN, M.A., LL.B. [8 December 1975]. Apprentice to Alexander James Ramsay Bisset and Others of Baillie & Gifford.—Son of Robert Hamilton, Farmer, Burdiehouse Mains, Liberton, Edinburgh. *Born* 26 August 1951. *Married* 3 June 1977, Fiona Margaret, daughter of Kenneth Matthews, Civil Servant. Depute Clerk of Court and Legal Assessor to Scottish Land Court.

HAMILTON, WILLIAM [22 November 1680]. Apprentice to John Sempill.—Son of Archibald Hamilton of Hallcraig, Lanarkshire. *Born* 1636.

HAMILTON, WILLIAM [29 October 1697]. Apprentice to James Hamilton of Pencaitland.—Third son of Robert Hamilton of Presmennan, East Lothian. *Born* 1665. *Died* unmarried.

HAMILTON, WILLIAM [22 February 1793]. Apprentice to John Tait, Sen.—Son of William Hamilton, Writer in Mauchline. *Died* 24 December 1822.

HAMILTON, WILLIAM HUGH, OF CAIRNS [27 March 1899]. Apprentice to Patrick Murray, Wm. Campbell Johnston, and R. D. Beith.—Son of William Hamilton of Cairns, Kirknewton, Mid-Lothian. *Born* 31 December 1874. *Married* 7 April 1920, Florence Marguerite (*died* 22 April 1981), third daughter of the Rev. Matthew Gardner, Minister of Hyndland, Glasgow. During Great War was Acting Paymaster, Scottish Command, 1915-19. *Died* 7 June 1956.

HANDYSIDE, HUGH [29 June 1827]. Apprentice to Robert Paul.—Son of Hugh Handyside, Merchant in Edinburgh. *Married* 3 September 1834, Ann Innes (*died* 1870), fourth daughter of Captain William Anderson, 96th Regiment. *Died* 3 November 1867, aged 64.

HANDYSIDE, WILLIAM [12 July 1791]. Apprentice to Charles Innes.—Son of Robert Handyside at Whitehill. *Born* 19 June 1764. *Married* 5 June 1797, Jane (*died* 28 November 1840), daughter of William Cunningham of Bridgehouse. Father of Lord Handyside. *Died* 17 January 1816.

HANIFORD, PAUL SYDNEY, M.A., LL.B. [9 December 1980*].—Son of Isaac Haniford, Company Director, Glasgow. *Born* 26 November 1955.

HANNAY, JOHN, OF OVER-LAGGAN [22 November 1821]. Apprentice to (1) Joseph Cauvin; and (2) James Carnegy.—Fourth son of James Hannay of Blarinie, Kirkcudbrightshire. *Born* 1798. *Married* 15 September 1824, Eliza Sproat, daughter of Captain James Kennedy, Dalton, Dumfriesshire. *Died* 26 April 1868.

HARDIE, IAN JAMES, LL.B. [13 May 1980*].—Son of James Lamb Hardie, Agricultural Scientist, Edinburgh. *Born* 11 November 1952. *Married* 23 July 1977, Vivian Evelyn, daughter of William John Corpe, Educational Adviser, Edinburgh. *Firm*—James & David W. B. Tait, Kelso.

HARDIE, NICOLL [26 November 1668]. Apprentice to John Muir.—Son of Robert Hardie, Burgess of Edinburgh. *Born* 1639. *Married* 25 July 1669, Mary, daughter of Alexander Clerk, Merchant Burgess of Edinburgh. *Died* February 1689.

HARDING-EDGAR, PAUL NICHOLAS ROBERT, B.L. [20 December 1937]. Apprentice to William Campbell Johnston and Others of Murray, Beith & Murray.— Son of George Harding-Edgar, Grain Merchant and Landowner, Edinburgh and East Lothian. *Born* 5 August 1914. *Married* (1) 25 September 1939, Bethia Iona, daughter of Patrick Keith Murray, W.S., Edinburgh and (2) 20 January 1967, Gabriele, daughter of Werner Kieschke of Berlin. Lieutenant Colonel R.A. 1939-45. Served Middle East. *Firm*—Lindsays (previously Cowan & Dalmahoy).

HARDMAN, ALASDAIR FRASER, LL.B. [9 December 1980]. Apprentice to J. S. Ritchie and Others of W. & J. Burness.—Son of Wilfred Hardman, Royal & Merchant Navy (Retired). Ballater, Aberdeenshire. *Born* 22 May 1952. *Married* 27 May 1977, Catriona Sarah Weir, daughter of William Adam, Linesman, Dunblane. *Firm*—W. & J. Burness.

HARDYMAN, JOHN HAY [15 November 1838]. Apprentice to Humphrey Graham.— Only surviving son of William Henry Hardyman, Commander in East India Company's Service. *Born* 2 July 1814. *Married* 28 November 1861, Annabella Gibson (*died* 28 June 1903), daughter of William Paton, Armagh, and relict of Stewart Maxwell. Assistant Extractor, Court of Session, 1853-71. *Died* 9 February 1871.

HARE, ALEXANDER MACONOCHIE [14 July 1864]. Apprentice to Robert Blair Maconochie.—Son of Stewart Bayley Hare of Calderhall, Mid-Lothian. *Born* 14 January 1838. *Died* 14 October 1876, unmarried.

HARLAW, JAMES [Before 1555].—Son of William Harlaw, Burgess of Edinburgh. *Married* Barbara Touris. *Died* 6 March 1586-7.

HARLAW, JAMES [1599]. Apprentice to Richard Cass.—Son of James Harlaw, W.S. *Born* 1573. *Married* 23 April 1606, Margaret Purves. Keeper of the Privy Seal. *Died* 28 August 1617.

HARLEY, HARRY HERBERT [14 January 1895]. Apprentice to W. H. Murray and John Maclachlan.—Youngest son of William Harley, residing at South Lawn, Fountainhall Road, Edinburgh. *Born* 28 October 1872. *Married* 8 June 1898, Fanny (*died* 18 March 1939), daughter of William Scott, Glasgow. (*Divorced* January 1912.) *Died* at Johannesburg, 6 April 1912.

HARPER, ALEXANDER [11 December 1905]. Apprentice to J. H. Sang and A. W. Hog.— Son of Duncan Harper, 139 Warrender Park Road, Edinburgh. *Born* 24 February 1881. Enlisted in A. and S. Highlanders, 1915; in France, 1916-18; received a Commission in Royal Scots. *Died* 16 January 1963.

HART, DAVID [Before 1605]. Being at the horn, suspended 27 January 1608.

HART, JOHN MILLAR, LL.B. [30 April 1973]. Apprentice to Patrick Arthur McLean and Others of Robson, McLean & Paterson. *Born* 24 March 1949. *Married* 14 July 1971, Margaret Ross Low.

HARTLEY, WILLIAM AUGUSTUS [11 April 1887]. Apprentice to F. Pitman, J. R. Anderson, W. H. Murray, and A. R. C. Pitman.—Son of William Hartley, Factor to the Earl of Mansfield at Comlongan Castle, Dumfriesshire. *Born* 15 July 1861. *Married* 16 January 1900, May Janet (*died* 3 January 1954), daughter of Sir John Skelton, K.C.B. *Died* 25 August 1928. *Firm*—Duncan & Hartley.

HARVEY, GEORGE WADDELL, M.B.E., T.D. [26 March 1928]. Apprentice to John Cowan and Others of Cowan & Dalmahoy.—Son of The Very Rev. James Harvey, D.D. *Born* 7 June 1898. *Married* 8 September 1926, Ellen McNaughton, daughter of Peter McNaughton Low. Major, R.A. Served U.K. 1939-45. *Died* 9 September 1977. *Firms*—(1) E. A. & F. Hunter & Co.; (2) E. A. & F. Hunter & Harvey; (3) Hunter, Harvey, Webster & Will.

HARVEY, JOHN [10 December 1798]. Apprentice to (1) Michael Nasmyth; and (2) Colquhoun Grant.—Second son of Dr John Harvey, Physician in London. *Died* 13 December 1832, aged 70, unmarried.

HARVEY, JOHN, B.L. [19 December 1932]. Apprentice to John Richardson of Scott Moncrieff & Trail.—Son of Colonel Charles Blundell Harvey, R.E., Marlborough, Wilts. *Born* 11 July 1909. *Married* 2 January 1959, Barbara, daughter of John Henry Alderson, Schoolmaster. Honorary Sheriff of North Strathclyde at Oban. *Firm*— Hosack & Sutherland, Oban. (Retired.)

HARVEY-JAMIESON, HARVEY MORRO, O.B.E., T.D., B.L. [16 December 1955]. Apprentice to Sir William Campbell Johnston and Others of Murray, Beith & Murray.—Son of Alexander Harvey Morro Jamieson, O.B.E., Advocate, Edinburgh. *Born* 9 December 1908. *Married* 23 January 1936, Frances, daughter of Colonel Julian Yorke Hayter Ridout, D.S.O. Lieutenant Colonel, R.A. Served U.K. and N.W. Europe 1939-45. Member of the Queen's Bodyguard for Scotland, Royal Company of Archers. Secretary and Legal Adviser to the Company of Merchants of the City of Edinburgh 1946-71. (Retired.)

HARVEY-JAMIESON, RODGER RIDOUT, LL.B. [6 December 1971]. Apprentice to Patrick Murray and Others of Murray, Beith & Murray.—Son of Harvey Morro Harvey-Jamieson, W.S., Edinburgh. *Born* 30 June 1947. *Married* 9 October 1971, Alison Mary, daughter of Edward Whitworth, Industrial Chemist. *Firm*—Murray, Beith & Murray.

HARVIE, THOMAS [Before 1592]. Servitor to John Henryson. *Married* Agnes Harlaw. Commissioner, 16 December 1594. *Died* 21 January 1602.

HASWELL, JAMES [12 November 1869]. Apprentice to Thomas Graham Murray.— Eldest son of George Haswell, Writer in Edinburgh. *Born* 31 May 1842. *Died* 18 March 1873, unmarried.

HATHORN, VANS, OF CHANGUE AND GARTHLAND [3 July 1781]. Apprentice to Thomas Tod.—Second son of Hugh Hathorn of Castlewigg, Wigtownshire. *Born* 1753. *Married* 19 September 1814, Jane, eldest daughter of Sir John Dalrymple Hay of Park Place, Bart. *Died* 14 October 1839.

HATTON, JAMES [2 July 1829]. Apprentice to (1) James Pedie; and (2) James Thomas Murray.—Son of David Hatton, Carver and Gilder in Edinburgh. *Married* Anne, daughter of John Traquair of Hillhead, Lasswade. *Died* 28 September 1866, aged 61.

HATTON, ROBERT [30 June 1831]. Apprentice to William Renny.—Son of David Hatton, Carver and Gilder in Edinburgh. *Married* 13 August 1830, Marion Joan (*died* 25 November 1891), daughter of John Traquair of Hillhead, Lasswade. *Died* 24 November 1838.

HAY, ADAM. *See* GORDON, ADAM HAY.

HAY, ALEXANDER.—Son of John Hay and grandson of Sir Alexander Hay of Easter Kennet. *Married* Jean (*died* 2 June 1666), daughter of Robert Winram of Liberton. Commissioner, 18 October 1631. Clerk of Council and Session, 27 November 1597. *Died* April 1636.

HAY, ALEXANDER [19 August 1718]. Apprentice to Patrick Murray.—*Married* (1) 1 June 1721, Jean, daughter of Mr Robert Cheyne, one of the Ministers of Edinburgh; and (2) 14 September 1735, Katherine, daughter of James Lumsden, Surgeon. *Died* 6 October 1744.

HAY, ALEXANDER, OF HARDENGREEN [1 July 1819]. Apprentice to Francis Wilson.—Son of James Hay, Assistant Clerk of Session. *Born* 11 August 1796. *Married* 24 November 1834, Jane (*died* 12 October 1850), youngest daughter of Robert Brown of Westbarns, East Lothian. *Died* 18 December 1854.

HAY, ANDREW, OF HAYSTOUN AND KINGSMEADOWS [Before 1612]. Apprentice to James Kinnear.—Son of John Hay of Kingsmeadows, Peeblesshire. Signs the Acts, 7 December 1612. *Married* Janet (*died* 30 August 1635), daughter of Peter Hay of Leys. *Died* 1655.

HAY, ANDREW, OF MONTBLAIRIE [23 November 1719]. Apprentice to John Stewart, Sen.—Son of Andrew Hay of Montblairie, Aberdeenshire. *Married* (1) Ann (*died* May 1719), second daughter of Sir Alexander Ogilvy of Forglen, one of the Senators of the College of Justice (Lord Forglen); and (2) (contract, 23 December 1721) Mary, daughter of George Allardice of that Ilk. *Died* 5 December 1750.

HAY, CHARLES [14 November 1800]. Apprentice to William Balderston.—Son of Alexander Hay of Mordington, Berwickshire. *Died* in Ceylon, 27 December 1819.

HAY, DANIELL [1594].—Second son of Alexander Hay of Easter Kennet. Writer to the Privy Seal. Reported not having an "open buith," 1607.

HAY, FRANCIS, OF BALHOUSIE [Before 1617]. Apprentice to James Kinnear.—Son of Peter Hay of Kirkland of Megginch, brother of George, first Earl of Kinnoull. *Married* (1) 2 July 1618, Janet, eldest daughter of James Halliburton of Essie; and (2) (contract, 26 April 1637) Elspeth, daughter of John Oliphant of Bachilton, Perthshire. Commissioner, 26 December 1627. Fined £2000 by Cromwell's Act of Grace and Pardon, 1654. *Died* before 1661.

HAY, HAROLD GORDON, B.L. [25 April 1955]. Apprentice to Charles R. Black and Another of Warden, Bruce & Co.—Son of the Rev. Henry Sutcliffe Hay, Edinburgh. *Born* 27 August 1924. *Married* 1 August 1950, Pauline Elizabeth Denholm. Captain, Queen's Own Cameron Highlanders. *Firm*—Hagart & Burn-Murdoch.

HAY, JAMES [Before 1627].

HAY, JAMES, OF CARRIBER [16 August 1671]. Apprentice to William Charters and John Kennedy.—Second son of David Hay of Woodcokdale, Linlithgow. *Married* 19 December 1672, Magdalen (*died* February 1713), daughter of —— Robertson, Goldsmith and Burgess of Edinburgh. *Died* December 1702.

HAY, JAMES, OF COCKLAW [9 December 1728]. Apprentice to Andrew Hay of Montblairie.—Second son of Mr Adam Hay of Asleid, Minister of Monquhitter. *Married* (1) July 1733, Ann, daughter of Alexander Farquharson, W.S.; and (2) July 1746, Agnes (*died* 18 February 1786), daughter of John Moodie of Ardbikie, Angus. Father of Charles Hay who became Lord Newton in 1806. *Died* 20 June 1771.

HAY, JAMES [3 August 1742]. Apprentice to Alexander Stevenson of Montgreenan.—Second son of Lord William Hay of Newhall, Mid-Lothian. *Married* October 1744, Jane (*died* 25 February 1758), daughter of John Henderson of Liston, Haddingtonshire. Warden of the Mint, 24 March 1744-79. *Died* 31 May 1779.

HAY, JAMES [3 July 1778]. Apprentice to Samuel Mitchelson.—Son of James Hay of Cocklaw, W.S. *Died* 6 June 1788.

HAY, JAMES [13 July 1780]. Apprentice to (1) William Hay; and (2) John Syme.—Eldest son of William Hay, W.S. *Died* 1794.

HAY, JAMES [30 June 1789]. Apprentice to Thomas Tod.—Eldest son of John Hay, younger of Hopes, East Lothian. *Born* 1764. *Married* 11 July 1798, Matilda Hay (*died* 29 January 1838), daughter of Captain John Clark, H.E.I.C.S., and widow of Alexander Falconar of Woodcot. *Died* 15 October 1821.

HAY, JOHN [Before 1595]. Commissioner, 4 December 1595. *Married* 26 May 1602, Maria Johnston.

HAY, JOHN, OF RESTALRIG [1 March 1726]. Apprentice to Hew Crawford.—Second son of Alexander Hay of Huntington, East Lothian, and brother of Thomas Hay who ascended the Bench as Lord Huntington in 1754. *Married* December 1727, Anne (*died* 27 June 1739), daughter and heiress of James Elphinston of Restalrig, Mid-Lothian. Fiscal, 1732-4. Treasurer, 1736-46. Substitute Keeper, 1725-41, 1742-4. Treasurer to Prince Charles, whom he accompanied to France. Attainted, 1746. *Died* 6 December 1784.

HAY, NEIL MOTHERWELL, M.A. LL.B. [8 December 1975]. Apprentice to Thomas Menzies McNeil of Allan McNeil & Son.—Son of Neil Thomson Hay, Analytical Chemist. *Born* 1 April 1927. *Married* 15 September 1956, Elizabeth Natalie, daughter of Thomas Ford. *Firm*—Allan McNeil & Son.

HAY, ROBERT [13 June 1646]. Apprentice to Thomas Forrest.—Eldest son of Robert Hay, Writer in Edinburgh. *Married* Christian (*died* 7 February 1671), daughter of John Rae, Burgess of Edinburgh. Re-admitted, 21 November 1661.

HAY, ROBERT COLQUHOUN, M.A., LL.B. [26 April 1971]. Apprentice to Charles Edward Stewart and Others of Murray, Beith & Murray.—Son of James Baird Hay, Dental Surgeon, Falkirk. *Born* 22 September 1933. *Married* 14 June 1958. Olive, daughter of J. C. Black, Farmer, Dumfriesshire. Procurator Fiscal Depute, Edinburgh, 1963-68. *Firm*—Bonar Mackenzie (formerly Bonar, Mackenzie & Kermack). (Resigned.)

HAY, WILLIAM, OF CRAWFORDTON [13 January 1755]. Apprentice to James Hay.—Son of James Hay, Merchant in Banff and brother-uterine of Alexander, Lord Banff. *Married* January 1752, Mary (*died* June 1790), daughter of Ludovick Cant of Thurston, East Lothian. *Died* 13 June 1776.

HAY, WILLIAM [20 June 1769]. Apprentice to James Hay of Cocklaw.—Son of Dr James Hay, Physician in Dumfries. *Married* Mary, daughter of Samuel Forbes of Knapperny, Aberdeenshire. *Died* 25 December 1796.

HAY, WILLIAM WARING. *See* NEWTON, WILLIAM WARING HAY.

HEART, J. [Before 1606]. Signs Minute of 17 January 1606.

HECTOR, DAVID [6 December 1827]. Apprentice to Charles Oliphant.—Youngest son of John Hector, residing in Aberdeen. *Born* 1802. *Married* 16 November 1855, Mary Charlotte (*died* 30 July 1908), daughter of William Hay of Laxfirth, Zetland. Admitted Advocate, 10 February 1837. Advocate-Depute, 1852. Sheriff of Galloway, 1861. *Died* 23 December 1874.

HEGGIE, GEORGE, OF PITLESSIE [15 May 1817]. Apprentice to David Wemyss.—Son of James Heggie, Merchant in Kirkcaldy, and grandson of George Heggie of Pitlessie, Fife. *Died* at Moulmein, East Indies, 5 January 1842, aged 50, unmarried.

HENDERSON, ALEXANDER [6 June 1691].—Son of William Henderson, W.S. *Born* 22 January 1654. *Married* 8 April 1690, Elizabeth Ranken (*died* 2 May 1734). *Buried* 14 December 1697.

HENDERSON, ALLAN MACFARLANE [9 July 1894]. Apprentice to (1) W. F. Skene; (2) William Garson.—Son of Alexander Henderson of Stemster, Caithness. *Born* 25 May 1869. Served with 1st Volunteer Batt. The Royal Scots. *Died* 23 March 1955. *Firm*—Henderson and Jackson.

HENDERSON, CHARLES STEWART, M.B.E., M.A., LL.B. [17 December 1934]. Apprentice to Alexander Burn-Murdoch.—Son of Robert Brown Henderson, H.M. Civil Service. *Born* 20 May 1910. Lt. Col. R.A.S.C. Served U.K., Africa, Sicily, Italy, Middle East and Austria 1939-45. Knight Commander of St Mary of Bethlehem 1945. Moderator of the High Constables and Guard of Honour of Holyroodhouse 1962-64. *Died* 26 December 1969. *Firm*—Patrick & James.

HENDERSON, DAVID JAMES THOMAS, LL.B. [11 December 1979*].—Son of James Henderson, Local Government Officer, Falkirk. *Born* 12 July 1950. *Married* 28 July 1972, Morag Jane Wilson, daughter of David McLeod. *Firm*—Campbell Smith & Co.

HENDERSON, GEORGE FRANCIS, M.C. [27 March 1899]. Apprentice to Henry Todd and Henry Tod Jun.—Son of James Henderson, Merchant, Dundee. *Born* 14 September 1875. *Married* 16 October 1937, Doris Evelyn Haeffner, or Robertson, daughter of F. A. C. J. Haeffner, Merchant, London. Served with Scottish Horse and Lovat Scouts, 1914-19, in Gallipoli, Egypt, Macedonia, and France. Promoted Major. Awarded M.C. Treasurer, 1935. *Died* 2 March 1968. *Firm*—Cowan and Dalmahoy.

HENDERSON, HUGH JOHN STEWART [17 July 1972]. Apprentice to Alan Forrest Stark and Others of Morton Fraser & Milligan.—Son of James Henderson, Schoolaster, Edinburgh. *Born* 24 February 1941. *Married* 29 August 1966, Sheila Margaret, daughter of The Rev. John Stewarton Sinclair, Edinburgh. *Firm*—Morton, Fraser & Milligan.

HENDERSON, JAMES, of Pittadro [11 December 1682]. Apprentice to, and eldest son of, William Henderson, W.S.—*Born* 27 January 1644. *Married* Mary, daughter of John Foulis of Ravelston, and widow of James Hamilton of Marktonhall. *Died* January 1707.

HENDERSON, JOHN [Before 1586]. *Married* Agnes, daughter of John Schort in the Canongate. *Died* 9 September 1591.

HENDERSON, JOHN [25 November 1824]. Apprentice to William Inglis.—Second son of William Henderson of Scotscalder, Sheriff-Substitute of Caithness. *Born* 21 December 1800. *Married* 10 August 1829, his cousin Barbara (*died* 1859), daughter of William Henderson, Edinburgh. Author of *Notes of Caithness Family History. Died* 25 August 1883.

HENDERSON, JOHN GEORGE BARRON [9 July 1894]. Apprentice to Patrick Blair and N. J. Finlay.—Son of William Horn Henderson, Solicitor, Linlithgow. *Born* 26 June 1870. County Clerk of West Lothian. *Firm*—Glen and Henderson, Linlithgow. *Died* 11 October 1947.

HENDERSON, RICHARD [7 June 1797]. Apprentice to Charles Stewart.—Eldest son of Archibald Henderson, Merchant in Glasgow. *Married* 16 June 1803, Jean, third daughter of Alexander Fisher, Greenock. Town Clerk of Glasgow. *Died* 30 June 1820.

HENDERSON, ROBERT [30 June 1831]. Apprentice to (1) William Forbes; and (2) Hugh Tod.—Son of Robert Henderson, Writer in Stirling. *Born* 17 April 1807. Admitted Advocate, 26 November 1836. *Died* 27 October 1852, unmarried.

HENDERSON, THOMAS [14 July 1859]. Apprentice to David Smith.—Son of William Henderson, Inspector, National Bank of Scotland. *Born* 2 June 1835. *Died* 8 October 1866, unmarried.

HENDERSON, THOMAS [19 October 1891]. Apprentice to George Bennet Clark.—Son of Charles Henderson, S.S.C., Edinburgh. *Born* 20 August 1868. *Married* 29 August 1899, Gertrude Helen (*died* 29 April 1933), second daughter of William Hawthorn of Wreighburn, Rothbury. *Died* 3 June 1915.

HENDERSON, or HENRYSON, WALTER, of Easter Granton [Before 1586]. *Married* Elizabeth Hepburn, relict of Robert Hepburn of Furde. Commissioner, 15 December 1594.

HENDERSON, or HENRYSON, WILLIAM [15 May 1643]. Apprentice to Robert Pringle.—Son of John Henryson, Servitor to William Hay, one of the Clerks of Session. *Married* Elizabeth (*died* 3 January 1685), daughter of Mungo M'Kaill. Re-admitted, 21 November 1661.

HENDERSON, WILLIAM JAMES CARLAW, B.L., [8 December 1981]. Apprentice to Ian Maxwell Ferguson and Others of Patrick & James.—Son of James Henderson, Schoolmaster, Edinburgh. *Born* 26 September 1948. *Firm*—Allan McDougall & Co.

HENDERSON, WILLIAM M'KELVIE [8 July 1901]. Apprentice to John Ramsay Anderson and William Hugh Murray.—Son of John Henderson, Solicitor, Dumfries. *Born* 16 January 1877. *Died* 7 July 1959.

HENDERSON, WILLIAM SCOTT [20 May 1845]. Apprentice to William Charles Balderston and John Scott.—Second son of Robert Henderson of Abbotrule, Roxburghshire. *Born* 8 October 1821. *Died* 3 February 1859, unmarried.

HENDRY, DAVID [Before 1605].

HENDRY, JOHN [13 November 1862]. Apprentice to John Stewart.—*Born* 18 November 1833. Author of *A Manual of Conveyancing*, 1859, and other works. *Died* 18 May 1863, unmarried.

HENDRY, JOHN EDMUND GORDON, LL.B. [11 December 1979*].—Son of Andrew Gilbert Hendry, Solicitor, Forfar. *Born* 28 September 1949. *Married* 14 July 1979, Gillian Margaret, daughter of David Young, Oil Company Operations Manager. *Firm*—Brodies.

HENRY, GEORGE ARCHIBALD, M.A., LL.B. [30 November 1964]. Apprentice to F. H. Simpson and Others of Fyfe, Ireland & Co.—Son of George G. Henry, Cashier, Edinburgh. *Born* 22 October 1929. *Married* 1st August 1959, Heather Gordon, daughter of William Taylor. *Firm*— Fyfe, Ireland & Co.

HENRY, GEORGE LOVAT FRASER, B.L. [13 March 1939]. Apprentice to Sir Ernest Maclagan Wedderburn and Others of Shepherd & Wedderburn.—Son of George Henry, Armourer Sergeant, Edinburgh. *Born* 12 April 1910. *Married* 19 March 1942, Jane Gibson, daughter of William Murdoch. Flight Lieutenant, R.A.F. Served U.K., North Africa, Malta and Cyprus 1941-45. Professor of Conveyancing, University of Edinburgh 1955-73; Member of Lord Reid's Committee on Registration of Title 1963; Chairman of Committee appointed to prepare a scheme of Registration of Title 1965. *Firm*—Shepherd & Wedderburn.

HENRY, MATTHEW, M.B.E. [16 July 1888]. Apprentice to J. R. M. Wedderburn.—Son of John Henry, S.S.C. *Born* 10 May 1864. *Died* 9 September 1954. *Firm*— Henry and Scott.

HEPBURN, JOHN BUCHAN, OF CASTLE DYKES [24 November 1831]. Apprentice to Morrison and Burnett.—Third son of Sir John Buchan Hepburn of Smeaton, Bart. *Born* 2 May 1808. *Married* 30 May 1837, Margaret Sophia, youngest daughter of A. F. Swinton, Warsash House, Hants. Solicitor to Court of Exchequer. *Died* 14 December 1874.

HEPBURN, JOHN STEWART, OF COLQUHALZIE [8 December 1808]. Apprentice to John Campbell of Annfield.—Son of Thomas Hepburn of Colquhalzie, Perthshire. *Born* July 1783. *Married* 19 September 1815, Helen (*died* April 1874), second daughter of Adam Stewart of Clunie. *Died* 20 September 1872.

HEPBURN, PATRICK [Before 1489].

HEPBURN, ROBERT, OF STONISLATE AND BAADS [14 May 1705]. Apprentice to John Macfarlane.—*Born* 1674. *Married* 13 August 1707, Katherine, daughter of Sir David Home, Lord Crossrig. *Died* 27 October 1738.

HERD, JAMES CEDRIC [27 March 1946]. Apprentice to George Waddell Harvey of Hunter & Harvey.—Son of James Herd, S.S.C., Dysart. *Born* 4 October 1894. *Married* 23 June 1948, Margaret Elizabeth Victor, daughter of W. W. Jones, Farmer, South Africa. Served First World War Royal Scots. Wounded twice. Transferred to R.G.A. 1916. *Died* 6 February 1951. *Firm*—Hunter, Harvey, Webster & Will.

HERD, JAMES PETER, M.B.E.(MIL.) [15 July 1949]. Apprentice to Archibald Campbell and Another of Archibald Campbell & Harley.—Son of Walter Herd, Solicitor, Kirkcaldy. *Born* 18 May 1920. *Married* 5 August 1943, Marjory Phimister, daughter of James Mitchell, Herring Curer and Exporter, Shetlands and Aberdeen. Major, Black Watch. Served U.K. and South East Asia 1939-46. *Firm*—Beveridge, Herd & Whyte, Kirkcaldy.

HERDMAN, JOHN JAMES [19 October 1891]. Apprentice to R. R. Simpson.—Son of James Herdman, Millowner, Edinburgh. *Born* 31 March 1869. *Married* 29 June 1899, Anne Robin (*died* 20 April 1951), younger daughter of William Greenlees, M.D., Edinburgh. *Died* 6 March 1940. *Firm*—Duncan and Black.

HERIOT, JAMES, OF RAMORNIE [4 October 1798]. Apprentice to Andrew Stuart.—Second son of Captain the Hon. Frederick Maitland of Rankeillor, Fife. *Born* 11 September 1774. *Married* 31 December 1813, Margaret (*died* 18 January 1869), second daughter of William Dalgleish of Scotscraig, Fife. Assumed name of Heriot in place of Maitland on succeeding to Ramornie. *Died* 26 April 1848.

HERON, JAMES, OF DALMORE [19 November 1835]. Apprentice to Tod and Hill.—Son of James Heron, Merchant in Ayr. *Born* 2 March 1811. *Died* 23 November 1849, unmarried.

HERRIES, WILLIAM YOUNG, OF SPOTTES [18 November 1817]. Apprentice to, and only son of, Alexander Young of Harburn, W.S.—*Born* 3 July 1794. *Married* 3 September 1822, Hon. Amelia (*died* 7 December 1838), youngest daughter of James, first Lord De Saumarez. Assumed name of Herries, 1823. *Died* 12 February 1872.

HEWAT, PETER [Before 1577]. Commissioner, 15 December 1594. Prebendary of Kells.

HEWAT, PETER [21 December 1809]. Apprentice to Michael Linning.—Son of Peter Hewat, Baxter in Edinburgh. *Born* 1782. *Married* 12 March 1819, Isabella (*died* 1871), eldest daughter of Andrew Taylor of Westbarns. *Died* 4 December 1832.

HIGGINS, JOHN ALEXANDER, OF NEWCK [10 March 1789]. Apprentice to James Ferrier.—Only son of John Higgins of Newck, Stirlingshire. *Born* 17 September 1765. *Died* 26 September 1822, unmarried.

HIGGINS, MICHAEL CALLANDER [7 December 1903]. Apprentice to A. Burn-Murdoch, C. H. Urmston, and J. V. Hagart.—Son of William Higgins, Falkirk. *Born* 8 January 1869. *Died* 6 March 1916, unmarried. *Firm*—Hagart & Burn-Murdoch.

HILL, ANDREW [29 November 1821]. Apprentice to Francis Brodie and George Imlach.—Third son of Dr Andrew Hill, Physician in Greenock. *Born* 1797. *Died* 19 March 1874, unmarried.

HILL, DAVID [15 July 1929]. Apprentice to James Watt and William Blair.—Son of Charles Hill, Manufacturer, Forfar. *Born* 17 May 1873. *Married* 8 March 1902, Elizabeth Beattie (*died* 15 February 1961), daughter of Thomas Alexander Hume, Merchant, Edinburgh. Served with Volunteer Batt. The Royal Scots during Great War. Author of *Parliament House Sketches*, 1901-2, pen-and-ink drawings of Judges and Counsel. *Died* 29 June 1959. *Firm*—Davidson and Syme.

HILL, HENRY DAVID [5 March 1818]. Apprentice to Walter Cook.—Fourth son of George Hill, Principal of St Mary's College, St Andrews. *Born* 22 June 1791. *Died* 25 July 1858, unmarried.

HILL, JAMES [4 July 1822]. Apprentice to, and eldest son of, Robert Hill, W.S.—*Born* 1800. *Married* ——(*died* 26 February 1877). *Died* February 1841.

HILL, JAMES LAWSON [5 March 1835]. Apprentice to Walter Cook.—Son of Charles Hill of Luthrie, Fife. *Born* 27 April 1812. *Married* (1) 19 November 1838, Margaret (*died* 15 November 1851), youngest daughter of James Dunlop, Glasgow; and (2) 26 April 1853, Sibella (*died* 21 December 1898), daughter of John James Boswell, Surgeon, H.E.I.C.S. Commissary Clerk of Mid-Lothian, 1860-83. *Died* 26 February 1883.

HILL, JOHN BOSWELL [21 July 1879]. Apprentice to, and son of, James Lawson Hill, W.S.—*Born* 11 December 1855. *Died* 2 November 1892 (killed in railway accident at Thirsk), unmarried.

HILL, LAWRENCE, OF BARLANERK [12 July 1779]. Apprentice to (1) John Bell; and (2) Alexander Menzies.—Son of James Hill of Cathcart, Writer in Glasgow. *Born* 9 March 1755. *Married* Christian Dreghorn (*died* 18 December 1830). *Died* 11 December 1792.

HILL, NINIAN [30 June 1801]. Apprentice to Robert Hill.—Eighth son of James Hill of Cathcart, Writer in Glasgow. *Born* 4 May 1775. *Married* 13 December 1801, Isabella (*died* 11 March 1810), eldest daughter of John Lang, Writer, Glasgow. *Died* 27 March 1814.

HILL, ROBERT, OF FIRTH [12 March 1795]. Apprentice to (1) Lawrence Hill; and (2) Harry Davidson.—Sixth son of James Hill, Writer in Glasgow. *Born* 11 June 1771. *Married* 4 August 1794, Barbara (*died* 24 August 1860), daughter of Robert Geddes, Banker and Merchant, Cupar. *Died* 10 February 1842.

HILL, ROBERT, OF ROSEBANK [19 June 1812]. Apprentice to John Anderson.—Son of Robert Hill, Kilmarnock. *Married* Jane Caldwell (*died* 5 February 1863). *Died* 11 August 1813.

HILL, ROBERT [17 March 1859]. Apprentice to Walter and John Cook.—Third son of Rev. Alexander Hill, D.D., Professor of Divinity in the University of Glasgow. *Born* 14 April 1831. *Married* 26 March 1861, Mary (*died* 23 November 1911), daughter of Thomas Croil, Merchant, Barbadoes. *Died* at Glasgow, 15 April 1898.

HIRD, THOMAS LEONARD, M.A., LL.B. [26 December 1933]. Apprentice to David Maxwell and Another of Maxwell, Gill & Pringle.—Son of Walter Duncan Hird, Draper, Arbroath. *Born* 20 July 1909. *Died* 9 November 1975.

HODGE, ALEXANDER MITCHELL, G.C., V.R.D., D.L., M.A., LL.B. [23 November 1944]. Apprentice to Sir John Prosser and Others of Morton, Smart, Macdonald & Prosser.—Son of James Mackenzie Hodge, Solicitor, Blairgowrie. *Born* 23 June 1916. *Married* 14 December 1944, Pauline Hester Winsome, daughter of William John Hill, Bristol. Captain, R.N.V.R. Served East Indies, Mediterranean, South Atlantic, Russian and North Atlantic convoys, Home waters and Pacific, 1939-45. Awarded George Cross 1940. *Firm*—Cowan & Stewart.

HODGE, GEORGE MACKENZIE, V.R.D., M.A., LL.B. [12 July 1937]. Apprentice to John Roger Orr and Another of Simpson & Marwick.—Son of James Mackenzie Hodge, Solicitor, Blairgowrie. *Born* 5 October 1912. *Married* 23 December 1947, Helen Russell, daughter of Rev. William Maxwell. Lieutenant Commander R.N.V.R. Served Home Waters and Eastern Fleet 1939-45. *Firm*—J. M. Hodge & Son, Blairgowrie.

HODGE, JAMES SINCLAIR, LL.B. [26 November 1966]. Apprentice to Sir Hugh Watson and Others of Dundas & Wilson.—Son of James Davidson Hodge, Solicitor, Blairgowrie. *Born* 30 November 1942. *Married* 5 March 1969, Barbara Katharine, daughter of James Craig, W.S., Edinburgh. *Firm*—Dundas & Wilson.

HODGE, JOHN MAXWELL, LL.B. [3 December 1973]. Apprentice to David Charles Scott-Moncrieff and Others of Tods, Murray & Jamieson.—Son of George Mackenzie Hodge, W.S., Blairgowrie. *Born* 13 May 1950. *Married* 13 June 1981, Christine Mary, daughter of A. S. Macdonald, Knitwear Production Controller, Edinburgh. *Firm*—Balfour & Manson.

HOG, ALAN WELWOOD, B.A. [15 January 1894]. Apprentice to C. B. Logan, Hon. J. W. Moncreiff, and G. G. Soote.—Son of Thomas Alexander Hog of Newliston. *Born* 28 July 1868. *Married* 17 April 1900, Winifred Alice, youngest daughter of Ralph Dundas, W.S. *Died* 12 August 1947. *Firm*—Pearson, Robertson, and Maconochie.

HOG, WILLIAM [24 December 1673]. Apprentice to John Wilkie. *Married* April 1676, Rachel, daughter of Rev. John Sinclair, Minister of Ormiston. *Buried* 26 November 1686.

HOGARTH, ANDREW [23 June 1829]. Apprentice to George Hogarth.—Son of David Hogarth of Hilton, Berwickshire. *Born* 1806. *Married* 25 March 1834, Dorothy, daughter of Patrick Dickson of Whitecross, Berwickshire. *Died* 22 March 1884.

HOGARTH, DAVID JAMES, M.A., LL.B. [8 May 1967]. Apprentice to Maurice Nicholson Durlac and Another of Allan, Dawson, Simpson & Hampton.—Son of James Hogarth, Under Secretary, Scottish Home & Health Department, Edinburgh. *Born* 22 May 1941. *Married* 24 October 1970, Barbara Gillian, daughter of Leslie G. North, Principal, Fareham Technical College, Fareham, Hants.

HOGARTH, GEORGE [22 June 1810]. Apprentice to J. A. Higgins.—Eldest son of Robert Hogarth, Farmer in Carfrae, Berwickshire. *Born* 6 September 1783. *Married* 1 June 1814, Georgina, daughter of George Thomson, Principal Clerk to the Hon. Board of Trustees. Sub-Editor *Morning Chronicle*. Author of *Musical History, Biography and Criticism*, 1835, and other works. Secretary of the Royal Philharmonic Society, 1850-1864. Father-in-law of Charles Dickens, Novelist. *Died* 12 February 1870.

HOGG, ANDREW [28 July 1690]. Apprentice to William Hog.—*Married* 17 June 1687, Jean, daughter of Rev. John Sinclair, Minister of Ormiston. *Buried* 6 October 1691.

HOGGAN, EDWARD [5 July 1821]. Apprentice to Francis Napier.—Son of George Hoggan of Waterside, Dumfriesshire. *Married* 1834, Elizabeth Craigie (*died* 1875). *Died* 20 February 1867.

HOGUE, THOMAS JOHN [11 July 1838]. Apprentice to Alexander Hunter.—Second son of Arthur Hogue, residing at Barron House, Somersetshire. *Born* 23 November 1815. *Died* at Chittagong, 27 July 1844, unmarried.

HOLE, GILBERT LINDSAY DOUGLAS [2 April 1906]. Apprentice to C. S. Rankine Simson.—Second son of William Brassey Hole, R.S.A., Edinburgh. *Born* 28 June 1882. *Married* 11 July 1906, Grace Chalmers (*died* 16 September 1977), eldest daughter of Alexander Watt Blackie, Merchant, Liverpool, and granddaughter of the late Rev. William Hanna, D.D., LL.D., Edinburgh. Served with Liverpool Scottish during Great War. Commission, January 1917. *Died* 10 November 1967. *Firm*—Gillespie and Paterson, and previously Hope, Simson, and Lennox.

HOME, ALEXANDER [27 November 1673]. Apprentice to William Chieslie.—Son of John Home of Manderstoune, Berwickshire. *Married* (1) 1 June 1676, Anna Home (*died* 14 September 1690); and (2) (contact dated 26 October 1693), Euphan (*died* July 1713), daughter of Thomas Young of Leny, Mid-Lothian, W.S. Writer to Treasury, 1694. Commissary of Lauder, 1690-1702. *Died* 15 May 1702, aged 56.

HOME, GEORGE, OF WEDDERBURN AND PAXTON [8 July 1763]. Apprentice to James Purves.—Second son of Alexander Home of Jardenfield, Berwickshire. Principal Clerk of Session, 26 July 1781 to 11 November 1808. *Died* 10 February 1820.

HOME, HENRY [29 July 1762]. Apprentice to John Davidson.—Eldest son of Alexander Home, Writer in Duns. *Born* 1732. *Married* 4 February 1767, Elizabeth, daughter of Rev. Andrew Boyd, Minister of Twynholm. *Died* May 1803.

HOME, JAMES, OF GAMELSHEILLS [2 March 1686]. Apprentice to Andrew Young.—Son of George Home of Gamelsheills. *Married* 14 February 1696, Agnes, only daughter of Andrew Arrett of Dunbarn. *Died* 1719.

HOME, SIR JAMES, OF BLACKADDER, BART. [20 June 1726]. Apprentice to Robert Hepburn.—Second son of Sir John Home of Blackadder, Bart. *Married* Catherine, daughter of George Livingstone, Depute Clerk of Session. Commissary of Lauder, 15 December 1739. *Died* 28 March 1755.

HOME, JAMES [25 November 1765]. Apprentice to (1) Robert Hepburn; and (2) Thomas Baillie.—Eldest son of Alexander Home, Collector of Excise, Stirling. *Married* 1754, Mary (*died* 26 July 1806), daughter of William Mitchelson, Builder in Edinburgh. Depute Clerk of Session, May 1768. *Died* 9 October 1768.

HOME, JAMES, OF LINHOUSE [19 March 1782]. Apprentice to Samuel Mitchelson.—Only son of James Home, W.S. *Born* 17 December 1755. *Married* 20 August 1802, Catherine (*died* 29 October 1827), eldest daughter of William Mitchell, Edinburgh. Lyon-Depute, 8 August 1796. *Died* 2 January 1819.

HOME, JOHN [20 February 1812]. Apprentice to John Davidson.—Eldest son of George Home, Town Clerk of Leith. *Born* 1758. *Married* (1) Janet Halliday; and (2) Jean Morrison (*died* 29 December 1829). Substitute Keeper of the Signet, 1785-1831. *Died* 13 October 1831.

HOME, JOHN [12 January 1866]. Apprentice to John and Henry Gordon Gibson.—Son of William Home, W.S. *Born* 20 May 1838. *Died* 10 April 1890, unmarried.

HOME, PATRICK, OF BASTLERIG [13 July 1695]. Apprentice to Robert Carstairs.— *Married* Helen, daughter of Alexander Home of Linthill. Treasurer, 1703-10. Commissary of Lauder, 10 July 1703. *Died* August 1717.

HOME, WILLIAM [19 June 1823]. Apprentice to, and son of, John Home, W.S.—*Married* 8 April 1829, Charlotte Helen (*died* 21 October 1879), daughter of John Burne of Kingston. *Died* 6 May 1846, aged 50.

HOPE, ARTHUR HENRY CECIL, O.B.E.(MIL.), T.D., B.L. [31 July 1922]. Apprentice to James Arthur Hope and Another of Hope, Todd & Kirk.—Son of James Arthur Hope, W.S., Edinburgh. *Born* 18 July 1896. *Married* 2 April 1937, Muriel Ann Neilson, daughter of James Anderson Collie, Commercial Traveller. First World War, Captain, 4th Seaforth Highlanders; R.F.S. and R.A.F. Second World War, Lieutenant Colonel, R.A., 52nd Searchlight Regiment. *Firms*—Hope, Todd & Kirk and Gillespie & Paterson. (Retired.)

HOPE, DAVID [12 December 1707]. Apprentice to Thomas Pringle.—Fourth son of Sir Archibald Hope, on of the Senators of the College of Justice (Lord Rankeillor). Procurator-Fiscal, Edinburgh Commissariat. *Died* December 1736, unmarried.

HOPE, HUGH [8 February 1838]. Apprentice to Walker, Richardson, and Melville.— Fourth son of Sir John Hope of Pinkie, Bart. *Born* 3 June 1813. *Married* 1 August 1848, Catherine (*died* 17 March 1875), daughter of Lieut.-Colonel Archibald Spens of Manor House, Inveresk, H.E.I.C.S. *Died* 15 August 1876.

HOPE, JAMES [1 March 1799]. Apprentice to James Walker.—Third son of Dr John Hope, Physician in Edinburgh, Professor of Materia Medica and Botany. *Born* 7 September 1769. *Married* 16 July 1805, Jane (*died* 6 April 1822), daughter of James Walker of Dalry, Edinburgh. Lieut.-Colonel Royal Edinburgh Volunteers, 1803. *Died* 14 November 1842.

HOPE, JAMES [4 July 1828]. Apprentice to James Hope.—Third son of Rt. Hon. Charles Hope of Granton, Lord President of the Court of Session. *Born* 28 May 1803. *Married* 2 December 1828, Elizabeth (*died* 20 July 1880), daughter of David Boyle of Shewalton, Lord President of the Court of Session. Joint Deputy Keeper of the Signet, 1828-50; sole Deputy Keeper, 1850. *Died* 14 February 1882.

HOPE, JAMES, OF BELMONT [10 December 1840]. Apprentice to, and second son of, James Hope, W.S. *Born* 1 July 1818. *Married* 16 April 1850, Hon. Gertrude Elphinstone (*died* 29 March 1894), daughter of Lieut.-Colonel James Drummond Buller Elphinstone, and sister of William, fifteenth Baron Elphinstone. *Died* 10 July 1903, the Father of the Society.

HOPE, JAMES ARTHUR, LL.B., V.D. [28 October 1889]. Apprentice to John Kirk.— Only son of David Boyle Hope, Advocate, Sheriff of Dumfries and Galloway. *Born* 21 January 1865. *Married* 17 April 1895, Geraldine Lucy (*died* 20 April 1949), youngest daughter of Rev. Charles Hope Robertson, M.A., Rector of Smeeth. As Colonel raised Army Service Corps Unit for two Scottish Horse Brigades in Great War. Acted as Military Representative to the City of Edinburgh Tribunal. *Died* 2 March 1925. *Firm*— Hope, Todd, and Kirk.

HOPE, JAMES EDWARD [31 October 1879]. Apprentice to (1) James Hope; and (2) A. Howe, J. S. Tytler, and W. MacGillivray.—Eldest son of James Hope of Belmont, W.S. *Born* 6 November 1852. *Married* 1 June 1880, Sophia (*died* 19 February 1924), fifth daughter of Sir William Edmonstoune of Duntreath, Bart. Solicitor of Inland Revenue. *Died* 8 December 1917.

HOPE, JAMES LOUIS, T.D., M.A., LL.B. [15 December 1930]. Apprentice to Henry E. Richardson and Others of Gillespie & Paterson.—Son of James Arthur Hope, W.S., Edinburgh. *Born* 31 January 1906. *Married* 6 June 1939, Kathleen Colquhoun Sconce (*died* 16 October 1968). Lieutenant Colonel Royal Scots. Served U.K. and West Africa 1939-45. *Firm*—Gillespie & Paterson and Hope, Todd & Kirk. (Consultant.)

HOPE, JOHN [12 November 1829]. Apprentice to, and eldest son of, James Hope, W.S.— *Born* 12 May 1807. Philanthropist. *Died* 25 June 1893, unmarried.

HOPE, REGINALD JOHN [1 April 1907]. Apprentice to (1) James Hope; and (2) C. S. Rankine Simson.—Son of James Edward Hope of Belmont, W.S., and grandson of said James Hope. *Born* 18 January 1885. *Married* 30 April 1923, Eileen, daughter of Roland Philipson, Colliery Owner, Tynemouth. *Died* 8 October 1952.

HOPKIRK, JOHN GLASSFORD [15 November 1811]. Apprentice to Sir James Gibson-Craig.—Second son of James Hopkirk of Dalbeth, Lanarkshire. *Born* 1789. *Married* 12 September 1815, Jessie (*died* 7 August 1824), second daughter of John Hamilton of Polmont Bank, Stirlingshire. *Died* 2 August 1859.

HORE, HENRY JAMES [11 December 1905]. Apprentice to George F. Bryce; thereafter to L. J. Cadell and W. B. Wilson.—Son of William Henry Hore, Manager of the London Assurance Corporation. *Born* 19 April 1880. *Married* 15 June 1912, Aimee Hay (*died* 6 June 1922), third daughter of Surgeon-General David Sinclair, C.S.I., I.M.S., 11 Mortonhall Road, Edinburgh. *Died* 1 March 1924. *Firm*—Chalmers & Hore.

HORNE, DONALD, OF LANGWELL [6 July 1813]. Apprentice to James Horne, his uncle.—Second son of John Horne of Stirkoke, Caithness. *Born* 20 May 1787. *Married* 1 June 1821, Jane (*died* 30 May 1834), daughter of Thomas Elliot Ogilvie of Chesters, Roxburghshire. *Died* 23 June 1870.

HORNE, JAMES, OF LANGWELL [16 November 1781]. Apprentice to James Marshall.—Son of William Horne, Tacksman of Scouthill, Watten, Caithness. *Died* 29 September 1831, aged 79.

HORNE, THOMAS [3 May 1881]. Apprentice to, and eldest son of, Thomas Elliot Ogilvie Horne, W.S. *Born* 26 June 1854. *Married* 6 August 1885, Horatia Georgina Ramsay (*died* 14 September 1944), second daughter of Major James Wardlaw, Belmaduthy, and widow of William G. C. Asher, Farmer, Belmaduthy. *Died* 24 September 1934. *Firm*—Horne and Lyell.

HORNE, THOMAS ELLIOT OGILVIE [24 June 1852]. Apprentice to, and son of, Donald Horne, W.S. *Born* 1 January 1829. *Married* Priscilla Moore (*died* 15 October 1884). *Died* 26 June 1884.

HORSBRUGH, CHARLES EDWARD [15 July 1890]. Apprentice to D. Beith, R. D. Beith, A. Forrester, and P. Murray.—Son of William Horsbrugh, Cupar, Fife. *Born* 16 July 1865. *Married* 24 July 1900, Marion Graham (*died* 18 April 1939), second daughter of Allan Graham Barns Graham of Limekilns, and Craigallian, Stirlingshire. *Died* 17 May 1937.

HORSBURGH, WALTER [27 February 1818]. Apprentice to John Tweedie.—Son of Thomas Horsburgh, Tenant in Yair, Selkirkshire. *Born* 1792. *Married* 21 September 1830, Elizabeth (*died* 1866), daughter of Rev. Andrew Murray, D.D., Minister of Auchterderran. *Died* 22 June 1858.

HOSSACK, CAMPBELL [13 January 1890]. Apprentice to Alexander Paterson Purves.—Youngest son of Robert Campbell Hossack, Master Mariner, Bonnington Grove. *Born* 26 August 1865. *Died* 14 April 1930, unmarried. *Firm*—Hossack & Hamilton.

HOTCHKIS, DUNMORE RICHARD ALEXANDER, B.A.(OXON), LL.B. [17 December 1934]. Apprentice to James Hotchkis Jameson and Others of Boyd, Jameson & Young.—Son of Robert Dunmore Hotchkis, M.D., Paisley. *Born* 19 December 1909. *Married* 10 January 1953, Betsy, daughter of Sir William Dishington Scott, Glasgow. Captain, Infantry. Served U.K. and Madagascar, India, Persia, Iraq, Central Mediterranean and North West Europe 1939-45. Wounded in Italy January 1944. Great-grandson of James Hotchkis, W.S. *Firms*—(1) J. N. Hotchkis & Co., St Andrews; (2) Pagan & Osborne, St Andrews and Cupar; (3) Pagan, Osborne & Grace, St Andrews and Cupar. (Retired.)

HOTCHKIS, JAMES [23 June 1820]. Apprentice to Richard Hotchkis and James Tytler.—Only son of Richard Hotchkis, W.S. *Born* 16 August 1795. *Married* 20 July 1824, Margaret (*died* 9 February 1876), youngest daughter of Major Thomas Hart of Castlemilk, Dumfriesshire. *Died* 24 March 1865.

HOTCHKIS, JAMES NAPIER [12 July 1887]. Apprentice to George Dunlop.—Eldest son of Major Richard James Hotchkis, and grandson of James Hotchkis, W.S. *Born* 16 July 1863. Served in South African War, 1900-1 (Queen's Medal and four clasps), and in Great War, 1914-19. Captain R.F.A. and H.L.I. *Died* 14 July 1948.

HOTCHKIS, RICHARD, OF TEMPLEHALL [1 August 1788]. Apprentice to (1) John Bell; and (2) James and William Tytler.—Son of James Hotchkis of Hoxwood, Shropshire, Brewer in Edinburgh. *Born* 5 May 1759. *Married* 1 July 1791, Isobel (*died* 26 April 1820), only daughter of Richard Gardner, Comptroller-General of Customs of Scotland. Treasurer, 1792-1824. *Died* 23 February 1824.

HOULDSWORTH, DAVID HENRY, LL.B. [28 May 1979]. Apprentice to T. G. Dempster and Another of Brodies.—Son of Ian George Henry Houldsworth, Farmer and Land Agent, Dallas, Morayshire. *Born* 19 February 1953. *Married* 9 May 1981, Sarah Jane, daughter of John Hogg, Insurance Broker, London. *Firm*—Brodies.

HOUSTOUN, ARCHIBALD [29 December 1699]. Apprentice to Robert Carstairs.—Fifth son of Sir Patrick Houstoun of that Ilk, first Baronet. *Married* 27 October 1702, Esther, daughter of Robert Carstairs, W.S. Clerk to Commission of Parliament, 1704. *Killed* in a brawl by Gilbert Kennedy, younger of Auchtyfardle, 20 March 1705.

HOUSTON, ROBERT GEORGE ALBERT, B.L. [20 December 1948]. Apprentice to Hon. A. G. Watson and Others of Brodie, Cuthbertson & Watson. *Born* 5 November 1922. *Married* 25 March 1950, Muriel Aina Baddon. Major, India and Burma 1942-46. *Firm*—Thorburn & Fleming, Keith, Banffshire. Resigned Commission 1959.

HOWATSON, WILLIAM, OF HAZLIEBRAE [16 June 1818]. Apprentice to Alexander Goldie.—Eldest son of William Howatson of Hazliebrae, Kirkmichael, Dumfriesshire. *Born* 1793. *Died* 7 May 1821.

HOWDEN, ANDREW [19 June 1818]. Apprentice to John Mowbray.—Son of James Howden, Watchmaker in Edinburgh. *Married* 16 July 1827, Laura (*died* 1873), daughter of Robert Richard Maitland, Edinburgh. *Died* 27 March 1861, aged 66.

HOWDEN, ANDREW CASSELS [26 May 1825]. Apprentice to John Renton and Joseph Grant.—Second son of Alexander Howden, Merchant in Leith. *Born* 1801. *Married* (1) 3 September 1827, Catherine Sinclair (*died* 29 April 1833), only child of Adam Robinson of Pearmont; and (2) Miss Fulton. *Died* 19 March 1875.

HOWDEN, ROBERT [9 July 1821]. Apprentice to William Dallas.—Eldest son of Francis Howden, Goldsmith in Edinburgh. *Born* 1797. *Married* 27 November 1852, Eliza Sophia, daughter of H. C. Burnet, York, and widow of W. H. S. James, Calcutta. *Died* 20 June 1858.

HOWE, ALEXANDER [8 November 1849]. Apprentice to (1) John Mackenzie Lindsay; and (2) Thomas George Mackay.—Son of Charles Howe, residing in Forfar. *Born* 26 April 1820. *Died* 24 May 1907, unmarried.

HOWIE, ROBERT STEUART, LL.B. [1 December 1969]. Apprentice to Alexander James Ramsay Bisset and Others of Baillie & Gifford.—Son of T. W. Howie, Firebrick Manufacturer, Falkirk. *Born* 21 April 1946. *Married* 30 December 1972, Diana Margaret, daughter of A. L. Keen, Timber Importer.

HUGHES, GEORGE [15 November 1832]. Apprentice to George Turnbull.—*Born* 17 August 1808. *Married* 7 August 1838, Helen Magniac, youngest daughter of David Erskine of Elambazar, Bengal. *Died* 6 November 1873.

HUME, JOHN [12 August 1783]. Apprentice to David Anderson.—Third son of John Hume of Ninewells, Berwickshire. *Died* 10 October 1806.

HUME, MATHEW NORMAN MACDONALD, OF BERNISDALE [17 November 1815]. Apprentice to Michael Linning.—Son of Norman Macdonald of Scalpay, Inverness-shire. *Born* 1793. *Married* (1) 5 March 1818, Catherine Finnan (*died* 5 March 1825); (2) 26 July 1831, Grace (*died* 5 January 1837), daughter of Sir John Hay of Smithfield and Haystoun, Bart.; and (3) 25 April 1843, Agnes Hume (*died* 4 March 1864), of Ninewells, second daughter of the Hon. David Hume, Baron of Exchequer. *Died* 7 July 1878.

HUNT, JAMES, OF NAVITY [31 May 1860]. Apprentice to (1) John Cosens; and (2) James Charles Murray.—Eldest son of William Hunt, W.S. *Born* 9 February 1828. *Died* 13 October 1879, unmarried.

HUNT, WILLIAM, OF NAVITY [25 June 1819]. Apprentice to James Mackenzie and William Innes.—Eldest son of Charles Hunt, Dunfermline. *Married* 17 April 1826, Mary (*died* 20 June 1862), only daughter of James Normand of Baltilly, Fife. *Died* 9 October 1854, aged 59.

HUNTER, ALEXANDER [22 November 1813]. Apprentice to, and fourth son of, John Hunter of Doonholm, Ayrshire, W.S.—*Born* 9 January 1790. *Married* 26 April 1819, Maria (*died* 14 July 1862), third daughter of Alexander Maclean of Coll, Argyllshire. Sheriff-Clerk of Ayrshire, 1827-58. *Died* 28 September 1858.

HUNTER, ALEXANDER GIBSON, OF BLACKNESS [7 June 1797]. Apprentice to John Anderson.—Eldest son of David Hunter of Blackness, Angus. *Born* 1771. *Married* 29 August 1800, Ann (*died* 18 December 1843), daughter of Alexander Gibson Wright of Cliftonhall, Mid-Lothian. Became a partner of A. Constable and Co., Publishers, 1803, and retired to his estate, 1811. *Died* 9 March 1812.

HUNTER, DOUGLAS MUNRO, LL.B. [9 December 1980]. Apprentice to Alexander John McDonald and Others of Thorntons & Dickies, Dundee.—Son of Thomas Munro Hunter, W.S., Edinburgh. *Born* 2 February 1954. *Married* 22 November 1980, Carol Ann, daughter of Raymond Carroll Williams, Manager, Warrenpoint, N. Ireland.

HUNTER, EDWARD PATRICK FRANK de PLUMPTON, B.L. [23 April 1951]. Apprentice to Sir William Haldane and Others of W. & F. Haldane.—Son of Patrick Constable Hunter, Arngask, Glenfarg, Perthshire. *Born* 31 January 1928. *Firm*— Jameson, Mackay & Hunter, Perth. (Retired.)

HUNTER, EVAN ALLAN [15 June 1848]. Apprentice to John M. Lindsay.—Son of Alexander Hunter, W.S. *Born* 19 June 1825. *Married* 15 June 1871, Ernestine Eglinton (*died* 16 December 1874), daughter of John Stuart Hay Newton of Newton, Mid-Lothian. Sheriff-Clerk of Ayrshire, 1858-90. *Died* 16 April 1890.

HUNTER, EVAN AUSTIN, C.B.E., B.A. [9 December 1912]. Apprentice to Harry Cheyne, Francis John Gordon Borthwick, Ian MacIntyre, and J. G. Kirkpatrick.—Son of Frank Hunter, W.S. *Born* 28 September 1887. *Married* (1) 8 January 1913, Jane Ritchie (*divorced* 31 May 1927), only child of Thomas Smith Kay, Edinburgh, and (2) 31 October 1940, Joan Pierrepoint Hunter. Served with Scottish Horse Brigade, T. and S. Column, in France. Staff-Captain (Q.M.G.3), War Office. Mentioned in Despatches. *Died* 31 January 1954.

HUNTER, FRANK [28 October 1881]. Apprentice to Evan Allan Hunter, his uncle.—Son of Alexander Maclean Hunter, residing at Balla-Balla, Cranbourne, Australia. *Born* 26 July 1858. *Married* 31 March 1886, Elizabeth Agnes (*died* 15 November 1929), daughter of Rev. John Mein-Austin, Minister of St Mungo, Dumfriesshire. *Died* at Dixons, Lockerbie, 11 October 1930.

HUNTER, HUGH BLACKBURN, D.S.O. [29 March 1905]. Apprentice to James Bruce, Thomas Kerr, and John Burns.—Son of the Rev. David Hunter, D.D., Minister of the Parish of Galashiels. *Born* 3 July 1880. *Married* 26 August 1913, Helen Brown (*died* at Victoria, B.C. March 1942), daughter of John Finlay, 8 Kilmaurs Road, Edinburgh. Served in France and Belgium, 1915-19. Major on Divisional Train, R.A.S.C. Twice mentioned in Despatches. D.S.O., 1918. *Died* 30 October 1956.

HUNTER, JAMES REID, M.A., LL.B. [30 November 1964]. (By Rule IX(a).)—Son of Robert Hunter, Draper, Edinburgh. *Born* 24 March 1925. *Married* 18 July 1952, Catherine Stewart, daughter of Charles Taylor Smith, Wine and Spirit Merchant, Edinburgh. Sub-Lieutenant Royal Navy, 1943-46. *Firms*—(1) Miller Thomson & Robertson (formerly J. Miller Thomson & Co.) and (2) Marwicks.

HUNTER, JOHN, OF DOONHOLM [26 June 1769]. Apprentice to John Bell.—Second son of Andrew Hunter of Abbotshill, Ayrshire, Writer in Edinburgh. *Born* 21 April 1746. *Married*, proclaimed 12 December 1773, Jane (*died* 4 July 1838), second daughter of William Fergusson of Doonholm and Bonnytoun, Ayrshire. *Died* 24 April 1823.

HUNTER, JOHN [22 November 1821]. Apprentice to William Mackenzie and Alexander Monypenny.—Son of David Hunter, Brewer in Aberdeen. *Married* —— (*died* in 1867). *Died* 21 January 1848.

HUNTER, JOHN, LL.D. [6 July 1826]. Apprentice to Walter Cook.—Eldest son of Dr James Hunter, Professor of Logic in University of St Andrews. *Born* 15 March 1801. *Married* 18 September 1829, Helen (*died* 25 August 1885), daughter of Richard Vary of Crossford, Lanarkshire. Auditor of Court of Session, 1849-66. *Died* 3 December 1869.

HUNTER, RICHARD [15 November 1838]. Apprentice to Mackenzie and Sharpe.—Son of Richard Hunter, of the Hon. East India Company's Service. *Born* 20 June 1817. *Died* July 1844, unmarried.

HUNTER, ROBERT LESLIE COCKBURN, M.A., LL.B. [27 April 1964]. Apprentice to (1) James Louis Hope and Others of Hope, Todd & Kirk and (2) Charles Stewart Henderson and Another of Patrick & James.—Son of Robert Leslie Hunter, T.D., Director of Allied Ironfounders Ltd., Edinburgh. *Born* 31 December 1934. *Married* 26 December 1960, Joan Gwendolen, daughter of the Rev. Alfred Gregory Mappin.

HUNTER, THOMAS [11 November 1647]. Apprentice to James Farquharson.—Son of Thomas Hunter, Bailie in Carsland, Ayrshire. *Married* Margaret Dishington. *Buried* 26 October 1684.

HUNTER, SIR THOMAS [30 October 1893]. Apprentice to J. P. Wright and T. M. Murray.—Son of Robert Hunter, Merchant in Hawick. *Born* 9 June 1850. Town Clerk of Edinburgh, 1895 to 1918. Knighted, 1911. *Died* at London, 25 August 1919.

HUNTER, THOMAS JAMES GIBSON [25 March 1901]. Apprentice to Sir T. D. Brodie and D. Wardlaw.—Son of David Hunter of Blackness, Angus. *Born* 4 April 1875. *Married* 21 April 1927, Elizabeth, youngest daughter of Alexander Crerar, Edinburgh. During Great War in 7th A. and S.H. and Labour Corps; Lieutenant. *Died* 12 October 1961. *Firm*—Hunter and Fraser.

HUNTER, THOMAS MUNRO [14 July 1947]. Apprentice to Percy Furneaux Dawson of Allan, Dawson, Simpson & Hampton.—Son of Robert Marshall Hunter, Actuary, Edinburgh. *Born* 19 June 1917. *Married* 9 April 1949, Meta Kennedy, daughter of James Wilkie Douglas. Major R.A. Served U.K. *Firm*—Allan Dawson, Simpson & Hampton.

HUNTER, WILLIAM [30 December 1647]. Resigned his Commission, 15 October 1663, on account of his age. *Married* Anna Douglas. *Died* before June 1697.

HUNTER, WILLIAM CONSTABLE OF ARNGASK, GLENFARG [19 March 1888]. Apprentice to David S. Dickson and David Shaw.—Son of Patrick Hunter of Waterybutts, Perthshire. *Born* 14 March 1865. *Married* 8 September 1893, Isabel Agnes (*died* 21 March 1951), second daughter of David Salmond Salmond, Shipping Agent, Glasgow. *Died* 26 November 1941. *Firm*—Mill, Bonar, and Hunter, till 1903; thereafter Bonar, Hunter, and Johnstone.

HUNTER, WILLIAM VARY [17 March 1864]. Apprentice to Charles Morton.—Son of John Hunter, W.S., Auditor of the Court of Session. *Born* 30 September 1839. *Died* 18 January 1872, unmarried.

HUTCHESON, JAMES [1 August 1707]. Apprentice to Adam Fullerton.—Son of James Hutcheson of Underwood, Ayrshire. *Married* 25 January 1706, Margaret, daughter of John Scougall, Limner, Edinburgh. *Died* 1726.

HUTCHESON, JAMES [27 June 1878]. Apprentice to George Dalziel.—*Born* 10 August 1846. *Died* 2 March 1899, unmarried.

HUTCHINSON, ALEXANDER [4 February 1830]. Apprentice to James Arnott.—Son of Captain John Hutchinson, Commander of the Irish Revenue Cutter *Nepean*. *Married* (1) 1834, Jane Charlotte Gordon; and (2) 19 June 1851, Elizabeth (*died* 29 May 1892), daughter of Rev. James Watt, of the Grammar School, Aberdeen. *Died* 14 November 1869, aged 71.

HUTCHISON, ANDREW EADIE [23 March 1925]. Apprentice to J. L. Mounsey, A. G. Brown, and K. R. Maitland.—Son of —— Hutchison, Bailie, Kinross. *Born* 3 August 1882, *Married* 29 June 1911, Jane Balmain (*died* 28 April 1942), daughter of Alexander Clark, Joppa. *Died* 11 January 1934.

HYNDMAN, DAVID GILCHRIST, M.A., LL.B. [2 December 1968]. (By Rule IX(a).)— Son of William Hyndman, Bank Manager, Ardrossan. *Born* 26 September 1933. *Firm*— Jas. Campbell & Co., Saltcoats.

HYNDMAN, JOHN BLAIR, OF SPRINGSIDE [12 December 1816]. Apprentice to Coll Macdonald.—Son of Robert Hyndman of Springside, Ayrshire. *Died* 20 January 1843, aged 50, unmarried.

HYSLOP, WILLIAM AIRD [20 October 1884]. Apprentice to Charles Baxter.—Son of James Macadam Hyslop, M.D., residing in Edinburgh. *Born* 24 December 1859. *Married* 24 February 1891, Marion Newton (*died* 26 May 1941), third daughter of Alexander Dudgeon, Humbie, Kirkliston. *Died* 3 June 1920.

IMLACH, GEORGE [7 March 1788]. Apprentice to John Tait.—Eldest son of Rev. Alexander Imlach, Minister of Murroes. *Born* 23 August 1753. *Married* Mary Cunningham. *Died* 1812.

IMLACH, GEORGE [22 February 1813]. Apprentice to John Dickson.—Only son of George Imlach, W.S. *Married* 14 June 1813, Agnes (*died* 31 December 1872), daughter of Robert Wight, Murrays, East Lothian. *Died* 3 February 1823.

INCHCOK, FRANCIS [Before 1498].

INGLIS, ANDREW [17 July 1862]. Apprentice to, and eldest son of, Henry of Torsonce, Mid-Lothian, W.S.—*Born* 4 January 1833. *Married* 28 July 1862, Eliza Louisa (*died* 6 August 1914), eldest daughter of Major-General Frederick Hope. *Died* 27 June 1892.

INGLIS, GEORGE [3 July 1632]. Apprentice to John Learmonth.—*Married* Jean Fortoun. *Died* before 1663.

INGLIS, HARRY HERBERT [16 July 1873]. Apprentice to Frederick Pitman.—Younger son of the Right Hon. John Inglis of Glencorse, Mid-Lothian, Lord Justice-General. *Born* 21 July 1848. *Died* 6 October 1907, unmarried.

INGLIS, HARRY MAXWELL, OF LOGANBANK [1 July 1828]. Apprentice to Archibald Gibson.—Eldest son of Rev. John Inglis, D.D., one of the Ministers of Edinburgh, and brother of Right Hon. John Inglis, Lord Justice-General. *Born* 1800. Principal Clerk of Session, 3 June 1858 to 1880. *Died* 7 May 1883, unmarried.

INGLIS, HENRY, OF TORSONCE [13 November 1828]. Apprentice to, and son of, William Inglis, W.S. *Born* 6 November 1806. *Married* (1) 2 April 1832, Marianne, daughter of Andrew Stein of Wester Greenyards; and (2) 27 January 1880, Ann Kinnear (*died* 11 September 1929). Author of *The Briar of Threave and the Lily of Barholm*, 1855, and other poems. Name removed from List of Society on 14 April 1879. Was a Director of the City of Glasgow Bank. *Died* 3 April 1885.

INGLIS, IAN BROWNLIE, LL.B. [26 April 1971]. Apprentice to the Hon. David A. Balfour and Others of Shepherd & Wedderburn.—Son of Charles Inglis, Steelworker. *Born* 6 February 1941. *Married* 31 July 1965, Eleanor McLuckie, daughter of Richard Mitchell Taylor. *Firm*—Shepherd & Wedderburn.

INGLIS, IAN GODFREY, B.A.(OXON), LL.B. [13 May 1980*].—Son of John Godfrey Inglis, Farmer and Company Director, Fairlie, Ayrshire. *Born* 21 July 1934. *Married* 11 March 1961, Rosemary, daughter of Major Hugh King, Landowner. Member of Phillimore Committee on Contempt of Court. *Firm*—Maclay, Murray & Spens.

INGLIS, JAMES CRAUFUIRD ROGER, B.A.(CANTAB), LL.B. [17 November 1952]. Apprentice to John Herbert Richardson and Others of Dundas & Wilson.—Son of Lieutenant Colonel John Inglis, C.M.G., D.S.O., Regular Soldier, Grangemuir, Pittenweem, Fife. *Born* 21 June 1925. *Married* 25 July 1952, Phoebe Aeonie, daughter of Edward Mackenzie Murray-Buchanan. *Firms*—(1) Dundas & Wilson; (2) Shepherd & Wedderburn.

INGLIS, JOHN, OF AUCHINDINNIE AND LANGBYRES [7 August 1691]. Apprentice to Archibald Nisbet.—Son of John Inglis of Langbyres, Lanarkshire, Writer in Linlithgow. *Born* 1663. *Married* (1) 9 November 1688, Helen (*died* 17 November 1694), daughter of Alexander Hay, Merchant Burgess of Edinburgh, King's Bowyer; (2) 1695, Catherine, daughter of Archibald Nisbet, W.S. *Died* 31 January 1731.

INGLIS, JOHN, OF ABERHOLDOUN [9 December 1717]. Apprentice to John Inglis.—*Died* 24 November 1726.

INGLIS, JOSEPH [11 July 1898]. Apprentice to John Philp Wood and W. Babington.—Second son of Joseph Ellis Inglis of Messrs. Hawthorns and Co., Engineers, Leith and Granton. *Born* 8 February 1862. *Married* 18 June 1888, Christina Dobson (*died* 20 May 1950), daughter of George Dobson, Timber Merchant, Leith. *Died* 29 July 1937. *Firm*—Melville and Lindesay.

INGLIS, JOSEPH ELLIS, M.C. [9 December 1913]. Apprentice to (1) Horatius Bonar and W. C. Hunter; and (2) W. Babington and Joseph Inglis.—Son of Joseph Inglis, W.S. *Born* 5 May 1889. *Married* 21 February 1918, Rhoda Gordon (*died* 14 July 1962), daughter of James Fenton, Jeweller, Edinburgh. During Great War, Major in R.G.A.; served in France and mentioned in Despatches; awarded Military Cross. *Died* 26 January 1949. *Firm*—Melville and Lindesay.

INGLIS, WILLIAM [25 June 1632]. Apprentice to John Gilmour.—*Married* (contract, 26 February 1633) Anna, daughter of Sir James Pringle of Galashiels. *Died* 1647.

INGLIS, WILLIAM, OF MIDDLETON [26 June 1789]. Apprentice to Andrew Stuart.— Second son of Laurence Inglis, Writer in Edinburgh, and his wife Richmond (after whom Richmond Street, Edinburgh, was named), second daughter of Colonel James Gardiner of Bankton, who fell at the battle of Prestonpans. *Married* 16 March 1797, Jane (*died* in America in 1847), daughter of James Stein of Kilbagie, Clackmannanshire, and sister-in-law to General the Hon. Sir Alexander Duff of Delgaty, son of the third Earl of Fife. Deputy Secretary to the Prince of Wales in Scotland, 1796. Commanded Loyal Edinburgh Spearmen, 1807. Portrait by Raeburn in Freemasons' Hall, Edinburgh. *Died* at Sainte Adresse, near Havre de Grâce, 20 June 1830.

INNES, ALBERT JAMES HACKETT [25 November 1963]. Apprentice to Richard Morison Ireland of Ketchen & Stevens.—Son of Albert James Hackett Innes, Aberdeen. *Born* 26 November 1912. *Married* 1 February 1941, Catherine Mildred, daughter of Ambrose Tamblin. Captain, Royal Scots, and previously 2nd Battalion Argyll & Sutherland Highlanders. Served in Germany. *Firm*—Connell & Connell.

INNES, ALEXANDER [5 December 1699]. Apprentice to Robert Innes, his brother.—Son of Alexander Innes of Blairtown, Aberdeenshire. Name removed from Roll, not having paid his fees.

INNES, ALEXANDER [6 August 1768]. Apprentice to John Davidson.—Eldest son of Alexander Innes of Cathlaw, Linlithgowshire. *Born* 1747. *Married* 14 January 1775, Janet (*died* 29 June 1845), youngest daughter of Thomas Shairp of Houston, Linlithgowshire. Went to Jamaica. *Died* 1782.

INNES, CHARLES, OF CLERKSEAT [25 November 1780]. Apprentice to David Anderson.— Son of Alexander Innes of Clerkseat, Advocate in Aberdeen. *Died* 27 September 1808.

INNES, EDWIN SANDYS MITCHELL [16 November 1871]. Apprentice to John M. Lindsay and Alexander Howe.—Second son of George Mitchell Innes of Bangour, Linlithgowshire. *Born* 4 July 1846. *Died* 29 August 1913, unmarried.

INNES, GILBERT [16 December 1895]. Apprentice to (1) W. C. M'Ewen and A. S. Blair; and (2) A. S. Blair and R. Strathern.—Son of Charles Innes, Solicitor, Inverness. *Born* 17 November 1872. *Died* 25 December 1897, unmarried.

INNES, JAMES [28 February 1811]. Apprentice to James Fraser, Francis Brodie, and David Wemyss.—Son of John Innes of Leuchars, W.S., residing in Durris. Merchant in China. *Died* 1842, aged 57.

INNES, JOHN, OF LEUCHARS [22 November 1776]. Apprentice to Charles Gordon.—Son of Robert Innes, Merchant in Elgin. *Born* 13 October 1747. *Married* 2 September 1780, Euphemia, daughter of James Russel of Earlsmill. Sheriff-Substitute of Kincardineshire, 1808-27. Father of Cosmo Innes, the Antiquary. *Died* 10 May 1827.

INNES, JOHN, OF COWIE [16 January 1800]. Apprentice to George Robinson.—Eldest son of Alexander Innes of Breda, Commissary of Aberdeen. *Born* 1776. *Married* (1) 25 July 1800, Una Cameron (*died* 26 September 1809), eldest daughter of Robert Barclay of Urie, Kincardineshire; and (2) Janet, eldest daughter of William Rogers, Sawyer, Edinburgh. *Died* 17 April 1832.

INNES, JOHN ALEXANDER DAVIDSON, B.A.(CANTAB), LL.B. [3 December 1965]. Apprentice to Sir Hugh Watson and Others of Dundas & Wilson.—Son of Richard Threlfall Innes, Solicitor, Kirkcaldy. *Born* 28 April 1940. *Married* 6 September 1968, Elizabeth Reid, daughter of John Reid Maclaren, C.A., Edinburgh. *Firm*—Dundas & Wilson.

INNES, JOHN BROWN [16 November 1837]. Apprentice to, and son of, William Innes, W.S.—*Born* 26 September 1814. *Married* 20 October 1855, Emily, daughter of Rowland Burdon Cotgrave, Pinner, Middlesex. *Died* 2 February 1883.

INNES, JOHN COTGRAVE [28 April 1882]. Apprentice to J. B. Innes, John Logan, and C. B. Logan.—Only son of John Brown Innes, W.S. *Born* 23 December 1857. *Died* 6 September 1900, unmarried.

INNES OF EDINGIGHT, MALCOLM ROGNVALD, M.A., LL.B. [27 July 1964]. Apprentice to George D. Cheyne and Another of W. H. Mill, McLeod & Rose.—Son of Sir Thomas Innes of Learney, G.C.V.O., LL.D. Advocate and formerly Lord Lyon King of Arms. *Born* 25 May 1938. *Married* 19 October 1963, Joan, daughter of Thomas D. Hay, C.A. Carrick Pursuivant 1958; Marchmont Herald 1971; Lyon Clerk and Keeper of the Records 1966. Lord Lyon King of Arms 1981.

INNES, MICHAEL WEMYSS, B.A.(OXON) [18 December 1950]. Apprentice to John Douglas Hamilton Dickson and Others of Tods, Murray & Jamieson.—Son of John Lockhart Innes, Solicitor, Kirkcaldy. *Born* 14 October 1924. *Married* 4 October 1956, Sarah, daughter of William B. Robertson, D.L., Dunfermline. Flying Officer R.A.F. 1943-46. *Firm*—A. & J. L. Innes, Kirkcaldy.

INNES, ROBERT, OF BLAIRTOUN [11 May 1680]. Apprentice to William Thomson.—Eldest son of Alexander Innes of Blairtoun, Aberdeenshire. *Married* Sophia Smith (*died* 11 November 1716). Lyon-Depute, 4 November 1677 to 1689. M.P. for Anstruther Easter, 1685-6. *Buried* 17 January 1699.

INNES, THOMAS, OF MONEILLE [11 January 1758]. Apprentice to (1) Andrew Hay of Montblairie; and (2) Andrew Burnett.—Second son of Thomas Innes of Muryfold, Banffshire. *Born* 15 November 1730. *Married* Elizabeth (*died* 19 March 1822), daughter of John Innes of Edingight. *Died* 6 September 1779.

INNES, THOMAS [8 March 1821]. Apprentice to John Innes, Jun.—Third son of John Innes, W.S. *Born* 1798. *Married* 2 February 1832, Mary (*died* 5 May 1881), daughter of Archibald Bogle, Merchant in Glasgow. *Died* 17 December 1844.

INNES, WILLIAM [4 January 1671]. Apprentice to (1) Robert Alexander; (2) William Chalmer; (3) James Cheyne.—Son of William Innes of Tibbertie. *Married* February 1690, Jean, second daughter of David Murray of Clairden.

INNES, WILLIAM [18 March 1704]. Apprentice to Robert Innes.—*Married* Janet (*died* 29 December 1758), daughter of Sir William Cunningham of Caprington, Bart., and widow of George Primrose of Dunipace. *Died* June 1746.

INNES, WILLIAM [18 May 1801]. Apprentice to Archibald Milne.—Eldest son of John Innes of Blackhills, Elginshire. *Married* 18 August 1810, Mary (*died* 25 December 1855), eldest daughter of George Brown of Linkwood, Elginshire. *Died* 8 August 1841, aged 66.

IRELAND, RICHARD MORISON [13 December 1910]. Apprentice to (1) A. D. Mutter-Napier; and (2) Neil Macvicar.—Son of Robert Alexander Ireland, I.S.O., Chief Assistant Keeper, H.M. General Register of Sasines. *Born* 24 November 1887. *Married* 2 October 1919, Erna Marie (*died* 13 January 1943), only daughter of William Herrmann, Vice-President of San Francisco Bank, San Francisco, California. During Great War, Captain in 5th and 9th Royal Scots in Gallipoli, France, and Germany. Staff Officer, Intelligence Corps. Wounded at Beaumont Hamel. *Died* 5 February 1944. *Firm*—Ketchen and Stevens.

IRONS, DAVID EBENEZER BLACKWELL [15 January 1894]. Apprentice to (1) James F. Mackay; (2) J. P. Wood.—Eldest son of James Campbell Irons, S.S.C., Edinburgh. *Born* 4 July 1868. *Died* 23 January 1898, unmarried.

IRONSIDE, THOMAS DAVID, LL.B. [9 December 1980]. Apprentice to Edward Graham Marquis and Others, of J. & F. Anderson.—Son of William Bickerstaff Ironside, Farmer, Wick. *Born* 2 June 1955.

IRVINE, JOHN [25 August 1698]. Apprentice to William Thomson.—Son of Robert Irvine of Cults, Aberdeenshire.

IRVING, DOUGLAS ROBERT, LL.B. [28 April 1975]. Apprentice to George William Tait of G. W. Tait & Sons.—Son of Thomas Kerr Irving, Architect, Stranraer. *Born* 24 May 1951.

IRVING, GEORGE, OF NEWTON [8 February 1720]. Apprentice to Alexander Home.—Only son of James Irving, Usher of the Privy Council. *Married* (contract, 2 November 1711), Sarah, daughter of Thomas Weir, Surgeon in Edinburgh. Clerk to the City of Edinburgh, 1720, and Solicitor to the City in succession to Ronald Campbell, 1726. As Agent for the City he had to attend in the House of Lords in connection with the murder of Captain Porteous. *Died* 19 June 1742.

IRVING, GEORGE [20 November 1828]. Apprentice to, and eldest son of, John Irving, W.S.—*Born* 1805. *Died* 19 February 1841, unmarried.

IRVING, JOHN [10 July 1794]. Apprentice to John Tait.—Second son of George Irving of Newton, Lanarkshire. *Born* November 1770. *Married* 2 July 1804, Agnes Clerk (*died* 10 July 1823), eldest daughter of Lieut.-Colonel Lewis Hay, R.E. *Died* 26 May 1850.

IRVING, PATRICK, OF INVERAMSAY [19 November 1797]. Apprentice to Lachlan Duff.—Son of John Irving of Auchmunzie. *Born* 23 September 1773. *Married* 1 June 1803, Margaret (*died* 10 June 1851), daughter of Patrick Orr of Bridgeton, Kincardineshire. Author of *Considerations of the Inexpediency of the Law of Entail*, 1826, and other legal works. *Died* 3 February 1854.

IRVING, ROBERT [28 July 1751]. Apprentice to Thomas Goldie.—Third son of William Irving of Bonshaw, Dumfriesshire. *Born* 26 June 1704. *Married*, proclaimed 8 January 1764, Mary (*died* 1 December 1765), daughter of William Veitch of Eliock, Dumfriesshire, W.S. *Died* 17 November 1772.

IVORY, HOLMES [19 April 1876]. Apprentice to Alexander F. Adam and John Kirk.—Eldest son of William Ivory, Advocate, Sheriff of Inverness. *Born* 21 March 1851. *Married* 21 December 1877, Margaret Dick (*died* 1 March 1933), eldest daughter of John Dick Peddie, R.S.A., Architect, Edinburgh. Receiver of Crown Rents. *Died* 14 October 1914.

IVORY, WILLIAM [23 November 1827]. Apprentice to Thomas Mackenzie.—Son of Thomas Ivory, residing in Dundee. *Married* 30 April 1846, Robina (*died* 13 July 1878), daughter of Robert Cox of Gorgie, Mid-Lothian. Compiled a *Catalogue of the Law Books in the Library of the Society of Writers to Her Majesty's Signet*, 1856. *Died* 21 May 1868, aged 70.

IVORY, WILLIAM HOLMES [30 March 1908]. Apprentice to A. Peddie Waddell and Holmes Ivory.—Son of Holmes Ivory, W.S. *Born* 4 April 1883. *Married* 30 July 1915, Helen (*died* 23 July 1969), eldest daughter of Henry Brown Marshall of Rachan, Broughton, Peeblesshire. Lieutenant, Royal Scots: served in France, 1917-18. *Died* 6 February 1967.

JACK, JAMES GORDON [13 July 1914]. Apprentice to W. Traquair Dickson and Another of Traquair, Dickson & Maclaren.—Son of George Jack, S.S.C., Dalkeith. *Born* 6 June 1889. *Married* 17 April 1917, Irene Winifred, daughter of Edwin James Castiglione, Estate Agent, Carlisle. Served in France during First World War, 2nd Lieutenant, H.L.I. *Died* 24 April 1977. *Firm*—L. & L. L. Bilton.

JACK, JOHN M'GREGOR BRUCE [7 July 1913]. Apprentice to William Babington and Joseph Inglis.—Son of James M'Gregor Jack, S.S.C., Edinburgh. *Born* 8 April 1888. *Married* 8 April 1921, Helena Colburn (*died* 18 February 1932), eldest daughter of Robert Colburn Buchanan, Edinburgh, Cinema Proprietor. *Died* 25 January 1943. *Firm*—J. and J. Jack.

JACKSON, GEORGE ERSKINE, OF KIRKBUDDO, O.B.E., M.C. [12 December 1898]. Apprentice to Sir T. D. Brodie.—Only son of James Rawlinson Jackson of Kirkbuddo, in the County of Angus, Deputy Surgeon-General I.M.D. *Born* 13 March 1872. Served with C.I.V. in South African War, 1900. In Great War, 1914-18, Staff Captain Highland Mounted Brigade. D.A.A.G. Australian Mounted Division. *Died* 2 August 1945. *Firm*—Henderson and Jackson.

JACKSON, GIDEON [23 September 1736]. Apprentice to Alexander M'Millan.—Son of Robert Jackson of Lowherelds. *Married* Mary Hepburn. Resigned his Commission, 15 March 1746. Clerk to the Tolbooth, 1755. *Died* 11 August 1773.

JACKSON, IAIN CARLYLE, LL.B. [28 November 1966]. Apprentice to (1) Ian Hauxwell Mellor of M. J. Brown, Son & Co. and (2) Ronald Kenneth Watson and Another of Brodie, Cuthbertson & Watson.—Son of George Sturdy Jackson, Bookseller, Bridge of Allan. *Born* 22 January 1924. *Married* 9 January 1952, Barbara, daughter of E. D. Jehring, C.A., Horley, Surrey. Sub. Lieutenant, Black Watch. Served N.W. Europe and Middle East 1943-46. *Firm*—Brodies.

JACKSON, PATRICK CHARLES [14 March 1892]. Apprentice to F. Pitman, J. R. Anderson, W. H. Murray, and A. R. C. Pitman.—Third son of the Rev. Gidart Jackson of St James' Episcopal Church, Leith. *Born* 14 November 1868. *Married* 5 July 1894, Kathleen Mary (*died* 15 March 1946), daughter of Lauritz La Cour, 17 Inverleith Row, Edinburgh. *Died* at Broughton-in-Furness, 21 October 1917.

JAMES, ARTHUR HOOD [15 December 1924]. Apprentice to (1) John James Herdman; and (2) J. A. Will.—Son of Robert Hood James, S.S.C., Edinburgh. *Born* 20 June 1901. *Married* (1) 23 November 1925, Norah Elliot (*died* 26 November 1926), eldest daughter of Robert Graham, Electrical Engineer, Edinburgh; and (2) 4 September 1928, Julia Margaret (*died* 12 July 1971), youngest daughter of William Morris, Building Contractor, Edinburgh. Pilot Officer, R.A.F. *Died* on active service 23 September 1940. *Firm*—Webster, Will, and Co.

JAMESON, ANDREW [17 November 1836]. Apprentice to William Bell.—Son of John Jameson, residing in Dublin. *Born* 19 September 1812. *Married* 14 March 1852, Margaret Cochrane. Sheriff-Clerk of Clackmannan, 1841-72. *Died* January 1872.

JAMESON, ANDREW ST CLAIR [18 December 1922]. Apprentice to J. H. Jameson and Another of Boyd, Jameson & Young.—Son of James Hotchkis Jameson, W.S. *Born* 20 April 1894. *Married* 25 September 1924, Margaret Eleanor (*died* 9 January 1982), daughter of Alfred Lennox, Mining Engineer, Wallsend. Lieutenant 3rd Battalion, attached 2nd Battalion, Seaforth Highlanders, 1914-17. Wounded, July 1916 and invalided out of Service. *Died* 7 November 1977. *Firm*—Boyd, Jameson & Young.

JAMESON, GEORGE GRANT [21 November 1833]. Apprentice to (1) David Ramsay; (2) John Donaldson.—Son of the Rev. John Jameson, D.D. *Born* 1 April 1805. *Died* December 1834, unmarried.

JAMESON, JAMES HOTCHKIS [4 August 1880]. Apprentice to J. B. Innes and John and C. B. Logan.—Son of Andrew Jameson, Advocate, Sheriff of Aberdeen and Kincardine. *Born* 4 January 1855. *Married* 25 March 1884, Virginia (*died* 7 June 1940), elder daughter of William Ker, Manila. Fiscal, 1918-28. *Died* 27 January 1937. *Firm*—Boyd, Jameson, and Young.

JAMESON, JAMES NEIL ST CLAIR, B.L. [30 November 1964]. Apprentice to Robert Carfrae Notman and Another of Morton, Smart, Macdonald & Milligan.—Son of Andrew St Clair Jameson, W.S., Edinburgh. *Born* 31 January 1938. *Firms*—(1) Boyd, Jameson & Young (1965-73); (2) Morton, Fraser & Milligan.

JAMESON, WILLIAM, OF ROSEFIELD [13 December 1793]. Apprentice to Robert Boswell.—Only son of William Jameson, Mason and Deacon Convener of the Trades, Edinburgh. *Married* (1), proclaimed 21 November 1795, a daughter of John Spottiswoode, Merchant in Edinburgh; and (2) Elizabeth Jane Turnbull (*died* 20 May 1837). *Died* at Annfield, Newhaven, 26 June 1825.

JAMIESON, HARVEY MORRO. *See* HARVEY-JAMIESON.

JAMIESON, JAMES AULDJO [15 March 1861]. Apprentice to John Dundas, William Wilson, and A. M. Bell.—Son of James Jamieson, Doctor of Medicine in Aberdeen and afterwards in Edinburgh. *Born* 25 September 1832. *Married* 17 November 1863, Isabella (*died* 8 February 1939), only daughter of James Powrie of Reswallie, Forfarshire. Crown Agent, 1874-80, 1885, 1886. *Died* 13 November 1907.

JAMIESON, JOHN HARRY IRVINE AULDJO [28 March 1904]. Apprentice to J. Auldjo Jamieson, his uncle.—Son of George Auldjo Jamieson, C.A., Edinburgh. *Born* 10 March 1878. *Married* 2 November 1905, Elizabeth (*died* 4 October 1973), eldest daughter of James Mylne, W.S. In Great War served with 8th Royal Scots and Machine Gun Corps. Acting Major. *Died* 10 December 1944.

JAMIESON, ROBERT, OF HERIOT HILL [2 January 1759]. Apprentice to John Watson.— Son of Robert Jamieson, Merchant in Aberdeen. *Married* (1), proclaimed 3 September 1758, Jean (*died* 29 September 1769), daughter of William Richardson, Smith, Edinburgh; and (2), proclaimed June 1770, Catherine (*died* 17 February 1809), daughter of John Lockhart of Cleghorne, Lanarkshire. *Died* 31 October 1808.

JAMIESON, ROBERT [23 March 1796]. Apprentice to, and son of, Robert Jamieson, W.S.—*Married* 19 April 1796, Jane (*died* 21 February 1834), daughter of Alexander Christie, Provost of Montrose. *Died* 7 December 1832, aged 63.

JAMIESON, ROBERT [2 July 1829]. Apprentice to Robert Strachan.—Eldest son of Robert Jamieson, W.S. *Died* at Melbourne, 14 February 1850.

JAMIESON, ROBERT WILLIAM [23 June 1829]. Apprentice to Adam Gib Ellis.—Son of Thomas Jamieson, Soap-boiler in Leith. *Born* 1805. *Married* 2 April 1835, Christina (*died* 22 July 1883), daughter of Major-General John Pringle of Symington, Mid-Lothiam. Author of *Nimrod: a Dramatic Poem*, 1848, and other works. Father of Dr Leander Starr Jamieson of the Transvaal Raid. *Died* at London, 10 December 1868.

JAPP, WILLIAM BUCHAN. *See* FENTON, WILLIAM BUCHAN JAPP.

JARDINE, SIR HENRY, OF HARWOOD [25 June 1790]. Apprentice to John Davidson.—Son of Rev. John Jardine, D.D., one of the Ministers of Edinburgh. *Born* 30 January 1766. *Married* 26 April 1794, Catherine (*died* 4 September 1838), youngest daughter of George Skene of Rubislaw, Aberdeenshire. Solicitor of Taxes, 1793. Lieutenant Royal Edinburgh Volunteers, 1794. Depute King's Remembrancer in Exchequer, 1802; King's Remembrancer, 1820-31. Knighted, 20 April 1825. Author of a *Report relative to the Tomb of King Robert the Bruce and the Cathedral Church of Dunfermline*. *Died* 11 August 1851.

JARDINE, JAMES [16 January 1834]. Apprentice to, and youngest son of, Sir Henry Jardine, W.S.—*Born* 7 October 1810. *Married* 30 January 1834, Ann, daughter of Colonel Tomlinson and widow of Captain Windowe. *Died* 15 November 1839.

JEFFRAY, JAMES STUART ALLAN, M.A.(OXON) [12 May 1981*].—Son of William Allan Jeffray, C.A., Broughty Ferry. *Born* 3 April 1947. *Married* 12 July 1975, Ann Shirley Wyndham, daughter of Dr Robert Wyndham Henn-Gennys Harris, General Practitioner, Natal, South Africa. *Firm*—Fyfe, Ireland & Co.

JINKINS, THOMAS MUIRHEAD [14 July 1947]. Apprentice to James Harrower Guild and Others of Russell & Dunlop.—Son of Thomas Gilliland Jinkins, Sales Representative, Edinburgh. *Born* 3 October 1906. *Married* 1 October 1938, Maida Margaret Balfour, daughter of Robert Scott, Builder, Portobello. *Died* 5 May 1979. *Firm*—Russell & Dunlop.

JOBSON, GEORGE LIVINGSTONE, B.L. [15 December 1947]. Apprentice to Joseph Ellis Inglis and Another of Melville & Lindesay.—Son of John Charles Jobson, Writer, Edinburgh. *Born* 28 April 1915. *Married* 19 August 1943, Mary Lawrie Jeffrey, daughter of James Hendry, Master Printer. *Died* 18 February 1980. *Firms*—(1) Melville & Lindesay; (2) Tods, Murray & Jamieson.

JOHNSTON, ALEXANDER [13 November 1817]. Apprentice to John Pollock.—Eldest son of George Johnston of Hillhouse. *Married*. *Died* 31 December 1864, aged 75.

JOHNSTON, ALEXANDER, OF VIEWFIELD [8 July 1831]. Apprentice to James Arnott,—Fourth son of William Johnston of Viewfield, Merchant in Aberdeen. *Born* 4 June 1809. *Married* 1 January 1836, Christina Martha (*died* 21 April 1878), second daughter of John Leith Ross of Arnage, W.S. *Died* 14 June 1880.

JOHNSTON, ALEXANDER GRAHAM, B.A.(OXON), LL.B. [26 April 1971]. Apprentice to Sir Alastair C. Blair and Others of Davidson & Syme.—Son of The Hon. Lord Kincraig, Senator of the College of Justice. *Born* 16 July 1944. *Married* 22 January 1972, Susan Gay, daughter of Ian Hunter Horne. *Firm*—Hagart & Burn-Murdoch.

JOHNSTON, ALEXANDER TAYLOR, B.L. [20 July 1950]. Apprentice to Robert Somerville and Another of Graham, Johnston & Fleming.—Son of Alexander Johnston, Engineer, Falkirk. *Born* 14 December 1912. *Married* 10 August 1940, Mary Margaret, daughter of James Meikle. Agent for the Crown in *Ultimus Haeres* Cases. *Firm*—Laing & Motherwell.

JOHNSTON, CHARLES, M.A., LL.B. [28 April 1969]. Apprentice to Andrew Macgregor Young and Another of J. & R. A. Robertson.—Son of Charles Johnston, Draper, Edinburgh. *Born* 11 June 1939. *Married* 8 July 1965, Valerie Elizabeth, daughter of Robert Faulds, Civil Engineer, Toronto, Canada. *Firm*—J. & R. A. Robertson.

JOHNSTON, DAVID [11 July 1904]. Apprentice to John Cowan, J. A. Dalmahoy, and E. J. M'Candlish.—Son of Henry Johnston, one of the Senators of the College of Justice (Lord Johnston). *Born* 5 June 1876. *Lost* in the wreck of the *Empress of Ireland* in the Gulf of the St Lawrence, 29 May 1914.

JOHNSTON, GEORGE [1 August 1786]. Apprentice to Walter Scott.—Second son of Thomas Johnston of Templehall, Berwickshire. *Born* 1762. *Died* 1801.

JOHNSTON, JAMES, OF STRAITON [5 July 1661]. Apprentice to Robert Hamilton.—Eldest son of Rev. James Johnston, Minister of Stonehouse. *Married* 25 November 1664, Ann, third daughter of Quentin Hamilton of Barncluith, Lanarkshire. *Buried* 18 May 1684.

JOHNSTON, JOHN [Before 1552]. *Married* Margaret Clark. *Died* 14 May 1597.

JOHNSTON, ROBERT [6 March 1828]. Apprentice to Charles Cunningham and Carlyle Bell.—Son of Robert Johnston, Tenant of Slateheugh, West Calder. *Married* 1835, Elspeth Duff (*died* 1872). *Died* 1853, aged 66.

JOHNSTON, ROBERT [13 November 1828]. Apprentice to (1) William Dymock; and (2) John Dymock.—Only son of John Johnston of Middlefield. *Born* 12 August 1805. *Married* 21 May 1829, Isabella (*died* 11 December 1879), eldest daughter of Joseph Johnston, Register House. *Died* 12 May 1869.

JOHNSTON, ROBERT BRUCE [17 January 1861]. Apprentice to Jardine, Stodart, and Fraser.—Son of Robert Johnston, W.S. *Born* 29 April 1835. *Married* 8 June 1864, Agnes Cockburn (*died* 24 April 1924), daughter of James Nelson Smith, Merchant, London and Sydney. Procurator-Fiscal of Edinburgh, 1868-88. *Died* 4 February 1888.

JOHNSTON, ROBERT FLEMING [21 January 1874]. Apprentice to John Richardson.—Son of John Smith Johnston, S.S.C. *Born* 22 February 1840. *Married* 22 May 1872, Isabella Anne Catherine (*died* 22 June 1916), second daughter of Rev. Charles Irving, Rector of Donoughmore. *Died* 12 July 1902.

JOHNSTON, ROBERT HERBERT [13 January 1890]. Apprentice to W. S. Fraser.—Eldest son of Robert Bruce Johnston, W.S. *Born* 1 May 1865. *Married* 11 February 1890, Edith (*died* 19 January 1942), younger daughter of John Comrie Thomson, Advocate. *Died* 15 February 1910 at University Club Ball, Edinburgh.

JOHNSTON, WILLIAM, OF BANKS [19 March 1782]. Apprentice to (1) Robert Irving; and (2) John Syme.—Only son of James Johnston of Nether Banks, Dumfriesshire. *Married* 1 November 1781, Nancy (*died* 8 January 1811), daughter of William Shortred of Colmslie, Roxburghshire. *Died* at Lockerbie, 16 November 1789.

JOHNSTON, WILLIAM [4 March 1805]. Apprentice to John Dickson.—Only son of George Johnston, Supervisor of Excise for the Ayr District. *Born* 1780. *Married* 29 December 1806, Sarah, daughter of Robert Riddle of Carzield, Dumfriesshire. Attorney-General, Prince Edward Island, Canada. *Died* in Prince Edward Island, 1828.

JOHNSTON, SIR WILLIAM CAMPBELL, LL.D. [13 July 1885]. Apprentice to John Cowan and James A. Dalmahoy.—Son of Henry Johnston, Surgeon in the Hon. East India Company's Service. *Born* 24 November 1860. *Married* 24 July 1889, Alicia Christina (*died* 11 March 1943), daughter of Major-General R. D. Macpherson, Bengal Staff Corps. Member of the King's Bodyguard for Scotland, Royal Company of Archers, 1897. Collector of Widows' Fund, 21 July 1922. Deputy Keeper of the Signet, 1924-35. Knighted, February 1934. Agent of the Episcopal Church in Scotland. *Died* 6 October 1938. *Firm*—Murray, Beith, and Murray.

JOHNSTONE, DAVID ALEXANDER, M.A., LL.B. [13 May 1980*].—Son of Anthony Johnstone, Commercial Traveller, Castle Douglas, Kirkcudbrightshire. *Born* 23 January 1938. *Married* 31 March 1967, Christine Janet Adams, daughter of Dr Haldane Philp Tait, Medical Practitioner, Edinburgh. *Firm*—G. W. Tait & Sons.

JOHNSTONE, IAN TEMPLE, M.A.(CANTAB). LL.B. [19 December 1949]. Apprentice to Sir Hugh Watson and Another of Dundas & Wilson.—Son of John Johnstone, Solicitor, Edinburgh. *Born* 25 February 1923. *Married* 29 March 1958, Frances Helen, daughter of the Rev. Campbell Ferenbach, Edinburgh. Captain, Royal Artillery. Served U.K. and India 1939-45. Appointed Treasurer to the Society 1974. *Firm*—Biggart, Baillie & Gifford. (Formerly Baillie & Gifford.)

JOHNSTONE, JOHN [Before 1547]. Commissioner, 16 December 1594.

JOHNSTONE, WILLIAM [30 January 1880]. Apprentice to John Gibson, Jun., and Robert Strathern.—Elder son of Christopher Johnstone of Croftheads, Dumfriesshire, General Manager of the Caledonian Railway Company. *Born* 25 August 1855. *Married* 28 June 1887, Janet (*died* 11 November 1945), eldest daughter of John James Malcolm Borthwick, Billholm, Dumfriesshire. *Died* 5 March 1893.

JOHNSTONE, WILLIAM CHARLES [12 January 1891]. Apprentice to John Turnbull.—Son of James Johnstone, Farmer, Hunterheck, in the Parish of Moffat and County of Dumfries. *Born* 16 June 1867. *Married* 22 August 1895, Mary Charlotte (*died* 30 March 1950), eldest daughter of Walter Pringle of Langlands. *Died* 4 June 1930.

JOLLIE, JAMES [12 December 1783]. Apprentice to James Forrest.—Son of Walter Jollie, Tailor in Edinburgh. *Born* 1755. *Married* 14 September 1790, Christian (*died* 27 November 1807), daughter of Rev. John Hart, Minister of Kirkinner. Clerk to the Merchant Company. One of the Trustees for Sir Walter Scott's creditors. *Died* 30 August 1846.

JOLLIE, WALTER [5 March 1818]. Apprentice to (1) James Jollie; and (2) James Dundas.—Eldest son of James Jollie, W.S. *Married* 19 August 1825, Hannah Lycette (*died* 30 May 1860), eldest daughter of Lieut.-General Avarne of Rugely, Stafford. *Died* 12 May 1859, aged 68.

JONES, ARCHIBALD WILSON [12 January 1891]. Apprentice to John William Young and John Blair.—Son of Alexander Fair Jones, late Captain in His Majesty's Fourth Regiment of Hussars. *Born* 21 June 1868. Resigned Commission, 5 December 1893. Admitted Advocate, 14 December 1894. Lieut.-Colonel Highland Light Infantry. Magistrate in Northern Nigeria. *Died* suddenly at Hawick on 21 February 1917. unmarried.

JONES, IAN QUAYLE, M.A., LL.B. [29 July 1968]. Apprentice to D. C. Scott-Moncrieff and Others of Tods, Murray & Jamieson.—Son of Arnold B. Jones, Motor Trader. *Born* 14 July 1941. *Married* 28 February 1968, Christine Ann, daughter of Kenneth Macrae, W.S., Edinburgh. *Firm*—Cowan & Stewart. (Resigned.)

JONES, THOMAS WILLIAM, V.D. [18 July 1861]. Apprentice to Charles Morton.—Son of Edmund Morse Jones, Surgeon. *Born* 5 July 1834. *Married* 4 April 1872, Elizabeth Macfarlane (*died* 5 January 1883), youngest daughter of James Greig of Eccles, W.S., and widow of James Charles Henderson, S.S.C. In Sasine Office. *Died* 3 March 1927.

JOPP, JOHN [31 May 1827]. Apprentice to John Russell.—Second son of Andrew Jopp, Advocate in Aberdeen. *Born* 18 July 1805. *Married* 7 September 1841, Margery (*died* 10 February 1893), eldest daughter of John Smith of Drongan, Ayrshire. *Died* 31 October 1857.

JOSSE, ROBERT [Before 1530].

JUNNER, JOHN CLARK [10 March 1870]. Apprentice to William Ferguson.—Son of John Mackenzie Junner, S.S.C. *Born* 22 March 1846. *Married* 18 March 1875, Margaret Balfour (*died* 16 July 1891), eldest daughter of A. B. Wright, Edinburgh. *Died* 9 April 1892.

KARR, ANDREW, OF KIPPILAW [2 October 1696]. Apprentice to James Hay.—Only son of Lieut.-Colonel Andrew Karr of Kippilaw, Roxburghshire. *Born* 28 July 1659. *Married* Jean, elder daughter of Rev. John Stirling, Minister of Bara, East Lothian. *Died* 16 October 1744.

KAY, JAMES, OF PINCARTAIN [1594]. Signs Minute of 16 December 1594. *Married* 17 September 1595, Elizabeth Scott.

KEAY, WILLIAM ALEXANDER, LL.B. [19 December 1927]. Apprentice to Sir John Prosser, A. Gray Muir, J. H. Macdonald and D. G. Prosser.—Son of William Keay, Solicitor, Blairgowrie. *Born* 3 November 1903. *Died* 15 June 1976. *Firm*—Keay & Hodges, Blairgowrie (latterly William Keay & Co.).

KEILL OR KYLE, ROBERT [29 November 1673]. Apprentice to James Carnegie.—*Married* Sarah (*died* 15 January 1697), daughter of John Cockburn, Tailor Burgess of Edinburgh.

KEITH, ALEXANDER, OF RAVELSTON AND DUNOTTAR [15 July 1763]. Apprentice to (1) Hew Crawford; and (2) John Mackenzie of Delvine.—Eldest son of Alexander Keith of Ravelston, Depute Clerk of Session. *Married* 24 April 1811, Margaret, youngest daughter of Lawrence Oliphant of Gask, Perthshire. *Died* 26 February 1819.

KEITH, JAMES, OF AUQUHORSK [7 March 1664]. Apprentice to James Cheyne and others.—Son of John Keith of Auquhorsk. *Born* 1630. *Married* Barbara Boyes. Sheriff of the Mearns, 1705.

KEITH, ROBERT, OF AUQUHORSK [Before 1631]. Commissioner, 18 October 1631. *Died* before 1663. His daughter Elizabeth got authority from the Town Council of Edinburgh, in 1663, to "keep a chope within this burgh and to sell such lawful commodities and merchand waire therein as her abilities can reache to."

KEITH-MURRAY, PATRICK [23 March 1903]. Apprentice to W. C. M'Ewen.—Second son of Sir Patrick Keith-Murray of Ochtertyre, Crieff, Baronet. *Born* 28 November 1878. *Married* 15 July 1903, Cecilia Mary Dorothea (*died* 3 November 1964), second daughter of General John Sprot of Riddell, Roxburghshire. Captain Lothian and Border Horse in Great War. *Died* 11 June 1937. *Firm*—Hope, Todd, and Kirk.

KELLAS, ALEXANDER JOHN, LL.B. [23 April 1951]. Apprentice to Maurice G. Kidd of Maurice G. Kidd & Co.—Son of John F. Kellas, Solicitor, Edinburgh. *Born* 6 July 1926. *Married* 4 April 1953, Esmee Louise, daughter of Dobson Wellbourne. *Firm*— Beveridge & Kellas (formerly John F. Kellas & Co.).

KELLIE, T. [Before 1606]. Signs Minute of 17 January 1606.

KELLIE, WILLIAM, OF EASTBARNS [Before 1598]. Son of —— Kellie of Newtonlees. *Married* (1) Marjorie Murray; and (2) Jean (*died* 24 November 1639), daughter of James Barron of Kinnaird. *Died* February 1632.

KELLIE, WILLIAM [1627]. *Married* Jean Borram (*died* 24 November 1639).

KELSO, WILLIAM, OF DANKEITH [13 May 1707]. Apprentice to John Cunningham of Enterkine.—Second son of John Kelso of Kelsoland, Ayrshire. *Married* April 1697, Mary, eldest daughter of John Dunlop of that Ilk. *Died* about 1721.

KEMP, DAVID EDWARD, M.A., LL.B. [25 April 1977]. Apprentice to Edward Graham Marquis and Others of J. & F. Anderson.—Son of James F. F. Kemp, F.R.I.C.S., Estate Factor, Glamis, Angus. *Born* 19 April 1947. *Married* 19 April 1974, Elizabeth Myron, daughter of Dr C. S. Philip. *Firm*—Boyd, Jameson & Young.

KENE, JOHN [Before 1586]. Commissioner, 16 December 1594.—Son of Thomas Kene, Writer in Edinburgh. *Married* Janet, daughter of Andrew Strang, Tutor of Balcaskie, and widow of Martin Balfour, Burgess of Kinghorn. *Died* about 1597.

KENE, RICHARD [21 February 1599].—Son of John Kene, W.S.

KENE, THOMAS [Before 1525].

KENNAWAY, ANDREW LAURIE [17 January 1888]. Apprentice to Charles Baxter.— Son of Robert Kennaway, Farmer, Polton Mains, Mid-Lothian. *Born* 30 August 1863. *Died* in New Zealand, 24 February 1920, unmarried.

KENNAWAY, CHARLES GRAY, LL.B. [9 April 1920]. Apprentice to Sir William S. Haldane, F. G. Haldane, and William Purves.—Son of James Peebles Kennaway, Solicitor, Auchterarder. *Born* 7 January 1894. *Married* 23 April 1924, Marjory Helen, M.B., Ch.B. (*died* 10 November 1979), daughter of George Turnbull Ewing, Pitkellony, Muthill. Served in Great War 1914-19. Captain Grenadier Guards, and Staff Captain 3rd Guards Brigade. Appointed to Ministry of Justice in Egypt, 1920. Resigned. Depute Clerk of Peace for Central Perthshire, 1921. *Died* 31 January 1941. *Firm*—Kennaway and Co., Auchterarder.

KENNEDY, ALEXANDER [1 December 1825]. Apprentice to John Forman.—Youngest son of Rev. Thomas Kennedy, Minister of St Madoes. *Born* 25 February 1802. *Died* 19 April 1868, unmarried.

KENNEDY, DUNCAN, M.B.E., B.L. [30 March 1908]. Apprentice to William Thomson.—Son of James Kennedy, 21 Bernard Terrace, Edinburgh. *Born* 14 November 1881. *Married* 24 July 1909, Janet Bald (*died* 3 November 1965), second daughter of Matthew Wilson, 143 Warrender Park Road, Edinburgh. Captain R.A.O.C.; served in Balkans, 1916-19. Awarded M.B.E. Clerk and Treasurer to Forth Conservancy Board 1924-47. *Died* 13 September 1947. *Firm*—T. & T. Gibson & Kennedy, Falkirk.

KENNEDY, GEORGE, OF ROMANNO [2 November 1711].—Younger son of Robert Kennedy of Auchtyfardle, Lanarkshire. *Married* (1) February 1714, Janet, daughter of Andrew Pringle of Clifton, Selkirkshire; (2) October 1721, Anne, daughter of Adam Cleghorn, Merchant and Bailie of Edinburgh; and (3) January 1731, Anne, daughter of George Stirling, Surgeon in Edinburgh. Under Keeper of the Signet, 1711-13. Warden of the Mint. Fiscal, 1722-3. *Died* 1743.

KENNEDY, HUGH [24 January 1822]. Apprentice to Walter Cook.—Second son of Captain George Kennedy, younger of Romanno, Peeblesshire. *Born* 7 September 1797. *Died* 4 May 1876, unmarried.

KENNEDY, JAMES NOEL, LL.B. [4 December 1972]. Apprentice to John Kenneth Finlayson and Another of Bonar, Mackenzie & Kermack.—Son of James Duncan Kennedy, C.B.E., County Clerk of Stirlingshire, Stirling. *Born* 25 December 1948. *Married* 15 August 1975, Mary Isobel Sinclair. *Firm*—Bonar Mackenzie.

KENNEDY, JOHN [29 June 1661]. Apprentice to, and son of, Quintin Kennedy, W.S.—*Died* 1686.

KENNEDY, JOHN, OF UNDERWOOD [8 December 1808]. Apprentice to James Dundas.—Third son of John Kennedy of Underwood, Ayrshire. *Born* 1785. *Married* 4 January 1814, Margaret Buchanan (*died* 1 May 1825), youngest daughter of Neil Snodgrass of Cunninghamhead, Ayrshire. *Died* 3 March 1862.

KENNEDY, JOHN, OF UNDERWOOD [18 July 1844]. Apprentice to Richard Campbell.—Eldest son of John Kennedy, W.S. *Born* 22 August 1816. *Married* 6 August 1851, Margaret Elizabeth (*died* 7 October 1893), daughter of Colin Macrae of Inverinate, Ross-shire, Merchant in London. *Died* 28 January 1902.

KENNEDY, JOHN, OF UNDERWOOD [19 July 1877]. Apprentice to, and eldest son of, John Kennedy, W.S.—*Born* 12 September 1852. *Married* 6 January 1884, Jessie Edwards (*died* 29 August 1935), daughter of Alexander Reid. *Died* 1 March 1920 in a railway accident at Wimbledon.

KENNEDY, MATTHEW DUNCAN, T.D., B.L. [20 March 1950]. Apprentice to (1) Duncan Kennedy and Another of T. T. Gibson & Kennedy, Falkirk, and (2) Frederick Patterson Milligan of Martin Milligan & Macdonald.—Son of Duncan Kennedy, W.S., Falkirk. *Born* 29 December 1914. Major, Argyll & Sutherland Highlanders. Served with 9th Scottish Commandos 1940-45 in Gibraltar, North Africa, Italy and Greece. Wounded in Italy in 1943. Honorary Sheriff-Substitute, Tayside, Central and Fife. *Died* 28 April 1980. *Firm*—T. & T. Gibson & Kennedy, Falkirk.

KENNEDY, QUINTIN [Before 1625].—Grand-nephew of James Kennedy, Merchant Burgess of Aberdeen. *Married* 1 February 1619, Catherine Wylie. *Buried* 19 January 1659.

KENNEDY, ROBERT [1 July 1822]. Apprentice to Patrick Tennent.—Son of Rev. Thomas Kennedy, Minister of St Madoes. *Born* 7 October 1798. *Died* 17 March 1840, unmarried.

KENNEDY, THOMAS ROBERT, B.A., B.SC.(Oxon), LL.B. [13 July 1936]. Apprentice to Robert F. Shepherd and Others of Shepherd & Wedderburn.—Son of Robert Kennedy, Engineer, Edinburgh. *Born* 21 June 1909. Squadron Leader, R.A.F.V.R., Royal Signals Branch. Served U.K. and India 1939-46.

KENNEDY, WILLIAM [28 June 1827]. Apprentice to Francis Brodie and George Imlach.—Third son of William Kennedy of Kirkland, Dumfriesshire. *Born* 1800. *Married* 28 September 1841, Sarah (*died* 4 November 1850), daughter of William Carrick, Carlisle. *Died* 23 April 1877.

KENNWYE, JAMES [15 January 1634]. Apprentice to John Ker.—Town Clerk of Culross.

KER, ALLAN EBENEZER, V.C. [7 December 1908]. Apprentice to, and son of, Robert Darling Ker, W.S.—*Born* 5 March 1883. *Married* 29 April 1916, Vera Irene Gordon, daughter of Alfred Barham Gordon Skinner, Director of Public Companies, London. Joined Gordon Highlanders, 1915, with Commission as Lieutenant. Served in France, Salonica, etc. Awarded the V.C. for a conspicuous act of gallantry at St Quentin on 21 March 1918. Second World War Major, Gordon Highlanders. Served U.K. General Staff, War Office. Awarded Knight of Order of Military Merit (Brazil) 1944. *Died* 12 September 1958.

KER, JOHN [Before 1623]. Commissioner, 1631. *Married* 30 August 1614, Janet (*died* February 1633), daughter of Edward Ker, Tailor Burgess of Edinburgh. *Died* February 1633.

KER, JOHN, OF KERFIELD [22 November 1799]. Apprentice to Alexander Young.—Second son of William Ker of Kerfield, Peebleshire. *Born* 1773. *Died* 22 September 1838, unmarried.

KER, ROBERT DARLING [18 January 1886]. Apprentice to William Smith.—Son of Robert D. Ker, wholesale Corn Merchant, residing at St Leonard's House, Edinburgh. *Born* 15 January 1853. *Married* 20 April 1882, Johanna (*died* 8 May 1931), daughter of Daniel Johnston, Wood Merchant, Edinburgh. *Died* 24 April 1940. *Firm*—Ker and Winchester.

KERMACK, GEORGE [14 July 1884]. Apprentice to John Cook.—Youngest son of William Ramsay Kermack, W.S. *Born* 9 Febuary 1860. *Married* 17 April 1917, Margaret (*died* 24 December 1939), elder daughter of Arthur E. Woodbridge, Bognor, Sussex. *Died* at London, 24 April 1935.

KERMACK, JOHN [10 July 1810]. Apprentice to Robert Cathcart.—Son of John Kermack, Writer in Edinburgh. *Born* 9 September 1781. *Married* 9 October 1815, Jane Ogilvie (*died* 2 February 1834), daughter of Rev. William Ramsay, Minister of Cortachy. *Died* 3 April 1860.

KERMACK, JOHN [30 November 1871]. Apprentice to, and eldest son of, William Ramsay Kermack, W.S.—*Born* 2 May 1847. *Died* 10 March 1899, unmarried.

KERMACK, WILLIAM RAMSAY [8 June 1843]. Apprentice to, and youngest son of, John Kermack, W.S.—*Born* 3 September 1820. *Married* 3 June 1846, Elizabeth (*died* 13 October 1894), daughter of Henry Armstrong, Edinburgh. Fiscal, 1872-83. *Died* 8 May 1883.

KERR, ALAN THURSFIELD, M.A., LL.B. [30 November 1959]. Apprentice to William Watt and Another of Davidson & Syme.—Son of Samuel Kerr Gifford Kerr, W.S., Edinburgh. *Born* 2 November 1913. *Married* 28 May 1960, Dorothy Joan, daughter of the Rev. David Cattanach, Hobkirk, Roxburghshire. Served in West African Frontier Force 1939-42 with Gold Coast Regiment in East Africa 1941-42. *Died* 6 June 1972. *Firm*—Charles & R. B. Anderson, Jedburgh.

KERR, ALLEN, LL.B. [3 December 1973]. Apprentice to George William Tait of G. W. Tait & Son.—Son of Harry White Kerr, Transformer Designer, Edinburgh. *Born* 30 August 1950. *Firm*—G. W. Tait & Son.

KERR, ANDREW MARK, B.A.(CANTAB), LL.B. [28 November 1966]. Apprentice to Alastair Campbell Blair and Others of Davidson & Syme.—Son of William Mark Kerr, W.S., Edinburgh. *Born* 17 January 1940. *Married* 23 September 1967, Jane Susanna, daughter of J. C. Robertson, C.B.E., Oldhamstocks, East Lothian. *Firm*—Bell & Scott, Bruce & Kerr.

KERR, CHARLES, OF ABBOTRULE [10 March 1789]. Apprentice to David Erskine.—Eldest son of Patrick Kerr, W.S. *Born* 21 January 1767. *Married* Mary Thomson, Douglas, Isle of Man. *Died* 17 November 1821.

KERR, GORDON JOHN, LL.B. [9 December 1980*].—Son of John Kerr, Wages Clerk, Rutherglen. *Born* 6 August 1954. *Firm*—Morton, Fraser & Milligan.

KERR, JOHN GIBSON, C.B.E., F.R.S.E. [25 March 1929]. Apprentice to Donald McCallum Smith and Another of W. & J. Burness.—Son of George William Kerr, Wine Merchant, Edinburgh. *Born* 26 April 1905. *Married* 10 September 1958, Noreen Patricia, daughter of Walter Home Sutherland. *Firm*—J. Gibson Kerr & Co.

KERR, JOHN NEILSON, LL.B. [9 December 1980]. Apprentice to George Stuart Russell and Others of Strathern & Blair.—Son of John Kerr, Civil Servant, Edinburgh. *Born* 23 September 1956.

KERR, PATRICK, OF ABBOTRULE [6 July 1768]. Apprentice to (1) Francis Pringle; and (2) Walter Scott.—Second son of William Kerr of Abbotrule, Roxburghshire. *Married* 27 March 1766, Jean (*died* 7 June 1793), daughter of Thomas Hay of Huntington, one of the Senators of the College of Justice (Lord Huntington). *Died* 10 July 1791.

KERR, RONALD WILLIAM, LL.B. [13 December 1931]. Apprentice to Robert William Dundas, R. Nevill Dundas, David Marshall, and John H. Richardson.—Son of Colonel Frederic Walter Kerr, D.S.O., Gordon Highlanders. *Born* 24 May 1906. *Married* 15 November 1939, Barbara Helen Crawford. Lieutenant R.N.V.R. 1939-44. *Died* 29 May 1972.

KERR, SAMUEL KERR GIFFORD, M.A., LL.B. [9 December 1901]. Apprentice to William J. Kirk and Another of Hope, Todd & Kirk.—Son of Thomas Kerr, W.S., Edinburgh. *Born* 4 July 1876. *Married* (1) 26 June 1909, Olive Mary (*died* 20 December 1921), daughter of Alfred Read, Liverpool; (2) 18 September 1926, Ella Margaret Jordan (*died* 2 February 1962), daughter of David Douglas Chisholm, Bank Manager, Wellingborough. Served Royal Scots Volunteer Battalion First World War. *Died* 27 January 1975. *Firm*—Bruce & Kerr.

KERR, THOMAS [22 February 1821]. Apprentice to James Greig.—Youngest son of Rev. Alexander Kerr, Minister of Stobo. *Born* 20 September 1798. *Died* 18 June 1832, unmarried.

KERR, THOMAS, LL.B. [28 June 1878]. Apprentice to James Bruce.—Son of Rev. Samuel Kerr, Minister of Yester. *Born* 2 October 1848. *Married* 29 July 1875, Jane (*died* 8 December 1943), younger daughter of William Mills, Leehouses, Haddington. *Died* 3 March 1916.

KERR, WILLIAM MARK, M.A., LL.B. [17 December 1934]. Apprentice to William Constable Hunter and Another of Bonar, Hunter & Johnstone.—Son of Samuel Kerr Gifford Kerr, W.S., Edinburgh. *Born* 3 October 1910. *Married* 11 April 1939, Katharine Marjorie Anne, daughter of James Laing Stevenson, Bank Manager. Major, R.A. Served U.K. 1939-45. *Firm*—Bell & Scott, Bruce & Kerr (formerly Bruce & Kerr).

KETCHEN, WILLIAM THOMAS [18 January 1886]. Apprentice to James Hotchkis Jameson.—Son of William Robinson Ketchen, Solicitor, Elie. *Born* 27 September 1858. *Married* (1) 15 December 1896, Catherine Alexandra (*died* 18 February 1906), eldest daughter of John Fraser, Temple, Glenurquhart; (2) 16 April 1912, Helen (*died* 31 December 1948), youngest daughter of John Fraser, Temple, Glenurquhart, Inverness-shire. Keeper of the Register of Sasines, 4 January 1911 to 1928. *Died* 25 April 1946.

KETTLE, ALEXANDER. *See* YOUNG, ALEXANDER KETTLE.

KEYDEN, WILLIAM, OF LYNEDALE [22 November 1799]. Apprentice to Alexander Young.—Son of Rev. William Keyden, Minister of Penpont. *Born* 15 September 1769. *Died* at West Linton, 5 January 1826.

KID, ALEXANDER [Before 1587].

KIDD, DAVID HAMILTON, LL.B., LL.M. [8 December 1981*].—Son of David Kidd, S.S.C., Edinburgh. *Born* 21 September 1949. Thesis of Legal Information (Edinburgh 1978), and Contributor to "Law and Legal Information" (1981). *Firm*—Biggart Baillie & Gifford.

KIDD, JAMES TURNBULL, O.B.E., T.D., D.L., LL.B. [17 December 1928]. Apprentice to E. M. Wedderburn, R. F. Shepherd, and R. W. Cockburn.—Son of James Kidd, M.P., Solicitor, Linlithgow. *Born* 22 March 1904. *Married* 23 April 1935, Stella Hermione Margaret McIver. Deputy Lieutenant. County of West Lothian. Lt.-Col. R.A. Served U.K. and Middle East 1939-44; War Office 1944-5. *Died* 21 December 1972. *Firm*—Peterkin and Kidd, Linlithgow.

KIDD, MAURICE GRAHAM, B.L. [11 July 1932]. Apprentice to Sir Charles Connell of Connell & Connell.—Son of David Archibald Kidd, Grain Merchant, Edinburgh. *Born* 30 October 1906. *Married* 26 February 1960, Catherine Anne. daughter of John Smith Wells, C.A. Captain R.A.S.C. Served U.K. 1940-45. Founder Member of The Stair Society. *Firm*—Maurice Kidd & Co. (incorporating Sturrock & Sturrock and Lister Shand & Lindsay).

KILGOUR, ROBERT M'CONNOCHIE, LL.B. [17 December 1928]. Apprentice to John D. Boswell and Wm. R. Milne.—Son of Alex. Kilgour, Linen Manufacturer, Kirkcaldy. *Born* 27 September 1903. *Married* 17 August 1935, Nancy Elizabeth Mary Bell. Flight-Lieutenant R.A.F.V.R. U.K. 1940-44. *Died* 28 November 1969. *Firm*—Ferguson Reekie and Kilgour.

KILPATRICK, NICHOLAS COLIN, LL.B. [11 July 1977]. Apprentice to Ronald K. Watson and Others of Brodies.—Son of Colin Kilpatrick, Hotelier, Gatehouse of Fleet. *Born* 24 October 1953. *Married* 18 September 1976, Penelope, daughter of Ian George Barsby.

KINLOCH, ROBERT [28 July 1882]. Apprentice to George Robertson and John Hope Finlay.—Son of Alexander John Kinloch of Park, Aberdeenshire. *Born* 25 July 1855. *Married* 8 January 1880, Mary Isabella (*died* 17 November 1937), only daughter of Henry Dundas Murray, of the Ochtertyre family. *Died* 13 April 1918.

KINNEAR, GEORGE BALFOUR. *See* BALFOUR-KINNEAR, GEORGE PURVIS-RUSSELL-.

KINNEAR, GEORGE THOMAS BALFOUR-, OF CROSS. *See* BALFOUR-KINNEAR, GEORGE THOMAS.

KINNEAR, GEORGE WILLIAM BALFOUR-. *See* BALFOUR-KINNEAR, GEORGE WILLIAM.

KINNEAR, JAMES, OF WESTER FORRET [Before 1602]. Apprentice to Harry Bickartoun.— *Married* 6 May 1601, Margaret, daughter of Harry Bickartoun, W.S. Commissioner, 1 June 1607. *Died* October 1617.

KINNEAR, JAMES [1 December 1634]. Apprentice to Robert Pringle.—Son of James Kinnear, W.S. *Married* (1) 24 February 1642, Elizabeth Alexander (*died* May 1642); and (2) 29 December 1646, Elspeth Reid, widow. Re-admitted, 21 November 1661. *Died* 1 November 1665.

KINNEAR, JAMES [1 March 1832]. Apprentice to Richard Mackenzie and William Sharpe.—Seventh son of George Kinnear, Banker in Edinburgh. *Born* 2 December 1810. *Married* 6 March 1831, Mary Henrietta (*died* 9 February 1871), eldest daughter of William Balfour of Trenaby, Orkney. *Died* at Cadiz, 21 June 1849.

KINNEAR, JAMES BALFOUR-, OF CROSS. *See* BALFOUR-KINNEAR, JAMES.

KINNEAR, THOMAS [25 May 1826]. Apprentice to Walter Dickson.—Son of Thomas Kinnear of Kinloch, Fife. *Died* at Toronto, 27 July 1843, aged 40, unmarried.

KINNINMONTH, GEORGE OGILVIE [24 July 1967]. (By Rule IX(a).)—Son of Andrew Farmer Kinninmonth, Wine Merchant, Burntisland. *Born* 25 February 1924. *Married* 3 September 1949, Dorothy Margaret, daughter of William Cook, Farmer, Wisbech, Cambridgeshire. Flying Officer in R.A.F. 1943-47. *Firm*—Jas. Campbell & Co., Saltcoats.

KINROSS, 4th BARON (DAVID ANDREW BALFOUR), O.B.E., T.D., D.L. [14 December 1941]. Apprentice to the Hon. James Moncrieff Balfour and Others of Shepherd & Wedderburn.—Son of The Rt. Hon. Patrick, Baron Kinross of Glasclune, K.C., Edinburgh. *Born* 29 March 1906. *Married* (1) 10 June 1936, Araminta, daughter of Lieutenant Colonel Willoughby Ewart Peel, Landed Proprietor; (2) 17 April 1948, Helen Ann (*died* 2 May 1969), daughter of Alan Welwood Hog, W.S., Edinburgh; (3) 15 December 1972, Ruth Beverley, daughter of William Henry Mill, S.S.C., Edinburgh. Lieutenant Colonel, R.A. Served U.K., India and Burma 1939-45. Mentioned in Despatches. Deputy Lieutenant for the County of Edinburgh. *Firm*—Shepherd & Wedderburn.

KIRK, COLIN [5 May 1715]. Apprentice to Colin Campbell of Carwhin.—Eldest son of Mr Robert Kirk, Minister of Aberfoyle. *Married* 20 June 1715, Jean, second daughter of George Stirling of Herbertshire, Stirlingshire. *Died* 18 March 1725.

KIRK, JOHN [18 July 1849]. Apprentice to James Hope and Robert Oliphant.—Son of Douglas Kirk, Surgeon, R.N. *Born* 23 July 1820. *Married* 17 January 1854, Frances (*died* 13 February 1900), third daughter of William Berry of Tayfield, Fife. Director of Chancery, 1873-89. *Died* at Cape Town, 27 April 1889.

KIRK, WILLIAM JOHN [28 April 1882]. Apprentice to James Hope.—Son of John Kirk, W.S. *Born* 5 February 1859. *Married* 29 April 1886, Helen Liddell Niven (*died* 2 February 1922), youngest daughter of John Jeffrey, Brewer, Edinburgh. *Died* 8 June 1915. *Firm*—Hope, Todd, and Kirk.

KIRKCALDIE, ROBERT DAVID CAIRD, LL.B. [7 December 1970]. Apprentice to A. J. R. Bisset and Others of Baillie & Gifford.—Son of R. L. Kirkcaldie, C.A., Axminster, Devon. *Born* 5 May 1947.

KIRKPATRICK, IAN DENBEIGH, M.A., LL.B. [27 April 1965]. Apprentice to (1) D. C. Scott-Moncrieff and Others of Tods, Murray & Jamieson, and (2) A. Muir Sturrock of Turnbull, Simson & Sturrock, Jedburgh.—Son of Ebenezer Kirkpatrick, Solicitor, Jedburgh. *Born* 15 December 1940. *Married* 6 August 1964, Jean Seton, daughter of R. Hunter Thyne, Farmer, Rhodesia. *Firms*—Turnbull, Simson & Sturrock, Jedburgh and P. & J. Stormonth Darling, Kelso, both incorporating Messrs. Lang & Steedman, Selkirk.

KIRKPATRICK, IVONE [20 March 1933]. Apprentice to Francis John Gordon Borthwick and Others of Mackenzie & Kermack.—Son of James Ivone Kirkpatrick, Stockbroker. *Born* 29 November 1907. *Married* 15 January 1936, Ruth, daughter of William Rufus Peterson. Wing Commander, A.A.F. Served U.K. 1939-45. *Firm*—Mackenzie & Kermack until 1946; since then resident in South Africa.

KIRKPATRICK, JOHN GEORGE [15 July 1886]. Apprentice to J. O. Mackenzie, W. R. Kermack.—Second son of Roger Kirkpatrick of Lagganlees, Dumfriesshire. *Born* 27 January 1864. *Died* 10 January 1940. *Firm*—Mackenzie and Kermack.

KIRKWOOD, JAMES [30 June 1628]. Apprentice to Robert Kirkwood.—Nephew of William Kirkwood of West Barns. *Married* 16 November 1631, Jean Measone (*died* 25 February 1677). *Died* 1646.

KIRKWOOD, ROBERT [1606]. Servitor to Thomas Lawtie. Signs Minute of 17 January 1606. *Married* 4 October 1610, Sibylla, daughter of Nicol Gilbert, Edinburgh. *Died* before 1642.

KNARSTON, JAMES ROGNVALD LEARMONTH, B.L. [20 December 1937]. Apprentice to Samuel Kerr Gifford Ker and Another of Bruce & Kerr.—Son of James Laughton Knarston, Master Builder, Stromness, Orkney. *Born* 4 January 1913. *Married* 20 September 1947, Vera Fenton, daughter of William Thomas Lawson. Lieutenant Colonel, Seaforth Highlanders, attached 5th Royal Gurkha Rifles, India, Burma and S.E.A.C. 1940-46.

KNOX, JOHN [28 February 1684]. Apprentice to John Campbell of Succoth.—*Married* 9 December 1684, Marjory Dundas (*died* 27 September 1695). *Died* 6 December 1705, aged 46.

KNOX, ROBERT, M.A., LL.B. [9 December 1980*].—Son of Robert Knox, Industrial Chemist, Bramhall, Cheshire. *Born* 23 May 1935. *Married* 23 April 1962, Jill, daughter of Ian Mackness, Master Printer, Bedford. Member of Lord Maxwell's Scottish Committee on Jurisdiction and Enforcement. *Firm*—Boyd, Jameson & Young.

KYD, JOHN DAVID, B.A.(CANTAB) [17 July 1972]. Apprentice to Kenneth Macrae and Others of Murray, Beith & Murray.—Son of John Proctor Kyd, Solicitor, Dundee. *Born* 22 March 1946. *Firm*—Shield & Kyd, Dundee.

KYNCAID, JOHN [1606]. Signs Minute of 17 January 1606. *Married* Janet Pringle. *Died* before July 1615.

KYNNIE (R), JAMES [Before 1627].

LAIDLAW, JAMES [16 November 1784]. Apprentice to Robert Jameson,—Son of Robert Laidlaw, Tenant in Peile. *Married* (1), proclaimed 29 January 1781, Janet (*died* 1798), daughter of Andrew Pitcairn, N.P., Edinburgh; and (2) 11 August 1801, Jean (*died* 12 October 1830), daughter of John Pitcairn, Merchant and Provost of Dundee. *Died* 1 May 1831.

LAIDLAW, JOHN BEDFORD RUTHERFORD [16 December 1924]. Apprentice to G. F. Dalziel and H. A. Jamieson.—Son of James Kinlay Laidlaw, S.S.C. *Born* 27 September 1900. *Married* 24 December 1928, Isabella Thomson, younger daughter of Mrs Elizabeth S. Muir, 60 Ashley Terrace, Edinburgh. Resigned Commission April 1958.

LAING, CHRISTOPHER ALAN LOUTTIT [7 July 1902]. Apprentice to (1) A. H. M'Lean; and (2) H. H. Harley.—Son of Alexander Laing, S.S.C. *Born* 20 April 1876. *Married* 20 June 1912, Mary (*died* 27 November 1971), fourth daughter of Peter Hastie, F.E.I.S., Leadhills, Lanarkshire. *Died* 20 April 1934.

LAING, GEOFFREY CHARLES MCARTHUR, LL.B. [21 July 1970]. Apprentice to (1) Charles Snow Campbell of Alex. Morison & Co.; (2) Michael Rutherfurd Clark Gillespie of Lidderdale & Gillespie, Castle Douglas.—Son of Charles McArthur Laing, Solicitor, Castle Douglas. *Born* 21 April 1944. *Married* 25 September 1970, Catherine Ann Kimberley, daughter of William Johnston. *Firm*—Lidderdale & Gillespie, Castle Douglas.

LAING, NIGEL OR NEIL (also entered under LAYNG) [Before 1544]. Keeper of the Signet. *Married* Elizabeth Danielston. *Died* 1 July 1586.

LAING, WILLIAM [Before 1586].

LAKE, RICHARD [25 November 1780]. Apprentice to James Stuart.—Son of Richard Lake, Merchant in Edinburgh, and Jean, daughter of Archibald Campbell, W.S. *Born* 9 January 1753. *Married* 17 February 1778, Isabella, daughter of Robert Watson of East Rhynd, Perthshire. Admitted Attorney of the Court, United States, 1798. *Died* in America, December 1798.

LAMB, ALAN MACKINTOSH [1 December 1969]. Apprentice to (1) Ronald Kerr Will and Others of Davidson & Syme; (2) James Doughty Lyon of George Gray & Co., Duns.—Son of James Crawford Lamb, Chemist and Optician, Linlithgow. Born 24 September 1945. *Married* 31 May 1969, Caroline Jane, daughter of Patrick Radford, Company Director.

LAMB, ANDREW HENRY COWAN, LL.B. [9 December 1907]. Apprentice to A. T. Steele Scott and John Glover.—Son of Alexander Neilson Lamb, Corn Factor, Glasgow. *Born* 3 March 1883. *Married* 29 June 1927, May Elena, younger daughter of Frazer Cunningham Park, Shipping Agent, Bilbao, Spain. During Great War served as Captain and Paymaster in Army Pay Department. *Died* 29 November 1945.

LAMB, JAMES JOHN, O.B.E., T.D., M.A., LL.B. [21 March 1949]. Apprentice to Charles Ritchie Black of Warden, Bruce & Co.—Son of George Robb Lamb, O.B.E., Solicitor, Edinburgh. *Born* 5 May 1916. Colonel, R.A.O.C. Served in A.A. Command and in Middle East, North Africa and Central Mediterranean 1939-45. Mentioned in Despatches 1945. *Firms*—(1) Warden, Bruce & Co. 1946-66); (2) Stuart & Stuart. Cairns & Co. (formerly Stuart & Stuart); Also Wilkie & Dundas, Kirriemuir and Brooke & Brown, Dunbar.

LAMBIE, JAMES [29 November 1673]. Apprentice to Robert Alexander.—*Married* 30 June 1670, Janet Rae.

LAMBTON, STEPHEN [11 July 1833]. Apprentice to William Renny.—Son of Arthur Lambton, residing in Norwich. *Born* 25 February 1809. *Married* 4 December 1833, Frances Elizabeth (*died* 18 August 1880), second daughter of Major George Brown, 4th Dragoons. *Died* 1851.

LAMONT, ALEXANDER, OF KNOCKDOW [21 May 1812]. Apprentice to Craufurd Tait.—Eldest son of James Lamont of Knockdow, Argyllshire. *Born* 17 March 1784. *Married* 3 April 1827, Jane (*died* 12 March 1880), daughter of Alexander Chrystie of Balchrystie, Fife. *Died* 21 August 1861.

LAMONT, WILLIAM [1 July 1819]. Apprentice to (1) Henry Jardine; and (2) Richard Hotchkis.—Son of Peter Lamont, Brewer in Edinburgh. Was twice married. *Died* 26 July 1858, aged 69.

L'AMY, JOHN RAMSAY, OF DUNKENNY [22 February 1838]. Apprentice to George Combe.—Eldest son of James L'Amy of Dunkenny, Forfarshire, Advocate. *Born* 9 April 1813. *Married* (1) 10 June 1845, Mary Riche Macleod (*died* 27 April 1875), only daughter of William Mitchell Innes of Ayton, Berwickshire; and (2) 10 November 1885, Adeline (*died* 28 February 1915), daughter of Captain James Attye and widow of James Malcolm. *Died* 26 March 1892.

LANG, JAMES [16 November 1812]. Apprentice to Ninian Hill.—Son of John Lang, Dean of Faculty of Procurators, Writer in Glasgow. *Married* 14 April 1818, Eliza (*died* 20 November 1872), fourth daughter of John Dickson of Kilbucho, Peeblesshire. *Died* 2 April 1869, aged 79.

LANG, WILLIAM [27 February 1818]. Apprentice to Robert Fleming.—Son of John Lang, Sheriff-Clerk of Selkirkshire. *Born* 1791. *Married* 27 April 1830, Isabella (*died* 30 March 1891), daughter of Rev. Andrew Murray, D.D., Minister of Auchterderran. *Died* 12 January 1837.

LAUDER, DAVID [7 April 1694]. Apprentice to George Dallas.—*Married* 18 December 1696, Isabel, daughter of John Thomson, Merchant, Edinburgh. *Died* 20 January 1709, aged 46.

LAUDER, ROBERT [Before 1609]. *Married* 18 October 1610, Margaret, daughter of Rev. John Clapperton, Minister of Coldstream. *Died* before 1620.

LAURIE, JAMES WALLACE, M.A., LL.B. [25 November 1963]. Apprentice to Charles Gibson Connell and Others of Connell & Connell.—Son of James Laurie, Bank Manager, Inverness. *Born* 13 January 1921. *Married* 9 March 1963, Sarah Morton, daughter of Frank Smith Vanderbrouk, Somers, Connecticut, U.S.A. Lieutenant, R.A. Served in North Africa and Italy 1941-46. *Firm*—Connell & Connell.

LAURIE, ROBERT BERTRAM, O.B.E., B.L. [3 June 1946]. Apprentice to Robert Francis Shepherd and Others of Shepherd & Wedderburn.—Son of Robert Laurie, Master Joiner. *Born* 15 June 1909. *Married* 4 April 1942, Sheila Margaret Irvine Hunter, daughter of William Whyte, Civil Servant. Flight Lieutenant, R.A.F. Served U.K., France, Holland and Germany 1939-45. Secretary of the Law Society of Scotland. (Retired.)

LAURIE, WILLIAM ALEXANDER, OF ROSSEND [27 June 1823]. Apprentice to William Inglis.—Son of Alexander Laurie, Depute Gazette Writer. *Born* 1800. *Married* (1) 6 February 1821, Harriet Oakley (*died* 31 December 1831), youngest daughter of Robert Beatson of Kilry, Fife; and (2) 16 August 1864, Isabella Taylor (*died* 2 March 1918), daughter of Captain William Riddock, 4th Regiment. *Died* 27 October 1870.

LAURIE, WILLIAM FRANCIS HUNTER [20 February 1834]. Apprentice to Archibald Watson Goldie.—Son of Rev. Harry Laurie, Minister of Lochmaben. *Born* 26 June 1806. *Married* 23 December 1834, Christina, daughter of Rev. Kenneth Bayne, Minister of Gaelic Church, Greenock. *Died* 2 March 1869.

LAW, CHRISTOPHER RAMSAY, LL.B. [3 December 1973]. Apprentice to Hon. D. A. Balfour and Others of Shepherd & Wedderburn.—Son of Ramsay Hammond Law, W.S., Edinburgh. *Born* 14 July 1948. *Married* 2 April 1977, Catriona Margaret Allan.

LAW, JAMES, OF BOGIS OR BOGNESS [28 December 1629].—Son of James Law, Snowdon Herald. *Married* Marion Tweedie. Deputy Keeper of the Signet, 26 December 1627. *Died* 1 May 1640.

LAW, JAMES [17 February 1825]. Apprentice to Walter Dickson.—Son of James Law of Elvingstone, Surgeon in Edinburgh. *Married* 29 July 1828, Mary (*died* 29 January 1885), only daughter of John Bennet, Surgeon in Edinburgh. *Died* 7 October 1867, aged 67.

LAW, RAMSAY HAMMOND, B.A.(CANTAB), LL.B. [25 April 1960]. Apprentice to Euan Barclay Robertson and Others of J. & R. A. Robertson.—Son of W. R. Law, Helensburgh. *Born* 19 January 1917. *Married* 7 September 1940, Jill, daughter of John M. Pringle. Lieutenant, R.N.V.R. *Firm*—J. & R. A. Robertson.

LAWSON, ALEXANDER [Before 1601].—Son of William Lawson, Burgess of Edinburgh. *Married* Janet Mowbray. *Died* December 1605.

LAWSON, GEORGE MURRAY [9 December 1912]. Apprentice to P. W. Campbell, F. J. Martin, and F. P. Milligan.—Son of John Murray Lawson, S.S.C. *Born* 28 April 1889. Served during War with Royal Fusiliers. Wounded, 1917. *Died* 19 March 1971. *Firm*—Murray, Lawson, and Macdonald.

LAWSON, JAMES [19 June 1818]. Apprentice to James Laidlaw.—Eldest son of Peter Lawson, Seedsman in Edinburgh. *Married* April 1826, Margaret (*died* 10 December 1879), youngest daughter of John Clark, Edinburgh. *Died* 27 February 1864, aged 70.

LAWSON, JOHN, OF CAIRNMUIR [21 May 1805]. Apprentice to (1) Hugh Robertson; and (2) James Dundas.—Eldest son of William Lawson of Cairnmuir and Netherurd, Peeblesshire, by Macfarlane, daughter of John Spottiswoode of Spottiswoode, Berwickshire. *Born* 1780. *Married* (1) 5 January 1808, Isabella (*died* 27 August 1822), daughter of William Robertson, Deputy Keeper of the Records; and (2) 25 January 1825, Janet (*died* 21 May 1852), second daughter of James Brown of Edmonston, Lanarkshire. 22nd representative of family of Lawson of Humbie, Highriggs, and Cairnmuir.

LAWTIE, ADAM, OF SAUGHTONHALL [Before 1586]. Commissioner, 1594.—Son of David Lawtie, W.S., Edinburgh. *Married* Janet Anderson. *Died* June 1629.

LAWTIE, DAVID [Before 1577]. *Married* Marion Weir. Clerk of Justiciary, 15 February 1582-83. On 27 March 1571 he was "invaded by Thomas Douglas and the maist part of his forefinger strucken fra him" (*Diurnal of Remarkable Occurrents*, 1513-75). *Died* before 1596.

LAYNG, JOHN, OF SPITTALS [Before 1586]. *Married* Rebecca Dennistoun. Depute Secretary and Keeper of the Signet, 16 December 1594. *Died* 14 February 1612.

LAYNG, NEILL OR NIGEL (also entered under LAING) [Before 1544]. *Married* Elizabeth Danielston. Keeper of the Signet. *Died* 1 July 1586.

LEADBETTER, JAMES GREENSHIELDS GREENSHIELDS, M.C. [31 July 1922]. Apprentice to Sir George M. Paul, R. N. Dundas, and David Marshall.—Son of Thomas Greenshields Leadbetter of Spittal Tower, Denholm, Roxburghshire. *Born* 11 August 1891. Served in Gallipoli and Egypt; attached Imperial Camel Corps, Palestine; also New Zealand Machine Gun Squadron in Palestine and Syria, including capture of Damascus, 1918. Member of the King's Bodyguard for Scotland, Royal Company of Archers, 1920. Clerk, Kelso District Committee, 1925-30, and to Kelso District Council, 1930. *Died* 29 February 1964. *Firm*—James and David W. B. Tait, Kelso.

LEARMONTH, JOHN [Before 1624]. Apprentice to Richard Cass.—*Married* Margaret, daughter of Andrew Hutchison, Merchant Burgess, Edinburgh, and widow of Rev. John Nymbill, Minister of Cranston. Commissioner, 18 October 1631. *Died* November 1649.

LEARMONTH, WILLIAM WADDELL [20 December 1921]. Apprentice to James Balfour-Kinnear and G. Purvis-Russell-Balfour-Kinnear.—Son of Andrew Smillie Robertson Learmonth, Farmer, Essex. *Born* 13 November 1874. *Married* (1) 22 December 1906, Margaret (*died* 24 January 1924), daughter of Peter Livingstone, Merchant, North Queensferry; and (2) 18 March 1931, Janet Maclaren (*died* 20 April 1953), daughter of James Davie, Dunfermline. *Died* 17 May 1954. *Firm*—Hamilton, Kinnear, and Beatson.

LEE, GEORGE AUGUSTUS JAMES [10 July 1893]. Apprentice to William F. Skene.—Son of the Hon. Robert Lee, one of the Senators of the College of Justice (Lord Lee). *Born* 23 June 1870. *Married* 13 February 1904, Harriet Mary Ann Catherine (*died* 27 September 1966), eldest daughter of Bernard James Cuddon-Fletcher of Dunans, Argyllshire, and Somerton Hall, Norfolk. Deputy Keeper of the Records, October 1903-28. Keeper of the Registers and Records of Scotland, 1928. Deputy Keeper of Great Seal, April 1931. *Died* 26 December 1948.

LEES, JOHN CARR GILLESPIE [11 July 1898]. Apprentice to Thomas Paterson and H. E. Richardson.—Son of Sir John M'Kie Lees, K.B.E., Sheriff of Stirling, Dumbarton, and Clackmannan. *Born* 1 March 1875. *Married* 11 September 1901, Helen (*died* 1 July 1961), elder daughter of William Brown, Dunkinty, Elgin. Member of the King's Bodyguard for Scotland, Royal Company of Archers, 1899. Served in Great War with British Red Cross Society. *Died* 15 June 1947. *Firm*—Gillespie and Paterson.

LEGAT, ROBERT [16 July 1858]. Apprentice to Adam Paterson.—Only son of Robert Legat of Esk Park, Musselburgh. *Born* 11 April 1831. *Married* 3 February 1866, Emily (*died* 3 December 1923), youngest daughter of James Eddowes, Surgeon, Royal Artillery. *Died* 6 December 1877.

LEGGAT, ALASTAIR MORISON, B.L. [7 September 1948]. Apprentice to Archibald Blair and Others of Davidson & Syme.—Son of John Morison Leggat, Farmer, Earlston, Berwickshire. *Born* 16 May 1919. *Married* 22 December 1941, Elsie Margaret, daughter of Samuel Campbell, Bangor, Co. Down. Captain, R.A. Served U.K., France, Belgium and Germany, 1939-45. *Firm*—J. Gibson Kerr & Co. (retired 1978).

LEGGAT, JOHN BRIAN, LL.B. [6 December 1971]. Apprentice to William Dunnett of Lindsay Duncan & Black.—Son of James Leggat, Banker, Edinburgh. *Born* 29 July 1948. *Married* 29 April 1972, Iona Laird, daughter of Wallace Aitken. *Firm*—Dundas & Wilson.

LEISHMAN, JOHN [19 November 1835]. Apprentice to William Fraser.—Only son of Rev. Robert Leishman, Kinross. *Born* June 1807. Married 3 March 1840, Hannah Elizabeth (*died* 5 January 1888, daughter of John Weatherly, Whickham House, Durham. *Died* 18 September 1867.

LEISHMAN, STRUAN, LL.B. [26 April 1971]. Apprentice to Maurice Nicholson Durlac and Another of Allan, Dawson, Simpson & Hampton.—Son of John Stuart Leishman, Management Consultant, Bridge of Allan, Stirlingshire. *Born* 26 July 1947. *Married* 5 May 1979, Charlotte Isobel Badenach-Nicolson. *Firm*—Allan, Dawson, Simpson & Hampton.

LEITCH, IAN WILSON, LL.B. [12 May 1981*].—Son of Dr Mathew Blackwood Leitch, Consultant Radiologist, Brora, Sutherland. *Born* 18 August 1949. *Firm*—J. Gibson Kerr & Co.

LEITH, JOHN ROSS. *See* Ross, John Leith.

LENY, GRAHAM, OF GLINS [17 May 1799]. Apprentice to (1) William Anderson; and (2) Robert Dundas.—Second son of George Leny of Nether Glins. *Died* 21 January 1827.

LESLIE, ALEXANDER [21 February 1655]. Apprentice to Francis Hay.—Eldest son of Lachlane Leslie of Miltoun in Balvanie, Banffshire. *Married* (1) Magaret (*died* 2 December 1665), daughter of —— Scott, City Clerk of Edinburgh; and (2) 13 October 1668, Jean Lindsay. Re-admitted, 8 July 1661. *Buried* 9 February 1672.

LESLIE, ALISTAIR EDWARD, B.L. [8 May 1967]. Apprentice to Maurice Kidd of Maurice Kidd & Co.—Son of Albert Edward Leslie. *Born* 3 August 1934. *Married* 21 August 1962, Janet Christine, daughter of Norman Cyril Philip Tyack.

LESLIE, ARCHIBALD RICHARD STEWART, C.M.G., T.D., OF KININVIE [12 December 1898]. Apprentice to C. B. Logan, Hon. J. W. Moncrieff and G. G. Soote.—Son of Lieut.-Colonel Archibald Young Leslie, of Kininvie. *Born* 7 October 1873. *Married* 18 January 1910, Margaret Ysobel (*died* 28 January 1951), daughter of Colonel Edward William Horne of Stirkoke, Caithness. Major Scottish Horse; served at Dardanelles till September 1915, when invalided home; then attached to War Office Staff. Promoted Lieut.-Colonel; awarded C.M.G. and mentioned in Despatches. *Died* 1 May 1928. *Firm*—Alex. Morison & Co.

LESLIE, SIR JOHN, OF WARDIS AND FINDRASSIE, BART. [16 November 1784]. Apprentice to Andrew Smart.—Son of Charles (John ?) Leslie, Writer in Edinburgh. *Married* 15 July 1794, Caroline Jemima (*died* 1810), only daughter and heir of Abraham Leslie of Findrassie, Elginshire. Claimed and assumed Baronetcy as fourth Baronet. *Died* 30 October 1825.

LESLIE, KENNETH ALEXANDER STEWART, B.A.(CANTAB), LL.B. [17 December 1945]. Apprentice to John Carr Gillespie Lees and Others of Gillespie & Paterson.—Son of Archibald Stewart Leslie, W.S., Edinburgh. *Born* 21 June 1914. *Married* 27 April 1945, Jean Frances David, daughter of Lt. Comm. David Douglas, R.N. Squadron Leader, R.A.F.V.R. Served U.K., Rhodesia, Middle East, Iraq and Persia. *Died* 10 February 1979. *Firm*—Gillespie, Macandrew & Co. (formerly Gillespie & Paterson, Hope, Todd & Kirk).

LESLIE, WILLIAM [22 November 1776]. Apprentice to Alexander Robertson.—Son of Thomas Leslie, Merchant in Montrose. *Died* 16 October 1798.

LESLIE, WILLIAM, T.D., B.A.(CANTAB), LL.B. [28 November 1955]. Apprentice to James Little Mounsey and Others of John C. Brodie & Sons.—Son of Norman Leslie, Shipbroker and Herring Exporter, Aberdeen. *Born* 13 April 1926. *Married* (1) 14 April 1956, Priscilla Anne Forgie, daughter of Algernon Ross-Farrow, Amisfield, Dumfriesshire, and (2) 29 November 1969, Elizabeth Jennis, daughter of Ralph Philip Bowden-Smith, Ecclefechan, Dumfriesshire. Lieutenant, Seaforth Highlanders (attached 2nd H.O.S.B.) Served India 1944-47. *Firms*—John C. Brodie & Sons; Brodie, Cuthbertson & Watson; Brodies (1955-77).

LEVEN, JOHN [8 June 1804]. Apprentice to John Tait.—Son of John Leven, General Supervisor of Excise. *Born* 1780. *Married* 31 August 1826, Janet (*died* 26 June 1891), youngest daughter of Rev. James Wemyss, Minister of Burntisland. *Died* 3 April 1862.

LIDDELL, ANDREW COLIN MACDUFF, B.A.(OxON), LL.B. [9 December 1980]. Apprentice to Alan George Laurie Baxter and Another of Pagan, Osborne & Grace, Cupar.—Son of Ian Donald Macduff Liddell, W.S., Pitlochry. *Born* 21 June 1954. *Married* 11 August 1979, Katrina Louise, daughter of Dr Kenneth Terence Gruer. *Firm*—J. & H. Mitchell, Pitlochry.

LIDDELL, BUCKHAM WILLIAM [24 March 1902]. Apprentice to J. E. Guild and Alfred Shepherd.—Son of John Liddell, 44 Leamington Terrace. *Born* 26 May 1870. *Married* 2 July 1907, Katharine (*died* 16 January 1967), elder daughter of James MacDuff of Tomnagrew, Strathbran, Dunkeld. *Died* 22 December 1950. *Firm*—J. and H. Mitchell, Pitlochry.

LIDDELL, HAMISH GEORGE MACDUFF, B.A.(OxON), LL.B. [19 December 1949]. Apprentice to Francis Borthwick and Others of Mackenzie & Kermack.—Son of Buckham William Liddell, W.S., Pitlochry. *Born* 20 February 1924. *Married* 9 July 1965, Mary Elizabeth, daughter of Leslie Milliken. Lieutenant, Black Watch (R.H.R.); Seconded King's African Rifles. Served East Africa, India and Burma. *Firm*—J. & H. Mitchell, Pitlochry.

LIDDELL, IAN DONALD MACDUFF, B.A.(OxON), LL.B. [17 December 1934]. Apprentice to Francis John Gordon Borthwick and Others of Mackenzie & Kermack.—Son of Buckham William Liddell, W.S., Pitlochry. *Born* 13 January 1911. *Married* 29 August 1939, Barbara MacDuff, daughter of Oscar Dixon, Company Director, Grimsby. Major, Infantry. Served U.K. and Europe 1939-45. Mentioned in Despatches 1945. *Died* as the result of a car accident, 15 November 1976. *Firm*—J. & H. Mitchell, Pitlochry.

LIDDIARD, JOHN KENDALL, M.A.(OxON), LL.B. [19 November 1951]. Apprentice to Charles Edward Stewart and Others of Murray, Beith & Murray.—Son of Major George Kendal Liddiard, M.B.E., Edinburgh. *Born* 19 February 1927. *Married* 1 May 1953, Sheila Margaret Blyth (*died* 1 May 1974), daughter of Donald Cameron, Master Tailor. Petty Officer, Writer (Legal Aid Section), R.N. 1944-47. *Firm*—Melville & Lindesay.

LIDDLE, JOHN STEWART, LL.B., C.A. [2 December 1974]. Apprentice to Alastair J. Gordon and Another of W. & J. Burness.—Son of Robert Black Liddle, Civil Servant, Melrose. *Born* 25 December 1944. *Married* 1 May 1970, Denise Moira, daughter of William Maxwell Johnstone, General Manager, Royal Bank of Scotland Ltd.

LIDDLE, WILLIAM, M.A. [9 December 1912]. Apprentice to Harry Cheyne, F. J. G. Borthwick, George Kermack, Ian MacIntyre, and J. G. Kirkpatrick.—Son of Thomas Liddle, S.S.C. *Born* 3 March 1887. Captain Royal Scots. *Died* on active service, 27 September 1918.

LIND, ARCHIBALD [10 March 1808]. Apprentice to Robert Trotter.—Fourth son of David Lind of Bearlawholme. *Died* 1811.

LIND, ROBERT ALAN, LL.B. [28 May 1979]. Apprentice to Charles Snow Campbell and Others of Alex. Morison & Co.—Son of Dr Robert Stirling Lind, Dunfermline. *Born* 20 October 1944. *Married* 15 September 1973, Lindsey Claire, daughter of Gordon Edmiston, Civil Servant, London.

LINDESAY, JAMES [22 June 1837]. Apprentice to Walker, Richardson, and Melville.—Son of William Lindesay, Merchant in Leith. *Born* 16 April 1812. *Died* 12 January 1888, unmarried.

LINDSAY, HENRY INGLIS [10 July 1899]. Apprentice to (1) W. P. Lindsay; (2) R. Dundas, W. J. Dundas, G. M. Paul, and R. N. Dundas.—Son of John Kyle Lindsay, S.S.C., Edinburgh. *Born* 23 May 1875. *Married* 10 February 1920, Janet Jordan Beattie (*died* 18 October 1970), widow of Captain T. R. Jackson, M.C., Duke of Cornwall's Light Infantry, and daughter of William H. Beattie, Builder, Edinburgh. *Died* at Mullion, Cornwall, 18 April 1922.

LINDSAY, JAMES [1 March 1832]. Apprentice to John Mowbray.—Son of George Lindsay, residing in Edinburgh. *Born* 4 July 1806. *Married* 27 September 1849, Jessie Brand (*died* 18 June 1889), daughter of Robert Kellie Douglas, Birmingham. *Died* 6 December 1891.

LINDSAY, JAMES WILLIAM [23 April 1873]. Apprentice to Patrick Blair.—Son of William Lindsay of Hermitage Hill, Leith. *Born* 5 October 1849. *Died* 11 October 1938.

LINDSAY, JOHN MACKENZIE [17 November 1814]. Apprentice to Alexander Pearson.—Fourth son of James Lindsay Carnegie of Boysack, Forfarshire. *Born* 15 March 1792. *Married* 22 July 1835, Florence (*died* 2 October 1857), daughter of Rev. Charles Brown of Whitestone Rectory, Devon. Director of Chancery, 25 June 1858-73. Principal Clerk of Session, 26 February 1847 to 6 July 1858. *Died* 4 August 1873.

LINDSAY, ROBERT JOHN [7 June 1872]. Apprentice to James Lindsay, his uncle.—Son of Robert Lindsay, Pharmaceutical Chemist in Edinburgh. *Born* 16 February 1848. *Married* 6 April 1887, Isabella Littlejohn (*died* 30 September 1903), daughter of Adam Paterson, LL.D. Writer in Glasgow. *Died* 23 May 1938. *Firm*—Lindsay and Wallace.

LINDSAY, ROBERT STRATHERN, M.C. [15 March 1920]. Apprentice to Robert Strathern, A. S. Blair, and C. J. Penn.—Son of William Percival Lindsay, W.S. *Born* 1 October 1893. *Married* 3 June 1924, Margaret Ferrier (*died* 10 August 1974), elder daughter of Arthur Hamilton Gardiner, Redholme, Campbeltown. Served in France during Great War. Captain 9th Batt. (Highlanders) The Royal Scots. Author of *History of Lodge Holyrood House (St Luke's), No. 44, and Roll of Members, 1734-1934. Died* 25 October 1963. *Firm*—J. K. and W. P. Lindsay.

LINDSAY, WILLIAM [7 August 1956]. Apprentice to R. Morison Ireland of Ketchen & Stevens.—Son of William Lindsay, Draper. *Born* 11 September 1917. *Married* 3 April 1946, Susan Penman, daughter of Alfred Thomson, Joiner. *Died* 2 June 1976. *Firm*—Ketchen & Stevens.

LINDSAY, WILLIAM, OF CAROLINA PORT [14 July 1789]. Apprentice to Archibald Tod.—
Third son of Martin Lindsay, Writer in Edinburgh. *Born* 30 March 1767. *Married* 20
February 1792, Alison (*died* 15 July 1844), daughter of John Mackenzie, Merchant in
Stirling. Became a Corn Merchant in Dundee, and Provost of Dundee, 1831-35. *Died* 17
April 1849.

LINDSAY, WILLIAM PERCIVAL [8 October 1883]. Apprentice to (1) Henry Inglis; and
(2) John W. Young and John Blair.—Son of John Kyle Lindsay, S.S.C. *Born* 25 April
1861. *Married* 7 December 1892, Edith Mary (*died* 15 June 1963), eldest daughter of
Robert Strathern, W.S. *Died* 1 January 1901.

LINNING, MICHAEL, OF CUMBERHEAD [18 June 1801]. Apprentice to James
Drummond.—Son of Rev. Thomas Linning, Minister of Lesmahagow. *Born* 24
September 1774. *Married* 29 April 1800, a daughter (*died* 1861) of Henry Patrick
Wilson, H.E.I.C.S. *Died* 17 February 1838.

LISTER, DAVID, OF KININMOUTH [9 July 1805]. Apprentice to Edward Bruce.—Son of
James Lister, Farmer, Pitlessie Mill, Fife. *Married* 14 February 1801, Janet (*died* 13
August 1816), daughter of James Blyth of Kininmouth, and widow of Andrew Fernie of
Wester Kilmux, Fife. *Died* 18 December 1827, aged 66.

LITTLE, JAMES [2 March 1804]. Apprentice to Thomas Cranston.—Youngest son of John
Little of Stewarton. *Died* 9 September 1816.

LITTLE, JOHN DRYDEN, LL.B. [1 December 1969]. Apprentice to John Henry
Constable Wishart and Others of Bonar, Mackenzie & Kermack.—Son of John Dryden
Little, Executive Engineer. *Born* 10 January 1944.

LITTLE, ROBERT. *See* GILMOUR, ROBERT LITTLE.

LIVINGSTONE, JOHN [3 July 1828]. Apprentice to John Murray.—Son of John
Livingston, Merchant in Strathblane. *Born* 1800. *Died* 24 November 1838, unmarried.

LIVINGSTON, JOHN CHRISTIAN [17 March 1890]. Apprentice to Robert Strathern.—
Son of James Livingston, Merchant, Edinburgh. *Born* 14 January 1866. *Married* 14
April 1897, Anne Cathie (*died* 7 July 1952), second daughter of Francis Briggs, Timber
Merchant, Glasgow. *Died* 11 January 1935. *Firm*—Livingston and Dickson.

LLOYD, JAMES BARRON [24 March 1941]. Apprentice to Francis Chalmers and
Another of Skene, Edwards & Garson.—Son of Richard Lloyd, Master Fishmonger
and Poulterer, Edinburgh. *Born* 5 February 1904. *Married* 26 June 1936, Jean Stobo
Whitelaw, daughter of Alexander McCallum, Master Painter and Decorator. *Firm*—
Skene, Edwards & Garson. (Retired.)

LOCH, JAMES [4 July 1769]. Apprentice to James Syme.—Third son of William Loch of
Hawkshaw, Writer in Edinburgh. *Married* 29 May 1786, Margaret, daughter of James
Loch of Drylaw. H.M. Remembrancer to the Court of Exchequer. *Died* 2 September
1793.

LOCKE, MARGARET LUISE STIRLING, B.A. [9 December 1980*].—Daughter of
James Stirling Locke, Engineer, Edinburgh. *Born* 30 August 1955.

LOCKHART, EPHRAIM, OF BARMAGATCHAN [25 February 1803]. Apprentice to (1)
William Blair; and (2) Campbell Adie.—Son of Ephraim Lockhart of the Customs,
Leith. *Married* 22 April 1818, Janet (*died* 4 February 1857), daughter of John
Learmonth, Parkhall, Stirlingshire. *Died* 26 November 1850, aged 74.

LOCKHART, NORMAN, OF TARBRAX [21 May 1805]. Apprentice to William Macdonald.—Third son of Charles Lockhart of Muiravonside. *Married* 3 January 1806, Phillis Barbara (*died* 5 September 1825), daughter of John Macmurdo, Dumfries. *Died* 5 March 1853, aged 73.

LOCKHART, WILLIAM [8 December 1662]. Apprentice to John Semple.—Son of James Lockhart of Cleghorne, Lanarkshire. *Married*——, daughter of Auchenleck of that Ilk. Having been appointed Commissary of Lanark, suspended 8 January 1666.

LOGAN, ALEXANDER CHRISTOPHER [18 April 1877]. Apprentice to A. Hamilton, G. T. Kinnear, and Robert Beatson.—Son of Alexander Stuart Logan, Advocate, Sheriff of Forfarshire. *Born* 7 May 1851. *Died* 10 May 1916, unmarried.

LOGAN, Sir CHARLES BOWMAN [9 February 1860]. Apprentice to, and son of, John Logan, W.S.—*Born* 3 May 1837. *Married* 16 July 1863, Margaret Carrick (*died* 21 January 1910), daughter of Robert Romanes of Craigerne, Peeblesshire. Fiscal, 1883-87. Crown Agent, 1883-85, and February to June 1886. Deputy Keeper of the Signet, 15 December 1887. Knighted, 1899. Resigned office of Deputy Keeper, 21 May 1905. *Died* 2 March 1907. *Firm*—Mackenzie, Innes & Logan.

LOGAN, DAVID [1612] *Married* 11 April 1611, Martha Mure. *Died* 19 January 1614.

LOGAN, EDMUND [4 February 1830]. Apprentice to James Hope.—Fourth son of William Logan of Clarkston. *Died* 24 January 1865, aged 61, unmarried.

LOGAN, GEORGE [12 December 1822]. Apprentice to William Bell.—Eldest son of Robert Logan, Milldown, Berwickshire. *Born* 1799. *Married* 5 August 1823, Marion (*died* 5 August 1882), second daughter of Thomas Manson, Lambeth. Clerk of Teinds, 1841-77. *Died* 18 July 1877.

LOGAN, JOHN [19 November 1829]. Apprentice to James Mackenzie and William Innes.—Son of Robert Logan, residing in Lanark. *Born* 5 August 1792. *Married* 7 August 1833, Helen (*died* 2 April 1879), daughter of Charles Bowman, Depute Clerk of Teinds. *Died* 11 July 1883.

LOGAN, WILLIAM BRUCE, B.A.(CANTAB), LL.B. [6 December 1971]. Apprentice to James Stewart Ritchie and Others of W. & J. Burness.—Son of Dr Robert Logan, Medical Practitioner, Forfar. *Born* 7 September 1941. *Married* 25 July 1969, Jennifer Mary, daughter of James Walker Smith, Bank Manager, Melrose. *Firm*—W. & J. Burness.

LOGIE, WILLIAM [1 March 1832]. Apprentice to Gibson and Oliphant.—Son of Major Logie, 97th Regiment. *Born* 18 December 1808. *Married* 1 June 1837, Jane Hewat (*died* 1 June 1905), eldest daughter of James Black, Glasgow. Sheriff-substitute at Airdrie, 1858-72. *Died* 15 November 1872.

LONGMORE, JOHN ALEXANDER, OF DEANSHAUGH [12 November 1835]. Apprentice to John Donaldson.—Only son of Adam Longmore, Jun., of the Exchequer. *Born* 28 October 1812. *Died* 16 April 1875, unmarried. The Longmore Hospital of the Edinburgh Association for Incurables was called after him in recognition of a grant of £10,000 from his trustees.

LORIMER, GEORGE [25 March 1901]. Apprentice to William Stuart Fraser.—Son of George Lorimer, Brewer, 2 Abbotsford Crescent, Edinburgh. *Born* 31 May 1877. *Married* 19 July 1913, Else Winifred (*died* 6 November 1972), third daughter of Prebendary H. A. Mason, Vicar of St Stephen's Bow, Rural Dean of Poplar. War Service: wilth R.G.A. in France and Belgium. *Died* 7 April 1959.

LORIMER, JAMES BANNERMAN [23 March 1903]. Apprentice to Sir John Prosser and A. G. Muir.—Elder son of John Campbell Lorimer, K.C., Sheriff of Aberdeen, etc., Edinburgh. *Born* 8 May 1879. Captain Cameron Highlanders. *Killed* in action on 3 May 1917.

LORIMER, MICHAEL, O.B.E., B.A.(Cantab), LL.B. [15 July 1940]. Apprentice to Carr Lees and Others of Gillespie & Paterson.—Son of Sir Robert Stodart Lorimer, K.B.E., R.S.A., Architect, Edinburgh. *Born* 11 June 1912. *Married* 8 May 1945, Jean Mary, daughter of Major Joseph Monteith, C.B.E., Cleghorn, Lanarkshire. Secretary, Scottish Landowners' Federation 1945-68. *Firm*—Henderson & Jackson. (Retired.)

LOTHIAN, EDWARD [7 July 1795]. Apprentice to Charles Innes.—Son of Rev. William Lothian, D.D., Minister of Canongate. *Born* 20 September 1769. Admitted Advocate, 3 June 1815. *Died* 12 April 1840.

LOTHIAN, JAMES HUGH [7 July 1820]. Apprentice to Craufurd Tait.—Eldest son of Rev. Andrew Lothian, Minister of the Associate Congregation of Portsburgh. *Died* 3 April 1831.

LOUDON, CHARLES EDWARD [15 July 1889]. Apprentice to R. B. Ranken.—Son of William Louden, Administrator-General, Bombay. *Born* 6 January 1865. *Died* 4 January 1915.

LOUDON, JOHN ALEXANDER, M.A., LL.B., C.A. [24 April 1978]. (By Rule IX(a).)—Son of William Forgie Loudon, Fire clay manufacturer. *Born* 23 June 1930. *Married* 10 October 1970. Susan Margaret, daughter of Edward Willis Gocher, Solicitor, King's Lynn, Norfolk. *Firm*—Brodies (formerly Brodie, Cuthbertson & Watson).

LOUDON, MARY VEDA, M.A., LL.B. [11 December 1979*].—Daughter of Dr William George Todd, Medical Practitioner, Kemnay, Aberdeenshire. *Born* 28 May 1954. *Married* (1) 7 August 1976, Christopher Richard, son of Richard Noxon, Civil Servant, Glasgow; and (2) 16 April 1981, Alasdair John Loudon, Solicitor, Edinburgh.

LOUTFOOT, JOHN [3 October 1671]. Apprentice to George Sibbald.—Son of John Loutfoot, Tailor Burgess of Edinburgh, representative of the family of Orchil. *Married*, proclaimed 21 May 1665, Sarah Elder. Treasurer, 1699-1703. Keeper of the Privy Seal. *Died* 1709.

LOW, GEORGE [23 April 1873]. Apprentice to John Brown Innes.—Youngest son of James Low of Laws, Berwickshire. *Born* 7 March 1849. *Married* 27 April 1880, Agnes Elizabeth (*died* 19 February 1920), third daughter of Major John Jocelyn Ffoulkes of Eriviatt, Denbighshire. *Died* 22 April 1899.

LOW, HENRY MALCOLM [3 July 1820]. Apprentice to Samuel Charteris Somerville (his brother-in-law) and Charles B. Scott.—Son of Robert Low of Clatto, Fife. *Born* 4 February 1798. *Died* at Meadi, Pegu, Burma, 5 April 1858, unmarried.

LOWE, WILLIAM DUNCAN [18 March 1889]. Apprentice to J. A. Jamieson, G. Dalziel, J. Craik, and J. W. Tod.—Fourth son of John Duncan Lowe, Publisher, Edinburgh. *Born* 22 April 1849. *Married* 2 April 1890, Edith Campbell (*died* 15 May 1923), daughter of Rev. Robert Gordon Balfour, of New North Free Church, Edinburgh. *Died* 1 July 1927. *Firm*—Tods, Murray, and Jamieson.

LOWNIE, JOHN DONALDSON [30 March 1908]. Apprentice to David Shaw.—Son of John Lownie, Building Contractor, Edinburgh. *Born* 1 May 1881. Served in Great War with Royal Scots and Machine Gun Corps; Lieutenant. *Died* 2 March 1960. *Firm*—H. Brougham Paterson and Co.

LOWNIE, RALPH HAMILTON, M.A., LL.B. [28 July 1952]. Apprentice to T. J. Carlyle Gifford and Others of Baillie & Gifford.—Son of James H. W. Lownie, Building Contractor. *Born* 27 September 1924. *Married* 12 November 1960, Claudine Therese, daughter of Pierre Lecrocq, Reims, France. Served R.E. 1943-47. Admitted to Faculty of Advocates 1959; to English Bar (Inner Temple) 1962. Resident in Bermuda.

LOWSON, JOHN HUGH [8 July 1912]. Apprentice to James F. Mackay.—Son of the late William Boyack Lowson, Stockbroker, Belfast. *Born* 15 January 1888. *Married* 12 April 1924, Adele Joan, daughter of Frank C. Luxton, Stockbroker, Melbourne. Lieutenant Royal Scots, and R.F.C. Wounded and captured, 1916. Appeared on the stage under the name of J. Herbert Leslie. Played with Anna Neagle in "The Glorious Days" at the Empire Theatre, Edinburgh, December-January 1952/53. *Died* 24 December 1953.

LOY, NOEL JOHN MICHAEL, M.A., LL.B. [27 July 1964]. Apprentice to Edmund Menzies and Others of Allan, Dawson, Simpson & Hampton.—Son of John Hugh Loy, Warehouse Manager, Edinburgh. *Born* 24 December 1939. *Married* 8 July 1968, Sheena, daughter of Robert Arthur Irving Ritchie, Farmer, Gretna. *Firm*—John Henderson & Sons, Dumfries.

LUMSDAINE, WILLIAM [24 February 1778]. Apprentice to Samuel Mitchelson.—Fourth son of James Lumsdaine of Strathtyrum. *Married* 14 October 1781, Ann (*died* 27 March 1794), eldest daughter of Sir Alexander Gordon of Lesmore, Bart. *Died* at Blandfield, 19 January 1794, from water in his head.

LUMSDEN, CLEMENTS [8 July 1823]. Apprentice to Richard Hotchkis and James Tytler.—Son of Harry Lumsden of Belhelvie, Aberdeenshire. *Born* 24 March 1796. *Married* 3 July 1827, Jane (*died* 20 December 1883), third daughter of James Forbes of Echt, Aberdeenshire. Admitted to Society of Advocates in Aberdeen, 5 July 1825. *Died* 27 November 1853.

LUMSDEN, HUGH HARLEY, B.L. [2 May 1966]. Apprentice to G. B. L. Motherwell and Another of Laing & Motherwell.—Son of H. M. Lumsden, Sales Manager. *Born* 22 September 1932. *Married* 2 August 1958, Nora Douglas, daughter of J. B. Rintoul, Wine Merchant.

LUMSDEN, JOHN, OF BLANERNE [3 February 1701]. Apprentice to William Thomson.—Second son of Robert Lumsden of Stravithie, Fife. *Married* 10 October 1717, Rachel, daughter of James Graham, Bailie, Edinburgh. *Died* 27 December 1757.

LUNDIE, ARCHIBALD [9 August 1782]. Apprentice to (1) Robert Menzies; and (2) John Moir.—Only son of Rev. Henry Lundie of Trinity College Church, Edinburgh. *Born* 1748. *Married* Jean (*died* 23 April 1826), daughter of Rev. James Lundie, Minister of Erskine. *Died* 4 May 1841.

LYALL, DAVID [4 December 1823]. Apprentice to Richard Cowan.—Eldest son of Alexander Lyall, Comptroller of the Customs, Aberdeen. *Died* 17 October 1826.

LYELL, DAVID, V.D., D.L. [28 January 1881]. Apprentice to Thomas E. O. Horne.—Son of David Lyell, S.S.C., Edinburgh. *Born* 19 May 1857. *Married* (1) 14 June 1887, Florence (*died* 23 September 1919), eldest daughter of William Tolson, Fazeley, Stafford; and (2) 7 February 1924, Jeannie Macgrath (*died* 8 April 1976), eldest daughter of Andrew Robertson of Kilwinning and Olten, Warwickshire. Served in Great War; twice mentioned in Despatches. *Died* 17 November 1926. *Firm*—Horne and Lyell.

LYN, JAMES [About 1500]. He graduated at St Andrews.

LYNCH, EDWARD BRENDAN, B.L. [27 April 1965]. Apprentice to Patrick James Oliphant and Others of Pearson, Robertson & Maconochie.—Son of Hubert William Lynch, Civil Servant, St Andrews, Fife. *Born* 10 January 1936. *Married* 13 February 1965, Harriet, daughter of John Hoskyns-Abrahall.

LYNCH, WILLIAM FERGUSON STUART, LL.B. [26 April 1976]. Apprentice to G. S. P. Bain and Others of Campbell Smith & Co.—Son of Patrick Stuart Lynch, Bank Manager, Elgin. *Born* 4 December 1950.

LYON, DAVID [11 August 1682]. Apprentice to John Lyon.—Son of William Lyon of Easter Ogil. *Married* (1) May, daughter of Mr Alexander Guthrie, Minister of Stracathro, Angus; (2) (contract, 16 June 1687), Jean (*died* 5 July 1690), second daughter of James Graham, Merchant Burgess, Edinburgh. Commissary of Brechin, 1690. *Died* 1726.

LYON, GEORGE, OF WESTER OGIL [15 June 1810]. Apprentice to Alexander Duncan.— Eldest son of Hugh Lyon, Captain in the service of the East India Company. *Born* 18 November 1787. *Married* 28 March 1810, Catherine Menzies (*died* 28 January 1862), third daughter of Rev. Thomas Fleming, D.D., Minister of Lady Yester's Church, Edinburgh. *Died* 14 November 1866.

LYON, GEORGE TRAILL, B.L. [12 May 1981*].—Son of Rev. James E. Lyon, Anstruther, Fife. *Born* 5 November 1944. *Married* 2 October 1971, Marjorie Anne, daughter of Hope Vere Anderson, Retired Civil Servant.

LYON, JAMES DOUGHTY [23 July 1951]. Apprentice to Joseph Ellis Inglis and Another of Melville & Lindesay.—Son of The Rev. Ritchie Doughty Lyon. *Born* 27 April 1925. *Married* 8 March 1952, Barbara Harriet, daughter of Dr Joseph Primrose Leckie, F.R.C.P. Lieutenant (A) R.N.V.R. Served Fleet Air Arm 1943-47. Resigned Commission. *Firm*—A. & P. Deas, Duns.

LYON, JAMES TRAILL, M.A., LL.B., LL.M. [30 April 1969]. Apprentice to (1) Professor A. J. McDonald of W. B. Dickie & Sons, Dundee; (2) F. R. Gould of J. & R. A. Robertson; (3) James Stewart of Shepherd & Wedderburn.—Son of The Rev. James E. Lyon, Kilconquhar. Elie, Fife. *Born* 15 April 1934. *Married* 6 August 1971, Katharine Cäcilia, daughter of Jakob Villiger, Farmer and Hotelier, Switzerland. Resident in Canada.

LYON, JOHN [2 December 1672]. Apprentice to Alexander Leslie.—Natural son of John, second Earl of Kinghorne (legitimated, 11 February 1676). *Married* 1 March 1667, Helen Ramsay.

LYON, WILLIAM KIRK [11 December 1906]. Apprentice to James Burness.—Son of Jonathan Lyon, Auctioneer, Edinburgh. *Born* 14 June 1879. Served in R.A.M.C.(V.) 1917-18. *Died* 30 January 1947.

LYONS, MATTHIAS [1 March 1799]. Apprentice to Horatius Cannan.—Eldest son of Matthias Lyons, Merchant in Lerwick. *Died* 1837.

MACALISTER, CHARLES [20 November 1818]. Apprentice to Walter Cook.—Youngest son of Alexander Macalister of Strathaird, Skye. Drowned on board the steamer *Comet* off Gourock, 21 October 1825.

MACALLAN, ALLAN BERTRAM [18 November 1858]. Apprentice to David Smith.— Son of James Macallan, W.S. *Born* 26 June 1836. *Married* 19 August 1875, Agnes Gertrude (*died* 18 July 1937), eldest daughter of David Laing Burn, St Andrews. *Died* 19 March 1888.

MACALLAN, HARRY BERTRAM WEDDERBURN, B.L. [20 July 1950]. Apprentice to John Pitman and Others of J. & F. Anderson.—Son of William Henry Macallan, Colonial Administrative Service. *Born* 14 August 1920. *Married* 24 October 1963, Grace Edwards. Sergeant, Intelligence Corps; Served in North Africa, Sicily, Italy, Greece, India and Malaya 1939-45. *Firm*—Maclay, Murray & Spens, Glasgow.

MACALLAN, JAMES [12 December 1816]. Apprentice to Francis Wilson.—Son of Thomas Macallan, Officer of Excise, Edinburgh. *Married* (1) 30 April 1822, Catherine (*died* 1 June 1823), eldest daughter of Robert Ainslie, W.S.; and (2) 27 July 1826, Cecilia (*died* 7 June 1870), daughter of William Bertram of Nisbet, Lanarkshire. *Died* 16 June 1868, aged 76.

MAKCALYEANE, JOHN [Before 1585]. *Married* Janet Gottray (Guthrie).

MCANDREW, ALAN JAMES, LL.B. [6 December 1976]. Apprentice to Ian Grant Smith and Another of Brodies.—Son of Alexander McAndrew, Solicitor and Bank Official, Edinburgh. *Born* 31 March 1953. *Firm*—Brodies.

MACANDREW, JOHN (LEWIS) MACLEAN [3 May 1881]. Apprentice to Robert Macandrew and J. P. Wright.—Only son of John Macandrew, S.S.C., Edinburgh. *Born* 17 July 1857. *Married* 29 January 1889, Elsie Mabel (*died* 24 August 1944), only daughter of Major-General W. Lambert Yonge of Westwood, Frimley, Surrey. Major 3rd Seaforth Highlanders. *Died* 11 October 1917.

MACANDREW, ROBERT [12 July 1860]. Apprentice to William Ramsay Kermack.—Son of Robert Macandrew of the Chancery Office, Edinburgh. *Born* 7 October 1832. *Died* 18 February 1876.

MACAO, WILLIAM ROSS [24 January 1824]. Apprentice to Joseph Gordon.—Son of William Macao, Accountant of Excise, Edinburgh. *Born* 1799. *Married* (1) April 1832, Caroline, daughter of Alexander Anderson of Udoll; and (2) 19 August 1879, Adeline Louise (*died* 4 April 1893), daughter of Chauncey Marshall, Merchant, State of New York. *Died* 25 September 1881.

MACARA, JAMES [23 January 1818]. Apprentice to Robert Fleming.—Son of the Rev. John Macara, Minister of the Antiburgher Congregation, Path of Struie. *Born* 1788. *Married* 11 July 1834, Elizabeth (*died* 5 October 1885), daughter of Peter Halkerston, S.S.C., LL.D. Author of *The Four Leading Doctrines of the New Jerusalem*. *Died* 22 January 1855.

MACARA, LAURENCE MUDIE [19 December 1833]. Apprentice to Æneas Macbean.—Son of Robert Macara, Merchant in Dunfermline. *Born* September 1804. *Died* 15 December 1875, unmarried.

MACARTHUR, IAN CAMPBELL, D.F.C., M.A., LL.B. [19 December 1949]. Apprentice to J. H. Macdonald and Others of Morton, Smart, Macdonald & Prosser.—Son of Neil Macarthur, Solicitor, Inverness. *Born* 14 March 1918. *Married* 7 November 1944, Doctor Mary Helen Reid (*died* February 1959). Served Queen's Own Cameron Highlanders. *Firm*—Stewart, Rule & Co. (now Macarthur & Co., Inverness).

MACARTNEY, JOHN [Before 1636]. *Married* 16 April 1628, Agnes Kincaid. Intimation to be given him, May 1636.

MACARTNEY, WILLIAM [Before 1586]. Servitor to John Young.—*Married* Marjorie, second daughter of William Rowane, Burgess of Aberdeen. King's Agent and Solicitor, 21 December 1587. *Died* before 1614.

MACAULAY, ALFRED CHARLES [17 December 1923]. Apprentice to H. E. Richardson, V. A. Noel Paton, and J. Carr G. Lees.—Son of Sir Alfred Newton Macaulay, Solicitor, Golspie. *Born* 23 August 1899. Served in Royal Flying Corps in Great War; 2nd Lieutenant R.A.F. *Died* 26 March 1958. *Firm*—A. N. Macaulay and Co., Golspie.

MACAULAY, DONALD DUNCAN, B.L. [17 November 1952]. Apprentice to Gilbert Lindsay Douglas Hole and Others of Gillespie & Paterson.—Son of Donald Boyd MacAulay, Stockbroker, Edinburgh. *Born* 29 March 1928. *Married* 12 July 1952, Evelyn Gertrude, daughter of John B. Duncan, C.A., London. *Firm*—Bonar Mackenzie (formerly Bonar, Mackenzie & Kermack).

MACAULAY, THOMAS (OTHERWISE M'AWLAY) [Before 1616]. Servitor to Peter Hewat.—Son of Allan Macaulay, Merchant Burgess of Edinburgh. *Married* (1) 30 November 1597, Elspeth Fairlie; and (2) Katherine Wallace (*died* April 1636). Clerk to Society. *Died* about 1647.

MACBAYNE, JOHN CLERIHEW [30 November 1792]. Apprentice to John Smyth.— Only son of Lachlan Macbayne, Grocer, Edinburgh. *Married* 24 September 1787, Susanna, daughter of John Kerr, Gardener, Kelso. *Died* 14 November 1800.

MACBEAN, ÆNEAS [27 November 1807]. Apprentice to Archibald Milne.—Son of Alexander Macbean, Merchant in Campbeltown. *Born* 11 September 1776. *Died* 30 August 1857, unmarried.

MACBEAN, ÆNEAS [16 November 1848]. Apprentice to Æneas Macbean, his uncle.— Son of Rev. Hugh Macbean, Minister of Ardclach. *Born* 13 June 1820. *Married* 15 April 1852, Mary Ann (*died* 5 April 1891), second daughter of Harry Gordon, Liverpool. Circuit Clerk of Justiciary, 1864-99. *Died* 17 March 1899.

MACBEAN, HARRY HAVELOCK [25 May 1883]. Apprentice to, and son of, Æneas Macbean, W.S.—*Born* 1 November 1857. *Married* 31 July 1915, Annie Frances (*died* 7 March 1966), youngest daughter of Surgeon-Colonel Alexander Allan, M.D., R.A.M.C. The Harry H. Macbean Memorial Fund was founded by his widow. *Died* 24 July 1922.

MCCALL, IAN STEWART [16 July 1934]. Apprentice to R. K. Blair and Others of Blair & Cadell.—Son of Martin McCall, S.S.C., Edinburgh. *Born* 3 June 1910. *Married* 30 June 1950, Phyllis Catherine, daughter of Major Frederick Woolner, R.E. Lieutenant Commander, R.N., 1940-45. *Firm*—McCall & Forsyth. (Retired.)

M'CALLUM, GEORGE KELLIE, OF BRACO [18 November 1825]. Apprentice to John Forman.—Only son of George M'Callum of Thornhill, Perthshire, Surgeon, R.N. *Born* 1804. *Married* 21 July 1841, Margaret Ann (*died* 9 November 1887), only surviving daughter of George Kellie, M.D., Leith. *Died* 2 June 1884.

M'CANDLISH, EDWARD JOHN, T.D., B.A.(OXON), [16 January 1893]. Apprentice to John Cowan and James A. Dalmahoy.—Son of John M'G. M'Candlish, W.S. *Born* 8 May 1867. *Married* 11 April 1899, Elizabeth Mackenzie (*died* 20 February 1955), youngest daughter of Thomas Chalmers Hanna, C.A., Edinburgh. Joint Agent, Church of Scotland. *Died* 30 March 1949. *Firm*—Cowan and Dalmahoy.

M'CANDLISH, JOHN M'GREGOR [12 June 1845]. Apprentice to John Archibald Campbell.—Son of William M'Candlish, Receiver-General of Taxes for Scotland. *Born* 12 January 1821. *Married* 20 August 1863, Mary Sibbald (*died* 26 July 1900), eldest daughter of Patrick Dalmahoy, W.S. General Manager and Actuary of the Scottish Union and National Insurance Company. President of the Faculty of Actuaries in Scotland. *Died* 10 November 1901.

M'CHEYNE, ADAM [15 December 1814]. Apprentice to Robert Graham.—Son of William M'Cheyne, Thornhill. *Born* 1781. *Married* 1 November 1802, Lockhart Murray (*died* 15 May 1854), daughter of David Dickson of Locharwoods, Dumfriesshire. *Died* 24 February 1854.

M'CHEYNE, DAVID THOMAS [30 November 1826]. Apprentice to, and son of, Adam M'Cheyne, W.S.—*Born* 1804. *Died* 8 July 1831, unmarried.

M'CLELLAND, GEORGE HUTCHISON [27 February 1823]. Apprentice to Alexander Young.—Third son of Thomas M'Clelland, Agent for the Bank of Scotland, Ayr. *Born* 26 December 1800. Author of *Predestination and Election Vindicated from the Dependence on Moral Necessity*, 1848. *Died* 19 October 1867, unmarried.

MCCLURE, ALEXANDER LOGAN, B.A.(Oxon), LL.B. [26 December 1933]. Apprentice to Adam West Gifford and Others of Mackenzie & Black.—Son of Sheriff Alexander Logan McClure, K.C., Sheriff of Argyll, Edinburgh. *Born* 1 December 1908. *Married* 16 July 1936, Christine Mary, daughter of Peter Forbes Jones, Ironfounder, Gosport. Captain R.A. Served U.K. 1939-43. *Firm*—Mackenzie & Black (now amalgamated with Brodies). (Consultant.)

MCCLURE, PETER LOGAN HUGH, B.A.(Oxon), LL.B. [28 November 1966]. Apprentice to Sir Hugh Watson and Others of Dundas & Wilson.—Son of Alexander Logan McClure, W.S., Edinburgh. *Born* 29 December 1939. *Married* 4 April 1974, Ellen, daughter of Kristoffer Johan Lenvik, School Master, Harstad, Norway. *Died* as a result of a fishing accident 24 August 1978. *Firm*—Brodies (formerly Mackenzie & Black, prior to amalgamation).

MACCOLL, ALASDAIR DONALD, B.L. [9 December 1980]. Apprentice to Richard Tyrrell Watt, of Pitcairns.—Son of John MacColl, London. *Born* 2 October 1947. *Firm*—Pitcairns.

MCCONNACHIE, DUNCAN CAMPBELL, T.D., M.A., LL.B. [21 March 1949]. Apprentice to William Blair and Others of Davidson & Syme.—Son of William McConnachie of Knowsie, Longmay, Aberdeenshire. *Born* 1 April 1913. *Married* (1) 29 July 1935, Jessie, daughter of William Sinclair, Fishery Officer (Marriage dissolved 7 July 1965), and (2) 3 August 1965, Lilian Margaret, daughter of William Ewart Robinson, Hotel Proprietor. Major, R.A. Served France 1939-40. *Firm*—Dundas & Wilson (formerly Davidson & Syme).

M'COOK, JAMES [23 November 1813]. Apprentice to George Robinson.—Eldest son of James M'Cook, Advocate in Aberdeen. *Baptized* 29 November 1787. *Married* 25 April 1820, Ann (*died* 10 May 1854), only daughter of Thomas Laing. *Died* 28 April 1847.

MACCORMICK, ROBERT JAMES ARCHIBALD, B.L. [2 May 1979]. (By Rule IX (a).)—Son of Ian MacCormick, Company Director, Gullane. *Born* 15 May 1940.

MCCOSH, EDWARD HASELL, LL.B. [9 December 1980]. Apprentice to Ronald K. Watson and another of Brodies.—Son of Bryce Knox McCosh, Biggar, Lanarkshire. *Born* 4 February 1949.

M'COSH, ROBERT, O.B.E., M.C., B.A.(CANTAB) [11 December 1911]. Apprentice to Robert Strathern and Alexander Stevenson Blair.—Son of Andrew Kirkwood M'Cosh, D.L., Iron and Coal Master, Gartsherrie. *Born* 14 April 1885. *Married* 9 September 1913, Agnes Dunlop, younger daughter of Bryce Muir Knox of Redheugh, Kilbirnie, Ayrshire. Served in Great War with Lanarkshire Yeomanry in Egypt, Sinai, and Palestine. Major; D.A.Q.M.G. Awarded Order of the Nile 4th Class, and mentioned in Despatches. *Died* 21 December 1959. *Firm*—Gillespie and Paterson.

MCCULLOCH, ANDREW JAMESON, B.L. [2 May 1966]. Apprentice to Patrick Murray and Others of Murray, Beith & Murray.—Son of Walter Jameson McCulloch of Ardwall, Gatehouse of Fleet. *Born* 21 September 1935. *Married* 7 March 1969, Marcia Ann, daughter of Captain A. V. Priestley, Coldstream Guards.

M'CULLOCH, JOHN SHEPPARD [13 January 1890]. Apprentice to R. L. and J. G. Stuart.—Son of John M'Casland M'Culloch, Teller, British Linen Bank, Edinburgh. *Born* 18 June 1867. *Married* 11 October 1923, Catherine Stewart (*died* 20 January 1944), daughter of Samuel Aitken Miller, Planter, Wynaad, Madras Presidency, India. *Died* 6 November 1946.

M'CULLOCH, WALTER, OF ARDWALL [11 March 1830]. Apprentice to John Gibson, Jun.—Second son of James Murray M'Culloch of Ardwall, Kirkcudbrightshire. *Born* 21 November 1807. Steward-Clerk of Kirkcudbright, 1849-59. *Died* 25 March 1892, unmarried.

MCCULLOCH, WALTER JAMESON, M.C., T.D., B.A.(CANTAB) [14 December 1931]. Apprentice to Robert William Dundas and Others of Dundas & Wilson.—Son of Major General Sir Andrew Jameson McCulloch of Ardwall, K.B.E., C.B., D.S.O., D.C.M. and grandson of Andrew Jameson, one of the Senators of the College of Justice (Lord Ardwall). *Born* 25 August 1906. *Married* 6 April 1934, Katharine Harriet, daughter of John Alexander Inglis, K.C., of Auchindinny and Redhall, King's and Lord Treasurer's Remembrancer. Honorary Sheriff Substitute at Kirkcudbright, 1966. *Firm*—Macandrew, Wright & Murray. (Retired.)

MACDONALD, ALEXANDER, OF CALLEY [24 November 1774]. Apprentice to Alexander Cunningham.—Eldest son of Duncan Macdonald, Writer in Edinburgh. *Married*, proclaimed 4 February 1778, Margaret, daughter of William Currie, Selkirk. *Died* 6 February 1813.

MCDONALD, ALEXANDER JOHN, M.A.(CANTAB), LL.B., S.S.C. [19 December 1949]. Apprentice to Percy Furneaux Dawson and Others of Allan, Dawson, Simpson & Hampton.—Son of John McDonald, Tea Planter, Polmont. *Born* 15 March 1919. *Married* 24 March 1951, Doreen Mary, daughter of Frank Cook, O.B.E., Company Director, Hull. Lieutenant, R.A. (Heavy A.A.) Served U.K., India and Burma 1939-45. Professor of Conveyancing, University of Dundee. *Firm*—Thorntons & Dickies, Dundee (formerly W. B. Dickie & Sons and Dickie, Gray, McDonald & Fair).

MACDONALD, ALEXANDER STUART [13 July 1936]. Apprentice to Alexander Buist Fleming and Others of Graham, Johnston & Fleming.—Son of Alexander Robert Macdonald, S.S.C., Edinburgh. *Born* 8 May 1913. *Married* 3 March 1945, Margaret Austin, daughter of Dr W. E. Graham, Dublin. Captain, R.A. Served U.K., Middle East, Central Mediterranean and North West Europe 1939-45. Mentioned in Despatches January 1945. *Died* 11 March 1979. *Firm*—Will & Philip, Brechin. (Retired.)

MACDONALD, COLL, OF DALNESS [18 March 1788]. Apprentice to William Macdonald.—Eldest son of James Macdonald of Dalness, Argyllshire. *Born* 1762. *Married* 22 October 1796, Elizabeth Barbour (*died* 31 March 1856), daughter of Captain Donald Macbean, 10th Regiment. *Died* 1 January 1837.

MCDONALD, DONALD PRINGLE, M.A., LL.B. [29 November 1960]. Apprentice to H. M. Braine and Others of Gordon Falconer & Fairweather.—Son of Sheriff T. P. McDonald. *Born* 10 July 1934. *Married* 19 November 1960, Evelyn Bjorg, daughter of E. W. K. Arnthal. *Firm*—J. & J. Miller, Perth.

MACDONALD, DONALD SOMERLED [21 July 1924]. Apprentice to (1) Thomas M. Murray and Kenneth Murray; and (2) Andrew Thomas Steele Scott and John Glover.—Son of Henry Macdonald, Barrister-at-Law. *Born* 21 November 1900. *Married* 22 March 1930, Margaret Henderson Kidd (Dame Margaret Kidd, D.B.E. (1975), Q.C., LL.B., Advocate the first woman called to the Bar in Scotland), daughter of James Kidd, Solicitor, Linlithgow, and M.P. for West Lothian. *Died* 24 May 1958. *Firm*—Scott and Glover.

MACDONALD, DUNCAN [7 March 1833]. Apprentice to, and son of, Coll Macdonald, W.S.—*Born* 9 November 1809. *Died* at Demerara, 8 June 1842, unmarried.

MACDONALD, GEORGE RAINY, OF KYLEATRIM, SKYE [24 October 1885]. Apprentice to Thomas S. Maclaren and William Traquair, Jun.—Son of Harry Macdonald, Writer and Banker in Portree. *Born* 11 September 1860. Tea-planter at Barah, India. *Died* 27 June 1918.

MACDONALD, HAROLD KENNEDY, B.A.(CANTAB) [19 December 1938]. Apprentice to R. Nevill Dundas and Another of Dundas & Wilson.—Son of James Harold Macdonald, W.S., Edinburgh. *Born* 24 February 1912. Flight Lieutenant R.A.F. Mentioned in Despatches. *Killed in action* over London, 28 September 1940.

MACDONALD, HECTOR *See* BUCHANAN, HECTOR MACDONALD.

MACDONALD, IAN HAY, M.A., LL.B. [19 November 1951]. Apprentice to Charles Edward Stewart and Others of Murray, Beith & Murray.—Son of John Macdonald, Accountant, Edinburgh. *Born* 19 July 1915. *Married* 30 March 1951, Joyce Wighton, daughter of Robert Wightman Handyside, Engineer. Served in Indian Civil Service 1938-47. *Firm*—John C. Brodie & Sons (now Brodies). (Retired.)

MACDONALD, JAMES [28 October 1874]. Apprentice to John Auld.—Son of John Macdonald, Accountant, Edinburgh. *Born* 3 July 1850. *Married* (1) 18 December 1889, Isabella Wilhelmina, younger daughter of Rev. William Cousin, Melrose; and (2) 30 November 1897, Agnes Madeline Eleanora (*died* 4 July 1937), daughter of Rev. David C. A. Agnew. Deputy Keeper of Great Seal. *Died* 17 July 1923. *Firm*—Auld & Macdonald.

MACDONALD, JAMES CUMMING RAFF [14 July 1884]. Apprentice to Charles Baxter.—Son of James Macdonald, LL.D., Rector of Ayr Academy. *Born* 13 August 1858. *Married* 19 January 1907, Catherine Isabella (*died* 8 September 1932), daughter of Rev. John Paton, D.D., Minister of St Michael's, Dumfries. *Died* 26 January 1921. *Firm*—Symons & Macdonald, Dumfries.

MACDONALD, JAMES HAROLD, C.V.O., T.D., LL.B. [28 March 1904]. Apprentice to Ralph Dundas, W. J. Dundas, G. M. Paul, and R. N. Dundas.—Son of James Macdonald, S.S.C. *Born* 1 March 1878. *Married* 27 April 1907, Isa May (*died* 18 December 1940), younger daughter of Donald Kennedy, Kirkton Lodge, Murrayfield, Edinburgh. Served in France during Great War; wounded. *Died* 4 August 1955. *Firm*— Morton, Smart, Macdonald, and Prosser.

MCDONALD, JOHN BLAIR, B.L. [13 May 1980*].—Son of Robert McDonald, Chartered Mechanical Engineer, Kelso. *Born* 29 February 1936. *Married* 17 September 1963, Janette Jamieson Wishart, daughter of J. H. C. Gilmour. *Firm*—James & David W. B. Tait, Kelso.

MACDONALD, NORMAN ALEXANDER MACKINTOSH, M.A.(Oxon), LL.B. [25 November 1963]. Apprentice to T. J. Carlyle Gifford and Others of Baillie & Gifford.— Son of Sheriff Norman Macdonald. *Born* 6 March 1929. *Married* 21 November 1953, Jean Mary, daughter of Professor J. C. Mitcheson. *Firm*—Biggart, Baillie & Gifford (formerly Baillie & Gifford).

MACDONALD, MATHEW NORMAN *See* HUME, MATHEW NORMAN MACDONALD.

MACDONALD, PETER FREDERICK, LL.B. [8 May 1967]. Apprentice to Arthur Woodman Blair and Others of Strathern & Blair.—Son of H. F. Macdonald, Schoolmaster, Edinburgh. *Born* 2 May 1942. *Married* 29 July 1972, Kirstine Margaret, daughter of George K. Mowat. *Firm*—MacNeill & Critchley, Inverness.

MACDONALD, Sir PETER GEORGE [28 March 1927]. Apprentice to Donald M. Smith and Another of W. & J. Burness.—Son of William Macdonald, Darnaway, Forres. *Born* 20 February 1898. Married 18 September 1929, Rachel Irene, daughter of the Rev. Robert Forgan, D.D., Edinburgh. Served with Scottish Horse, 9th Battalion Black Watch, Lovat Scouts and R.G.A., First World War. Knighted 1963. Deputy Lieutenant, Edinburgh 1966. Hon. Life President United Biscuits Ltd. and McVitie & Price Ltd. (Chairman 1948-67 and 1947-64 respectively). *Firm*—W. & J. Burness. (Consultant.)

MACDONALD, RANALD FRASER, M.A., LL.B. [9 December 1980]. Apprentice to Thomas Dunsire and Others of Morton, Fraser & Milligan.—Son of Alastair Donald Macdonald, Architect, Dalguise, Perthshire. *Born* 7 May 1947.

MACDONALD, RANALD GEORGE MEYRITT [12 November 1835]. Apprentice to John Russell.—Fourth son of Lieut.-Colonel Robert Macdonald of Inchkenneth, Argyllshire. *Born* 25 February 1810. *Married* (1) 24 May 1836, Alicia Jane (*died* 5 January 1875), eldest daughter of Rev. Nathaniel Bridges, Vicar of Hensbridge; (2) 16 September 1875, Mary Ann (*died* 11 December 1893), daughter of W. Horsman and widow of E. Sandys Bain of Easter Livilands, Stirlingshire, Serjeant-at-Law. *Died* 19 September 1875.

MACDONALD, ROBERT IAIN, LL.B. [12 May 1981*].—Son of Robert Lindsay MacDonald, Accountant, Edinburgh. *Born* 20 February 1954. *Firm*—Bell & Scott, Bruce & Kerr.

MACDONALD, ROBERT IAIN FERGUSON, LL.B. [24 April 1978]. Apprentice to David Campbell MacPherson and Another of Wallace & Guthrie.—Son of Rev. Donald Ferguson Macdonald, Paisley. *Born* 29 August 1950. *Married* 14 September 1972, Irene Davina, daughter of Walker Moffat, Civil Servant, Scarborough. *Firm*— Wallace & Guthrie.

MACDONALD, THOMAS [19 July 1779]. Apprentice to William Macdonald.—Eldest son of James Macdonald of Falside, Sheriff-Substitute of Kincardine. *Married* 1 June 1780, Sarah, second daughter of George Skene of Skene (divorced August 1784). *Died* 1821.

MACDONALD, WILLIAM, of St Martins [11 January 1762]. Apprentice to Robert Grant.—Eldest son of James Macdonald of Ranathan, Perthshire. *Born* 1732. *Married* 4 January 1772, Cecilia (*died* 6 January 1785), daughter of David Kinloch of Kilry, Perthshire. *Died* 17 May 1814.

MACDONELL, ALEXANDER [25 May 1826]. Apprentice to James Macdonell.— Youngest son of Alexander Macdonell, Writer in Inverness. Sheriff-Substitute of Wigtownshire, 1829-47. *Died* 11 August 1851, aged 50, unmarried.

MACDONELL, JAMES, of Milnfield [17 May 1811]. Apprentice to Coll Macdonald.— Eldest son of Alexander Macdonell, Writer in Inverness. *Born* 1785. *Married* 4 January 1813, Mary Proby (*died* 30 November 1854), second daughter of George Mackenzie of Pitlundie. *Died* 23 November 1841.

MACDOUGALL, ALLAN, of Gallanach and Glenlochan [25 June 1770]. Apprentice to Colquhoun Grant.—Eldest son of Dugald Macdougall of Gallanach, Argyllshire. *Married*, proclaimed 7 August 1768, Margaret (*died* January 1838), second daughter of John Hay of Newhall, Mid-Lothian, a sister of George, seventh Lord Tweeddale. Agent for the Commissioners of Annexed Estates. *Died* 24 December 1807.

MACDOUGALL, ALLAN, of Hayfield [26 February 1824]. Apprentice to John Young.—Fourth son of Patrick MacDougall of MacDougall, Dunollie, Argyllshire. *Born* 1798. *Died* 3 August 1876, unmarried.

MACDOUGALL, JAMES ARCHIBALD, B.L. [15 July 1940]. Apprentice to T. J. Carlyle Gifford and Another of Baillie & Gifford.—Son of John Macdougall, Solicitor, Edinburgh. *Born* 26 August 1910. *Married* 25 June 1936, Valerie Jean, daughter of Patrick Haggart Fraser, C.A., Colombo, Ceylon. Advocate of High Courts of Kenya, Uganda and Tanzania. *Died* 16 February 1982. *Firm*—Baillie & Gifford (until 1946).

MACDOUGALL, PATRICK, of Crichen [20 July 1704]. Apprentice to Harry Nicoll.— Son of Robert Macdougall of Crichen. *Married* 20 March 1701, Elizabeth, daughter of Robert Martin of Burnbrae. *Died* May 1734.

MACDOUGALL, PATRICK, of Gallanach [27 June 1839]. Apprentice to John Patten.— Eldest son of Dugald Macdougall of Gallanach, Argyllshire. *Born* 26 November 1817. *Died* 5 April 1866, unmarried.

MACDOWALL, CHARLES [5 July 1821]. Apprentice to John Campbell, *quartus*.— Youngest son of Archibald Macdowall, Surveyor of Customs at Leith. *Born* 1796. *Married* 26 November 1832, Jane Margaret Sawers (*died* 1873), daughter of John Finnie of Swanston. *Died* 27 June 1837.

MACDUFF, ALEXANDER, of Bonhard [14 November 1839]. Apprentice to David Welsh.—Eldest son of Alexander Macduff of Bonhard, Perthshire. *Born* 5 December 1816. *Married* 21 September 1842, Mary (*died* 4 September 1865), daughter of Francis Brown of Jordanhill, Trinidad. *Died* 20 March 1866.

MACDUFF, ALEXANDER, of Bonhard [28 January 1876]. Apprentice to Colin Mackenzie, A. D. M. Black, and J. M. Mackenzie.—Son of Alexander Macduff of Bonhard, W.S. *Born* 29 July 1849. *Married* 16 May 1883, Edith Alexandrine (*died* 28 June 1936), younger daughter of John Shiell of Smithfield, Angus. *Died* 3 January 1936.

MACEWAN, KENNETH [27 March 1911]. Apprentice to (1) R. R. Simpson and Alexander P. Melville; and (2) to William Blair and James Watt.—Son of William MacEwan, 32 Gilmore Place, Edinburgh. *Born* 11 October 1880. *Married* 15 April 1922, Mary (*died* 7 December 1968), daughter of James Halliday, Dunmuck, Southwick. *Died* 2 June 1962. *Firm*—W. H. Mill and Co.

MACEWAN, WILLIAM, OF MUCKLY [25 February 1740]. Apprentice to Archibald Stewart.—Eldest son of John MacEwan of Muckly, Commissary Clerk of Dunkeld. *Married* (1) Grizel, third daughter of Dr Thomas Rattray of Craighall, Perthshire; and (2) November 1757, Mark (*died* 15 August 1812), third daughter of Thomas Douglas of Cavers family. Commissary Clerk, Dunkeld, 1742. *Died* 7 February 1765.

MACEWAN, WILLIAM [4 July 1809]. Apprentice to Coll Macdonald.—Eldest son of Daniel MacEwan, Cattle-dealer at Burn of Ruskie. *Married* 1 August 1814, E—— (*died* 1864), daughter of —— Lindsay, Stockbridge, Edinburgh. *Died* 3 October 1821.

M'EWEN, DAVID CAMPBELL [13 December 1910]. Apprentice to (1) W. J. Kirk, J. A. Hope, and P. Keith Murray; and (2) W. C. M'Ewen.—Son of William Campbell M'Ewen, W.S. *Born* 20 October 1885. *Died* 10 April 1917 of wounds received in action, as 2nd Lieutenant in Royal Scots.

MACEWEN, EWYN ALASTAIR, M.C. AND BAR [31 July 1922]. Apprentice to and son of William Campbell MacEwen, W.S., of J. & A. F. Adam. *Born* 9 July 1888. *Married* 27 March 1916, Lilian Cushla (*died* 26 November 1966), daughter of Dr George Fisher Parker, London. Commissioned in 3rd Battalion Argyll & Sutherland Highlanders; Attached 1st Cameron Highlanders and 2nd Argyll & Sutherland Highlanders. *Died* 21 December 1976. *Firm*—J. & A. F. Adam.

M'EWEN, JAMES, OF BARDROCHAT [16 December 1830]. Apprentice to Thomas Grierson.—Son of Robert M'Ewen, Factor for Lady Crawford at Rozelle, Ayrshire. *Born* 21 July 1801. *Died* 13 July 1874, unmarried.

M'EWEN, WILLIAM CAMPBELL, OF LERAGS [28 January 1876]. Apprentice to Alexander F. Adam and John Kirk.—Son of John M'Ewen of Broomhill, Inverness. *Born* 17 September 1849. *Married* 29 July 1882, Margaret (*died* 23 May 1944), second daughter of David Croall of Southfield, Mid-Lothian. *Died* at Achiltibuie, Ross, 18 June 1929. *Firm*—J. & A. F. Adam.

MACFARLANE, JAMES, OF BALWILL [6 June 1833]. Apprentice to Alexander Young.— Son of James Macfarlane of Balwill, Stirlingshire. *Born* 3 June 1809. *Died* 18 June 1870, unmarried.

MACFARLANE, JOHN [24 December 1678]. Apprentice to John Bayne.—*Married* (1) 16 April 1680, Euphan Ritchie (*died* 29 March 1699); and (2) June 1700, Christian, daughter of John Hamilton of Bangour, Linlithgowshire. Treasurer, 1691-7. *Died* 3 November 1709, aged 65.

MACFARLANE, JOHN [12 November 1709]. Apprentice to, and son of, John Macfarlane, W.S.—*Born* 14 August 1685. *Married* (1) ——, daughter of Colonel Charles Straiton (she was accused of the murder of Captain John Cayley in 1716, see Chambers's *Traditions of Edinburgh*); and (2) January 1733, Elizabeth (*died* 17 September 1772), daughter of Sir Henry Wardlaw of Pitreavie, Bart. *Died* 30 April 1771.

MACFARLANE, ROBERT [29 June 1827]. Apprentice to James Greig.—Only son of Parlan Macfarlane, Tacksman of Glenmallashan, Dunbartonshire. *Born* 30 July 1802. *Married* 21 October 1843, Grace Addison (*died* 4 June 1870), daughter of James Greig of Eccles, W.S. Admitted Advocate, 9 March 1838. Appointed Sheriff of Renfrewshire, 1853, he was raised to the Bench with the title of Lord Ormidale, February 1862. *Died* 3 November 1880.

MACFARLANE, WILLIAM [19 November 1782]. Apprentice to Colquhoun Grant.—Son of Daniel Macfarlane, Brewer in Portsburgh. *Born* 1749. *Married*, proclaimed 18 August 1784, Barbara Waugh (*died* 25 March 1804), widow of Captain John Grant; and (2) 19 April 1811, Jane (*died* 2 February 1853), eldest daughter of James Sommers, Writer, Edinburgh. *Died* 12 July 1831.

MACFARQUHAR, JOHN [1 August 1788]. Apprentice to William Charles Craigie.—Son of George Macfarquhar, Coachpainter in Edinburgh. *Married* 15 October 1793, Bethia (*died* 16 February 1846), daughter of Lawrence Brown of Edmonston. *Died* 10 June 1817.

MACFIE, ALEXANDER, M.A., LL.B. [17 December 1928]. Apprentice to Andrew Thomas Steele Scott and Another of Scott & Glover.—Son of Robert Macfie, W.S., Whithorn. *Born* 10 January 1904. *Married* 22 March 1934, Ida Pauline, daughter of Frank Harrison, Solicitor, Northampton. Major, K.O.S.B. Served U.K. and North West Europe 1941-45. *Died* 3 December 1978. *Firm*—Scott & Glover (now amalgamated with Haldanes, McLaren & Scott).

MACFIE, JOHN HARRISON, B.L. [26 November 1962]. Apprentice to H. M. Braine and Others of Gordon, Falconer & Fairweather.—Son of Alexander MacFie, W.S., Edinburgh. *Born* 22 March 1938. *Married* 30 September 1967, Dorothy Charlotte, daughter of Dr R. T. Cooke, Middlesbrough. *Firm*—A. C. Bennett & Fairweather (after amalgamation with Gordon, Falconer & Fairweather).

MACFIE, JOHN STEWART, M.B.E., T.D., M.A., LL.B. [16 December 1935]. Apprentice to Patrick Keith Murray and Others of Hope, Todd & Kirk.—Son of Samuel Macfie, Solicitor, Edinburgh. *Born* 27 July 1910. *Married* (1) 14 October 1939, Jean Anne Robertson, daughter of David Arnot, Farmer, Edzell, Angus; (2) 26 October 1959, Kathleen Elizabeth, daughter of Cochrane Welsh, Landowner, Carnowen, Co. Monaghan, Eire. Major, Infantry. Served U.K., France and Central Mediterranean Forces 1939-45. Mentioned in Despatches January 1945. *Died* 22 April 1980. *Firm*—Tods, Murray & Jamieson.

MACFIE, ROBERT, LL.B. [6 July 1896]. Apprentice to W. Traquair Dickson and T. S. Maclaren.—Son of Alexander Macfie, Agent at Whithorn of the Clydesdale Bank Ltd. *Born* 30 June 1872. *Married* 15 April 1903, Annie Alexander (*died* 18 May 1961), third daughter of Alexander Mitchell, Edinburgh. *Died* 12 September 1937.

MCGEACHY, ALISTAIR LAIRD, LL.B. [28 April 1975]. Apprentice to (1) Thomas Munro Hunter of Allan, Dawson, Simpson & Hampton and (2) Francis Hugh Simpson and Another of Fyfe, Ireland & Co.—Son of William Laird McGeachy, Solicitor, Glasgow. *Born* 2 April 1949. *Married* 22 April 1978, Jennifer Heather Macleod.

MACGILL, JOHN [Before 1586].—Second son of David Macgill of Cranston Riddell, one of the Senators of the College of Justice (Lord Nisbet). *Married* 6 August 1606, Marion Sandilands.

MACGILLIVRAY, IAN [15 December 1930]. Apprentice to William Alex. MacGillivray and John Parker Watson.—Son of William Alexander MacGillivray, W.S. *Born* 21 April 1907. *Died* 16 March 1959. *Firm*—Lindsay, Howe, and Co.

MACGILLIVRAY, WILLIAM [3 November 1870]. Apprentice to (1) John Dundas; and (2) Alexander Howe.—Son of Alexander MacGillivray, residing in Carron Terrace, Stonehaven. *Born* 30 May 1823. *Married* 29 July 1868, Margaret (*died* 7 March 1894), youngest daughter of John Dods, Brewer, Dunbar. *Died* 23 November 1917.

MACGILLIVRAY, WILLIAM ALEXANDER [16 January 1893]. Apprentice to (1) G. T. Kinnear, R. Beatson, E. Hamilton, and James Kinnear; (2) A. Howe, W. MacGillivray, J. Buchanan, and A. Yeaman.—Eldest son of William MacGillivray, W.S. *Born* 21 September 1869. *Married* 10 June 1896, Janet Robertson (*died* 4 November 1955), second daughter of James Kellie Morton, J.P., Secretary of the Union Bank of Scotland, Edinburgh. *Died* 19 September 1942. *Firm*—Lindsay, Howe, and Co.

M'GLASHAN, JEFFREY BLACKSTOCK, LL.B. [14 July 1919]. Apprentice to Horatius Bonar and W. C. Hunter.—Son of Rev. Robert Blackstock M'Glashan, F.C. Minister of Gatehouse-of-Fleet. *Born* 2 February 1888. *Married* 18 September 1925, Marion Thomson, only daughter of Alexander Fraser, Chemist, Paisley. Depute J.P., Procurator-Fiscal at Paisley. Served in France and Italy during Great War with 9th Royal Scots, and as Lieutenant A. and S. Highlanders. *Died* 9 February 1956. *Firm*— Hart, Abercrombie, and Lang, Paisley.

MACGLASHAN, ROBERT, of EASTERTYRE [9 March 1814]. Apprentice to Robert Graham.—Second son of Major Alexander Macglashan of Eastertyre, Perthshire. *Died* 1 August 1825.

MACGOWAN, JOHN [24 January 1712].—Son of William Macgowan, Town Clerk, Whithorn. *Married* 1 April 1713, Margaret, daughter of Francis Borthwick of Hartsyde, Surgeon. *Died* 18 August 1762.

McGREGOR, ALISTAIR GERALD CRICHTON, B.A.(OxoN), LL.B. [27 April 1965]. Apprentice to D. G. McGregor, Edinburgh.—Son of James Reid McGregor, Permanent Under Secretary of State for War (Retired), Sevenoaks, Kent. *Born* 15 October 1937. *Married* 7 August 1965, Margaret Lees, daughter of D. Lees, Civil Servant. Member of the Faculty of Advocates.

MACGREGOR, AUGUSTUS WALLACE, LL.B. [11 January 1892]. Apprentice to George Dunlop and J. A. S. Miller.—Son of Rev. John Macgregor, Minister of the Free Church at Hawick. *Born* 18 August 1867. Lieutenant in 4th K.O.S.B., 1915-19. Author of *Some Aspects of Scottish Lawn Tennis*, 1911, and *Fifty Years of Scottish Lawn Tennis*, 1927. *Died* 23 October 1937.

M'GREGOR, CAMPBELL [10 July 1911]. Apprentice to Sir Henry Cook and Charles Cook.—Son of Rev. Charles M'Gregor, D.D., of Lady Yester's, Edinburgh. *Born* 23 July 1886. *Died* 31 August 1949.

McGREGOR, DUNCAN GERALD, A.F.C. [23 July 1923]. Apprentice to Robert Strathern and Others of Strathern & Blair.—Son of the Rev. Duncan McGregor, Torphins, Aberdeenshire. *Born* 9 November 1897. *Married* 19 September 1934, Elizabeth Alice Muir, daughter of John Reith, Rector of Bo'ness Academy. Sub-Lieutenant R.N.A.S., 1916. Captain R.A.F., 1917-18. Awarded Air Force Cross and Mentioned in Despatches, 1918.

MACGREGOR, JOHN [16 January 1888]. Apprentice to John W. Young and John Blair.—Eldest son of Malcolm MacGregor, S.S.C., Edinburgh. *Born* 6 January 1864. *Married* 6 October 1898, Marion Galloway (*died* 25 July 1956), daughter of George Robertson, Edinburgh. Procurator-Fiscal of Lyon Court, 1918. Clerk to Admission of Notaries, 23 April 1931. *Died* 9 September 1937. *Firm*—M. MacGregor and Co.

MACGREGOR, MALCOLM ROBERTSON, LL.B. [26 March 1928]. Apprentice to James Mylne and Archibald B. Campbell.—Son of John MacGregor, W.S. *Born* 15 February 1904. *Married* 3 June 1931, Doris (*died* 7 December 1971), elder daughter of Richard Henry Godwin, 14 Dalkeith St., Joppa. Lieutenant R.N.V.R. U.K., 1941-45. Joint Procurator-Fiscal of Lyon Court, 1933. *Died* 24 July 1960. *Firm*—M. MacGregor and Co.

MACGREGOR, RONALD [18 July 1854]. Apprentice to Edmund Baxter.—Eldest son of James Macgregor, Writer in Fort-William. *Born* 17 May 1830. *Married* 30 April 1860, Duncana M'Lachlan (*died* 2 January 1915), youngest daughter of Alexander Cumming of Grieshernish, Isle of Skye. *Died* 19 February 1868.

MACHARG, JAMES [7 March 1788]. Apprentice to John Hunter.—Son of Archibald Macharg, Writer in Edinburgh. Lieutenant 99th Foot. *Died* at Dublin, 19 November 1794.

MCINNES, IAN WHITTON, T.D., M.A., LL.B., [21 July 1924]. Apprentice to William C. Hunter of Bonar, Hunter & Johnstone.—Son of John Alexander McInnes, Headmaster, Leven. *Born* 27 March 1900. *Married* 23 July 1936, Lucy Margaret, daughter of John Currie Wilson, Solicitor. 2nd Lieutenant Black Watch, First World War; Major, R.A.C. Served U.K. and N.W. Europe 1939-45. Vice President of the Law Society of Scotland 1959-60. *Died* 1 April 1976. *Firm*—Drummond, Johnstone & Grosset, Cupar.

M'INTOSH, CHARLES [13 July 1775]. Apprentice to Robert Jamieson.—Second son of John M'Intosh, Bailie and Merchant in Inverness. *Died* 26 November 1812, aged 71.

M'INTOSH, DONALD [4 March 1816]. Apprentice to Kenneth Mackenzie.—Eldest son of Campbell M'Intosh of Dalmigavie, Writer in Inverness. *Born* 1792. *Died* 19 October 1832, unmarried.

M'INTOSH, GEORGE [27 October 1882]. Apprentice to Hew Hamilton Crichton.—Eldest son of George M'Intosh, S.S.C., Edinburgh. *Born* 5 October 1859. *Died* at Vichy, France, 28 August 1923. *Firm*—Waddell, M'Intosh, and Peddie.

MCINTOSH, JAMES DONALD HUNTER [15 March 1937]. Apprentice to A. St. Clair Jameson and Another of Boyd, Jameson & Young.—Son of John George Hunter McIntosh, W.S., Edinburgh. *Born* 9 October 1912. *Married* 24 October 1939, Angela Stiles (*died* 5 September 1968), daughter of S. G. Rome. 2nd Lieutenant, R.A.C. Served U.K. and France 1939-40. *Firm*—Boyd, Jameson & Young.

M'INTOSH, JOHN GEORGE HUNTER [7 December 1903]. Apprentice to John Blair, William Blair, and James Watt.—Son of James Beveridge M'Intosh, S.S.C. *Born* 21 January 1876. *Married* 5 April 1904, Minnie Catherine Moir (*died* 3 April 1917), eldest daughter of James Alexander Robertson-Durham of Boghead, Linlithgowshire. Captain Scottish Horse and The Lovat Scouts. Served during Great War in Gallipoli, Egypt, Salonica, and France. *Died* 3 September 1935. *Firm*—J. B. M'Intosh and Son.

MCINTYRE, DERRICK WILLIAM McEWEN, LL.B. [4 December 1972]. Apprentice to Francis James Stewart and Others of Murray, Beith & Murray.—Son of Donald McEwen McIntyre, Tea Planter (Retired), Lochearnhead, Perthshire. *Born* 16 June 1944. *Married* 3 February 1973, Janet Anna, daughter of Ian Scott Fraser, Ph.D., United Nations Official. *Firm*—Scott Moncrieff & Trail.

MACINTYRE, DUNCAN [26 March 1928]. Apprentice to Robert Beveridge Smith.—Son of Ian MacIntyre, W.S., ex-M.P. *Born* 30 December 1902. *Died* 12 June 1930.

MACINTYRE, IAN, LL.B. [30 October 1893]. Apprentice to John Ord Mackenzie, H. Cheyne, and J. Kermack.—Son of Duncan MacIntyre of James Currie and Co., Shipowners, Leith. *Born* 27 November 1869. *Married* (1) 5 September 1896, Ida (*died* 8 February 1942), daughter of Charles John Van der Gucht, Shipowner, and (2) 14 July 1942, Gwendoline Mand Coates (*died* 28 April 1959). Member of Edinburgh Town Council, 1918-20. M.P. for West Edinburgh, 1924-9. Member of the King's Bodyguard for Scotland, Royal Company of Archers, 1910. *Died* 29 June 1946. *Firm*—Mackenzie & Kermack.

M'ISAAC, JAMES WATSON, LL.B. [22 March 1915]. Apprentice to William Babington and Joseph Inglis.—Son of James M'Isaac, Solicitor, Elgin. *Born* 1 January 1891. Lieutenant H.L.I. Served 1916-19 with Salonica Forces. County Collector, Elgin, 1927. *Died* 20 September 1957. *Firm*—Stewart and M'Isaac, Elgin.

MACIVER, ANTHONY DIGBY DUFFUS, LL.B. [28 April 1975]. Apprentice to Norman Angus Miller Mackay and Others of Baillie & Gifford.—Son of Donald Duffus Maciver, Edinburgh. *Born* 14 February 1948. *Married* 22 June 1974, Catherine Jennifer, daughter of Robert Gray, Stockbroker. *Firm*—J. & F. Anderson.

M'JANNET, WILLIAM ROBERT BENNY, LL.B. [13 December 1910]. Apprentice to Alexander Guild.—Son of John Douglas M'Jannet, Coalmaster, Woodlands, Stirling. *Born* 8 December 1885. *Married* 8 April 1913, Caroline Annie (*died* 25 January 1966), youngest daughter of Sir Thomas R. Fraser, M.D., F.R.S., Edinburgh. Captain Seaforth Highlanders. *Killed* in action, 15 July 1916.

MACK, AITCHISON ALEXANDER, OF BURNSIDE [28 June 1827]. Apprentice to Alexander Dallas and John Innes.—Sixth son of William Mack, Writer in Airdrie. *Born* 1803. *Married* 30 October 1829, Martha (*died* 22 April 1877), youngest daughter of John White, Memus, Angus. *Died* 25 April 1843.

MACK (OR MAK), GEORGE [Before 1586].—Son of George Mack, Writer in Edinburgh. Commissioner, 16 December 1594. Fiscal, 1604. *Married* Agnes Hay (*died* 15 February 1626). *Died* 3 November 1622.

MACK, GEORGE [7 November 1631]. Apprentice to William Kellie.—Nephew of George Mack, W.S. *Married* 20 August 1626, Isobel, daughter of Alexander Bynning, Merchant Burgess, Edinburgh. Treasurer, 1654-9. Re-admitted, 21 November 1661. *Died* December 1664.

MACK, HUGH ANTONY LOGAN [26 December 1933]. Apprentice to William C. Hunter and J. J. Bonar.—Son of James Logan Mack, S.S.C., Edinburgh. *Born* 31 July 1906. *Married* 13 February 1943. Ethel Joan Lorimer (*died* 9 June 1980). Major, Infantry, U.K. 1939-45. *Died* 4 September 1950. *Firm*—J. S. and J. L. Mack (latterly Rainnie & Mack).

MACK, JOHN [7 June 1667]. Apprentice to, and only son of, George Mack, W.S.—*Married* Mary Hepburn.

MACK, ROBERT [21 November 1820]. Apprentice to Walter Dickson.—Fifth son of William Mack, Writer in Airdrie. *Died* 12 December 1827.

MACKAY, ALAN DOUGLAS, LL.B. [28 April 1975]. Apprentice to Ian Maxwell Ferguson and Others of Patrick & James.—Son of Neil Edward Mackay, Assistant Chief Valuer, Inland Revenue for Scotland. *Born* 19 January 1944. *Married* 3 September 1971, Elizabeth Margaret, daughter of Thomas O'Loughlin, Education Officer. *Firm*—Patrick & James.

MACKAY, COLIN MORRICE, M.A., LL.B. [13 March 1939]. Apprentice to William Kerr Steedman and Another of Steedman, Ramage & Co.—Son of Alexander Morrice Mackay (The Hon. Lord Mackay), Senator of the College of Justice. *Born* 30 May 1911. Major, R.A. Served U.K., Western Desert and Middle East, 1939-45. *Firm*—Steedman, Ramage & Co. (Consultant.)

MACKAY, DONALD HUGH JAMES, B.L. [15 December 1930]. Apprentice to Charles M. Brown and Thomas J. Mackenzie.—Son of Robert Angus Mackay, Merchant, Durban, Natal. *Born* 21 May 1900. *Married* 3 March 1934, Jessie Marguerite, only daughter of John Grant M'Culloch, Stotfield Hotel, Lossiemouth. Served with Royal Engineers, 1918-19. Procurator-Fiscal Depute, Edinburgh, 1931. *Died* 25 January 1968.

MCKAY, ELIZABETH ANNE, M.A., LL.B. [11 December 1979]. Apprentice to Alasdair G. W. Dear of Alasdair G. W. Dear & Co.—Daughter of Joseph Elder McKay, Engineering Draughtsman, Aberdeen. *Born* 4 May 1954. Captain, Army Legal Corps.

MACKAY, JAMES [14 March 1867]. Apprentice to, and son of, Robert Mackay, W.S.—*Born* 16 April 1844. *Died* 25 December 1876, unmarried.

MACKAY, JAMES FRANCIS, C.B.E., V.D. [10 October 1877]. Apprentice to Donald Beith.—Fourth son of John Mackay of Inveralmond, Pharmaceutical Chemist in Edinburgh. *Born* 6 April 1855. *Married* 14 April 1886, Annie Alma (*died* 20 July 1926), daughter of David Croall of Southfield, Mid-Lothian. Colonel City of Edinburgh R.G.A. Military Representative to City of Edinburgh Military Tribunal, 1917-18. *Died* 21 March 1933. *Firm*—Mackay and Hay.

MACKAY, JAMES LYLE ELLIOT [13 July 1903]. Apprentice to P. Murray, W. C. Johnston, and R. D. Beith.—Son of William Mackay, Shipowner, Arbroath. *Born* 17 March 1879. *Died* 23 February 1953.

MACKAY, NIGEL HUGH, LL.B. [9 December 1980]. Apprentice to J. C. Millar and Others of Simpson & Marwick.—Son of Colonel Coryndon Luxmore Mackay, Army Officer, Edinburgh. *Born* 9 December 1947. *Married* 26 June 1970, Madeleine Christison, daughter of D. M. Oliver, Dunbar. *Firm*—Steedman, Ramage & Co.

MACKAY, NORMAN ANGUS MILLER, B.A.(Oxon), LL.B. [16 December 1946]. Apprentice to T. J. Carlyle Gifford and Another of Baillie & Gifford.—Son of William Miller Mackay, Rubber Planter, Johore Bahru, Malaya. *Born* 10 July 1915. *Married* 26 April 1940, Lesley Lonie Macgillivray, daughter of David Alison, R.S.A. Captain, Royal Scots; attached Mahratta Light Infantry (Indian Army). Served in India and Burma. Mentioned in Despatches. *Firm*—Biggart, Baillie & Gifford (formerly Baillie & Gifford).

MACKAY, NORRIS [28 March 1899]. Apprentice to F. Hunter and W. S. Dykes.—Son of Harbourne Marius Straughan Mackay, Banker and Land Surveyor in Elgin. *Born* 17 July 1873. *Died* 11 November 1911, unmarried.

MACKAY, ROBERT [24 November 1831]. Apprentice to Gibson and Oliphant.—Son of James Mackay, Jeweller in Edinburgh. *Born* 6 March 1807. *Married* 13 March 1835, Elinor (*died* 25 January 1872), only daughter of John Thorburn, Merchant in Leith. *Died* 11 May 1872.

MACKAY, THOMAS GEORGE [8 March 1827]. Apprentice to Richard Mackenzie.—Son of Captain Æneas Mackay of Scotston, Peeblesshire. *Born* 11 March 1803. *Married* 12 October 1838, Mary (*died* 6 November 1884), daughter of John Kirkcaldy of Baldovie, Angus. *Died* 1 May 1864.

M'KEAN, HUGH [16 November 1831]. Apprentice to (1) John M'Kean; (2) William Mackenzie; and (3) J. T. Gibson-Craig.—Son of Andrew M'Kean of Locharwoods, Dumfriesshire. *Born* 30 June 1809. *Married* 11 August 1840, Ann Hally (*died* 4 September 1902), third daughter of George Knight, Edinburgh. *Died* 15 August 1893.

M'KEAN, JOHN [6 March 1817]. Apprentice to (1) Robert Cathcart; and (2) John Kermack.—Son of Andrew M'Kean of Locharwoods, Dumfriesshire. *Born* 4 May 1794. *Married* 24 July 1820, Margaret (*died* 1869), youngest daughter of John Thomson, Leith. Manager of Scottish Widows' Fund. *Died* 3 January 1839.

MACKENZIE, ALEXANDER, OF DELVINE [15 December 1714]. Apprentice to Thomas Pringle.—Second son of John Mackenzie of Delvine, Perthshire. *Born* 8 February 1695. *Married* Anne, daughter of —— Fortheringhame of Powrie. Principal Clerk of Session, 12 December 1718 till death. *Died* 5 July 1737.

MACKENZIE, ALEXANDER, OF PORTMORE [15 July 1763]. Apprentice to John Mackenzie.—Eldest son of Alexander Mackenzie of Tolly, Bailie and Merchant in Dingwall. *Born* 5 February 1735. *Married* 25 October 1766, Anne (*died* 11 July 1823), eldest daughter of Colin Mackenzie of Kilcoy, Ross-shire. *Died* 4 September 1805.

MACKENZIE, ALEXANDER, OF MEIKLE SCATWELL [24 June 1835]. Apprentice to Alexander Monypenny.—Eldest son of William Mackenzie of Muirton, W.S. *Born* 28 February 1812. *Married* 6 January 1842, Marion Dalrymple (*died* 20 July 1872), daughter of John Mansfield of Midmar, Aberdeenshire. Keeper of the Register of Hornings, etc., 1839-44. *Died* 9 December 1891.

MACKENZIE, ALISTAIR JAMES ANTHONY, M.A., LL.B. [8 December 1975]. Apprentice to James Sinclair Hodge and Others of Dundas & Wilson.—Son of J. Strath Mackenzie, Advocate in Aberdeen. *Born* 17 July 1951. *Married* 6 April 1974, Felicity Diana Cooper.

MACKENZIE, ANDREW [3 July 1778]. Apprentice to John Mackenzie.—Second son of Kenneth Mackenzie, Professor of Civil Law in the University of Edinburgh. *Married* 30 April 1789, Janet, daughter of James Goodlet Campbell of Achlyne, Perthshire. *Died* 10 September 1793.

MACKENZIE, ANTHONY TRAIL, B.A.(OXON) [15 December 1919]. Apprentice to J. P. Wright and T. M. Murray.—Son of Sir William Mackenzie, Secretary and Managing Director of the Alliance Trust Co. (Ltd.), Dundee. *Born* 26 September 1884. *Died* 17 August 1944.

MACKENZIE, COLIN, OF ROSEND [25 July 1722]. Apprentice to Alexander Mackenzie.—Son of Colin Mackenzie of Rosend, Fife. *Died* 3 December 1746.

MACKENZIE, COLIN, OF PORTMORE [21 November 1790]. Apprentice to, and second son of, Alexander Mackenzie of Portmore, Peeblesshire, W.S.—*Born* 11 January 1770. *Married* 13 May 1803, Elizabeth (*died* 1851), daughter of Sir William Forbes of Pitsligo, Bart., Banker. Principal Clerk of Session, 14 November 1804 to 23 February 1828. Deputy Keeper of the Signet, 1820-8. *Died* 16 September 1830.

MACKENZIE, COLIN [14 July 1864]. Apprentice to, and eldest son of, James Hay Mackenzie, W.S.—*Born* 22 April 1841. Deputy Keeper of the Great Seal, 1866-82. *Died* 15 July 1882, unmarried.

MACKENZIE, DAVID, LL.B. [9 December 1907]. Apprentice to P. W. Campbell and F. J. Martin.—Son of George Alexander Mackenzie, Solicitor, Perth. *Born* 5 January 1882. *Married* 18 June 1927, Alison Walker, daughter of Dr John Laurie, Little Bridley, Worplesdon, Surrey. Captain Black Watch. Served in Mesopotamia in Great War. *Firm*—Condie, Mackenzie & Co., Perth. *Died* 13 September 1950.

MACKENZIE, DONALD [15 November 1872]. Apprentice to John Clerk Brodie.—Eldest son of Donald Mackenzie, Advocate, one of the Senators of the College of Justice. *Born* 10 July 1844. *Married* 13 July 1878, Laura Augusta Mackenzie (*died* 27 August 1919), second daughter of Lynedoch Douglas, fifth son of General Sir Kenneth Douglas, Bart. of Glenbervie. *Died* at Oxford, 16 December 1924.

MACKENZIE, DONALD GLADSTONE [29 March 1905]. Apprentice to Sir W. S. Haldane, F. G. Haldane and W. Purves.—Son of Alexander Donald Mackenzie, Horticultural Builder, and one of the Bailies of the City of Edinburgh. *Born* 22 July 1881. *Married* 27 January 1912, Charlotte Burrell (*died* 24 December 1955), only daughter of William Clark Sturrock, Solicitor, Edinburgh. Barrister-at-Law, and K.C., Calgary, Alberta, Canada. *Died* at Calgary 10 November 1945.

MACKENZIE, GEORGE [30 November 1675]. Apprentice to John Bayne.

MACKENZIE, GEORGE [15 July 1852]. Apprentice to (1) Arthur Campbell; and (2) John Ord Mackenzie, his brother.—Fifth son of Richard Mackenzie of Dolphinton, W.S. *Born* 12 September 1828. *Married* 16 April 1858, Agnes (*died* 26 February 1921), second daughter of James Valentine Hagart of Glendelvine, Perthshire. *Died* 16 September 1871.

MACKENZIE, IAN DRUMMOND, M.A., LL.B. [13 July 1936]. Apprentice to E. M. Wedderburn and Others of Shepherd & Wedderburn.—Son of John Edwin Mackenzie, B.Sc., Edinburgh. *Born* 21 May 1909. *Married* 16 March 1940, Rosemary Isobel Margaret Munro. Captain, Seaforth Highlanders. Served U.K., Middle East and North Africa. Killed in action at Djebl Roumana, Tunisia, 6 April 1943. *Firm*—Strathern & Blair.

MACKENZIE, JAMES [10 March 1806]. Apprentice to Alexander Grant.—Third son of Henry Mackenzie of the Exchequer, "The Man of Feeling." *Died* 7 February 1870, aged 90, unmarried.

MACKENZIE, JAMES DOUGLAS [11 December 1979*].—Son of J. H. A. Mackenzie, W.S., Edinburgh. *Born* 24 May 1953. *Firm*—Mowat & Mackenzie.

MACKENZIE, JAMES HAY [1 March 1831]. Apprentice to (1) William Mackenzie; and (2) Richard Mackenzie.—Second son of Colin Mackenzie of Portmore, W.S. *Born* 25 October 1809. *Married* (1) 11 April 1838, Janet Isabella (*died* 1 August 1853), eldest daughter of James Wedderburn, Advocate, Solicitor-General for Scotland; and (2) 4 March 1863, Selina Jane Norton (*died* 1869), widow of Donald Hume Macleod, 68th Regiment. Keeper of the Register of Inhibitions, etc., 1844-65. Deputy Keeper of the Great Seal, 1858-65. *Died* 16 February 1865.

MACKENZIE, JAMES HUGH ALEXANDER, B.L. [23 July 1951]. Apprentice to Andrew St. Clair Jameson and Others of Boyd, Jameson & Young.—Son of James Mackenzie, Solicitor, Edinburgh. *Born* 4 January 1928. *Married* 5 June 1952, Marjory Dean, daughter of John Douglas Mackay, Master Printer. *Firm*—Mowat & Mackenzie (formerly James Mackenzie & Son).

MACKENZIE, SIR JAMES MOIR, K.B.E., C.M.G. [27 March 1911]. Apprentice to P. Murray and Others of Murray, Beith & Murray.—Son of James Mackenzie, Shipowner, Melrose. *Born* 17 October 1886. *Married* 23 June 1914, Marguerite Stevenson (*died* 4 February 1975), daughter of Stevenson Haggie, Jesmond, Newcastle-upon-Tyne. Lieutenant, R.N.V.R., R.N. Division and Harwich Forces (Destroyers), First World War. Deputy Director, Federation of British Industries. Member, Queen's Bodyguard for Scotland, Royal Company of Archers. President, Scottish Rugby Union 1948-49. Played 14 times as Scottish Internationalist. Knighted 1951. *Died* 22 January 1963.

MACKENZIE, JOHN, OF DELVINE [1737]. Apprentice to Hugh Somerville.—Fourth son of John Mackenzie of Delvine. *Born* 1709. *Married* 1742, Cecilia Renton of Lamerton. Deputy Keeper of the Signet, 1770-8. Principal Clerk of Session, 8 March 1776. *Died* 14 June 1778.

MACKENZIE, JOHN, OF LETTEREWE [15 December 1825]. Apprentice to William Mackenzie and Alexander Monypenny.—Eldest son of Alexander Mackenzie of Letterewe, Ross-shire. *Died* 4 January 1834, aged 33, unmarried.

MACKENZIE, JOHN [23 June 1853]. Apprentice to, and son of, John Whitefoord Mackenzie, W.S.—*Born* 3 September 1830. *Died* 22 April 1911, unmarried.

MACKENZIE, JOHN [18 November 1861]. Apprentice to, and son of, John Ord Mackenzie of Dolphinton, Lanarkshire, W.S.—*Born* 1 March 1838. *Died* 22 August 1868, unmarried.

MACKENZIE, JOHN MANSFIELD, OF SCATWELL [18 March 1869]. Apprentice to (1) Thomas G. Mackay and Alexander Howe; and (2) Colin Mackenzie.—Second son of Alexander Mackenzie of Meikle Scatwell, Ross-shire, W.S. *Born* 20 January 1846. *Died* 3 March 1893, unmarried.

MACKENZIE, JOHN MONCREIFF ORD, B.A.(CANTAB), J.P. [15 March 1937]. Apprentice to Robert Ker Blair and Another of Blair & Cadell.—Son of Kenneth Mackenzie, W.S., Dolphinton House, Dolphinton. *Born* 13 August 1911. *Married* 15 October 1936, Delia Alice, daughter of Wyndham Damer Clark. Captain, R.A. Served U.K., India and North West Europe. *Firm*—Bonar Mackenzie (formerly Mackenzie & Kermack; Bonar, Mackenzie & Kermack). (Consultant.)

MACKENZIE, JOHN ORD, OF DOLPHINTON [26 June 1832]. Apprentice to, and eldest son of, Richard Mackenzie of Dolphinton, W.S.—*Born* 18 March 1811. *Married* (1) 23 April 1833, Margaret Hope (*died* 3 May 1873), daughter of Sir Thomas Kirkpatrick, Bart. of Closeburn, Dumfriesshire; and (2) 20 January 1881, Joanna (*died* 15 February 1928), elder daughter of William Spens, Manager of the Scottish Amicable Assurance Company, Glasgow. Father of Society. *Died* at Dolphinton, 14 March 1902. *Firm*—Mackenzie & Kermack.

MACKENZIE, JOHN WHITEFOORD [26 May 1818]. Apprentice to Francis Napier.—Eldest son of John Mackenzie, M.D., Edinburgh. *Born* 29 August 1794. *Married* 2 October 1826, Jane Campbell (*died* 16 September 1856), daughter of John Gordon of Carleton, Ayrshire, W.S. *Died* 8 November 1884.

MACKENZIE, KENNETH [21 November 1777]. Apprentice to John Fraser.—Second son of Kenneth Mackenzie of Dundonnell, Ross-shire. Registrar of Seizures of H.M. Customs. *Died* 4 November 1790.

MACKENZIE, KENNETH, OF INVERINATE [29 June 1786]. Apprentice to Alexander Mackenzie.—Son of John Mackenzie of Brae. *Married* 27 October 1787, Anne (*died* 4 September 1806), second daughter of Thomas Mackenzie of Applecross, Ross-shire. *Died* 20 November 1820.

MACKENZIE, KENNETH [15 December 1825]. Apprentice to Kenneth and Thomas Mackenzie.—Second son of Alexander Mackenzie of Hilton, Ross-shire. *Born* 1798. *Married* (1) 1831, Anne Urquhart, Aberdeen; and (2) 26 October 1853, Elizabeth Charlotte Jones (*died* 31 March 1879). *Died* in Canada, 19 May 1874.

MACKENZIE, KENNETH, B.A. [29 March 1909]. Apprentice to H. E. Richardson, Victor A. Noel Paton, and J. Carr G. Lees.—Son of John Ord Mackenzie, W.S. *Born* 10 March 1882. *Married* 4 October 1910, May Eudora (*died* 1 May 1979), eldest daughter of Henry Moncreiff Horsbrugh, C.A., Edinburgh. Captain Royal Scots. *Killed* in action on 27 August 1918.

MACKENZIE, LAWRENCE MILLAR [13 December 1897]. Apprentice to G. G. Turnbull and John Ewart.—Son of the Rev. James Mackenzie, Minister of Free Abbey Church, Dunfermline, Author of *A History of Scotland. Born* 4 January 1860. *Married* 5 September 1906, Anna Marion (*died* 18 March 1957), daughter of Rev. James M'Clymont, Denholm, Roxburghshire. *Died* 23 July 1932.

MACKENZIE, LIONEL RUSK SPROT, B.L. [15 December 1947]. Apprentice to F. P. Milligan and Another of Martin, Milligan & Macdonald.—Son of Brevet-Major L. D. A. Mackenzie, D.S.O., M.C. *Born* 20 January 1921. *Married* 8 September 1956, Margaret Ishbel, daughter of Professor A. Mackenzie Stuart. Flight Lieutenant, R.A.F. Served U.K. and South East Asia. *Firm*—Menzies Dougal & Milligan (after amalgamation with Martin, Milligan & Macdonald).

MACKENZIE, MURDOCH CAMPBELL, M.A., LL.B. [28 November 1966]. Apprentice to D. A. Balfour and Others of Shepherd & Wedderburn.—Son of the Rev. Duncan Murdo Mackenzie, Kinross. *Born* 12 December 1938. *Married* 24 November 1967, Sheila Bryce, daughter of David Stevenson McLaren. *Firms*—(1) McCormick & Nicholson, Newton-Stewart; (2) John Roddick & Co., Annan.

MACKENZIE, RICHARD, OF DOLPHINTON [8 March 1803]. Apprentice to Kenneth Mackenzie.—Son of John Mackenzie of Dolphinton, Advocate. *Born* 2 August 1780. *Married* 3 April 1810, Jane (*died* 30 December 1874), daughter of Captain John Hamilton, 73rd Regiment. Fiscal, 1820-4. Treasurer, 1824-8. Joint Deputy Keeper of the Signet, 1828-50. *Died* 22 March 1850.

MACKENZIE, ROBERT, OF SALACHURY [9 July 1801]. Apprentice to Kenneth Mackenzie.—Son of William Mackenzie, Writer in Inveraray. *Born* 1774. *Married* 18 May 1835, Mary (*died* 14 September 1845), widow of Duncan Campbell of Duncholgine, Argyllshire. *Died* 29 March 1838.

MACKENZIE, RODERICK [23 November 1819]. Apprentice to Æneas Macbean.—Son of George Mackenzie of Inniklet. *Born* 1793. *Married* 28 October 1822, Euphemia (*died* 24 April 1887), eldest daughter of Andrew Johnston of Rennyhill, Fife. *Died* 4 January 1844.

MACKENZIE, THOMAS, OF APPLECROSS [4 March 1816]. Apprentice to, and eldest son of, Kenneth Mackenzie of Inverinate, W.S.—*Born* 1793. *Married* 13 May 1817, Margaret (*died* 28 April 1876), daughter of George Mackenzie of Avoch, Ross-shire. M.P. for Ross and Cromarty, 1837-47. Solicitor to G.P.O. *Died* 9 June 1856.

MACKENZIE, THOMAS [13 November 1849]. Apprentice to Arthur Campbell.—Third son of Thomas Mackenzie, W.S. *Born* 28 November 1822. *Died* 11 March 1884, unmarried.

MACKENZIE, THOMAS JAMIESON [16 December 1924]. Apprentice to J. L. Mounsey, A. G. Brown, and Keith Ramsay Maitland.—Son of John Anderson Mackenzie, Solicitor, Glasgow. *Born* 4 February 1881. *Married* 24 September 1852 Agnes Margaret Gaunt, widow of William Burns, W.S. (*died* 15 November 1980). Served as Private and Lieutenant with A. and S. Highlanders, 1915-18. *Died* 15 May 1957. *Firm*—J. C. Brodie and Sons.

MACKENZIE, WILLIAM, OF MUIRTON [25 February 1803]. Apprentice to Colin Mackenzie, his brother.—Seventh son of Alexander Mackenzie of Portmore, W.S. *Born* 1 October 1780. *Married* (1) 6 July 1809, Mary (*died* 12 July 1818), eldest daughter of James Mansfield of Midmar, Aberdeenshire; and (2) 9 April 1821, Alice (*died* 28 January 1856), eldest daughter of Andrew Wauchope of Niddrie-Marischal, Mid-Lothian. Keeper of the Register of Hornings, etc., 1829-39. *Died* 28 April 1856.

MACKERSY, LINDSAY [15 March 1860]. Apprentice to, and eldest son of, William Mackersy, W.S.—*Born* 10 December 1831. *Married* 2 August 1859, Ann Helena (*died* 28 October 1920), youngest daughter of James Charles Stuart of Erncrogo, Kirkcudbrightshire. *Died* 14 August 1902.

MACKERSY, WILLIAM [8 July 1823]. Apprentice to Charles Tawse.—Son of Rev. John Mackersy, D.D., Minister of West Calder. *Born* 1795. *Married* 4 August 1829, Elizabeth, youngest daughter of Robert Walker of Sunny Bank, Fife. *Died* 3 October 1875.

MACKERSY, WILLIAM ROBERT [17 January 1888]. Apprentice to (1) Robert Pringle; and (2) George Dunlop.—Eldest son of Lindsay Mackersy, W.S. *Born* 1 December 1863. *Married* 10 June 1890, Mary Luke (*died* 25 July 1943), youngest daughter of John Bainbridge Callum, Edinburgh. Struck off Roll, 25 June 1924. *Died* 12 May 1933.

MACKIE-ROBERTSON, JAMES ANGUS, B.L. [7 September 1948]. Apprentice to (1) James Stormont Darling and Another of P. & J. Stormonth Darling, Kelso, and (2) the Hon. Adam George Watson and Others of Mackenzie, Innes & Logan.—Son of John Robertson, Depute County Clerk for Roxburghshire. *Born* 15 August 1918. *Married* (1) 21 June 1945, Janet Miller (divorced December 1948); and (2) 24 March 1949, Margery Elizabeth Bell, daughter of Arthur Bell Couper, Banker. Major, Black Watch (R.H.R.) and King's African Rifles 1939-46. Advocate of the High Courts of Kenya, Uganda and Tanzania; One of Her Majesty's Counsel for Kenya. *Firm*—Brodies (formerly Brodie, Cuthbertson & Watson).

MACKIESON, GEORGE [Before 1567]. *Married* Elspeth Menteith. *Died* 1594.

MACKINLAY, WILLIAM HENDERSON, B.L. [30 April 1962]. Apprentice to Charles R. Black of Warden, Bruce & Co.—Son of W. H. Mackinlay, Master Baker. *Born* 20 July 1922. *Married* 6 June 1951, Daphne Muriel, daughter of W. R. Glenny, Army Officer. Served R.A.F., Signals Branch, Middle East and Italy 1942-46. *Firm*—Tods, Murray & Jamieson.

MACKINNON, KENNETH ALASDAIR, B.A.(CANTAB), LL.B. [26 November 1962]. Apprentice to John Herbert Richardson and Others of Dundas & Wilson.—Son of Neil Mackinnon, W.S., Oban. *Born* 8 March 1936. *Married* 6 April 1963, Anne Clare, daughter of Francis John Valentine, Oilfield Manager, Burmah Oil Company. *Firm*— D. M. Mackinnon & Co., Oban.

MACKINNON, NEIL, T.D., M.A., LL.B. [18 July 1927]. Apprentice to J. Miller Thomson of J. Miller Thomson & Co.—Son of Alexander Dugald Mackinnon, O.B.E., Solicitor, Portree. *Born* 11 April 1904. *Married* (1) 16 September 1933, Janet Alison (divorced October 1945), daughter of Rt. Rev. Kenneth Mackenzie, Bishop of Argyll and The Isles, Ardconnell, Oban; (2) 18 May 1946, Aldyth, daughter of Matthew Joseph Martin, Chief Constable of Perthshire. Major, R.A. Served U.K. and France 1939-40. Prisoner-of-War 1940-45. Hon. Sheriff of Argyll at Oban. *Died* 25 April 1979. *Firm*—D. M. Mackinnon & Co. (Retired.)

MACKINTOSH, PATRICK TURNER [17 December 1917]. Apprentice to William Garson and James Garson.—Son of John Mackintosh, J.P., Ardchattan, Inverness. *Born* 30 March 1874, *Died* 30 June 1941. *Firm*—Skene, Edwards, and Garson.

MACKINTOSH, SIMON FRASER [15 January 1819]. Apprentice to Richard Hotchkis.— Son of James Mackintosh of Farr, Inverness-shire. *Died* 10 September 1842, aged 53, unmarried.

MACKINTOSH, THOMAS [12 April 1887]. Apprentice to John William Young and John Blair.—Son of Rev. Thomas Mackintosh, Minister of St Cyrus. *Born* 12 October 1863. *Married* 27 October 1903, Anna Dorothea (*died* 22 June 1967), youngest daughter of Rev. William Pinney, Rector of Llanvetherine, Monmouthshire. *Died* 1 October 1959. *Firm*—Mackintosh and Boyd.

MACKNIGHT, GEORGE SIMPSON, LL.B. [17 December 1942]. Apprentice to William Babington and Others of Melville & Lindesay.—Son of George Simpson Macknight, Procurator Fiscal of West Lothian, Linlithgow. *Born* 2 February 1917. *Married* 10 April 1943, Katherine Alice (*died* 22 July 1977), daughter of Sir John Usher, Bart. *Died* 18 December 1952.

MACKNIGHT, IAN ALASTAIR, D.S.C., M.A., LL.B. [14 December 1936]. Apprentice to William Babington of Melville & Lindesay.—Son of George Simpson Macknight, Procurator Fiscal of West Lothian, Linlithgow. *Born* 19 March 1913. *Married* 22 August 1938, Catherine Olivia, daughter of Hugh Rattray. Lieutenant Commander R.N.V.R. Served Atlantic and Arctic. County Clerk of Angus 1947-74.

MACKNIGHT, JAMES, OF DALSRAITH [5 December 1833]. Apprentice to James and Charles Nairne.—Son of Rev. Thomas Macknight, D.D., Minister of Old Church, Edinburgh. *Born* 23 September 1810. *Married* 28 April 1842, Helen (*died* 9 March 1896), third daughter of Commander Hugh Pearson, R.N., of Myrecairnie and Vellore. Edited, for the Abbotsford and Maitland Clubs, *Memoirs of Sir Ewen Cameron of Lochiel*, 1848. *Died* 6 November 1878.

MACKNIGHT, SAMUEL [7 March 1786]. Apprentice to (1) John Bell; and (2) John Tait.—Second son of Rev. James Macknight, D.D., Minister of Lady Yester's, Edinburgh. *Born* 23 January 1757. *Died* 24 August 1807.

MCKUNE, RONALD, M.A., LL.B. [11 December 1979]. Apprentice to Charles R. Black and Another of Warden, Bruce & Co.—Son of William Golding McKune, Pharmacist, Kirkcaldy. *Born* 27 March 1938. *Married* 12 July 1969, Margaret Anne, daughter of William Laughton, Edinburgh. *Firm*—Warden, Bruce & Co.

MACLACHLAN, CHARLES FELLOWES MONCRIEFFE [9 July 1907]. Apprentice to W. K. Steedman.—Son of Rev. Ivie Macrae Maclachlan, Minister at Uddingston. *Born* 10 April 1879. *Married* 10 April 1915, Alyce Swan (*died* 29 November 1972), third daughter of the Rev. William Fairweather, Maryton, Angus. Enlisted in Royal Scots, 1914; Commission, Gordon Highlanders, 1915. Served in France and Belgium. Mentioned in Despatches. Treasurer and Clerk, John Watson's Trust, 1935. *Died* 20 October 1964. *Firm*—Ronald and Ritchie.

MACLACHLAN, GEORGE, OF MACLACHLAN [30 November 1826]. Apprentice to Robert Mackenzie.—Fourth son of Donald Maclachlan of Maclachlan, Argyllshire. *Born* 1803. *Married* Mary (*died* 10 September 1903), daughter of John Thow. *Died* 7 August 1877.

MACLACHLAN, JOHN, OF MACLACHLAN [13 April 1885]. Apprentice to Frederick Pitman.—Second and eldest surviving son of George Maclachlan of Maclachlan, W.S. *Born* 3 January 1859. *Married* 26 February 1919, Frances Eva Marjorie (*died* 23 July 1949), daughter of Albert C. Macpherson of Cluny Macpherson, and widow of Donald Ninian Nicol of Ardmarnock. Member of the King's Bodyguard for Scotland, Royal Company of Archers, 1882. *Died* 18 September 1942. *Firm*—J. & F. Anderson.

MACLACHLAN, ROBERT [18 October 1886]. Apprentice to Colin Mackenzie, A. D. M. Black, and A. M. Mackenzie.—Third son of George Maclachlan of Maclachlan, W.S. *Born* 20 September 1860. *Married* 25 April 1883, Helen Louisa (*died* 6 June 1928), daughter of Captain Hale Monro of Ingsdon, Devon. *Died* 21 April 1914.

M'LACHLAN, WILLIAM MACKAY [20 October 1885]. Apprentice to William Campbell M'Ewen.—Son of Rev. James M'Lachlan, Minister of Inveravon, Banffshire. *Born* 19 November 1861. *Married* (1) 23 April 1895, Jeannette Commelia (*died* 8 December 1931), daughter of A. C. Bramwell, Blackaddie, Sanquhar; (2) 24 July 1934, Elizabeth Dundas (*died* 22 May 1957), daughter of George Syme, 7 Granby Road, Edinburgh. Foreign Mission Secretary of Church of Scotland. *Died* 9 February 1951.

MACLAGAN, DOUGLAS PHILIP [11 July 1892]. Apprentice to Charles Simson Rankine Simson.—Son of Robert Craig Maclagan, M.D., Edinburgh. *Born* 12 August 1867. *Married* 6 June 1896, Jane Elizabeth (*died* 16 September 1950), second daughter of James Melvin, 43 Drumsheugh Gardens, Edinburgh. Member of the King's Bodyguard for Scotland, Royal Company of Archers, 1897. *Died* 20 July 1948. *Firm*—Fyfe, Ireland, and Co.

MACLAGAN, ROBERT CHEEVER [1 April 1907]. Apprentice to Sir Charles B. Logan, Hon. J. W. Moncreiff, G. G. Soote, and E. J. Cuthbertson.—Son of Gilbert Charles Maclagan, 28 Stafford Street, Edinburgh. *Born* 21 February 1883. *Married* 1 March 1915, Winifred Ellen Donaldson (*died* 17 August 1971). *Died* 29 July 1944.

MACLAREN, ALASDAIR IAIN [23 March 1914]. Apprentice to A. D. M. Black, A. W. Gifford, and C. M. Black.—Son of Duncan MacLaren, S.S.C., Edinburgh. *Born* 21 July 1889. President, Court of First Instance, Baghdad, 1924-29. *Died* 13 December 1933, unmarried.

MCLAREN, JAMES FERGUS, M.A., LL.B. [11 December 1979*].—Son of Dr Robert Craik McLaren, Medical Practitioner, Edinburgh. *Born* 29 February 1948. *Firm*—Brodies.

M'LAREN, LAURENCE [14 July 1890]. Apprentice to John Rutherfurd.—Son of John M'Laren, Merchant, Edinburgh. *Born* 23 January 1865. *Married* 9 April 1904, Mary Wilson (*died* 30 December 1940), second daughter of Peter Stroyan, Liverpool. *Died* at Glasgow, 25 January 1929. *Firm*—L. and J. M'Laren.

MCLAREN, LAWRENCE FALCONER, B.A.(OXON), LL.B. [17 December 1934]. Apprentice to Robert Nevill Dundas and Others of Dundas & Wilson.—Son of John McLaren, Solicitor, Edinburgh. *Born* 25 April 1909. *Married* (1) 5 October 1940, Janet Logan (*died* 13 May 1959), daughter of George Soutar Dickson, Publishers' Editor; (2) 20 April 1963, Elizabeth Meta, daughter of Frederick Bauermeister, Bookseller, Edinburgh. Captain, R.A. Instructor in A.A. Gunnery. Served U.K. and Allied Land Forces, Norway, 1939-45. *Firm*—Haldanes, McLaren & Scott (formerly L. & J. McLaren, and Haldanes & McLaren).

MACLAREN, THOMAS SHAW, OF SHAWFIELD [15 July 1874]. Apprentice to William Traquair.—Son of James Maclaren of Dalnabrick, Perthshire. *Born* 7 August 1841. *Married* 25 January 1883, Isabella Davidson (*died* 21 January 1940), elder daughter of John Smith, Banker and Solicitor, Anstruther. *Died* 4 June 1907.

MACLAREN, WILLIAM ALEXANDER [20 January 1875]. Apprentice to Thomas Spalding.—Son of Thomas Maclaren. *Born* 4 May 1843. *Married* 20 March 1884, Sarah Louisa (*died* 27 December 1893), younger daughter of Benjamin Liddell of Press Castle, Berwickshire. *Died* 9 April 1886.

MACLAURIN, JOHN [10 March 1825]. Apprentice to (1) Donald Maclean; and (2) John and Walter Ferrier.—Youngest son of John Maclaurin, residing at Lochfynehead. *Born* 1799. *Married* 22 December 1830, Grace (*died* 20 December 1880), daughter of James Wylie of Airlywight, Perthshire. Sheriff-Substitute at Inveraray, 1834-60. Author of a *Digest of the Sheriff's Small Debt Act for Scotland*, 1838, and other works. *Died* 20 May 1880.

MACLEAN, ARCHIBALD [17 November 1836]. Apprentice to, and son of, Donald Maclean, W.S.—*Born* 13 December 1810. *Died* 24 September 1844, unmarried.

M'LEAN, ARTHUR HENRY [14 July 1891]. Apprentice to George Robertson, John Hope Finlay, and W. P. Robertson.—Son of the Rev. Daniel M'Lean, Minister of Bloomgate U.P. Church, Lanark. *Born* 23 October 1868. *Married* 1 October 1895, Isabel Cranstoun (*died* 18 September 1964), daughter of the Rev. Professor Robert Johnstone, D.D.; Edinburgh. Joint Agent, Church of Scotland, 1929. *Died* 18 April 1956. *Firm*—Robson, M'Lean and Paterson.

MACLEAN, CHARLES PETER BRUCE, M.A., LL.B. [11 December 1979]. Apprentice to P. A. Maclean and Others of Robson, McLean & Paterson.—Son of A. Bruce Maclean, Consultant General Surgeon, Carlisle. *Born* 23 August 1951.

MACLEAN, DAVID WILLIAM JAMES, LL.B. [8 December 1975]. Apprentice to Roy Wilson of Alan McNeil & Son.—Son of James Maclean, W.S., Edinburgh. *Born* 2 September 1950. *Married* 11 May 1974, Hilary Mary, daughter of Bertram Fraser Vernon, Insurance Official.

MACLEAN, DONALD, of Drimnin [26 February 1796]. Apprentice to Colquhoun Grant.—Son of Allan Maclean of Drimnin, Argyllshire. *Born* 15 January 1770. *Married* 24 April 1793, Lilias (*died* 30 December 1833), daughter of Colquhoun Grant, W.S. Solicitor to Court of Exchequer, 1822-37. *Died* 16 March 1853.

MACLEAN, FITZROY JEFFERIES GRAFTON [4 December 1845]. Apprentice to John Maclaurin.—Son of Donald Maclean, W.S. *Born* 30 August 1813. *Died* 20 March 1858, unmarried.

M'LEAN, HECTOR FREDERICK [22 May 1845]. Apprentice to Charles Cuningham and Carlyle Bell.—Third son of John M'Lean of Campbeltown. *Born* 9 November 1818. *Married* 1 June 1869, Marsali (*died* 11 February 1887), daughter of Æneas Ranaldson Macdonell of Glengarry. *Died* 10 July 1891. *Firm*—Bell & M'Lean.

MACLEAN, JAMES [26 April 1954]. Apprentice to James Barron Lloyd and Another of Skene, Edward & Garson.—Son of Donald MacLean, Smallholder, Elphin, Sutherland. *Born* 12 November 1924. *Married* 26 October 1946, Margaret, daughter of William Denham, Leather Merchant, Huddersfield. Corporal in Fleet Air Arm and R.A.F., Second World War. Clerk and Treasurer of John Watson's Trust. Honorary Sheriff at Dornoch. *Firm*—Skene, Edwards & Garson.

MCLEAN, JAMES ANGUS, B.A.(Cantab), LL.B. [4 December 1972]. Apprentice to J. P. Watson and Others of Lindsays.—Son of Angus McLean, S.S.C., Dunoon, Argyll. *Born* 25 April 1947. *Married* 18 September 1971, Carol Ann, daughter of George Inglis. *Firm*—W. & J. Burness.

MACLEAN, JOHN [24 January 1687]. Apprentice to John Macfarlane. *Died* April 1695.

MCLEAN, PATRICK ARTHUR, M.A., LL.B. [13 July 1931]. Apprentice to James Watt and Another of Davidson & Syme.—Son of Arthur Henry McLean, W.S., Edinburgh. *Born* 19 November 1907. *Married* 1 November 1938, Winifred Maud (*died* 19 February 1980), daughter of George Dunlop Dempster, Greenock and Edinburgh. Major, Queen's Own Cameron Highlanders. Served U.K. and India 1940-45. *Firm*—Robson, McLean & Paterson. (Retired 1978.)

MACLEHOSE, ANDREW CRAIG [1 July 1808]. Apprentice to Robert Ainslie.—Son of James Maclehose, Attorney-at-Law, Kingston, Jamaica, and his wife, Nancy Craig ("Clarinda"). *Born* 1778. *Married* 2 October 1809, Mary (*died* 21 April 1838), eldest daughter of John Goodrum of Shropham, Norfolk. *Died* 10 April 1839.

MCLELLAN, DAVID KENNETH, LL.B. [7 December 1970]. Apprentice to The Hon. David A. Balfour and Others of Shepherd & Wedderburn.—Son of Kenneth Archibald McLellan, W.S., Edinburgh. *Born* 27 July 1946. *Firm*—Dundas & Wilson.

MCLELLAN, KENNETH ARCHIBALD, M.B.E., M.A., LL.B. [22 June 1942]. Apprentice to Robert Nevill Dundas and Others of Dundas & Wilson.—Son of Henry Drysdale McLellan, Solicitor, Stirling. *Born* 5 October 1915. *Married* 20 June 1945, Elizabeth Mary, daughter of Percy Hamilton Maflin, Civil Engineer, Godalming. Lieutenant Commander R.N.V.R. Served Home Fleet 1939-40; U.K. 1940-45. Secretary to Admiral of the Fleet Lord Keyes 1941; Secretary to Admiral Lord Louis Mountbatten 1941; Secretary to Rear Admiral H. E. Horan 1941-45. Commended by Commander in Chief, Western Approaches, August 1945. *Firm*—Dundas & Wilson.

MACLENNAN, DAVID PETER HUGH, LL.B. [6 December 1971]. Apprentice to R. T. Peden and Another of Drummond & Co.—Son of Alexander Fraser Maclennan, S.S.C., Edinburgh. *Born* 6 September 1947. *Married* 3 April 1974, Joan Isobel, daughter of J. G. Milligan. *Firm*—Balfour & Manson.

MACLEOD, ALEXANDER [15 September 1704].—Brother to Norman Macleod, Tacksman of Wilkhaven. *Married* February 1699, Margaret, eldest daughter of William Montgomery of Macbiehill, Peeblesshire. Under Keeper of the Signet, 1704-5. *Died* June 1706.

MACLEOD, DONALD IAN KERR, M.A., LL.B. [18 July 1966]. Apprentice to Hon. D. A. Balfour and Others of Shepherd & Wedderburn.—Son of Angus MacLeod, C.B.E., Procurator Fiscal of Midlothian (retired), Edinburgh. *Born* 19 April 1937. *Married* 29 July 1966, Mary St. Clair, daughter of Professor I. C. Bridge, Rhu, Dunbartonshire. *Firm*—Shepherd & Wedderburn.

MACLEOD, EUAN RODERICK, LL.B. [4 December 1967]. Apprentice to Alastair Campbell Blair and Others of Davidson & Syme.—Son of Angus MacLeod, C.B.E., Procurator Fiscal of Midlothian (retired), Edinburgh. *Born* 17 January 1944. *Married* 29 August 1968, Fiona Margaret, daughter of John McDonald. *Firm*—Dundas & Wilson.

MACLEOD, KENNETH JOHN BAILLIE STEWART, LL.B. [12 May 1981]. Apprentice to John Munro Wotherspoon of Macandrew & Jenkins, Inverness.—Son of Roderick MacLeod, Crofter, Ullapool, Ross-shire. *Born* 8 January 1936. *Married* 9 August 1969, Rona Janet, daughter of Donald John Mackay, Director of Welfare Services for the County of Sutherland. Liberal Parliamentary Candidate for South Aberdeen, 1970.

MCLEOD, NEIL [3 December 1973]. Apprentice to Patrick Watson Turcan and Another of Dundas & Wilson.—Son of Norman McLeod, Medical Practitioner, St Andrews, Fife. *Born* 9 November 1944.

MACLEOD, NEIL ALASTAIR, LL.B. [1 December 1969]. Apprentice to Patrick Watson Turcan and Others of Dundas & Wilson.—Son of Angus MacLeod, Procurator Fiscal of Midlothian (retired). *Born* 28 April 1942. *Married* 16 October 1971, Bethia Walker, daughter of Alexander Laurie Alison. *Firm*—Dundas & Wilson.

MACLEOD, RODERICK, OF SUNBANK [7 March 1732]. Apprentice to (1) Ronald Campbell; and (2) John Buchanan.—Second son of William Macleod of Luskinder, Inverness-shire. *Married* (1) July 1736, Isabel, only daughter of Hector Bannatyne of Kames, Buteshire; and (2) Marjory (*died* 14 March 1772), daughter of John Taylor, Writer in Edinburgh. Father of Sir William Macleod Bannatyne (Lord Bannatyne), one of the Senators of the College of Justice. *Died* 26 June 1784.

MCLEOD, RODERICK [18 December 1939]. Apprentice to George Alexander Roger of McLeod & Rose.—Son of Alexander Mathers McLeod, S.S.C., Edinburgh. *Born* 9 July 1913. Captain, Royal Indian Army Service Corps. Served in India and Burma 1940-47. Latterly Major, Legal Staff, Burma Command Headquarters, Rangoon. Currently practising in Victoria, Australia.

MCLETCHIE, DAVID WILLIAM, LL.B. [11 December 1979*].—Son of James Watson McLetchie, Salesman, Edinburgh. *Born* 6 August 1952. *Married* 26 November 1977, Barbara Gemmell, daughter of Daniel Baillie, Farmer, by Dunfermline. Conservative Candidate, Central Edinburgh Constituency, General Election 1979. *Firm*—Tods, Murray & Jamieson.

MACLULLICH, DUNCAN [14 December 1925]. Apprentice to George F. Bryce.—Son of John Campbell Maclullich, Procurator-Fiscal of Argyllshire at Inveraray. *Born* 22 June 1883. Served with Royal Scots and A. and S. Highlanders in France. Promoted Lieutenant. Wounded, 1918. *Died* 10 January 1939. *Firm*—J. A. Campbell and Lamond.

M'MILLAN, ALEXANDER, OF DUNMORE [13 October 1726]. Apprentice to John Cuningham of Bandalloch.—Eldest son of Duncan M'Millan of Dunmore, Knapdale. *Married* (1) Margaret (*died* 5 January 1748), daughter of John Campbell, Lord Provost of Edinburgh; and (2) Jane Campbell (*died* 8 November 1785). Deputy Keeper of the Signet, 1726-42 and 1746-70. He was appointed D.K.S. before he joined the Society. *Died* 22 July 1770.

MACMILLAN, ALEXANDER [19 June 1834]. Apprentice to Thomas Peat.—Son of Alexander Macmillan, Merchant in Campbeltown. *Born* 28 June 1808. *Married* 5 July 1841, Basil Hamilton, second daughter of Captain Henry Dundas Beatson of H.M. Revenue Cruiser *Swift*. *Died* 30 June 1865.

MACMILLAN, ROBERT [6 March 1810]. Apprentice to John Syme.—Son of William Macmillan, Writer in Newton-Douglas. *Born* 1779. *Died* 19 May 1831, unmarried.

MACMILLAN, THOMAS, OF SHORTHOPE [17 November 1815]. Apprentice to David Wemyss.—Son of Thomas Macmillan of Shorthope, Selkirkshire. *Born* 22 April 1792. *Died* 10 June 1838, unmarried.

MACNAB, JOHN, OF NEWTON [4 July 1783]. Apprentice to John Davidson.—Eldest son of Archibald Macnab of Newton of Balquhidder. *Died* 4 August 1801.

MCNAIR, ALASTAIR JAFFREY, LL.B. [11 December 1978]. Apprentice to William James Gay and Another of Hagart & Burn-Murdoch.—Son of Thomas Jaffrey McNair, Consultant Surgeon, Edinburgh. *Born* 12 January 1954.

MCNALLY, TERENCE STEPHEN JAMES, LL.B., [8 December 1981*].—Son of Peter McNally, Headmaster, Glasgow. *Born* 13 August 1943. *Married* 13 October 1971, Diane Helen Bishop. *Firms*—(1) P. & J. Stormonth Darling, Kelso; (2) Turnbull, Simson & Sturrock, Jedburgh; (3) J. D. Clark & Allan, Duns.

MACNAUGHTAN, NEIL MURRAY, B.L. [23 April 1956]. Apprentice to Ralph Colley Smith and Others of Fraser, Stodart & Ballingall.—Son of John Monteath Cairns Macnaughtan. *Born* 18 April 1932. *Married* 21 August 1965, Faith, daughter of Edward Donaldson Jackson, Solicitor. *Firms*—(1) Maxwell Ferguson & Co.; (2) Courtney & Co.; (3) Baillie & Gifford (now Biggart, Baillie & Gifford).

MACNAUGHTON, DUNCAN, LL.B., F.R.S.E. [14 July 1919]. Apprentice to Sir Thomas Hunter.—Son of Peter Macnaughton, S.S.C., Edinburgh. *Born* 2 March 1892. Served in Belgium; 2nd Lieutenant, 1st Gordon Highlanders; Wounded 1915. Author of "*A Scheme of Babylonian Chronology*" and "*A Scheme of Egyptian Chronology*". *Died* 1 October 1973. *Firm*—J. S. & J. W. Fraser-Tytler.

MCNEIL, DAVID JOHN, M.A., LL.B. [30 November 1964]. Apprentice to Hon. William Douglas Watson and Others of Fraser, Stodart & Ballingall. *Born* 24 March 1937. *Married* 21 July 1962, Georgina Avril Sargent. *Firm*—(1) Fraser, Stodart & Ballingall; (2) Morton, Fraser & Milligan (after amalgamation).

MACNEIL, EWEN CAMERON [3 July 1828]. Apprentice to John and Alexander Smith.— Youngest son of Roderick Macneil of Barra, Inverness-shire. *Died* in Trinidad, 1847, aged 42, unmarried.

MACNEIL, HECTOR ARCHIBALD [25 November 1830]. Apprentice to Thomas Cranston.—Son of Captain Archibald Macneil of the 75 Regiment and 3rd Royal Veteran Battalion. *Married* 5 July 1842, Louisa (*died* 22 May 1899), daughter of James Sinclair of Forss, Caithness. *Died* 11 April 1875.

M'NEIL, THOMAS MENZIES, O.B.E., T.D. [19 December 1927]. Apprentice to John S. Pitman, Robert O. Pitman, and Patrick C. Smythe.—Son of Allan M'Neil, S.S.C., Edinburgh. *Born* 20 May 1902. *Married* 30 June 1947, Helen Shannon Ross. Group Captain, R.A.F. Served U.K., Gibraltar and North Africa 1939-45. Mentioned in Despatches 1940. Bailie of Abbey Court, Holyrood. Author of *Wills and Succession* (Popular Law Series), and other legal works. *Died* 5 October 1956. *Firm*—Allan M'Neil and Son.

M'NEILL, ARCHIBALD [18 June 1829]. Apprentice to (1) Robert Sym; and (2) John Maclaurin.—Fifth son of John M'Neill of Colonsay, Argyllshire. *Born* September 1803. *Married* 18 July 1836, Christina Erskine (*died* 3 August 1886), daughter of Major William Mitchell of the Royal Bengal Artillery. Director in Chancery, 1843-58. Principal Clerk of Session, 6 July 1858 till death. Author of *Notes on the Authenticity of the Poems of Ossian. Died* 2 June 1870.

MACNEILLIE, DAVID [4 July 1809]. Apprentice to Alexander Blair.—Son of John Macneillie, Marchfield, Castle-Douglas. *Born* 15 July 1779. *Married* 24 May 1819, Mary, daughter of John Falconer, Mains of Dalrulzian, Perthshire. *Died* 11 April 1850.

MACONOCHIE, ROBERT BLAIR, OF GATTONSIDE [23 November 1837]. Apprentice to Alexander Monypenny.—Second son of Alexander Maconochie of Meadowbank, Mid-Lothian, one of the Senators of the College of Justice (Lord Meadowbank). *Born* 21 May 1814. *Married* 6 January 1846, Charlotte Joanna (*died* 23 June 1901), daughter of John Tod of Kirkhill, Mid-Lothian. *Died* 4 October 1883.

MACPHAIL, GEORGE WASHINGTON [14 January 1895]. Apprentice to D. Beith, P. Murray, and R. D. Beith.—Third son of the Rev. James Calder Macphail, D.D., Pilrig Free Church, Edinburgh. *Born* 25 August 1865. *Married* 6 December 1911, Lilian Alina (*died* 18 July 1919), only daughter of Colonel C. W. St John, 94th Regiment, widow of Æneas J. G. Mackay, K.C. *Died* 12 July 1924.

MACPHAIL, PETER JOHN STEWART [22 March 1915]. Apprentice to A. R. C. Pitman and R. O. Pitman.—Son of Peter Macphail, 7 Craigmillar Park, Edinburgh. *Born* 10 August 1888. Lieutenant R.G.A.: wounded. *Died* at the Military Hospital, Winchester, 26 November 1918, unmarried.

MACPHEE, DUNCAN, LL.B. [13 May 1980*].—Son of Angus Macphee; Building Contractor, Fort William, Inverness-shire. *Born* 15 December 1951. *Firm*—Macarthur, Stewart & Orr, Fort William.

MACPHERSON, ALEXANDER FRASER [24 March 1930]. Apprentice to William H. Fraser, William Galbraith, and Ralph C. Smith.—Son of Thomas John Macpherson, 168 Braid Road, Edinburgh. *Born* 22 June 1896. *Married* 18 September 1930, Minnie Telfer Fraser, only daughter of Wm. Fraser, Solicitor, Tranent. Served with Royal Scots: wounded, 1917. 2nd Lieutenant H.L.I. *Died* 14 December 1968. *Firm*—Fraser, Stodart, and Ballingall.

MACPHERSON, DAVID CAMPBELL, M.A., LL.B. [28 November 1966]. Apprentice to David Swan Wallace of Wallace & Guthrie.—Son of Hugh Ross Macpherson, Headmaster, Edinburgh. *Born* 16 February 1931. *Married* 2 October 1962, Florence Lillian, daughter of Alexander Montgomery. *Firm*—(1) Wallace & Guthrie: (2) Skene, Edwards & Garson (after amalgamation—1979).

M'PHERSON, JOHN [26 January 1671]. Apprentice to James Cuningham.—Son of Dougall M'Pherson of Powrie. *Married* 8 October 1671, Mary Bruce. *Died* November 1675.

MACPHERSON, JOHN MORTON [18 October 1876]. Apprentice to Thomas Jarron Gordon.—Son of Andrew Macpherson, Feuar at Newmilns, Ayrshire. *Born* 26 May 1845. *Married* 27 December 1878, Louisa (*died* 10 March 1930), youngest daughter of Joseph Davies, Kensington, London. *Died* 11 March 1894.

MCPHERSON, MALCOLM HENRY, B.L. [12 May 1981]. Apprentice to Michael Lorimer of Henderson & Jackson.—Son of Douglas McPherson, Company Director, Edinburgh. *Born* 22 May 1954. *Married* 8 July 1977, Fiona Sutherland, daughter of William Hogg. *Firm*—Henderson & Jackson.

MACPHERSON, MICHAEL CROUMBIE, LL.B. [12 December 1977]. Apprentice to Patrick Arthur McLean and Others of Robson, McLean & Paterson.—Son of Norman Croumbie Macpherson, W.S., Edinburgh. *Born* 25 March 1948.

MACPHERSON, NORMAN CROUMBIE, B.A.(CANTAB). [24 April 1961]. (By Rule IX(a).)—Son of Sir Norman Macgregor Macpherson, S.S.C., Edinburgh. *Born* 21 March 1910. *Married* 11 June 1935, Irene Betty, daughter of Ralph Heasman, C.A. Served France 1939-40. Deputy Assistant Director of Claims, Claims Commission with rank of Major. Solicitor in Scotland to the Admiralty (now Admiralty Board, Ministry of Defence). *Firms*—(1) Norman Macpherson & Son; (2) Pitcairn & Mathers; (3) Robson, McLean & Paterson.

MACPHERSON, NORMAN RAMSAY [30 March 1908]. Apprentice to R. Pringle and A. T. Clay.—Son of John M. Macpherson, W.S. *Born* 13 February 1884. *Married* 10 September 1929, Nancy Hendry, L.R.A.M., youngest daughter of David M'Intosh, Glendoick, Glencarse. *Died* 13 January 1948. *Firm*—Small & Macpherson, Montrose.

MACPHERSON, ROBERT NORMAN, M.A., LL.B. [30 November 1964]. Apprentice to Robert Johnson Wightman and Others of Morton Fraser & Milligan.—Son of Norman Croumbie Macpherson, W.S., Edinburgh. *Born* 22 June 1937. *Married* 25 March 1964, Sheila Ann Boyd, daughter of Alexander Cameron, C.B.E., Largs, Ayrshire. *Firms*—(1) Drummond, Johnstone & Grosset, Cupar, Fife; (2) Stewart & Burnett, Dunoon, Argyllshire.

MACPHERSON, WILLIAM [16 February 1781]. Apprentice to Thomas Cockburn.—Son of James Macpherson, Architect at Dean. *Died* 9 May 1814, unmarried. Bacchanal but beneficent. See *Kay's Portraits, LXVI.*

MACQUEEN, HUGH [9 March 1814]. Apprentice to Coll Macdonald.—Second son of Donald Macqueen of Corrybrough, Inverness-shire. *Born* 1791. *Died* 11 March 1836, unmarried.

MCQUEENIE, JAMES PATRICK, LL.B. [30 April 1970]. Apprentice to John Graham Dickson and Another of Shiels & Macintosh.—Son of James Mulhill McQueenie, Sales Manager, Edinburgh. *Born* 17 January 1946. *Married* 15 August 1970, Rosemary (divorced 1977), daughter of Hugh Gibson, Weights and Measures Inspector. *Firms—* (1) Maclachlan & Mackenzie; (2) McQueenie & Co.

MACRAE, ALEXANDER WILLIAM URQUHART [13 December 1909]. Apprentice to William Babington and Joseph Inglis.—Son of Horatio Ross Macrae, W.S. *Born* 18 April 1885. Captain Royal Scots. Took part in actions in many places, being four times wounded and finally *killed* in action, 11 August 1918.

MACRAE, ANDREW MURISON [29 June 1826]. Apprentice to John Morison.—Second son of William Gordon Macrae of Wellbrook, Mid-Lothian. *Born* 17 August 1800. *Married* 25 September 1830, Georgianna Huntly Gordon (*died* 24 May 1890), Gordon Castle, Banff. *Died* at Melbourne, 24 July 1874.

MACRAE, SIR COLIN GEORGE, OF WELLBANK [16 November 1871]. Apprentice to (1) John Anthony Macrae; and (2) John Kennedy.—Second son of John Anthony Macrae, W.S. *Born* 30 November 1844. *Married* 22 June 1877, Flora Maitland (*died* 24 November 1921), daughter of John Colquhoun, Author of *The Moor and Loch.* Knighted, 1900. *Died* at Colinton, 9 December 1925.

MACRAE, DONALD JOHN [7 July 1902]. Apprentice to Sir Colin G. Macrae.—Son of Donald John Macrae, Invershiel, Ross-shire. *Born* 1 October 1871. *Married* 15 June 1916, Alice Emily Louise (*died* 6 August 1950), daughter of William Robson of Grove Hill, Kelso. Depute Keeper of the Minute Book of the Court of Session, 1912. Assistant Extractor of Court of Session, 1927. *Died* 16 September 1936.

MACRAE, HORATIO ROSS, OF CLUNES [15 October 1873]. Apprentice to James Mackenzie, J. B. Innes, and John and C. B. Logan.—Third son of John Anthony Macrae, W.S. *Born* 5 July 1846. *Married* 27 March 1884, Letitia May (*died* 13 March 1921), fourth daughter of Sir William Maxwell of Cardoness, Bart. *Died* 23 July 1931.

MACRAE, JOHN ANTHONY, LL.D., OF WELLBANK [2 July 1835]. Apprentice to John Bowie and William B. Campbell.—Eldest son of Colin Macrae of Inverinate, Ross-shire. *Born* 1 February 1812. *Married* 15 July 1841, Joanna Isabella (*died* 28 January 1890), youngest daughter of John Maclean of Dumfries Estate, Carriacou, Grenada. *Died* 23 May 1868.

MACRAE, KENNETH, T.D., M.A.(OXON), LL.B., [17 December 1934]. Apprentice to Mackenzie Smith Shaw of Thomson, Dickson & Shaw.—Son of Donald Macrae, S.S.C., Edinburgh. *Born* 27 June 1910. *Married* 12 September 1936, Margaret Elizabeth Isobel, daughter of John Norrie, Insurance Inspector, Edinburgh. Major, R.A.; Served U.K. and North West Europe 1939-45. Treasurer of the Society 1964-74. *Firms*—(1) Horne & Lyell; (2) Murray, Beith & Murray (after amalgamation).

MACRAE, ROBERT STEVEN, M.A., LL.B. [25 April 1955]. Apprentice to G. C. Dove-Wilson and Others of Mackenzie & Kermack.—Son of. Alexander MacRae, Sheriff Clerk Depute of Ross and Cromarty, Stornoway. *Born* 17 December 1930. *Married* 31 July 1959, Maureen Margaret, daughter of R. W. Smith, sometime County Assessor of Midlothian. *Firm*—A. & J. C. Allan & Co., Falkirk.

MACRITCHIE, THOMAS ELDER, OF CRAIGTON AND DENORK [4 March 1824]. Apprentice to (1) James Little; and (2) John Murray.—Eldest son of John MacRitchie of Denork, Fife. *Born* 6 June 1800. *Died* 29 December 1878, unmarried.

MACTAGGART, SCIPIO ALEXANDER [19 November 1835]. Apprentice to Walter Dickson and James Steuart.—Son of Daniel Mactaggart, Writer in Campbeltown. *Born* 15 March 1812. *Married* 4 November 1851, Katherine (*died* 5 January 1905), daughter of Colonel Hook, Ceylon Rifles. Sheriff-Clerk of Argyllshire, 1837-86. *Died* 25 June 1886.

MACTAGGART, WILLIAM FLEMING, LL.B. [30 April 1973]. Apprentice to Patrick Arthur McLean and Others of Robson, McLean & Paterson.—Son of Hugh Mactaggart, C.A., Edinburgh. *Born* 27 April 1944. *Married* 29 March 1969, Heather Jane, daughter of Sidney Fawcett Batey, Local Government Officer, Northumberland. *Firm*—Robson, McLean & Paterson.

MACTAVISH, DUGALD, OF DUNARDRY [9 March 1813]. Apprentice to (1) James Ferrier; and (2) John Ferrier.—Eldest son of Lachlan Mactavish of Dunardry. *Born* 1780. *Married* 30 April 1810, Letitia, only daughter of Rev. William Lockhart, D.D., Glasgow. Sheriff-Substitute at Campbeltown, 1823-48. *Died* 20 July 1855.

MACVICAR, NEIL [7 December 1903]. Apprentice to A. D. Mutter-Napier.—Eldest son of Neil Macvicar, Shipowner, Liverpool. *Born* 18 July 1880. *Married* 24 June 1919, Winifred Campbell (*died* 23 April 1968), daughter of the late Ruthven Campbell Todd, C.A., Glasgow. *Died* 7 November 1958. *Firm*—Fyfe, Ireland, and Co.

MCVIE, JOHN, B.L. [21 May 1963]. Apprentice to A. A. Innes Wedderburn of Alex. Morison & Co.—Son of John McVie, O.B.E., Solicitor and Keeper of the Registers of Scotland, Edinburgh. *Born* 7 December 1919. *Married* 14 July 1943, Lindsaye Woodburn Mair. Captain, 7/9 Battalion, The Royal Scots. Signals Officer, North West Europe. *Firms*—(1) Young & Anderson; (2) now Anderson & McVie, Haddington.

MCVITIE, ALASDAIR HUGH, M.A., LL.B. [29 July 1968]. Apprentice to A. J. Ambrose and Others of Macandrew, Wright & Murray.—Son of Richard McVitie, Civil Servant, Edinburgh. *Born* 4 September 1938. *Married* 12 October 1963, Joyce Swallow, daughter of John Richardson. *Firm*—Gillespie Macandrew & Co. (formerly Macandrew, Wright & Murray).

M'VITTIE, CHRISTOPHER RICHARDSON [20 March 1922]. Apprentice to Ebenezer Denholm Young.—Son of David Blacklock M'Vittie, Master Painter, Annan. *Born* 20 July 1881. *Married* 11 April 1911, Isabella M'Intosh (*died* 13 August 1972), daughter of John Turner, Coal Merchant, Davidson's Mains. Served during Great War with 4th and 12th Batts. The Royal Scots, in Gallipoli and France. Chairman of Courts of Referees for Edinburgh and Leith Districts under Unemployment Insurance Acts, 1930. *Died* 28 October 1959. *Firm*—Denholm Young and M'Vittie, and later L. & J. Mclaren.

MCVITTIE, JOHN CHRISTOPHER, M.A., LL.B. [15 July 1949]. Apprentice to Charles Edward Stewart and Others of Murray, Beith & Murray.—Son of Charles Richardson McVittie, W.S., Edinburgh. *Born* 14 December 1918. *Married* 28 January 1950, Margaret Jeffrey McKinnon, daughter of David Jeffrey Aitken, Solicitor. Captain, Royal Artillery 1939-45. *Firm*—L. & J. McLaren (now Haldanes, McLaren & Scott).

MCWHIRTER, ROY, M.A., LL.B. [8 May 1967]. Apprentice to William Robertson Milne and Others of Tait & Crichton.—Son of Robert McWhirter, Headmaster, Edinburgh. *Born* 6 January 1929. *Married* 27 March 1965, Helen McLean, daughter of Alexander McLean Lowe. *Firm*—Warden, Bruce & Co.

MABEN, THOMAS [Before 1537].

MADILL, WILLIAM MILLAR, B.L. [24 November 1958]. Apprentice to Andrew J. Smail of Cairns, McIntosh & Morton.—Son of Dr J. H. Madill, Physician Superintendent. *Born* 5 February 1933. *Married* 7 July 1960, Kate Robertson, daughter of John Macintosh. *Resigned* 28 August 1981. *Firms*—(1) Allan Dawson, Simpson & Hampton; (2) Macrae, Flett & Rennie.

MAIN, FREDERICK JAMES LILLEY, B.L. [23 November 1953]. Apprentice to John James Bonar, Hunter & Johnstone.—Son of James Frederick Main, Civil Engineer, Galashiels. *Born* 7 March 1927. *Married* 5 April 1952, Rosemary Anne, daughter of Major H. F. C. Govan. Sergeant, Black Watch and Royal Military Police 1945-48. *Firm*—Bonar, Hunter & Johnstone, then Bonar Mackenzie & Kermack, now Bonar Mackenzie. (Retired from practice.)

MAIR, GEORGE LEONARD ROBERTSON, B.A., LL.B. [28 May 1979]. Apprentice to H. A. Nicolson and Another of Morton, Fraser & Milligan.—Son of George Brown Mair, Surgeon and Author, Old Polmont. *Born* 5 September 1949. *Married* 6 August 1971, Joyce Isabel, daughter of Archibald Hawkins, Engineer, South Queensferry. *Firm*—Morton, Fraser & Milligan.

MAITLAND, AUGUSTUS [16 December 1824]. Apprentice to Sir James Gibson-Craig.—Third son of Sir Alexander Charles Gibson Maitland of Clifton Hall, Bart., Mid-Lothian. *Born* 27 March 1800. *Married* 1 June 1843, Elizabeth Jane (*died* 9 January 1891), daughter of Rev. William Page Richards. D.D. *Died* 26 January 1855.

MAITLAND, EDWARD FRANCIS, B.A.(OxoN) [28 March 1904]. Apprentice to A. Howe, W. MacGillivray, A. Yeaman, J. Brookman, and W. A. MacGillivray.—Son of Edward Francis Maitland, Linen Manufacturer, of Hazel Hall, Dundee. *Born* 31 March 1877. *Died* 5 June 1964.

MAITLAND, GEORGE RAMSAY [18 July 1849]. Apprentice to Augustus Maitland.—Second son of Alexander Gibson Maitland, younger of Clifton Hall, Advocate. *Born* 19 January 1821. *Married* 19 September 1848, Alice Ann (*died* 27 October 1869), eldest daughter of Josiah Nisbet of the East India Company's Service. *Died* 24 June 1866.

MAITLAND, KEITH RAMSAY [20 October 1890]. Apprentice to Sir Thomas Dawson Brodie.—Only son of Colonel Keith Ramsay Maitland, 79th Highlanders. *Born* 13 October 1865. *Died* at Belhaven, Dunbar, 27 July 1929, unmarried. *Firm*—John C. Brodie and Sons.

MALCOLM, EDWARD ELLICE [26 March 1901]. Apprentice to Robert Schaw Miller.—Son of George Malcolm, Estate Factor, Invergarry. *Born* 25 September 1875. *Married* 25 September 1906, Evelyn Nellie (*died* 14 September 1974), daughter of Alfred George Kirkup, Manufacturer, Duffield, Derbyshire. Commission in Volunteers, Home Defence, during Great War. *Died* 31 January 1939.

MALCOLM, WILLIAM FRASER, B.A., LL.B. [2 December 1974]. Apprentice to Patrick James Oliphant and Others of Pearson, Robertson & Maconochie.—Son of William Fraser Malcolm, Schoolmaster, Edinburgh. *Born* 14 November 1948. *Married* 19 September 1975, Shona Ruth Malcolm, daughter of Edward Alexander Meldrum. *Firm*—Pearson, Robertson & Maconochie.

MALCOLM-SMITH, JOHN GEORGE, M.A., LL.B. [30 November 1959]. Apprentice to Robert McCosh and Others of Gillespie & Paterson.—Son of Dr George Louis Malcolm-Smith, Physician, Edinburgh. *Born* 13 October 1931. *Married* 30 September 1961, Ruth Mary, daughter of Frederick William Derry, Solicitor, Iron Bridge, Shropshire. *Firm*—Boyd, Jameson & Young.

MALLACE, ALEXANDER BALFOUR, B.L. [19 December 1949]. Apprentice to James Harold Macdonald and Others of Morton, Smart, Macdonald & Prosser.—Son of Alexander Cross Mallace, Medical Practitioner, North Berwick. *Born* 6 April 1920. *Married* 2 December 1948, Margaret Helen Gilbert, daughter of Thomas George Macfarlane, Preserves Manufacturer, Glasgow. Served in Royal Air Force 1941-46, U.K. and India.

MANFORD, GILBERT CUMMING, M.C. [13 July 1914]. Apprentice to Sir John Prosser, A. G. Muir, John Smart, and J. H. Macdonald.—Only son of Simon Gilbert Manford, Agent, Royal Bank of Scotland, Newington, Edinburgh. *Born* 26 February 1890. *Married* 5 December 1914, Alice Mary (*died* 1 September 1961), daughter of Alex. Langlands, Montrose, and widow of —— Scott. Captain Highland Light Infantry. Served in France and was awarded Military Cross. *Died* at Elgin, 2 September 1929.

MANN, HENRY DARNEY, LL.B., Q.C. [10 July 1911]. Apprentice to Nelson Briggs Constable.—Son of William Mann, Schoolmaster, Kinghorn. *Born* 24 February 1886. *Married* 24 March 1915, Margaret Fairbairn, fifth daughter of Sir James Lawton Wingate, *P*.R.S.A., Edinburgh. Became a Barrister at Calgary, Alberta, Canada. *Died* 27 January 1971.

MANNERS, ALEXANDER [16 November 1819]. Apprentice to, and son of, Thomas Manners W.S.—*Married* 15 May 1820, Barbara (*died* 1861), eldest daughter of Stewart Murray Fullerton of that Ilk. *Died* 1856, aged 61.

MANNERS, THOMAS [14 July 1789]. Apprentice to John Tait.—Son of Alexander Manners, Merchant in Edinburgh. *Married* 18 August 1791, Juliana (*died* 14 June 1823), daughter of Archibald Hope, Collector of Excise. Depute Clerk of Session, 29 November 1814 till death. *Died* 8 September 1826.

MANSON, ANDREW [27 September 1630]. Apprentice to Robert Lauder.

MANSON, JAMES WILSON [26 March 1900]. Apprentice to John Ross.—Son of James Likley Manson, Agent, North of Scotland Bank Ltd., Old Meldrum, Aberdeenshire. *Born* 14 November 1874. *Married* 11 February 1911, Agnes (*died* 28 September 1960), elder daughter of Duncan Bell-Irving, M.D., Vancouver, B.C. Settled in Vancouver, B.C. *Died* 30 March 1960.

MANSON, THOMAS [17 March 1797]. Apprentice to David Campbell.—Son of John Manson, Merchant, Tain. *Married* —— (*died* in 1831). *Died* 21 July 1815.

MANSON, WILLIAM GEORGE, LL.B. [14 January 1895]. Apprentice to D. Beith and P. Murray.—Son of George Manson, Secretary to the Port Trust of Bombay. *Born* 8 January 1873. *Married* 11 September 1900, Jane Campbell (*died* 2 April 1922), daughter of David Murison, Grain Merchant, Dundee. *Died* 5 March 1944. *Firm*—W. G. Manson and Co.

MANUEL, TERTIUS PETER [7 December 1903]. Apprentice to James Burness.—Son of William Manuel, S.S.C. *Born* 5 March 1880. *Married* 2 April 1927, Mary Faulds (*died* 7 April 1966), youngest daughter of David Douglas Martin, one of the Bailies of the City of Edinburgh. Served abroad, 1915-17; Lieutenant Royal Scots. *Died* 17 August 1957. *Firm*—Manuel, Menzies, and Paton, latterly W. & T. P. Manuel.

MARJORIBANKS, ANDREW, OF THAT ILK [10 December 1702]. Apprentice to James Hay of Carriber.—Eldest son of Thomas Marjoribanks of that Ilk. *Married* 2 April 1700, Christian, daughter of James Hay of Carriber, Linlithgowshire, W.S., Commissary of Edinburgh. *Died* 13 April 1742.

MARJORIBANKS, ANDREW, OF THAT ILK [20 March 1739]. Apprentice to Archibald Campbell.—Eldest son of Andrew Marjoribanks of that Ilk, W.S. *Married* (1) 1 April 1744, Mary, daughter of Alexander Chalmers, Merchant, Edinburgh; and (2) February 1755, Jean, daughter of Thomas Boyes, Depute Clerk of Session. King's Writer in Ordinary, 1741. *Died* 20 February 1766.

MARQUIS, EDWARD GRAHAM, M.A., LL.B.(CANTAB) [23 July 1951]. Apprentice to J. D. H. Dickson and Others of Tods, Murray & Jamieson.—Son of Edward Marquis, Cotton Merchant, Birkenhead. *Born* 29 July 1915. *Married* 29 December 1951, Anne Guthrie, daughter of William Wilfrid Leete, Merchant, Liverpool. *Firm*—J. & F. Anderson.

MARSHALL, ARCHIBALD [2 June 1663]. Apprentice to Hugh Paterson.—*Married* 7 February 1665, Barbara, daughter of Gavin Hamilton of Raploch, and widow of John Kilpatrick of Gilgersland.

MARSHALL, DAVID [23 March 1914]. Apprentice (1) to Ralph Dundas and W. J. Dundas; and (2) to Sir George M. Paul, Robert W. Dundas, and R. N. Dundas.—Son of Robert Marshall, Cashier, Forfar. *Born* 15 August 1869. *Married* 3 August 1897, Marion Mitchell (*died* 13 January 1955), daughter of John Irons, Stationmaster, Forfar. *Died* 13 October 1945. *Firm*—Dundas and Wilson.

MARSHALL, JAMES [29 June 1759]. Apprentice to David Spens.—Eldest son of John Marshall, Writer in Strathaven, Lanarkshire. *Born* 1731. *Married* April 1761, Janet (*died* 27 January 1788), daughter of David Spens, W.S. Fiscal, 1796-1807. See *Kay's Portraits*, CXI. *Died* at Greenside House, 23 May 1807.

MARSHALL, JOHN [7 July 1680]. Apprentice to Andrew Aikman.—*Married* Marion Neilson.

MARSHALL, JOHN HANNAH, B.A.(OXON), LL.B. [31 March 1958]. Apprentice to T. J. Carlyle Gifford and Others of Baillie & Gifford.—Son of Robert Ian Marshall, C.A., Edinburgh. *Born* 16 August 1931. *Married* 6 December 1966, Elspeth Young, daughter of David Young Douglas, Banker. *Firm*—Dundas & Wilson.

MARSHALL, LAWRENCE DOUGAL, B.L. [26 November 1962]. Apprentice to Andrew White Young and Others of J. & R. A. Robertson.—Son of John Spiers Marshall, retired Rubber Planter, Helensburgh. *Born* 16 February 1935. *Married* 9 June 1969, Morag Lilian, daughter of Air Vice Marshal Andrew MacGregor, C.B., C.B.E., D.F.C., Crieff. *Firm*—W. & J. Cook.

MARSHALL, ROBERT [6 December 1799]. Apprentice to James Walker.—Eldest son of Robert Marshall, Merchant in Glasgow. *Married* 29 October 1819, Jane Cochran (*died* 30 January 1835), "late wife" of Captain Shirley. *Died* at Fernie Hill, 27 September 1823, aged 53.

MARSHALL, ROBERT DOWLING CALDER [17 March 1890]. Apprentice to Colin G. Macrae.—Son of John Dalrymple Marshall, Edinburgh. *Born* 25 August 1866. *Married* 7 June 1893, Harriet (*died* 15 April 1918), youngest daughter of William Gidden, Edinburgh. *Died* 22 May 1916. *Firm*—Calder Marshall and Walker.

MARSHALL, ROBERT WADDELL [11 October 1922]. Apprentice to John Little Mounsey and Others of John C. Brodie & Sons.—Son of John Marshall, Solicitor, Bo'ness. *Born* 12 March 1897. *Married* 15 April 1931, Jessie Victoria Hastie (*died* 17 June 1964), daughter of John Menzies, Coalmaster, Edinburgh. Served in France, First World War; 2nd Lieutenant, Rifle Brigade; Major, Indian Army Ordnance Corps 1939-1945. *Died* 12 June 1979. *Firm*—W. & J. Cook (formerly H. & H. Tod prior to amalgamation). (Retired.)

MARSHALL, STEWART YOUNG, M.A., LL.B. [3 December 1965]. Apprentice to Charles Law Forbes and Others of Aitken, Kinnear & Co.—Son of William Marshall, Bank Manager, Dalkeith. *Born* 25 October 1935. *Married* 15 October 1960, Elsie, daughter of Thomas Moore, Marine Engineer. *Firm*—Aitken, Kinnear & Co.

MARSHALL, WILLIAM, OF CALLANDER [1 July 1830]. Apprentice to Robert Macmillan.—Son of William Marshall, Merchant in Edinburgh, and Agnes, sister and co-heiress of George Hunter of Callander. *Born* 4 April 1806. *Married* 29 July 1845, Isabella (*died* 24 February 1913), eldest daughter of Hugh Auld, Cashier of the Commercial Bank of Scotland. *Died* 18 November 1851.

MARSHALL, WILLIAM HUNTER, OF CALLANDER [15 July 1874]. Apprentice to Patrick Blair.—Only son of William Marshall of Callander, Perthshire, W.S. *Born* 6 June 1846. *Died* 3 November 1926, unmarried.

MARSHALL, THOMAS ROGER [5 October 1873]. Apprentice to Alexander Hamilton and George T. Kinnear.—Third son of John Marshall, M.D. *Born* 26 June 1849. *Married* 3 June 1890, Agnes Stewart (*died* 24 May 1945), third daughter of Allan Gilmour of Eaglesham. *Died* 27 June 1913.

MARTIN, FRANCIS JOHN [19 April 1876]. Apprentice to, and son of, John Martin, W.S.—*Born* 19 March 1853. *Married* 14 April 1886, Jessie Agnes Helen (*died* 14 August 1946), eldest daughter of Robert Barclay, Glasgow. *Died* 28 March 1911.

MARTIN, JOHN [6 March 1834]. Apprentice to Charles James Fox Orr.—Son of Francis Martin of Davieland, Dean of the Faculty of Procurators in Paisley. *Born* 23 July 1811. *Married* 22 October 1850, Mary (*died* 25 May 1887), eldest daughter of Charles James Fox Orr of Thornly Park, Renfrewshire, W.S. Principal Clerk of Session, 1880. *Died* 26 March 1893.

MARTIN, ROBERT MONCRIEFF, M.A., LL.B. [26 November 1962]. Apprentice to David Blyth Bogle and Others of Lindsay, Howe & Co.—Son of Robert Watson Martin, W.S., Edinburgh. *Born* 12 March 1936. *Married* 4 January 1967, Margery, daughter of Thomas Colledge Halliburton, Tea Company Director. Secretary and Treasurer of Cockburn Association 1963-71 and Treasurer 1971 to date. *Firms*—(1) Simpson, Kinmont & Maxwell; (2) Lindsays.

MARTIN, ROBERT WATSON [23 July 1923]. Apprentice to Alexander Yeaman and Others of Lindsay, Howe & Co.—Son of Frederick William Martin, C.A., Edinburgh. *Born* 5 March 1899. *Married* 20 November 1930, Kathleen Moncrieff, daughter of Alexander Patrick Melville, W.S., Edinburgh. 2nd Lieutenant, Black Watch, 1918-19. Served U.K. *Firms*—(1) Simpson, Kinmont & Maxwell (formerly R. R. Simpson & Lawson, and Kinmont & Maxwell, also formerly T. & W. Liddle & Martin). Currently Consultant with Lindsays.

MARTIN, SAMUEL [13 July 1891]. Apprentice to C. C. Nisbet.—Son of William Martin of Dardarroch, Dumfriesshire. *Born* 4 August 1867. *Died* 3 August 1926.

MARTIN, WILLIAM ALEXANDER [21 May 1806]. Apprentice to Archibald Swinton.— Eldest son of Peter Martin, Cabinetmaker in Edinburgh. *Born* 1780. *Married* 3 October 1806, Margaret (*died* 27 February 1825), youngest daughter of John Davie of Gavieside. *Died* 26 September 1828.

MARWICK, CHARLES, T.D., B.L. [21 July 1970]. Apprentice to Ian Coshieville Menzies and Another of Menzies & White.—Son of John Craigie Marwick, Civil Servant, Edinburgh. *Born* 29 March 1923. *Married* 2 August 1949, Mary Thomson Aytoun, daughter of James Whitehead, Newtongrange. Captain, Royal Scots; Served Persia, Iraq and Middle East 1943-46; British Military Government, Eritrea 1946. *Firm*— Menzies & White (now Menzies, Dougal & Milligan).

MARWICK, DAVID WILLIAM, LL.B. [13 July 1885]. Apprentice to Peter Gardner.— Son of Sir James David Marwick, LL.D., Town Clerk of Glasgow. *Born* 4 July 1860. *Married* 3 October 1895, Louise Kenmure Maitland (*died* 3 June 1919), younger daughter of William Arthur Peterkin, General Superintendent, Local Government Board. Food Officer for City of Edinburgh during Great War. *Died* 19 March 1942. *Firm*—Simpson and Marwick.

MASON, CHARLES GROSVENOR, B.A.(Oxon), LL.B. [19 December 1932]. Apprentice to Sir John Prosser and Others of Morton, Smart Macdonald & Prosser.—Son of George Harold Mason, Shipping Merchant, Edinburgh. *Born* 28 July 1906. *Married* 14 December 1946, Margaret Grace, daughter of Charles Henry Luke, Chevalier of The Legion of Honour. Captain, Royal Scots; Seconded to West African Frontier Force (Gold Coast Regiment). Major, Judge Advocate General's Dept.

MASON, GEORGE STEWART, B.A.(Oxon), LL.B. [18 March 1935]. Apprentice to Robert Francis Shepherd and Others of Shepherd & Wedderburn.—Son of George Harold Mason, Shipping Merchant, Edinburgh. *Born* 14 June 1908. Worked for the Canadian Government in Ottawa—1939-44.

MASSON, ALAN JOHN, B.A., LL.B. [12 May 1981*].—Son of James Brown Masson, Edinburgh. *Born* 11 January 1952. *Firm*—Bell & Scott, Bruce & Kerr.

MASSON, HAMISH, O.B.E., M.A., LL.B. [15 December 1930]. Apprentice to Adam West Gifford and Others of Mackenzie & Black.—Son of Lt. Colonel James Masson, Surgeon, Indian Medical Service. *Born* 3 June 1906. *Married* (1) 28 July 1934, Mary Hilda Hamilton (*died* 15 October 1965), daughter of James Simpson, Company Director, Edinburgh; (2) 18 May 1967, Betty Denholm Pretsell or Walls, daughter of James Pretsell, Farmer. Flight Lieutenant, R.A.F., Balloon Command and attached to Army and R.A.F. Legal Aid Section, Scottish Command. 1941-44. Deputy Secretary, Law Society of Scotland 1949-71. *Died* 4 August 1980. *Firm*—Murray, Lawson & Macdonald (1932-44).

MASTERTON, CHARLES, OF PARKMILL AND GOGAR [February 1709]. Apprentice to Charles Row.—Eldest son of Francis Masterton of Parkmill, Clackmannanshire. *Born* 1 August 1682. *Married* 11 August 1713, his cousin Mary, daughter of John Kiery of Gogar, Perthshire. Substitute Keeper, 1708-9 and 1713-14. *Died* April 1744.

MATHERS, GEORGE FLEMING, LL.B. [15 January 1894]. Apprentice to James Hope of Belmont.—Son of Samuel Renny Mathers, Flaxspinner, Dundee. *Born* 16 January 1861. *Died* 20 August 1941. *Firm*—Pitcairn and Mathers.

MATHESON, ALEXANDER [14 July 1879]. Apprentice to James Barker Duncan.—Third surviving son of Alexander Matheson, Merchant in Edinburgh. *Born* 15 March 1855. *Married* 15 April 1896, Mrs Ada Emily Fraser or Norman (*died* 13 September 1941). *Died* at London, 11 August 1928.

MATHISON, ARCHIBALD DOUGLAS EDWARD [29 March 1905]. Apprentice to John Prosser and A. G. Muir.—Son of Archibald Mathison of 5 Carpenter Road, Edgbaston, Birmingham. *Born* 22 July 1881. *Died* 26 October 1926, unmarried.

MATTHEW, GORDON FINDLAY, LL.B. [6 December 1976]. Apprentice to Patrick James Oliphant and Others of Pearson, Robertson & Maconochie.—Son of Thomas Findlay Matthew, Farmer, Glencarse, Perthshire. *Born* 26 May 1952.

MATTHEWS, OLIVER HARWOOD [21 March 1932]. Apprentice to Ninian J. Finlay and Charles F. M. Maclachlan.—Son of Charles Edwin Matthews, M.D., M.R.C.S., of Tiverton, Devon. *Born* 13 May 1896. *Married* 29 August 1921, Ida Elizabeth Charlotte, daughter of Ninian J. Finlay, W.S. Served in Royal Navy, 1913-21. Temporary Secretary, Diplomatic Service, 1922-24. Paymaster-Commander, Royal Navy, Great Britain 1939-44. *Died* 21 September 1971. *Firm*—Bell, Bannerman, and Finlay, and later Dudgeon, Farmer, and Matthews.

MATTHEWS, PETER ALEXANDER HOPE, LL.B. [24 April 1978]. Apprentice to (1) David Cairns Fulton and Others of Tods, Murray & Jamieson, and (2) Ivor Reginald Guild and Another of Shepherd & Wedderburn.—Son of Baird Matthews, Solicitor, Newton Stewart. *Born* 30 December 1954. *Married* 10 January 1979, Mary Josephine Weatherill. *Firm*—A. B. & A. Matthews, Newton Stewart.

MAULE, DAVID [27 September 1714].—Sixth son of John Maule, son of George Maule of Cairncorthie. Subsitute Keeper and Clerk, 1713-14. *Died* 20 January 1744.

MAULE, HARRY [4 April 1707]. Apprentice to Robert Innes.—Third son of John Maule, son of George Maule of Cairncorthie. *Married* September 1705, Margaret, daughter of Major John Neilson. Lyon Clerk, 1709. Deputy Keeper of the Signet, 1713-14. *Died* 4 December 1734.

MAULE, JAMES [10 March 1789]. Apprentice to William Leslie.—Son of John Maule, Writer in Stonehaven. *Died* 11 April 1806.

MAWER, WALTER, OF MAWERSTON [Before 1586].—Son of William Mawer. *Married* Margaret Waus. Commissioner, 16 December 1594. *Died* 18 August 1605.

MAXWELL, DAVID, LL.B. [12 December 1898]. Apprentice to James Reid.—Son of David Maxwell, Farmer, Panlathy Mill, Carnoustie. *Born* 14 February 1869. *Married* 29 July 1924, Margaret Isabella Eckford (*died* 15 November 1947), daughter of Captain John Annan Simpson, Shipowner, Leith. *Died* 10 March 1943. *Firm*—Maxwell, Gill, and Pringle.

MAXWELL, GEORGE [3 June 1824]. Apprentice to Alexander Hunter.—Son of George Maxwell, Prior's Lynn, Dumfriesshire. *Born* 1797. *Married* 16 April 1857, Jane (*died* 29 August 1909), daughter of Andrew Wishart, Contractor. *Died* 10 December 1879.

MAXWELL, HAMILTON [14 April 1884]. Apprentice to J. R. Maclagan Wedderburn and G. G. Watson.—Younger son of Colonel James Maxwell, C.B., of the 1st West India Regiment. *Born* 6 January 1861. *Married* 28 July 1892, Catherine (*died* 31 May 1946), fourth daughter of D. M. Watson of Bullionfield, Dundee. *Died* 11 September 1932. *Firm*—Kinmont and Maxwell.

MAXWELL, JOHN [24 March 1924]. Apprentice to William Gibson and Others of Tait & Crichton.—Son of James Maxwell, Factor, Auchinleck, by Maybole, Ayrshire. *Born* 17 May 1899. *Married* 19 December 1944, Norah Mary, daughter of John Edward Scott. 2nd Lieutenant, Seaforth Highlanders, France 1918. *Firm*—Tait & Crichton. (Retired.)

MAXWELL, JOHN HERRIES, OF MUNCHES [27 November 1807]. Apprentice to Hugh Corrie.—Eldest son of Wellwood Maxwell of Barncleugh, Kirkcudbrightshire. *Born* 1784. *Married* 7 June 1813, Clementina (*died* 23 May 1858), daughter of William Maxwell, East Blackshaw, Caerlaverock. *Died* 1 March 1843.

MAXWELL, PATRICK [14 September 1631]. Apprentice to Andrew Nimmo. *Married* Marion Farquhar. Sheriff-Clerk of Perthshire.

MEGGET, THOMAS [6 December 1804]. Apprentice to James Buchan.—Son of John Megget, Tanner in Edinburgh. *Married* 4 August 1810, Jane Bell, daughter of Rev. Thomas Murray, Minister of Channelkirk. *Died* 19 February 1864, aged 82.

MEIK, HENRY HUNTER [13 July 1885]. Apprentice to James Hope and John Kirk.—Son of Thomas Meik, Civil Engineer, Edinburgh. *Born* 13 August 1860. *Died* 18 December 1923, unmarried.

MEIK, JOHN, OF FORTISSAT [9 March 1791]. Apprentice to James Horne.—Eldest son of William Meik of Fortissat, Lanarkshire. *Died* 20 January 1845, aged 76, unmarried.

MEIKLEJOHN, IAIN MAURY CAMPBELL, LL.B. [13 May 1980*].—Son of Arnold Peter Meiklejohn, Medical Practitioner, Edinburgh. *Born* 3 November 1954.

MEIKLEJOHN, JOHN [7 June 1821]. Apprentice to Richard Hotchkis and James Tytler.— Only son of William Meiklejohn, Torrie. *Born* 1786. *Married* (1) 18 November 1822, Catherine (*died* 26 September 1823), youngest daughter of Alexander M'Callum, Plewlands; and (2) Marian Hutton (*died* 8 July 1849). Fiscal to Lyon Court, 1837-51. *Died* 29 April 1851.

MEIN, JOHN [19 March 1723]. Apprentice to Patrick Pitcairn.—*Died* 3 January 1729.

MELDRUM, DAVID BAYNE [26 January 1854]. Apprentice to J. M. Melville, J. F. Walker Drummond, and James Lindesay.—Eldest son of Alexander Meldrum of Easter Kincaple, Fife, Advocate. *Born* 7 August 1829. *Died* 8 August 1906, unmarried.

MELDRUM, JAMES [Before 1532].

MELDRUM, WILLIAM [Before 1556].

MELLOR, IAN HAUXWELL [19 December 1938]. Apprentice to Percy Furneaux Dawson of Allan, Dawson, Simpson & Hampton.—Son of Herbert Mellor, S.S.C., Edinburgh. *Born* 1 June 1915. *Married* 6 January 1951, Mary Isabel, daughter of John Dick Nicoll, Company Director, Perth. Major, R.A., Deputy Assistant Judge Advocate General. Served U.K., India, Middle East, Greece and Italy. *Died* 19 February 1978. *Firm*—(1) M. J. Brown, Son & Co; (2) Simpson, Kinmont & Maxwell.

MELROSE, JAMES DOUGLAS LEITCH [13 December 1909]. Apprentice to Campbell Hossack.—Second son of James Melrose, Goshen Bank, Kelso. *Born* 5 October 1884. *Married* 12 August 1916, Jessie Macpherson, (*died* 20 February 1960), daughter of W. P. Jenkinson. Major R.G.A. *Died* of wounds received in action, 29 April 1918.

MELVILLE, ALEXANDER PATRICK [9 July 1894]. Apprentice to R. R. Simpson.—Son of the Rev. Andrew Melville, D.D., Principal Clerk to the General Assembly of the Free Church of Scotland, Edinburgh. *Born* 21 June 1870. *Married* 17 June 1897, Laura Moncrieff (*died* 21 July 1952), eldest daughter of David Lumsden of Fincastle, and Pitcairnfield, Perthshire. *Died* 14 April 1939. *Firm*— R. R. Simpson and Lawson.

MELVILLE, ANDREW, M.A., C.A. [13 July 1931]. Apprentice to Ernest M. Wedderburn and Others of Shepherd & Wedderburn.—Son of Alexander Patrick Melville, W.S., Edinburgh. *Born* 7 August 1901. *Married* 12 February 1935, Muriel Dorothy, daughter of Dr W. R. Martine, Haddington. *Firm*—R. R. Simpson & Lawson (later Simpson, Kinmont & Maxwell). (Retired.)

MELVILLE, ANDREW PATERSON [14 December 1896]. Apprentice to Charles Baxter and William Mitchell.—Son of Francis S. Melville, D.C.S., Edinburgh. *Born* 5 April 1867. *Married* 16 December 1897, Henrietta (*died* 3 April 1933), daughter of John Hutchison, R.S.A. During Great War joined City of Edinburgh Volunteer Batt. The Royal Scots, and was later Lieutenant in R.A.M.C.(V.). *Died* 19 May 1938. *Firm*— Mitchell and Baxter.

MELVILLE, ARCHIBALD [30 May 1844]. Apprentice to John Glassford Hopkirk.—Son of Robert Melville, residing in Falkirk. *Born* 2 September 1804. *Married* 14 May 1875, Margaret (*died* 23 October 1905), daughter of Edward Watson, Farmer, Crawfordjohn. *Died* 21 March 1884.

MELVILLE, DANIEL [Before 1627]. Apprentice to Adam Lawtie.—*Married* 26 December 1615, Beatrix Edmonstone. *Died* June 1651.

MELVILLE, EDWARD CHARLES, M.A., LL.B. [30 April 1973]. Apprentice to (1) Edmund Oliver St John and Another of Lindsays; (2) John Moncreiff Ord Mackenzie and Another of Bonar, Mackenzie & Kermack.—Son of Lt. Colonel C. L. Melville, Dorset. *Born* 15 May 1940. *Married* 22 July 1966, Alison Sinclair, daughter of Thomas Sinclair Fraser. *Firm*—Bonar Mackenzie.

MELVILLE, JAMES MONCRIEFF, OF HANLEY [15 May 1817]. Apprentice to Walter Dickson.—Son of Dr Thomas Moncrieff Melville, Physician in St Andrews. *Born* 28 September 1793. *Married* (1) 19 August 1832, Augusta (*died* 30 March 1837), youngest daughter of Vice-Admiral Lechmere of Steeple-Aston, Oxfordshire; and (2) 18 October 1839, Margaret (*died* 1863), third daughter of Patrick Lindsay of Wormiston, Fife. *Died* 28 September 1872.

MELVILLE, SIR JOHN [6 December 1827]. Apprentice to Alexander Manners.—Only son of George Melville, residing in Newington, Edinburgh. *Born* 1803. *Married* 19 June1838, Jane (*died*1873), daughter of William Marshall, Edinburgh. Lord Provost of Edinburgh, 1854-59. Knighted, 1859. Crown Agent, 1860. *Died* 5 May 1860.

MELVILLE, JOHN INGLIS BALFOUR. *See* BALFOUR-MELVILLE, JOHN INGLIS.

MELVILLE, ROBIN KENNETH CHRISTIAN, LL.B. [11 December 1978]. Apprentice to John Kenneth Finlayson and Another of Bonar, Mackenzie.—Son of Lt. Colonel Christian Landale Melville, D.S.O., Blandford Forum, Dorset. *Born* 28 October 1938. *Married* 24 June 1961, Elizabeth Mary Melville, daughter of Captain Melville Stewart Jameson, Blairgowrie, Perthshire. *Firm*—Bonar, Mackenzie.

MENTEATH, ALEXANDER STEUART [10 July 1834]. Apprentice to John Donaldson.—Son of Sir Charles Granville Steuart Menteath, Bart., of Closeburn, Dumfriesshire. *Born* 10 March 1809. *Married* 5 August 1841, Harriet (*died* 20 April 1891), youngest daughter of Major-General Patrick Agnew of Lochnaw, and Authoress of several poems. *Died* 11 August 1885.

MENZIES, ALAN LOCKHART [13 April 1886]. Apprentice to Ralph and W. J. Dundas, and G. M. Paul.—Eldest son of Sir William John Menzies, W.S. *Born* 2 April 1861. *Married* 10 June 1890, Katherine Helen (*died* 21 July 1927), youngest daughter of Henry Bruce of Ederline, Argyllshire. Agent, Church of Scotland, 1905-25. *Died* 12 November 1926, at Larchgrove, Balerno.

MENZIES, ALAN SCOTT, LL.B. [11 December 1979]. Apprentice to Edward Graham Marquis and Another of J. & F. Anderson.—Son of Alexander Menzies, Doctor of Medicine, Edinburgh. *Born* 31 May 1949. *Firm*—J. & F. Anderson.

MENZIES, ALEXANDER, OF CHESTHILL [25 June 1770]. Apprentice to Robert Menzies.— Eldest son of John Menzies in Culivulin, Rannoch. *Married* 5 November 1772, Eleanor Hamilton (*died* 20 February 1817), daughter of James Menzies of Culdares, Perthshire. Principal Clerk of Session, 10 December 1778 till death. *Died* suddenly, 9 June 1804.

MENZIES, ALLAN [17 December 1829]. Apprentice to Richard Mackenzie and William Sharpe.—Son of Rev. William Menzies, Minister of Lanark. *Born* 28 February 1804. *Married* 2 August 1833, Helen (*died* 21 November 1875), daughter of Alexander Cowan, Moray House, Edinburgh. Professor of Conveyancing in the University of Edinburgh, 1847-56. Author of *Conveyancing according to the Law of Scotland*, 1856, and other legal works. *Died* 13 February 1856.

MENZIES, ARCHIBALD [7 August 1661]. Apprentice to John Semple.—Youngest son of Sir Alexander Menzies of that Ilk. *Died* before 1676.

MENZIES, CHARLES, OF KINMUNDY [15 March 1697]. Apprentice to William Dykes.— *Married* April 1718, Barbara, daughter of Sir John Falconer of Balmakellie. *Died* August 1764.

MENZIES, EDMUND, B.L [27 March 1946]. Apprentice to Percy Furneaux Dawson of Allan, Dawson, Simpson & Hampton. *Born* 17 September 1907. *Married* 14 August 1947, Paule Germaine Marie Therese Michel, France. Squadron Leader R.A.F. (Intelligence Branch). *Firm*—Allan, Dawson, Simpson & Hampton.

MENZIES, GEORGE MACBETH, M.A.(OXON), LL.B. [8 December 1975]. Apprentice to Nigel Campbell Thomson and Others of W. & J. Burness.—Son of George Macbeth Menzies, Steelfounder, Edinburgh. *Born* 18 April 1943. *Married* 2 August 1967, Patricia Mary, daughter of Colin Davis. *Firm*—W. & J. Burness.

MENZIES, IAN COSHIEVILLE, O.B.E. [20 March 1922]. Apprentice to Richard White.—Son of Archibald Menzies, S.S.C., Edinburgh. *Born* 1 October 1882. *Died* 22 July 1949. *Firm*—Menzies and White.

MENZIES, JAMES [4 December 1685]. Apprentice to Andrew Young.—Brother to William Menzies, Merchant, Edinburgh. *Married* 11 August 1685, Christian Scott.

MENZIES, JAMES, OF PITNACREE [11 June 1829]. Apprentice to John Forman.—Eldest son of Archibald Menzies of Pitnacree, Perthshire. *Married* July 1833, Maria Elizabeth (*died* 3 February 1897), eldest daughter of Edward Menzies of Paradise Pen, Kingston, Jamaica. *Died* 3 April 1849, aged 42.

MENZIES, PATRICK DROUGHT NORTH [9 July 1906]. Apprentice to P. W. Campbell and F. J. Martin.—Son of Sir William John Menzies, W.S. *Born* 27 July 1880. *Married* 7 December 1912, Ruth Marjorie (*died* 23 August 1969), youngest daughter of Andrew Thomson, Timber Merchant, Edinburgh. In Great War, after serving in other corps, Lieutenant 5th Royal Scots Fusiliers. *Died* 25 February 1953. *Firm*—Menzies and Thomson.

MENZIES, ROBERT, OF CULTERALLERS [3 August 1742]. Apprentice to James Baillie.— Eldest son of John Menzies, M.D. *Married* December 1749, Margaret, daughter of Rev. John Thomson, Minister of West Liberton. *Died* 28 August 1769.

MENZIES, ROBERT, OF BOLFRACKS [23 November 1795]. Apprentice to John Graeme.— Eldest son of Robert Menzies, Chamberlain to Sir John Menzies of that Ilk. Depute Clerk of Session, 19 January 1802 till death. *Died* 22 January 1838, aged 72, unmarried.

MENZIES, WILLIAM, OF RAW [6 August 1675]. Apprentice to William Chieslie.—Son of Captain William Menzies of Castlehill, Lanarkshire. *Born* 1640. *Married* (1) (contract, 31 August 1664), Jean, second daughter of Rev. Oliver Colt, Minister of Inveresk (1651-1679; (2) 4 November 1706, Anna Mitchell, widow of George Kennedy, Merchant Burgess of Edinburgh. Joint-Fiscal, 1702-3. Chamberlain of Bishopric of Orkney. *Died* 2 September 1721.

MENZIES, SIR WILLIAM JOHN [25 November 1858]. Apprentice to (1) Allan Menzies; and (2) John Dundas and William Wilson.—Eldest son of Allan Menzies, W.S. *Born* 14 October 1834. *Married* (1) 12 July 1859, Helen (*died* 8 February 1867), daughter of Alexander Adie, and widow of James Marshall of Callander; (2) 28 July 1870, Ellen (*died* 2 May 1878), youngest daughter of William Young and widow of William Tweedie; and (3) 14 October 1879, Annie Percival (*died* 18 February 1923), eldest daughter of Captain J. A. Drought, Whigsborough, King's County, and widow of T. S. Jones of the National Bank of India, Bombay. Agent, Church of Scotland. Knighted, 12 May 1903. *Died* 14 October 1905.

MERCER, HUGH SMYTH [25 June 1790]. Apprentice to John Innes.—Son of Alexander Mercer, Merchant in Edinburgh. *Born* 1766. *Married* (1), proclaimed 4 July 1788, Euphemia (*died* 18 March 1789), daughter of Archibald Nisbet of Carphin; (2) 16 January 1792, Magdalene (*died* 31 May 1827), daughter of William Wilson of Blackleymill, Paisley. *Died* 15 October 1803.

MERCER, ROBERT, OF SCOTSBANK [5 July 1821]. Apprentice to William Scott.—Son of James Mercer of Scotsbank, Selkirkshire, Writer in Edinburgh. *Born* 1796. *Married* 27 October 1825, Elizabeth Scott, daughter of William Scott Moncrieff of Fossoway, Perthshire. *Died* 3 November 1875.

MERCER, WILLIAM [21 December 1820]. Apprentice to Robert Ainslie.—Son of Hugh Smyth Mercer, W.S.—*Born* 1793. *Married* 22 October 1821, Catherine (*died* 5 October 1848), eldest daughter of Robert Maxwell, Paisley. *Died* 24 February 1853.

METHUEN, JAMES, B.A.(Oxon) [17 March 1890]. Apprentice to Alexander Paterson Purves.—Eldest son of James Methuen, Merchant, Leith. *Born* 22 May 1862. *Married* 9 April 1891, Daisy Caroline (*died* 5 December 1924), second daughter of Major John Boulton, R.A. *Died* suddenly, 10 April 1933. *Firm*—Aitken, Methuen, and Aikman.

MICKEL, RODERICK GRAHAM, LL.B. [12 December 1977]. Apprentice to Edmund Menzies and Another of Allan, Dawson, Simpson & Hampton.—Son of Robert G. Mickel, Solicitor, Crieff. *Born* 17 October 1951. *Married* 22 October 1977, Pauline Ann, daughter of Walter McAndrew, C.A., Newcastle-upon-Tyne. *Firm*—S. Graham Mickel & Co., Crieff.

MIDDLETON, JONATHAN THOMAS, B.L. [15 July 1929]. Apprentice to William C. Hunter and John J. Bonar.—Son of John Munro Middleton, Solicitor, Inverness. *Born* 30 August 1904. *Married* 1 September 1939, Helen Hewitt (*died* 6 January 1964), daughter of Robert Hutton, Edinburgh. Secretary of the Royal Incorporation of Architects in Scotland 1936-51. *Died* 4 November 1951.

MIDDLETON, WILLIAM GEORGE SELBY [4 December 1967]. (By Rule IX(a).)—Son of Alexander Middleton, Solicitor, Montrose. *Born* 16 March 1913. *Married* (1) Maureen Gunn (marriage dissolved); (2) 18 September 1959, Rosalind, daughter of Hugh Henderson, Headmaster, Lanarkshire. Major in Army (Regiment not known); Served Middle East and North Africa. Wounded at El Alamein—transferred to R.A.S.C. *Died* 13 September 1970. *Firm*—Campbell, Middleton, Burness & Dickson, Montrose.

MILLAR, ANGUS GEORGE, B.A.(Oxon), LL.B. [28 November 1955]. Apprentice to T. J. Carlyle Gifford and Others of Baillie & Gifford.—Son of George William Russell Millar, Rubber Planter, Port Dickson, Malay States. *Born* 1 July 1928. *Married* 25 April 1959, Julia Mary, daughter of Alan Cathcart of Drumgrange, Kirkcudbrightshire.

MILLAR, COLIN DAVIDSON, LL.B. [19 July 1971]. Apprentice to David Charles Scott-Moncrieff and Others of Tods, Murray & Jamieson.—Son of Robert Millar, Edinburgh. *Born* 15 January 1947. *Married* (1) 31 March 1971, Helen Christine, daughter of John Watson Farquhar, C.A., and (2) 16 July 1980, Shelagh Jane Thomson. *Firm*—Nightingale & Bell.

MILLAR, FRANCIS ROBERT, B.L. [19 December 1949]. Apprentice to (1) David Blyth Bogle and Others of Lindsay, Howe & Co.; (2) Peter George Macdonald and Another of W. & J. Burness.—Son of Arthur David Millar, H.M. Inspector of Schools for Perthshire, Crieff. *Born* 1 June 1917. *Married* 12 September 1941, Jean, daughter of Joseph Bullen, Lancashire. Major, Royal Artillery, Second World War. *Firm*—W. & J. Burness (until 1952).

MILLAR, JOHN ALEXANDER STEVENSON, M.V.O. [16 July 1888]. Apprentice to Alexander J. Russell and George Dunlop.—Son of John Millar, Writer, Johnstone, Renfrewshire. *Born* 20 October 1854. *Married* 10 September 1878, Dora (*died* 19 July 1928), second daughter of Thomas Shillinglaw, Chief Clerk, Crown Office, Edinburgh. M.V.O., 1911. Chairman, Church of Scotland General Trustees, 1925, and Joint Agent, Church of Scotland, 1926. Member of Executive Committee British Red Cross. Author of contributions to *Juridical Styles, Green's Encyclopaedia,* and various magazines. *Died* 5 November 1938. *Firm*—Russell and Dunlop.

MILLAR, JOHN SYDNEY LAWRENCE [11 December 1906]. Apprentice to George Dunlop and J. A. S. Millar.—Son of John Alexander Stevenson Millar, W.S. *Born* 28 June 1879. *Married* (1) 14 October 1926, Jean Burtholme (*died* 23 November 1949), younger daughter of Albert E. Taylor, Mus. Doc., Lancaster, and (2) 3 April 1951, Phyllis, elder daughter of said Albert E. Taylor. Captain Lovat Scouts (Gallipoli and Egypt) in Great War. *Died* 12 December 1961. *Firm*—Russell and Dunlop.

MILLAR, PETER CARMICHAEL, O.B.E., M.A., LL.B. [22 November 1954]. Apprentice to Tertius Peter Manuel of W. & T. P. Manuel.—Son of the Rev. Peter Carmichael Millar, O.B.E., B.D., D.D., Aberdeen. *Born* 19 February 1927. *Married* 5 September 1953, Kirsteen Lindsay, daughter of David Carnegie, C.B., O.B.E., T.D., D.L., Deputy General Manager, Clydesdale Bank Ltd. Served in Royal Navy 1944-47. Clerk to the Society (appointed 1964). *Firm*—Aitken Kinnear & Co. (formerly W. & T. P. Manuel).

MILLAR, ROBERT JOHN, LL.B. [13 May 1980]. Apprentice to (a) George Stobie Preston Bain and Another of Campbell, Smith & Co. and (b) Thomas Norman Biggart of Biggart, Baillie & Gifford.—Son of William Lawrie Millar, Consulting Engineer, Kingston, Jamaica. *Born* 28 February 1954. *Firm*—Campbell Smith & Co.

MILLER, ALEXANDER [6 December 1827]. Apprentice to Donald Horne.—Eldest son of James Miller, Merchant in Leith, and brother of Sir William Miller of Manderston, Bart. *Born* 14 January 1804. *Married* (1) 11 April 1828, Margaret (*died* 8 August 1842), daughter of James Cornwall, Commissioner of Excise; and (2) 22 December 1849, Letitia, only child of George Burridge, Droitwich. *Died* 26 July 1864.

MILLER, ALEXANDER GRANT SCHAW, B.A.(CANTAB) [19 July 1920]. Apprentice to H. N. S. Callander and Euan B. Robertson.—Son of Robert Schaw Miller, W.S. *Born* 19 June 1890. *Married* 19 October 1921, Olive Elizabeth (*died* 24 January 1957), daughter of Montague Beart, Sawbridgeworth, Herts. Captain and Adjutant Fife and Forfar Yeomanry. *Died* 27 October 1965. *Firm*—Carmichael and Miller, incorporated in 1924 with Hamilton, Kinnear, and Beatson.

MILLER, ANDREW [5 July 1814]. Apprentice to (1) Richard Lake; and (2) John Campbell.—Son of James Miller, Glover in Edinburgh. *Married* 23 December 1791, Grace (*died* 27 March 1827), eldest daughter of James Hogg, Wine Merchant. Depute Clerk of the Bills, 1801-31. *Died* 27 January 1831.

MILLER, ARCHIBALD [Before 1586]. *Married* Katherine M'Gill.

MILLER, ARCHIBALD, OF GLENAVON [9 March 1791]. Apprentice to Lawrence Hill.— Fourth son of John Miller, Advocate, Professor of Law in the University of Glasgow. *Born* 26 April 1767. *Died* 21 February 1823.

MILLER, CHARLES [Before 1730]. *Married* Susannah Weir.

MILLER, CHARLES HAGART [24 November 1831]. Apprentice to (1) David Ramsay; and (2) John Donaldson.—Youngest son of James Miller of Milton. *Born* 16 September 1806. *Died* 4 January 1846, unmarried.

MILLER, CUTHBERT [Before 1628]. Apprentice to John Macgill.—Brother of John Miller, Advocate. *Married* (1) 16 December 1601, Elspeth Lees; (2) 7 February 1622, Margaret Leyes; and (3) 20 February 1628, Bethiah, daughter of James Cathkin, Bookseller, Edinburgh. *Died* 30 October 1631.

MILLER, GEORGE ANDERSON [18 October 1876]. Apprentice to J. M. Lindsay, Alexander Howe, and William MacGillivray.—Son of James Dick Miller, Solicitor in Perth. *Born* 20 September 1853. *Married* 21 June 1888, Margaret Barclay (*died* 16 May 1936), elder daughter of Isaac Wallace, M.D., Perth. *Died* 7 August 1930.

MILLER, HUGH [15 July 1889]. Apprentice to Sir J. Gillespie and Thomas Paterson.—Son of John Miller, Glenluce. *Born* 23 June 1867. *Married* (1) 1 October 1901, Elsie Providence (*died* 6 February 1903), only daughter of W. Wemyss-Anderson, Barnshot, Colinton; and (2) 13 July 1907, Mary Agnes (*died* 10 January 1950), daughter of Rear-Admiral Lewis Maitland of Lindores, Fife. *Died* at Berkeley, California, 6 October 1927.

MILLER, IAN DAVID, LL.B. [1 December 1969]. Apprentice to Henry Maurice Braine and Another of Gordon, Falconer & Fairweather.—Son of John M. Miller, Company Director, Edinburgh. *Born* 13 July 1945. *Married* 27 June 1970, Sheila Stewart, daughter of Alexander McLean, Innkeeper. Honorary Austrian Consul for Scotland. *Firm*—A. & W. M. Urquhart.

MILLER, JAMES [Before 1560]. *Married* 1566. Margaret Taillefour, a Sister of Penitence in Aberlour. He was a close friend of the Earl of Morton, Regent of Scotland.

MILLER, JAMES ALSTON GRAHAM [9 July 1895]. Apprentice to John Turnbull.—Son of Richard Kerr Miller, Consulting Engineer, 13 Lennox Street, Edinburgh. *Born* 29 November 1868. *Married* 28 July 1909, Phoebe Robina Gowan (*died* 4 July 1944), elder daughter of John Watson Miller, Mayfield, Battyeford, Yorks. *Died* 24 September 1942.

MILLER, JAMES CYRIL KING, B.L. [13 December 1926]. Apprentice to David William Marwick of Simpson & Marwick.—Son of James Duncan Miller, M.R.C.V.S., Port of Spain, Trinidad. *Born* 13 June 1903. *Married* 11 November 1943, Ella Elizabeth, daughter of John Walker, O.B.E. *Died* 15 August 1979. *Firm*—Simpson & Marwick. (Retired.)

MILLER, JOHN [Before 1554].

MILLER, JOHN [18 July 1634]. Apprentice to Robert Kirkwood. *Died* 1645.

MILLER, JOHN, OF STEWARTFIELD [4 March 1816]. Apprentice to Hugh Warrender.—Fourth son of Sir William Miller of Glenlee, Bart., one of the Senators of the College of Justice (Lord Glenlee). *Born* 28 December 1789. *Married* 15 March 1828, Mary (*died* 9 September 1875), eldest daughter of Nicolas Sutherland. *Died* 24 September 1863.

MILLER, JOHN ASHLEY LAING, LL.B. [11 December 1979*].—Son of George William Miller, Chemist, London. *Born* 4 August 1948. *Married* 6 July 1973, Sheila Elizabeth, daughter of R. B. Knowles, Accountant, Edinburgh. *Firm*—Brodies.

MILLER, JOHN CHARLES STRETTELL [18 January 1886]. Apprentice to Hugh Auld and James Macdonald.—Son of Captain John Miller of the P. and O. Service. *Born* 22 February 1858. *Married* 5 June 1890, Anna Eliza (*died* 30 June 1934), elder daughter of William Dent Robinson of Temple Sowerby, Westmorland. Interim Director of Chancery and Depute Keeper of Great Seal, 1895. *Died* 21 February 1931.

MILLER, JOHN KING, M.A., LL.B. [17 July 1972]. Apprentice to The Hon. David Andrew Balfour and Others of Shepherd & Wedderburn.—Son of James Cyril King Miller, W.S., Edinburgh. *Born* 20 January 1947. *Firm*—Simpson & Marwick.

MILLER, JOHN PARRY, M.A.(Oxon) [7 December 1970]. Apprentice to J. D. Cochrane and Another of Alston, Nairn & Hogg.—Son of A. S. Miller, Farmer, Bellrigg, Castle-Douglas, Kirkcudbrightshire. *Born* 30 November 1937. *Married* 24 April 1965, Zelda Jane, daughter of E. Garner, Civil Servant.

MILLER, RICHARD TWEEDIE, B.L. [14 July 1947]. Apprentice to Samuel Kerr Gifford Kerr of Bruce & Kerr.—Son of Robert Pairman Miller, S.S.C., Edinburgh. *Born* 11 April 1915. Staff Lieutenant, Intelligence, A.D.G.B., 94th H.A.A. Regiment, R.A., Second World War. *Firm*—Pairman, Miller & Murray.

MILLER, ROBERT SCHAW [16 January 1888]. Apprentice to Charles Morton and John Neilson.—Son of Robert Schaw Miller, sometime residing in Alloa, afterwards in Montreal, Canada. *Born* 3 March 1863. *Married* 29 August 1889, Jane Caroline (*died* 5 March 1931), only daughter of Alexander Grant, Hamilton. *Died* 24 March 1928.

MILLER, ROBERT GRANT SCHAW. *See* SCHAW MILLER.

MILLER, WILLIAM, OF GLENLEE AND BARSKIMMING [15 July 1719]. Apprentice to Robert Wallace of Holmstone.—Second son of Matthew Miller of Glenlee, Kirkcudbrightshire. *Married* Janet, eldest daughter of Thomas Hamilton of Shieldhall. Father of Sir Thomas Miller, Lord President. *Died* 26 September 1753.

MILLER, WILLIAM DOUGLAS, M.A., LL.B., C.A. [29 April 1974]. Apprentice to (1) Ronald Kenneth Watson and Another of Brodie, Cuthbertson & Watson and (2) Ian Maxwell Ferguson and Others of Patrick and James.—Son of Thomas Henderson Miller, Solicitor, Glasgow. *Born* 12 March 1929. *Married* 3 June 1967, Benita Daphne, daughter of Lieutenant Colonel W. B. R. Neave-Hill.

MILLER, WILLIAM RONALD CRAWFORD, M.A.(Cantab), LL.B. [19 December 1949]. Apprentice to David Porter and Others of Davidson & Syme.—Son of William Miller, M.A., LL.B., Taxation Specialist and Accountant, Edinburgh. *Born* 21 May 1919. Captain, 1st Battalion Duke of Wellington's (West Riding) Regiment. Served U.K., North Africa, Italy and Middle East. Wounded at Anzio. *Firm*—Steedman, Ramage & Co.

MILLIE, JOHN [27 February 1823]. Apprentice to John Forman.—Youngest son of John Millie of Bridgend. *Died* 1849, aged 54, unmarried.

MILLIGAN, FREDERICK PATTERSON [14 December 1896]. Apprentice to George Dunlop and J. A. S. Miller.—Son of the Rev. Professor William Milligan, D.D., Aberdeen. *Born* 14 August 1870. *Married* 6 August 1903, Helena Mary (*died* 24 May 1933), daughter of William Clarke, J.P., of the Hermitage, Gateshead. *Died* 17 May 1961. *Firm*—Martin, Milligan, and Macdonald.

MILLIGAN, JAMES [13 December 1909]. Apprentice to Sir Charles B. Logan, Hon. James W. Moncreiff, G. G. Soote, and E. J. Cuthbertson.—Son of John Milligan, W.S. *Born* 6 September 1884. *Married* 11 April 1923, Amy, third daughter of Professor J. Lorrain-Smith, LL.D., F.R.S. Assistant Clerk and Extractor of the Signet, 27 June 1919. Substitute Keeper and Clerk to the Society, 25 November 1931. *Died* 19 December 1953. *Firm*—J. and J. Milligan.

MILLIGAN, JOHN, OF TANNIELAGGIE [25 March 1869]. Apprentice to Alexander Forsyth Adam.—Son of James Milligan, S.S.C., Assistant Clerk and Extractor of the Signet. *Born* 13 October 1846. *Married* 8 September 1880, Mary (*died* 29 August 1945), eldest surviving daughter of Alexander Waugh, Solicitor, Newton-Stewart. Assistant Clerk and Extractor, 1876-85. Substitute Keeper of the Signet, 19 August 1885. *Died* 27 August 1904. *Firm*—J. and J. Milligan.

MILLIGAN, PATRICK FRASER [14 January 1895]. Apprentice to James Bruce and Thomas Kerr.—Son of the Rev. Peter Milligan, Minister of the Parish of Guthrie. *Born* 6 December 1867. *Died* 30 June 1930.

MILLIGAN, WILLIAM CHARLES ANSTRUTHER, B.A.(CANTAB), LL.B. [11 July 1932]. Apprentice to R. W. Dundas and Others of Dundas & Wilson.—Son of Wyndham Anstruther Milligan, Physician. *Born* 27 October 1904. *Married* 11 June 1959, Jeanne Marie-Magdeleine, daughter of Comte Georges de Bellescize, France. Major, Lothians & Border Horse. Served North Africa, Italy and Germany, 1939-46. Wounded in Italy July 1944. Mentioned in Despatches, 1945. *Firm*—Martin, Milligan & Macdonald. (Retired 1948.)

MILLS, FREDERICK SHARP, B.L. [28 July 1952]. Apprentice to Samuel Raleigh Simpson and Others of Simpson, Kinmont & Maxwell.—Son of Frederick Mills, Seedsman, Haddington. *Born* 30 May 1928. *Firms*—(1) Mackenzie & Black; (2) J. & F. Anderson.

MILN, ALEXANDER HAY, OF WOODHILL [10 June 1841]. Apprentice to Andrew Storie.— Eldest son of James Miln of Woodhill, Angus. *Born* 19 July 1817. *Married* 15 September 1859, Sarah Isabella (*died* 11 September 1883), eldest daughter of James Mackintosh of Lamancha, Peeblesshire. *Died* 5 February 1877.

MILN, ARCHIBALD, OF CHAPELTOWN [21 June 1787]. Apprentice to Lachlan Duff.—Elder son of Alexander Miln of Chapeltown, Elginshire. *Baptized* 2 August 1762. *Died* at Keith, 2 October 1812.

MILN, CHARLES [4 January 1699]. Apprentice to William Dykes.—Son of Robert Miln of Balfarge, Mason. *Married* (1) Susanne, niece of Walter Weir; and (2) January 1736, Helen, daughter of Alexander Nisbet, Farmer, Oldhamstocks. *Died* 4 May 1750.

MILNE, ALFRED ERNEST [10 July 1911]. Apprentice to (1) Alexander Wallace and Laurence A. Guthrie; and (2) Hamilton Maxwell.—Third son of James Milne, M.D., and Bank Agent, Huntly. *Born* 5 October 1882. *Married* 17 April 1912, Margaret (*died* 3 March 1973), youngest daughter of Ebenezer Erskine Scott, C.A., of Linburn, Mid-Lothian. Served with 4th and 10th Royal Scots; went to Russia in September, and was wounded in October 1918. *Died* 6 September 1954.

MILNE, NEIL ALEXANDER, M.A., LL.B. [20 December 1948]. Apprentice to James Miller Thomson of J. Miller Thomson & Co.—Son of Alexander C. Milne, Company Director, Blairgowrie. *Born* 23 November 1918. *Married* 2 September 1950, Katrine Jean, daughter of James Armour, Accountant. Captain, R.A. Served Middle East and Italy, 1940-46. *Firms*—(1) Miller, Thomson & Robertson (formerly J. Miller Thomson & Co.) and (2) Marwicks.

MILNE, SIR WILLIAM ROBERTSON [12 July 1915]. Apprentice to (1) James Reid; and (2) William Gibson.—Son of John Robertson Milne. *Born* 1 June 1880. *Married* 28 December 1916, Janet (*died* 24 August 1975), eldest daughter of John Young, Schoolmaster, Clunie, Perthshire. Crown Agent for Scotland 1941-45. Knighted 1954. *Died* 31 March 1959. *Firm*—Reid & Milne (latterly Tait & Crichton).

MILNES, KEITH [28 January 1799]. Apprentice to George Robinson.—Eldest son of Rev. James Milnes, Minister of Sandwich, Kent. Died 21 August 1857.

MILROY, ANDREW [21 December 1832]. Apprentice to Walter Cook.—Eldest son of Andrew Milroy, Jeweller in Edinburgh. *Born* 6 May 1803. *Married* 1 November 1842, Susannah, second daughter of Joseph Nixon, Edinburgh. Manager of the Bank of British North America at St John's, Newfoundland. *Died* 25 July 1867.

MIRTLE, JOHN, OF GRACEMOUNT [25 June 1829]. Apprentice to Charles and Adam Twase.—Eldest son of William Mirtle at Boon, Berwickshire. *Born* 1803. *Died* 9 February 1835, unmarried.

MITCHELL, ALEXANDER, OF CRAIGEND [3 March 1712]. Apprentice to Charles Bell.—Son of John Mitchell of Craigend, Stirlingshire. *Born* about 1678. *Married* 24 April 1713, Alison, daughter of Alexander Livingstone of Parkhall, Stirlingshire. *Died* 14 December 1738.

MITCHELL, ALEXANDER [16 July 1858]. Apprentice to Graham Binny.—Eldest son of Alexander Mitchell of the Exchequer, Edinburgh. *Born* August 1833. *Died* 23 May 1902, unmarried.

MITCHELL, DAVID [11 December 1810]. Apprentice to John Graeme.—Son of Thomas Mitchell, Factor on the estate of Airlie. *Died* 11 August 1815.

MITCHELL, DAVID HUGH ARTHUR, B.A.(OXON), LL.B. [16 December 1946]. Apprentice to Thomas Patrick Spens of Maclay, Murray & Spens, Glasgow.—Son of David Mitchell, Stockbroker, Glasgow. *Born* 27 February 1914. *Married* 5 March 1955, Elizabeth Johnstone, daughter of Dr Oliver Carlyle, Dumfries. (Descendant of Thomas Carlyle.)

MITCHELL, JAMES LAIDLAW [7 July 1820]. Apprentice to James Laidlaw.—Son of John Mitchell, Merchant in Edinburgh. *Died* 18 October 1852, aged 62, unmarried.

MITCHELL, JAMES THOMSON RANKIN, D.S.O. [8 December 1913]. Apprentice to William Thomson and P. F. Dawson.—Son of James Mitchell of Bannockburn House, Bannockburn. *Born* 26 March 1888. D.S.O., 1916. Lieut.-Colonel A. and S. Highlanders. Several times mentioned in Despatches. *Died* 1 April 1918 of wounds received in action.

MITCHELL, JOSEPH [26 May 1825]. Apprentice to William Fraser.—Son of Joseph Mitchell, Farmer at Whitestanes, Dumfriesshire. *Died* 22 April 1858, aged 56, unmarried.

MITCHELL, WILLIAM [28 October 1889]. Apprentice to Charles Baxter.—Son of William Mitchell, S.S.C., and grandson of James Stewart Ducat, W.S. *Born* 16 July 1863. *Retired* 1908. *Died* 10 December 1943. *Firm*—Mitchell and Baxter.

MITCHELSON, SAMUEL [12 March 1736]. Apprentice to Alexander Stevenson of Montgreenan.—Third son of John Mitchelson of Middleton, Mid-Lothian, Advocate. *Married*, proclaimed 21 October 1753, Jean, daughter of John Oliver of Dinleybyre, Roxburghshire. Fiscal, 1754-55. Treasurer, 1755-88. *Died* 21 January 1788.

MITCHELSON, SAMUEL, OF CLERMISTON [16 December 1760]. Apprentice to Samuel Mitchelson.—Son of James Mitchelson, Jeweller in Edinburgh. *Married*, proclaimed 20 March 1763, Katherine (*died* 23 August 1808), daughter of Alexander Birnie of Broomhall, Lanarkshire. Principal Clerk of Session, 16 June 1789 till death. *Died* 8 December 1793.

MOFFAT, ALEXANDER DOUGLAS, LL.B. [1 December 1969]. Apprentice to Charles Stewart Henderson and Others of Patrick & James.—Son of Robert Cuthbert Easton Moffat, Medical Practitioner Edinburgh. *Born* 13 March 1946. *Married* 27 June 1970, Alison Jane, daughter of James Duncan Kennedy, C.B.E. *Firm*—Patrick & James.

MOFFAT, DOUGLAS WILLIAM JOHN [8 December 1975]. Apprentice to John Stewart Macfie and Another of Tods, Murray & Jamieson.—Son of John R. Moffat, Medical Practitioner, Castle Douglas, Kirkcudbrightshire. *Born* 3 October 1947. *Married* 21 October 1972, Sheila Elizabeth, daughter of T. R. Foster, Farmer, Bridlington, Yorkshire. *Firm*—Tods, Murray & Jamieson.

MOFFETT, IAN WEATHERSTON, LL.B. [2 December 1974]. Apprentice to Ewen K. Cameron and Others of Dundas & Wilson.—Son of John Weatherston Moffett, Master Baker, Edinburgh. *Born* 25 April 1950. *Married* 23 March 1979, Jennifer Helen Margaret Lennox. *Firm*—Dundas & Wilson.

MOIR, JOHN, OF HILLFOOT [20 June 1769]. Apprentice to David Campbell.—Only son of James Moir, Writer in Stirling. *Married*, proclaimed 23 March 1766, Elizabeth (*died* 2 June 1783), daughter of Rev. Daniel Macqueen, Minister of St Giles', Edinburgh. *Died* November 1802.

MOIR, JOHN, OF HILLFOOT [17 March 1797]. Apprentice to, and son of, John Moir, W.S.— *Born* 1769. *Married* Mary Bell Gray (*died* 17 October 1805). *Died* through bursting a blood-vessel, 22 December 1804.

MOIR, ROBERT [17 May 1799]. Apprentice to David Balfour.—Fourth son of John Moir, Merchant in Edinburgh. *Born* 1769. *Died* 17 August 1805.

MOLLE, OR MOW, WILLIAM, OF MAINS [7 March 1788]. Apprentice to Thomas Cockburn.—Second son of John Mow of Mains, Berwickshire. *Born* 1765. *Married*, proclaimed 27 July 1795, Agnes (*died* 4 April 1855), daughter of Alexander Adam, Slater, Edinburgh, and niece of William Preston of Gorten. Assumed name of Molle, 1789. *Died* 20 March 1840.

MONCREIFF, HENRY [8 June 1804]. Apprentice to Alexander Duncan.—Third son of Rev. Sir Henry Moncreiff Wellwood, Bart., of Tullibole, Kinross-shire. *Born* 25 February 1778. *Married* 31 July 1809, Charlotte Erskine, daughter of Hugh James Paterson Rollo of Bannockburn. *Died* 16 April 1817.

MONCREIFF, JAMES FREDERICK [28 March 1899]. Apprentice to Sir Thomas Dawson Brodie.—Son of the Hon. James William Moncreiff, W.S. *Born* 18 September 1872. *Married* 21 November 1922, Elizabeth, daughter of Peter William Souter, Nelson Street, Edinburgh, and niece of Peter Crooks, W.S., Edinburgh. *Died* 12 July 1948.

MONCREIFF, HON. JAMES WILLIAM [30 March 1871]. Apprentice to John M. Lindsay and Alexander Howe.—Third son of the Right Hon. James, Baron Moncreiff of Tullibole, Lord Justice-Clerk. *Born* 16 September 1845. *Married* 19 March 1872, Mary Lillias (*died* 29 December 1910), eldest daughter of George Mitchell Innes of Bangour, Linlithgowshire. Substitute Keeper of the Signet, 1876-85. *Died* 30 January 1920. *Firm*—Mackenzie, Innes, and Logan.

MONCREIFF, JOHN, OF MORNEPEA [11 December 1690]. Apprentice to John Bayne of Pitcarlie.—*Married* Jean Leslie. Clerk to the Admission of Notaries, 3 December 1690. *Died* July 1697.

MONCRIEFF, ALEXANDER, OF TAYSIDE AND PITCASTLE [11 July 1837]. Apprentice to John Ker and Henry G. Dickson.—Eldest son of Robert Hope Moncrieff, Writer in Perth. *Born* 15 June 1815. *Married* 15 November 1843, Euphemia Dick (*died* 23 March 1890), daughter of General John Cunningham of Newton, Perthshire. *Died* 15 March 1886.

MONCRIEFF, DAVID SCOTT [16 December 1854]. Apprentice to John Gibson, Jun.—Fourth son of Robert Scott Moncrieff of Fossoway, Perthshire. *Born* 13 June 1829. *Married* (1) 8 August 1860, Elizabeth (*died* 17 January 1870), daughter of Robert Sym Wilson of Woodburn, W.S., a brother of Professor John Wilson; (2) 22 October 1872, Margaret Fisher (*died* 2 May 1908), daughter of George William Campbell, M.D., of Peaton, Dunbartonshire, Professor of Surgery, M'Gill University, Montreal; and (3) 10 June 1909, Agnes Campbell (*died* 4 August 1916), eldest daughter of Francis Brodie Imlach, F.R.C.S., Edinburgh. *Died* 10 August 1918. *Firm*—Scott Moncrieff and Trail.

MONCRIEFF, DAVID CHARLES SCOTT. *See* SCOTT-MONCRIEFF.

MONCRIEFF, JOHN KENNETH SCOTT. *See* SCOTT-MONCRIEFF.

MONCRIEFF, ROBERT HOPE [14 March 1872]. Apprentice to Thomas Graham Murray.—Eldest son of Alexander Moncrieff, W.S. *Born* 23 November 1849. *Married* 12 October 1886, Margaret (*died* 30 May 1931), daughter of Rev. John Anderson, D.D., Minister of Kinnoull. *Died* 21 January 1900.

MONCRIEFF, ROBERT SCOTT, OF DOWNHILL [15 July 1886]. Apprentice to D. S. Moncrieff and John A. Trail.—Eldest son of David Scott Moncrieff, W.S. *Born* 11 April 1862. *Married* 2 June 1891, Hamilton Lora Noel Paton (*died* 24 May 1921), daughter of Sir Joseph Noel Paton, R.S.A., H.M. Limner for Scotland. *Died* 9 January 1923. *Firm*—Scott Moncrieff and Trail.

MONILAWS, ALEXANDER GEORGE [14 November 1851]. Apprentice to Alexander and Christopher Douglas.—Eldest son of Rev. James Monilaws, Minister of Annan. *Born* 1 April 1828. *Died* 15 February 1858, unmarried.

MONRO, DAVID, OF ALLAN [18 July 1731]. Apprentice to John Steuart.—Son of Joseph Monro of Allan, Ross-shire. *Born* 1696. *Died* 6 December 1767, unmarried.

MONRO, HECTOR [26 May 1864]. Apprentice to George Greig.—Son of James Monro, Writer in Kinross. *Born* 21 March 1839. *Married* 5 June 1873, Isabella (*died* 19 December 1887), daughter of Dundas Simpson and widow of Robert Baird of Limerigg. *Divorce* 1880. *Died* 25 May 1894.

MONRO, HUGH [20 November 1671]. Apprentice to James Peter.—Son of Rev. David Monro, Minister of Killearn. *Buried* 12 February 1672.

MONRO, JOHN [Before 1586]. *Died* before 1594.

MONRO, JOHN [29 December 1683]. Apprentice to (1) James Carnegie; and (2) Alexander Ord. *Married* (1) 18 April 1672, Margaret Clunas; and (2) 17 June 1684, Susan Leirmont.

MONTEATH, HARRY HENDERSON, B.A.(Oxon), LL.B. [11 December 1911]. Apprentice to William Blair and James Watt.—Son of Henry Monteath, S.S.C. *Born* 26 June 1885. *Married* 1 March 1917, Margaret Frances Alice (*died* 15 July 1920), youngest daughter of T. A. Warrand, Lentran, Bridge of Allan; (2) 29 September 1925, Margaret Frew, youngest daughter of David Robert M'Neill, Corrie, Four Oaks, Warwickshire. In Great War, Captain R.A.S.C. Mesopotamian Expeditionary Force. Mentioned in Despatches. Professor of Conveyancing in the University of Edinburgh, 1935-55. *Firm*—Horne and Lyell. *Died* 5 March 1962.

MONTGOMERIE, JOHN, of Wrae [23 December 1687]. Apprentice to John Muir.—Fifth son of George Montgomerie of Broomlands. *Married* (1) 2 February 1689, Penelope, daughter of Sir Robert Barclay of Pierston, Ayrshire; and (2) September 1696, Janet, daughter of Thomas Gray, Merchant, Edinburgh. M.P. Linlithgowshire, 1704-7. Deputy Secretary for Scotland. *Died* 11 March 1725, aged 62.

MONTGOMERY, WILLIAM [Before 1580]. *Died* before 1594.

MONTGOMERY, WILLIAM [10 March 1806]. Apprentice to Alexander Blair.—Second son of William Montgomery, Wigmaker in Edinburgh. *Died* 22 September 1809.

MONTGOMERY, WILLIAM [19 February 1852]. Apprentice to Walter Jollie.—Third son of Robert Montgomery, Barrister-at-Law, residing in Edinburgh. *Born* 20 March 1822. *Married* 21 August 1860, Elizabeth Maxwell (*died* 22 October 1918), daughter of Colin Maceachran of Oatfield, Argyllshire. Clerk to the Admission of Notaries, 1869-1888. *Died* 2 March 1888.

MONYPENNY, ALEXANDER [18 May 1801]. Apprentice to Colin Mackenzie.—Fourth son of Lieut.-Colonel Alexander Monypenny of Pitmilly, Fife. Brother of Lord Pitmilly. *Born* 23 March 1778. Depute Clerk to the Admission of Notaries, 1814-32. One of the three trustees for the creditors of Sir Walter Scott. *Died* 15 June 1844.

MOODIE, ADAM WALTER DOUGLAS, B.L. [23 April 1956]. Apprentice to John Roger Orr and Another of Simpson & Marwick.—Son of Adam Wilson Moodie, Chief Conservator of Forests, Burma, latterly of Doonfoot, Ayr. *Born* 28 June 1925. *Married* 9 September 1954, Margaret Gilmour Wilson, daughter of John William Andrew, M.C., C.A. Major, 6th Gurkha Rifles, India and Burma. Solicitor to the Free Church of Scotland. *Firm*—Simpson & Marwick.

MOODIE, LYALL GEORGE WILLIAM, LL.B. [12 December 1977]. Apprentice to (1) J. K. Finlayson and Another of Bonar, Mackenzie; (2) N. J. M. Loy of John Henderson & Son, Dumfries.—Son of William G. Moodie, W.S., Edinburgh. *Born* 8 January 1954. *Married* 27 June 1975, Fiona, daughter of Richard C. Young, Civil and Structural Engineer. *Firm*—John Henderson & Sons, Dumfries.

MOODIE, STUART [28 June 1787]. Apprentice to William Dick.—Son of John Moodie, Merchant in London. Admitted Advocate, 26 January 1793. *Died* 7 April 1827.

MOODIE, WILLIAM GEORGE, B.L. [23 November 1953]. Apprentice to James Campbell Walker and Another of Steedman, Ramage & Co.—Son of George Moodie, S.S.C., Edinburgh. *Born* 16 October 1929. *Married* 5 September 1952, Margaret Orr, daughter of George Simpson William Knowles. *Firm*—Keir, Moodie & Co.

MORE, ERIC GEORGE MELVILLE, B.L. [20 July 1950]. Apprentice to Alexander Dougal of J. L. Hill, Dougal & Co.—Son of David Melville More, S.S.C., Edinburgh. *Born* 9 April 1924. Sergeant, Royal Scots. *Firms*—(1) J. L. Hill, Dougal & Co.; (2) Menzies, Dougal & Milligan (after amalgamation).

MORE, FRANCIS ADAM JOHN, LL.B. [8 December 1975]. Apprentice to R. K. Watson and Others of Brodies.—Son of Francis George More, C.A., Edinburgh. *Born* 28 May 1949. *Married* 16 September 1972, Gillian Helen, daughter of Hugh Macintyre Tucker, Medical Practitioner. *Firm*—Murray, Beith & Murray.

MORE, GEORGE. *See* GORDON, GEORGE MORE.

MORISON, HENRY [16 August 1671]. Apprentice to James Allan.—Eldest son of John Morison, Merchant Burgess, Edinburgh. *Married* 22 November 1672, Agnes, daughter of James Wilkie of Cammo. *Buried* 5 November 1673.

MORISON, JOHN, OF HETLANDHILL [14 June 1791]. Apprentice to John Taylor.—Son of Andrew Morison, Writer in Edinburgh. *Born* 1769. *Married* 20 August 1796, Jane (*died* 18 April 1833), daughter of Robert Farquhar of Newhall. *Died* 15 May 1837.

MORRIS, AUSTIN DOUGLAS, LL.B. [17 July 1939]. Apprentice to J. L. Mounsey and Others of John C. Brodie & Sons.—Son of Austin Robert Morris, Indian Civil Service. *Born* 25 June 1914. *Married* 26 June 1943, Molly Brown. Captain, Royal Army Pay Corps; Served U.K. 1939-45. *Died* 22 July 1959. *Firm*—John C. Brodie & Sons.

MORRISON, EDWARD FRANCIS ALLARDYCE [19 December 1938]. Apprentice to Kenneth Murray and Another of Macandrew, Wright & Murray.—Son of Edward Shaw Morrison, Factor, Fort William. *Born* 3 April 1914. Lieutenant, Infantry. Served U.K. and Belgium 1939-40. Killed in action, Belgium, 22 May 1940.

MORRISON, NAESMYTH [16 June 1818]. Apprentice to David Wemyss.—Son of David Morrison, Major in the service of the Hon. East India Company. Captain H.E.I.C.S. *Died* at Hyderabad, 10 December 1846, aged 53, unmarried.

MORTHLAND, MATTHEW, OF RINDMUIR [30 June 1741]. Apprentice to William Miller.—Son of Charles Morthland, Professor of Oriental Languages in the University of Glasgow. *Died* 15 October 1787, aged 74.

MORTON, CHARLES, OF GLENLOIN [8 July 1828]. Apprentice to James Greig.—Eldest son of Samuel Morton, Agricultural Implement Maker, Edinburgh. *Born* 21 January 1806. *Married* 7 August 1834, Isabella (*died* 3 October 1889), daughter of James Harvey, Grandholm, Aberdeen. Crown Agent, June and July 1866, 1868-74, 1880-83. *Died* 24 December 1892.

MORTON, JOHN STUART [16 December 1895]. Apprentice to Matthew Henry.—Son of James Morton, Manager of the Union Bank of Scotland Ltd., Edinburgh. *Born* 16 September 1871. *Married* 29 March 1928, Jean Wilson (*died* 13 December 1964), younger daughter of Robert Thorburn, Banker, Leith. Captain Royal Scots during Great War. *Died* 22 July 1958.

MORTON, WILLIAM [18 October 1886]. Apprentice to Henry Cairns.—Son of Alexander Morton, Banker, Edinburgh. *Born* 14 September 1851. *Married* 2 July 1889, Jessie Christiana (*died* 7 January 1935), daughter of Thomas Struthers, Edinburgh. Solicitor-at-Law. S.S.C., 1876. *Died* 20 January 1920. *Firm*—Cairns, M'Intosh, and Morton.

MOSMAN, HUGH, OF AUCHTYFARDLE [15 July 1885]. Apprentice to F. Pitman, A. B. Macallan, J. R. Anderson, and W. H. Murray.—Eldest son of Hugh Mosman of Auchtyfardle, Lanarkshire. *Born* 27 October 1860. *Died* 12 February 1916, unmarried.

MOSMAN, RICHARD [Before 1627]. Mentioned, 1 August 1633. *Died* before 1646.

MOTHERWELL, GAVIN BLACK LOUDON, O.B.E. [9 July 1900]. Apprentice to R. S. Miller.—Son of John Motherwell of Rawyards. *Born* 27 July 1874. *Married* 3 August 1927, Dorothy Sinclair, daughter of Francis Phillips Smith, Iron Merchant, Drungoyne, Helensburgh. Captain Royal Scots Fusiliers, afterwards Appeal Military Representative for the War Office in Counties of Stirling, Dumbarton, Clackmannan, and Argyll. Agent for the Crown in *Ultimus Haeres* 1940-59. *Died* 16 February 1959. *Firm*—Laing and Motherwell.

MOUNSEY, JAMES LITTLE, LL.B. [9 December 1912]. Apprentice to, and son of, John Little Mounsey. *Born* 29 October 1887. *Married* 2 April 1919, Marjory Manners (*died* 12 February 1952), second daughter of William Herbert Brookfield of Glen Cove, Chester, Nova Scotia. Civilian Prisoner of War in Ruhleben Prison Camp, Berlin, November 1914-18. *Died* 22 February 1958. *Firm*—John C. Brodie and Sons.

MOUNSEY, JOHN LITTLE, LL.D. [8 October 1883]. Apprentice to Sir Thomas Dawson Brodie. Son of Archibald Carlyle Mounsey, Rector of the Grammar School, Jedburgh, *Born* 30 October 1852. *Married* 21 June 1881, Margaret (*died* 31 May 1940), eldest daughter of John Jackson of Solway Bank, Annan. Professor of Conveyancing in the University of Edinburgh, 1900-19. *Died* 26 June 1933. *Firm*—John C. Brodie and Sons.

MOWAT, ALAN WALTER, B.L. [8 May 1967]. Apprentice to James Mackenzie of Mowat & Mackenzie.—Son of David Longmuir Mowat, S.S.C., Edinburgh. *Born* 2 November 1935. *Married* 28 August 1965, Heather Valerie, daughter of John Alexander Clarke. *Firm*—Mowat & Mackenzie.

MOWAT, JAMES, OF FAWSIDE [Before 1611]. *Married* (1) 29 October 1611, Margaret Rollock (*died* 2 June 1621); (2) Dame Anna Saltounstill; and (3) (contract, 24 and 28 August 1624), Jean, daughter of Sir Patrick Chirnside of East Nisbet. Sheriff-Clerk of Berwickshire, 14 November 1627. *Died* July 1657.

MOWBRAY, JOHN, OF HARWOOD [30 November 1792]. Apprentice to William Campbell of Crawfordton.—Second son of Robert Mowbray, Merchant in Edinburgh. *Born* 1768. *Married* (1) 7 April 1801, Elizabeth (*died* 1 November 1804), daughter of John Scougall, Merchant in Leith; and (2) 26 June 1807, Patricia Hodge (*died* 14 December 1852) of Awalls. *Died* 19 September 1838.

MOWBRAY, JOHN THOMSON, LL.D. [8 March 1832]. Apprentice to John Mowbray.— Son of Robert, Merchant in Leith. *Born* 12 May 1808. Treasurer, 1882. Author of *An Analysis of the Conveyancing (Scotland) Act*, 1874, and other legal works. *Died* 17 April 1892, unmarried.

MOYSIE, DAVID [Before 1607]. Probably son of James Moysie, Burgess, Edinburgh. Suspended, until he should obtain a proper admission, 22 November 1609. Probably Author of *Memoirs* published by Bannatyne Club.

MUDIE, JOHN [Before 1627]. Brother of William Mudie, Portioner of Athie. Mentioned, 1630. *Married* Marion Geddes (*died* July 1648). *Died* 1648.

MUIR, ANDREW GRAY [12 July 1887]. Apprentice to Thomas Jarron Gordon.—Son of George Watson Muir, Kirkhouse, Traquair. *Born* 27 January 1865. *Married* 22 July 1896, Mary Elizabeth (*died* 7 February 1937), elder daughter of James Thomson Henderson, Leghorn, Italy. Collector of Widows' Fund, 1925. Clerk to Royal College of Physicians of Edinburgh, 1908. *Died* 8 July 1940. *Firm*—Morton, Smart, Macdonald, and Prosser.

MUIR, ANDREW GRAY, B.A.(Oxon), LL.B. [29 November 1960]. Apprentice to David Blyth Bogle and Another of Lindsay, Howe & Co.—Son of W. E. Gray Muir, W.S., Edinburgh. *Born* 14 February 1934. *Married* 28 July 1962, Alexandra Mary, daughter of Brigadier W. A. Mackenzie of Gairloch. *Firms*—(1) Morton, Smart, Macdonald & Milligan (now Morton, Fraser & Milligan); (2) Alan R. Fairlie & Co.

MUIR, GEORGE, of Cassencarrie [7 January 1756]. Apprentice to John Davidson of Stewartfield.—Son of William Muir of Cassencarrie, Kirkcudbrightshire. *Married* 20 April 1762, Margaret (*died* 5 July 1767), eldest daughter of Alexander Mackenzie of Delvine, Perthshire. Principal Clerk of Justiciary. *Died* 3 September 1783.

MUIR, JOHN. *Married* Euphemia Lauder. *Died* November 1656.

MUIR, JOHN, of Nether Scheills [11 April 1661]. Apprentice to Alexander Douglas.— *Married* (contract, 4 July 1658), Catherine (*died* July 1703), daughter of Robert Monteith, Indweller in Edinburgh. *Died* 2 February 1686.

MUIR, JOHN. *See* Chalmer, John Muir.

MUIR, WILLIAM EDWARD GRAY [19 December 1927], Apprentice to William A. MacGillivray and John P. Watson.—Son of Andrew Gray Muir, W.S., Edinburgh. *Born* 25 September 1902. *Married* 23 June 1932, Elizabeth Margaret (*died* 23 March 1976), daughter of William Henry Montgomery, British Linen Bank House, North Berwick. Captain, Royal Scots. Served U.K. and France 1939-45. *Died* 28 January 1959. *Firm*—Morton, Smart, Macdonald & Prosser.

MUIRHEAD, CHARLES HERRIES, of Logan [23 June 1807]. Apprentice to Alexander Young of Harburn.—Son of Rev. James Muirhead, D.D., Minister of Urr. *Born* 1781. *Died* 6 February 1823.

MUIRHEAD, DAVID [Before 1586]. Signs Minute, 1606. *Married* Marion Lawson. *Died* January 1614.

MUNDELL, ALEXANDER [8 July 1790]. Apprentice to Lawrence Hill.—Son of Robert Mundell, Printer in Edinburgh. *Born* 1769. *Married* Susanna (*died* 1846), second daughter of Samuel Champneys of Bradmire, Hertfordshire. *Died* 19 March 1837.

MUNRO, ALEXANDER DANIEL [29 June 1943]. Apprentice to Patrick Drought North Menzies of Menzies & Thomson.—Son of William Munro, Inverness. *Born* 24 May 1909. *Married* 26 September 1936, Dorothy Mary Gordon, daughter of J. G. Thomson, S.S.C., Edinburgh. Lt. Colonel, Infantry. Served U.K., Middle East, Burma and India 1940-45. *Died* at Berlin, 30 October 1947.

MUNRO, HENRY GEORGE, C.B.E., T.D., M.A., LL.B. [20 December 1948]. Apprentice to John Herbert Richardson and Others of Dundas & Wilson. *Born* 26 August 1919. *Married* 1 November 1941, Christina Macdonald. Squadron Leader, R.A.F. 1939-45. Director and General Secretary, National Farmers' Union of Scotland 1954-77.

MURBY, DAVID FRIGAST, LL.B. [11 December 1979*].—Son of Leslie Murby, Publisher, Glasgow. *Born* 7 March 1947. *Married* 2 March 1973, Elma, daughter of Thomas Brown, Castle Douglas. *Firm*—Shepherd & Wedderburn.

MURDOCH, ALEXANDER BURN-, LL.B. [11 December 1911]. Apprentice to (1) A. Burn-Murdoch, C. H. Urmston, and M. C. Higgins; and (2) William Blair and James Watt.—Son of Archibald Burn-Murdoch, W.S. *Born* 21 August 1886. *Married* 20 July 1929, Aline (*died* 19 June 1969), daughter of Rev. W. J. Macdonald, Kirkcaldy, and widow of Cecil Blake. Commission in 8th Royal Scots. Afterwards served in France and Ireland during Great War. *Died* 7 June 1954. *Firm*—Hagart and Burn-Murdoch.

MURDOCH, ARCHIBALD BURN- [18 July 1861]. Apprentice to Thomas Graham Murray.—Fifth son of John Burn-Murdoch of Gartincaber, Perthshire. *Born* 10 December 1836. *Married* 4 November 1874, Mary Harriet Burn (*died* 26 February 1922), only daughter of William Burn Callander of Prestonhall, Mid-Lothian. *Died* 30 June 1916. *Firm*—Hagart and Burn-Murdoch.

MURDOCH, JAMES FERGUSON [12 November 1835]. Apprentice to John Mackenzie Lindsay.—Eldest son of Alexander Murdoch, Procurator-Fiscal of Ayrshire. *Born* 5 November 1812. *Married* 24 August 1841, Ann Cuninghame (*died* 10 October 1905), daughter of Rev. Robert Douglas, Minister of Kilbarchan. Procurator-Fiscal of Ayrshire, 30 January 1843. *Died* 6 October 1874.

MURRAY, ALFRED ALEXANDER ARBUTHNOTT, OF FIDDES [28 March 1898]. Apprentice to Robert Strathern.—Only son of Joseph Murray, Writer, Edinburgh. *Born* 25 March 1863. *Married* 4 July 1889, Mary (*died* 19 August 1946), youngest daughter of George Moir, Edinburgh. *Died* 17 June 1929.

MURRAY, ANDREW [13 February 1845]. Apprentice to George Dalziel.—Son of Patrick Murray, Writer in Glasgow. *Born* 11 October 1823. *Married* 8 June 1849, Mina Maria (*died* 28 February 1911), third daughter of James Balfour, Edinburgh. Crown Agent, 1860-66. *Died* 23 August 1869.

MURRAY, ANDREW, OF CONLAND [15 June 1837]. Apprentice to, and eldest son of, William Murray of Conland, Fife, W.S.—*Born* 19 February 1812. *Married* 4 September 1858, Jane Rodger (*died* 6 October 1885). Professor of Natural Science, New College, Edinburgh, 1857. Author of *Catalogue of the Coleoptera of Scotland* (1853). *Died* 11 January 1878.

MURRAY, ANDREW ERNEST [8 December 1902]. Apprentice to Patrick Murray, W. C. Johnston, and R. D. Beith.—Son of Patrick Murray, W.S. *Born* 21 September 1878. *Married* 4 June 1910, Hope (*died* 23 July 1954), youngest daughter of A. Dunn Macindoe, 18 Belhaven Terrace, Glasgow. *Died* 16 January 1920. *Firm*—Murray, Beith & Murray.

MURRAY, ANTHONY, OF DOLLERIE [26 May 1825]. Apprentice to (1) Hay Donaldson; and (2) John Gibson, Jun.—Eldest son of Anthony Murray of Dollerie, Perthshire. *Born* 1802. *Married* 19 October 1829, Georgina (*died* 18 April 1877), daughter of Sir Patrick Murray of Ochtertyre, Bart. *Died* 16 September 1884.

MURRAY, CHARLES KENNETH, T.D. [12 July 1948]. Apprentice to Kenneth Morton Oliphant and Another of Pearson, Robertson & Maconochie.—Son of Sir Kenneth Murray, W.S., of Geanies, Fearn, Ross-shire. *Born* 17 April 1920. *Married* 1 July 1949, Audrey, daughter of Dr D. A. R. Haddon, M.C., M.D., Hawick. Major, Lovat Scouts. Served U.K., Faroe Isles, Canada, Italy and Greece, 1939-46. Member of Queen's Bodyguard for Scotland, Royal Company of Archers (formerly Secretary). *Firm*—Gillespie, Macandrew & Co. (prior to amalgamation, Macandrew, Wright & Murray).

MURRAY, DAVID [3 July 1792]. Apprentice to Robert Trotter.—Son of David Murray, D.C.S., Writer in Edinburgh. *Died* 4 March 1845.

MURRAY, GEORGE JOHN [18 December 1856]. Apprentice to Andrew Murray, Jun.— Son of William Murray of Geanies, Banker in Tain. *Born* 13 September 1832. *Died* 13 November 1868, unmarried.

MURRAY, HENRY MONTAGUE SCOTT [22 June 1826]. Apprentice to William Young Herries.—Third son of John Murray of Tundergarth, Dumfriesshire. *Died* 1844, aged 41, unmarried.

MURRAY, JAMES [1 February 1630]. Apprentice to Robert Alexander.—Son of William Murray of Ochtertyre. *Died* 2 March 1632.

MURRAY, JAMES CHARLES [25 May 1848]. Apprentice to Donald Horne.—Son of David Murray, Comptroller of Excise for Scotland, afterwards Accountant in Edinburgh. *Born* 17 January 1816. *Died* 22 January 1878, unmarried.

MURRAY, JAMES THOMAS [1 July 1822]. Apprentice to David Murray.—Son of James Murray, Solicitor-at-Law. *Born* 1800. *Married* 21 July 1829, Mary (*died* 2 February 1886), daughter of William Goddard, Merchant, Leith. *Died* 22 January 1857.

MURRAY, JOHN [21 May 1806]. Apprentice to John Dundas.—Eldest son of William Murray, Agent for the Church. *Born* 1782. *Married* 24 August 1818, Ann Jane (*died* 17 January 1851), youngest daughter of James Borland, Glasgow. Agent for the Church. *Died* 13 September 1836.

MURRAY, JOHN, M.A., LL.B., [12 July 1937]. Apprentice to Robert Octavius Pitman and Others of J. & R. Anderson.—Son of Edward Murray, Farmer, Conheath, Dumfries. *Born* 24 October 1910. *Married* 30 January 1943, Marion Smith Murray, daughter of George Higgins, Furniture Designer. Lt. Commander, R.N.V.R. Combined Operations 1940-46. Flotilla Commander in Home Waters, Mediterranean and Far East. Mentioned in Despatches (three times). *Firm*—John Henderson & Sons, Dumfries.

MURRAY, JOHN, OF WOOPLAW [23 June 1853]. Apprentice to John Scott and Sir John Gillespie.—Eldest son of Andrew Murray, Jun., Advocate. *Born* 28 July 1829. *Married* 25 February 1867, Elizabeth, daughter of William Robertson. *Died* 1 December 1899.

MURRAY, SIR KENNETH, B.A.(OXON), J. P. [17 March 1919]. Apprentice to Sir George M. Paul and Others of Dundas & Wilson.—Son of Thomas Middleton Murray, W.S., Geanies, Fearn, Ross-shire. *Born* 23 August 1891. *Married* 5 June 1919, Edith Maud, daughter of W. J. Tustin, London. Served as Captain in Lovat Scouts during First World War; Served in Gallipoli, Egypt and Salonica. Discharged in 1918, due to wounds received in 1916. Knight Bachelor 1958. Chairman of The Royal Bank of Scotland (1946-55); Deputy Lieutenant for Ross and Cromarty. *Died* 11 April 1979. *Firm*—Macandrew, Wright & Murray. (Retired.)

MURRAY, PATRICK [23 January 1703]. *Married* 2 June 1709, Jean, daughter of Alexander Simson, Litster, Edinburgh, widow of John Prophet, Wine Merchant at Holyroodhouse. *Died* 1 May 1728.

MURRAY, PATRICK [15 October 1873]. Apprentice to (1) Andrew Murray, Jun.; and (2) Donald Beith.—Son of Andrew Murray, Jun., W.S. *Born* 29 May 1850. *Married* 5 July 1877, Agnes Evelyn (*died* 15 October 1933), youngest daughter of Rev. John Congreve, Rector of Tooting Graveney, Surrey. *Died* 27 July 1930. *Firm*—Murray, Beith, and Murray.

MURRAY, PATRICK [15 July 1935]. Apprentice to Sir John Prosser and Others of Morton, Smart, Macdonald & Prosser.—Son of Andrew Ernest Murray, W.S. *Born* 13 May 1911. *Married* 4 January 1941, Doris Herbert, daughter of George Herbert Green, Insurance Official. V.R.D., R.N.V.R. 1935-55; Commander; Served U.K. and Iceland. *Firm*—Murray, Beith & Murray. (Consultant.)

MURRAY, PATRICK KEITH. *See* KEITH-MURRAY, PATRICK.

MURRAY, ROBERT [21 October 1673]. Apprentice to William Thomson.—Eldest son of John Murray, Merchant Burgess of Edinburgh. *Married* Marion, daughter of John Pollock, Cordwainer, Burgess of Edinburgh. *Buried* 29 December 1676.

MURRAY, THOMAS GRAHAM, OF STENTON, LL.D. [22 November 1838]. Apprentice to Adam Gib Ellis and Robert Ellis.—Son of Andrew Murray of Murrayshall, Perthshire, Advocate. *Born* 24 November 1816. *Married* 19 December 1848, Caroline (*died* 19 April 1906), daughter of John Tod of Kirkhill. Crown Agent, 1866-68. Father of Andrew Graham Murray, first Viscount Dunedin. *Died* 10 May 1891.

MURRAY, THOMAS MIDDLETON, OF GEANIES [20 October 1884]. Apprentice to D. Beith, A. Forrester, P. Murray, and R. D. Beith.—Second son of Kenneth Murray of Geanies, Ross-shire. *Born* 27 March 1860. *Married* 8 June 1887, Caroline (*died* 15 February 1942), daughter of Walter Ross Macdonald, Barrister, Hamilton, Ontario, Canada. *Died* suddenly 21 February 1935. *Firm*—Macandrew, Wright, and Murray.

MURRAY, WILLIAM, OF POLMAISE [12 January 1706]. Apprentice to Alexander Glass.— Son of John Murray of Polmaise, Stirlingshire. *Born* 10 October 1679. *Married* (1) Cecilia Gibson, widow of John Bayne of Logie; and (2) 10 February 1738, Elizabeth, only daughter of Alexander Gibson of Pentland. *Died* 25 June 1758.

MURRAY, WILLIAM, OF CONLAND [23 February 1816]. Apprentice to Thomas Megget.— Son of Andrew Murray of Conland, Fife. *Born* 26 June 1783. *Married* Mary Thompson —— (*died* in 1871). *Died* 25 October 1848.

MURRAY, WILLIAM CLEGHORN [17 November 1864]. Apprentice to John Anthony Macrae.—Only son of John Murray, S.S.C. *Born* 4 October 1837. Name removed from the Roll, 5 February 1923, as he had not been heard of for a great many years.

MURRAY, WILLIAM HUGH [14 November 1872]. Apprentice to Frederick Pitman.— Son of William Murray, S.S.C. *Born* 5 March 1850. *Married* 14 February 1901, Ethel Natalie (*died* 16 March 1923), elder daughter of David Younger, Brewer, Edinburgh. *Died* at Dunbar, 24 September 1921. *Firm*—J. and F. Anderson.

MUSTARD, ALEXANDER LOW, LL.B. [9 December 1912]. Apprentice to William Blair and James Watt.—Son of Alexander Mustard, S.S.C. *Born* 23 January 1889. *Married* 14 September 1916, Eliza Russell (*died* 30 March 1976), second daughter of James M'Gregor Jack, S.S.C., Edinburgh. Captain Royal Scots; wounded, 1918. *Died* 16 April 1949. *Firm*—Grigor and Young, Elgin.

MUTCH, JOHN HAROLD, B.A.(CANTAB), LL.B. [21 July 1970]. Apprentice to Alexander James Ramsay Bisset and Another of Baillie & Gifford.—Son of Wilfred Ernest Mutch, Advertising Manager, Manchester. *Born* 18 September 1933. *Married* 15 July 1961, Rosemary Lindsay, daughter of James King Annand, Schoolmaster and Poet. *Firm*— Biggart, Baillie & Gifford (formerly Baillie & Gifford).

MUTTER-NAPIER, ARCHIBALD DAVID [30 October 1893]. Apprentice to W. T. Dickson.—Son of John Mutter, residing at 29 Chalmers Street, Edinburgh. *Born* 28 July 1868. *Married* 1 June 1897, Annie Thomson (*died* 14 February 1944), daughter of Rev. Alexander Thomson Cosens, Minister of Broughton, Peeblesshire. Assumed the name of Mutter-Napier, 1900. Major Northumberland Fusiliers in Great War. Mentioned in Despatches. *Died* 15 March 1944.

MYLLER, ARCHIBALD [Before 1595]. *Married* Agnes Creichie.

MYLNE, JAMES [20 February 1834]. Apprentice to Alexander Pearson.—Son of George Mylne, Manager of Edinburgh Life Assurance Company. *Born* 25 March 1807. *Married* 16 July 1839, Emelia Elizabeth (*died* 14 March 1896), second daughter of William Roberts, Banker, Glasgow. *Died* 3 December 1879.

MYLNE, JAMES [29 June 1871]. Apprentice to John M. Lindsay and Alexander Howe.—Third son of James Mylne, W.S. *Born* 8 April 1846. *Married* 5 November 1877, Jane Ramsay (*died* 9 November 1923), second daughter of William Ramsay Kermack, W.S. *Died* at North Berwick, 17 September 1927.

MYLNE, JAMES GRAHAM, B.A. [8 December 1913]. Apprentice to James Mylne and A. B. Campbell.—Son of James Mylne, W.S. (1871). *Born* 7 December 1886. Lieutenant The Royal Scots; served in Palestine and France. *Killed* in action on 2 September 1918.

MYLNE, JOHN MILLAR [11 December 1828]. Apprentice to George Dunlop.—Son of James Mylne, Professor of Moral Philosophy in the University of Glasgow. *Born* 5 July 1804. *Married* 28 January 1843, Margaret (*died* 1892), daughter of Dr John Thomson. *Died* 30 January 1880.

MYLNE, WILLIAM KERMACK [11 December 1905]. Apprentice to John Ord Mackenzie, H. Cheyne, G. Kermack, and F. J. G. Borthwick.—Son of William Roberts Mylne, C.A., Edinburgh. *Born* 19 February 1881. *Died* 16 September 1941.

NAIRN, AINSLIE JAMES WILLIAM, B.L., Ph.D.(FLORIDA) [24 April 1954]. Apprentice to (1) James Douglas Cochrane of Alston, Nairn & Hogg; (2) Andrew White Young and Others of J. & R. A. Robertson.—Son of Eric William Herbert Nairn, S.S.C., Edinburgh. *Born* 20 September 1930. *Married* (1) 14 February 1956, Sheila Hamilton Gunn (*died* 31 December 1962), daughter of Ben Gunn Fowler, and (2) 30 March 1964, Sheila, daughter of Duncan Don Donnelly. Baron of Ballencrieff in the Nobility of Scotland. *Firm*—Alston, Nairn & Hogg.

NAIRNE, CHARLES [29 May 1819]. Apprentice to James Nairne, his brother.—Youngest son of Rev. James Nairne of Claremont, D.D., Minister of Pittenweem. *Born* 23 December 1794. *Married* 20 September 1820, Amelia Forbes (*died* 20 March 1874), daughter of Rev. Andrew Bell of Kilduncan, Minister of Crail. *Died* 20 January 1837.

NAIRNE, JAMES, OF CLAREMONT [8 June 1804]. Apprentice to Edward Bruce.—Second son of Rev. James Nairne of Claremont, D.D., Minister of Pittenweem. *Born* 29 August 1782. *Married* 9 April 1807, Elizabeth (*died* 1869), eldest daughter of Dr John Hill of Brownhills, Fife, Professor of Humanity in the University of Edinburgh. Fiscal, 1824-1844. *Died* 20 October 1847.

NAIRNE, JAMES [16 November 1843]. Apprentice to James Nairne.—Eldest son of Charles Nairne, W.S. *Born* 8 August 1821. Secretary of the North British Railway Company, 1852-66. *Died* 26 March 1866, unmarried.

NAPIER, A. D. MUTTER. *See* MUTTER-NAPIER, ARCHIBALD DAVID.

NAPIER, ALEXANDER JOHN [8 July 1847]. Apprentice to (1) Richard Campbell; and (2) John Mackenzie Lindsay.—Youngest son of George Napier of Dales, Linlithgowshire, S.S.C. *Born* 7 November 1824. *Married* 18 October 1867, Elizabeth Isabella (*died* 8 November 1907), daughter of David Stevenson, C.E., Edinburgh. *Died* 27 December 1903.

NAPIER, ALISTAIR GRAHAM, LL.B. [11 December 1978]. (By Rule IX(a).)—Son of Edward George Napier, Accountant, Basingstoke, Hampshire. *Born* 27 September 1944. *Married* 3 June 1967, Irene Scott, daughter of Robert Baird, Accountant, Falkirk. *Firm*—Kippen, Campbell & Burt, Perth.

NAPIER, ANDREW, M.A., LL.B. [26 November 1962]. (By Rule IX(a).)—Son of Robert Andrew Napier, Gas Manager. *Born* 31 July 1914. *Married* 26 June 1943, Lilian Violet Ritchie. Served in Black Watch. Discharged after receiving severe burns in Gibraltar, 1941. *Died* as the result of an accident, 2 November 1967. *Firm*—Condie, Mackenzie & Co., Perth.

NAPIER, FRANCIS [10 July 1794]. Apprentice to Alexander Duncan.—Eldest son of Hon. Mark Napier, Colonel, 32nd Foot. *Born* 20 August 1770. *Married* 30 March 1796, Mary Elizabeth Jane Douglas (*died* 1838), eldest daughter of Colonel Archibald Hamilton of Innerwick, East Lothian. Collector of Widows' Fund, 1805-18. *Died* 11 June 1818.

NAPIER, MACVEY [6 December 1799]. Apprentice to John Campbell of Annfield.— Eldest son of John Macvey of Braes, Dunbartonshire. *Born* 12 April 1776. In 1789 he matriculated at Glasgow University as Napier Macvey. *Married* 24 April 1798, Catherine (*died* 17 March 1826), daughter of Captain David Skene of Pitfour. Librarian to the Society, 9 December 1805 to 20 June 1837. Professor of Conveyancing, 1816-47. Principal Clerk of Session, 12 May 1837 till death. Editor of *Edinburgh Review*, 1829, and of the *Encyclopaedia Britannica* (seventh edition). Author of *Lord Bacon and Sir Walter Raleigh*, 1853, and other works. His mother was a daughter of John Napier of Craigannat and he changed his name at request of his grandfather (*Dict. Nat. Biog.*). *Died* 11 February 1847.

NAPIER, WILLIAM [4 March 1824]. Apprentice to (1) Francis Napier; and (2) David Cleghorn.—Eldest son of George Napier of Dales, Linlithgowshire, S.S.C. *Born* 1801. *Married* 28 April 1828, Mary (*died* 25 May 1876), eldest daughter of Alexander Low, Aberdeen. *Died* 17 June 1849.

NASMYTH, MICHAEL [19 December 1767]. Apprentice to James Hay of Cocklaw.— Only son of Bailie Michael Nasmyth, Schoolmaster in Lochwinnoch, Renfrewshire. *Died* November 1777.

NEAVES, WILLIAM [7 March 1833]. Apprentice to Alexander Pearson.—Son of Charles Neaves, Writer in Edinburgh. *Born* 15 February 1810. *Died* at Demerara, 18 December 1841, unmarried.

NEILL, ROBERT [4 December 1655]. *Married* 25 January 1644, Isobel Measlet. *Buried* 7 September 1663.

NEILSON, JOHN [18 November 1861]. Apprentice to George Greig.—Eldest son of Alexander Neilson, Writer in Port Glasgow. *Born* 19 November 1836. *Married* 1 August 1867, Elizabeth Maxton (*died* 9 February 1920), youngest daughter of John Barr Cumming of Lloyd's, Greenock. *Died* 30 July 1892.

NEILSON, JOHN [7 December 1970]. Apprentice to Ronald Kenneth Watson and Another of Brodie, Cuthbertson & Watson.—Son of John Neilson, Surgeon, Dumfries. *Born* 22 August 1943. *Married* 5 November 1964, Mattine Macrae, daughter of Matthew Fleming, Businessman. *Firm*—Brodies.

NEILSON, STUART [21 November 1850]. Apprentice to John Irving.—Son of James Neilson of Millbank. *Born* 10 December 1809. *Died* 10 May 1886, unmarried.

NEILSON, WILLIAM [12 December 1627]. Servitor to Thomas Coutts. Admitted in his place. *Married* Marion Cunyngham (*died* 9 December 1667).

NEISCHE, WALTER, OF WESTER DUBHEADS.—Son of Walter Neische of Wester Dubheads; retoured heir to his father, 13 December 1637.

NEISH, CRAWFORD [19 May 1959]. (By Rule IX(a).)—Son of James Crawford Neish, Hotel Keeper. *Born* 8 July 1903. *Married* 12 July 1938, Gertrude Mary (*died* 15 September 1979), daughter of Charles Spier, Publican. *Died* 16 March 1977. *Firm*— J. C. & A. Steuart.

NEWALL, JOHN, LL.B. [24 April 1972]. Apprentice to James Barron Lloyd and Others of Skene, Edwards & Garson.—Son of John Hamilton Newall, Dumfries. *Born* 6 August 1942. *Married* 20 July 1967, Gaye, daughter of Norman Ronald Tuddenham, Laurieston. *Firm*—Skene, Edwards & Garson. (Resigned 1978.)

NEWALL, MARTIN, OF BARNEBACHALL [Before 1615]. Apprentice to John Buchanan.— *Married* Euphan Kincaid. *Died* about 1629.

NEWBIGGING, JOHN STEUART [26 June 1832]. Apprentice to Walter Dickson.—Son of Sir William Newbigging, Surgeon in Edinburgh. *Born* 20 January 1809. *Married* 30 June 1840, Elizabeth (*died* 16 December 1879), daughter of James Flemyng, Killiechassie, Perthshire. Sheriff-Clerk of Roxburghshire, 1841-49. *Died* 25 October 1849.

NEWLANDS, HARRY SCOTT, C.M.G. [8 December 1908]. Apprentice to John Ewart.— Son of Andrew Newlands, S.S.C. *Born* 9 February 1884. Assistant Commissioner Gold Coast, 1910. District Commissioner, 1912. Served with Togoland Field Force, 1914. Private Secretary to Governor of Gold Coast. Deputy Provisional Commissioner and Secretary for Native Affairs. Chief Commissioner, Ashanti, 1930. Governor and Commander-in-Chief of Barbados, 1932. *Died* in Barbados, 12 March 1933.

NEWLANDS, ROBERT [Before 1606]. Signs Minute of 17 January 1606.

NEWTON, JAMES, OF CASTLANDHILL [23 November 1819]. Apprentice to Craufurd Tait.— Eldest son of James Newton, Baker in Edinburgh. *Died* 18 June 1861, aged 65, unmarried.

NEWTON, WILLIAM WARING HAY, OF NEWTON [24 May 1821]. Apprentice to William Mackenzie.—Second son of William Hay Newton of Newton, Mid-Lothian. *Born* 20 September 1795. *Married* (1) 19 June 1821, Jane Frances (*died* 5 April 1833), only child of Thomas Gregson of Blackburn; and (2) 15 February 1844, Jane (*died* 1872), daughter of James Clark Rattray of Craighall, Perthshire, Advocate. *Died* 15 May 1860.

NIBLIE, ARCHIBALD [5 August 1777]. Apprentice to Walter Ross.—Son of Archibald Niblie, Tenant in Elphinstone. *Married*, proclaimed 27 November 1777, Margaret, only daughter of John Rannie of Myles. *Died* 21 March 1779.

NICHOLS, DAVID IAN, M.A.(CANTAB), Ph.D.(LEICESTER) [4 December 1972]. Apprentice to Kenneth Alexander Stewart Leslie and Others of Gillespie & Paterson.— Son of Hugh Glen Glendower Nichols, Solicitor. *Born* 3 March 1943. *Married* 7 April 1973, Janet Mary Cameron, daughter of Alexander Stewart Alison, Engineer. Major Scholar of Jesus College, Cambridge.

NICOLL, HENRY [3 January 1683]. Apprentice to James Cheyne.—*Married* 28 December 1677, Christian Leishman. *Died* December 1704.

NICOLL, JOHN [19 November 1609]. Apprentice to David Anderson.—*Married* (1) 21 October 1606, Bessie (*died* August 1627), daughter of James Thomson, Merchant Burgess, Edinburgh; and (2) (contract, 20 April 1628), Magdalen, daughter of Andrew Hutchison, Merchant Burgess, Edinburgh. Clerk of Society, 1647-54. His *Diary of Public Transactions* (1650-67) published by Bannatyne Club. Re-admitted, 21 November 1661. *Died* February 1668.

NICOLL, JOHN [13 April 1650].—Son of John Nicoll, W.S. *Died* before 1685.

NICOLSON, ARTHUR BADENOCH, OF GLENBERVIE [13 July 1891]. Apprentice to Alexander Howe, William MacGillivray, and Alexander Yeaman.—Elder son of James Badenoch Nicolson of Glenbervie. *Born* 18 May 1865. *Married* 1 July 1897, Elizabeth Isobel (*died* 24 March 1960), elder daughter of Alexander John Napier, W.S. *Died* 25 February 1924.

NICOLSON, HAROLD ALEXANDER, M.A., LL.B. [26 July 1954]. Apprentice to James Harold Macdonald and Others of Morton, Smart, Macdonald & Prosser.—Son of the Rev. Angus Nicolson, Ph.D., Edinburgh. *Born* 20 February 1925. *Married* 17 May 1958, Elizabeth, daughter of Thomas O'Beirne. Served R.N.V.R. (Fleet Air Arm) in Canada. Collector of the Widows Fund, 1975-. *Firm*—Morton, Fraser & Milligan (formerly Morton, Smart, Macdonald & Prosser and Morton, Smart, Macdonald & Milligan).

NICOLSON, JAMES [Before 1550].—Son of David Nicolson, Sheriff-Clerk, Aberdeen, and Vicar of Maryculter. Sheriff-Clerk of Aberdeenshire, 29 May 1563. Resigned his Commission before 9 February 1565-66.

NICOLSON, LIONEL RUTHERFORD [13 July 1914]. Apprentice to W. P. Robertson.— Third son of Sir Arthur Thomas Bennet Robert Nicolson of that Ilk and Lasswade, Bart. *Born* 29 September 1887. *Married* 20 December 1932, Kathleen Mary, daughter of Henry Gane Moon, Shepton Mallet, Somerset. Lieutenant R.N.V.R., 1915. *Died* 17 May 1957.

NICOLSON, ROBERT [Before 1621]. *Married* Dame Katherine Lyell who was buried in Canongate, March 1630. *Died* about 1628.

NIMMO, ADAM PRENTICE [25 March 1901]. Apprentice to William Black Rankin.— Son of the Rev. James Nimmo, The Manse, Springfield, Fife. *Born* 4 September 1870. *Married* 3 April 1902, Gertrude Mary (*died* 19 February 1949), only daughter of the Rev. Percival Wood Hulbert, M.A., St Vincent's Rectory, Edinburgh. Lieutenant 1st Volunteer Batt. The Royal Scots. *Died* 13 July 1953. *Firm*—W. B. Rankin and Nimmo.

NIMMO, ANDREW, PORTIONER OF WESTBARNS [Before 1623]. Signs the Acts, 26 December 1627. *Married* Marion Ritchie. *Died* 27 September 1647.

NIMMO, JOHN [8 March 1802]. Apprentice to H. M. Buchanan.—Eldest son of Peter Nimmo Brewer in Edinburgh. *Married* Margaret Nimmo (*died* 16 January 1853). *Died* 1812.

NIMMO, WILLIAM, M.C., B.A.(CANTAB), LL.B. [19 December 1949]. Apprentice to Edmund Menzies of Allan, Dawson, Simpson & Hampton.—Son of Alexander Nimmo, Writer, Falkirk. *Born* 21 March 1918. *Married* 16 March 1954, Anne Elinor, daughter of Harry Macdonald Simson, W.S., Edinburgh. Major, Argyll & Sutherland Highlanders. Served in Burma. *Firm*—Russel & Aitken.

NIMMO-SMITH, ANDREW JAMES, B.L. [20 July 1950]. Apprentice to Harry Henderson Monteath and Another of Horne & Lyell.—Son of Francis Clement Nimmo-Smith, W.S., Edinburgh. *Born* 2 July 1924. Captain, Royal Scots. Served with 8th Battalion in France 1944. Wounded in Normandy July 1944. *Firms*—(1) Simpson, Kinmont & Maxwell (to 1965); (2) Dudgeon, Farmer & Matthews.

NISBET, ADAM [c. 1680].

NISBET, ARCHIBALD, OF CARFIN [16 July 1661]. Apprentice to Robert Hamilton.—Son of James Nisbet of Ladytoun. *Married* (1) 1671, Euphan, daughter of John Scroggie, Tailor, Edinburgh; and (2) 18 November 1692, Jean (*died* February 1722), daughter of Thomas Baillie of Polkemmet. *Died* July 1695.

NISBET, ARCHIBALD CHARLES, B.A.(OXON) [19 December 1927]. Apprentice to George F. Dalziel and Another of Tods, Murray & Jamieson.—Son of Christopher Charles Nisbet, W.S., Edinburgh. *Born* 21 July 1903. *Married* 21 December 1926, Anne Armit, daughter of Peter Annand, Engineer. Observer Lieutenant and Scottish Training Officer, Royal Observer Corps. Depute Group Commandant of 31 Group (Edinburgh and Borders). *Died* 16 February 1981. *Firm*—Tawse & Bonar. (Retired.)

NISBET, CHRISTOPHER CHARLES, OF STOBSHIEL [21 October 1874]. Apprentice to John Wardrobe Tawse, his uncle.—Son of Rev. Robert Nisbet, D.D., Minister of West St Giles', Edinburgh. *Born* 31 August 1851. *Married* 3 October 1894, Janet (*died* 5 January 1950), eldest daughter of Archibald Steuart, W.S. Member of King's Bodyguard for Scotland, Royal Company of Archers, 1885. Grand Commander of the Ancient and Accepted Scottish Rite. Author of History of the Signet Club 1808. *Died* 11 October 1940. *Firm*—Tawse and Bonar.

NISBET, JOHN, OF NISBETFIELD [26 July 1693]. Apprentice to Thomas Gordon.—*Married* 28 September 1682, Agnes, daughter of Henry Riddell, Portioner of Bewlie, Roxburghshire. *Died* 1716.

NISBET, MARK POLLOK, B.A.(CANTAB), LL.B. [19 December 1949]. Apprentice to David B. Bogle and Others of Lindsay, Howe & Co.—Son of John Elson Sinclair Nisbet, East India Merchant, Gattonside, Melrose. *Born* 27 July 1921. *Married* 24 March 1948, Margaret Inglis, daughter of Hugh Crombie Falconer, Farmer. Lieutenant, K.O.S.B. Served in East Africa and Sicily. *Firm*—James & David W. B. Tait, Kelso.

NIVEN, NORMAN ROBERT WILLIAM, LL.B. [15 July 1949]. Apprentice to Francis J. G. Borthwick and Another of Mackenzie & Kermack.—Son of William Niven, Newsagent, Tobacconist and Stationer, Sanquhar. *Born* 21 November 1921. *Married* 15 September 1949, Janet Dickie (*died* 26 September 1954), daughter of Thomas Gray, Master Butcher, Sanquhar. Commissioned with the Gurkhas. *Died* 28 August 1953.

NIVEN, ROBERT WILLIAM [1 July 1819]. Apprentice to David Ramsay.—Eldest son of Rev. Alexander Niven, Minister of Dunkeld. *Born* 8 April 1795. *Married* 11 March 1817, only daughter (*died* 17 April 1828) of Robert Brown, Westmoreland, Jamaica. *Died* 1 December 1832.

NOBLE, ALEXANDER BERTRAM [25 March 1901]. Apprentice to H. Auld, James Macdonald, and J. C. Auld.—Son of Alexander Noble, Manufacturing Chemist, Edinburgh. *Born* 2 July 1875. *Married* 16 October 1915, Agnes Alison (*died* 20 August 1954), youngest daughter of Robert Tod, London. *Died* 28 December 1931. *Firm*—Auld and Macdonald.

NOBLE, ALEXANDER HUGH, T.D., B.A.(Cantab), LL.B. [15 December 1947]. Apprentice to Robert Somerville and Others of Graham, Johnston & Fleming.—Son of Alexander Bertram Noble, W.S., Edinburgh. *Born* 10 February 1917. *Married* 18 October 1958, Norma Elizabeth, daughter of Norman Charles Grant, S.S.C., Edinburgh. Served R.A. in Italy, Second World War. Collector of the Widows Fund 1964-75. *Firm*—Haldanes, McLaren & Scott (formerly Haldanes & McLaren).

NOBLE, DAVID, M.A., LL.B., J.P. [30 November 1964]. (By Rule IX(a).)—Son of Donald Noble, Solicitor, Inverness. *Born* 11 February 1923. *Married* 12 July 1947, Marjorie Scott, daughter of James Scott Smith, Company Director, Cheshire. Flight Lieutenant, R.A.F. Served Bomber Command, Europe, and Provost Units, Malaya, 1942-46. *Firm*—Miller, Thomson & Robertson (formerly J. Miller Thomson & Co.).

NOBLE, IAIN WILLIAM, M.A., LL.B. [25 April 1955]. Apprentice to John Herbert Richardson and Others of Dundas & Wilson.—Son of Donald Noble, Solicitor, Inverness. *Born* 6 December 1925. *Married* 5 August 1960, Mary Evelyn Cameron, M.A., Ph.D., daughter of William Edward Henry Bird, Farmer, Kenya. Lieutenant, R.A. and R.I.A. Served in India, Malaya and Java 1939-45. Professor of Conveyancing, University of Edinburgh, 1973-. *Firm*—Dundas & Wilson.

NORIE, FRANCIS JAMES [11 January 1892]. Apprentice to W. S. Fraser.—Eldest son of Henry Hay Norie, W.S. *Born* 14 August 1867. *Married* 22 March 1909, Esther Elizabeth, daughter of Henry John Smith, Bricklayer, Westminster, London. *Divorce* 10 December 1910. *Died* 1 January 1946.

NORIE, HENRY HAY [9 February 1860]. Apprentice to Walter Jollie.—Son of Evelyn Thomas Francis Norie, Commander R.N., residing in Elgin. *Born* 8 June 1837. *Married* 8 September 1864, Christina (*died* 11 March 1907), second daughter of James Moir, Banker, Alloa. Manager of Union Bank of Scotland, Edinburgh, 1881-1900. *Died* 11 May 1900.

NORMAND GEORGE PRENTICE [28 March 1898]. Apprentice to William Traquair Dickson.—Son of Patrick Hill Normand of Whitehill, Aberdour, Fife. *Born* 20 June 1873. *Married* 7 March 1906, Mary Margaret (*died* 15 May 1942), elder daughter of Robert Beatson, W.S. Acting Paymaster Scottish Command during Great War. Held Royal Humane Society's Bronze Medal for saving life from drowning. *Died* 16 December 1948. *Firm*—Traquair, Dickson, and MacLaren.

NORMAND, RICHARD JOHN, M.C., T.D., M.A., LL.B. [14 December 1936]. Apprentice to A. St Clair Jameson and Another of Boyd, Jameson & Young.—Son of Patrick Hill Normand (Superintendent of Transvaal Prisons, South Africa), Colonial Service. *Born* 28 January 1912. *Married* 10 August 1942, Audrey Mary, daughter of Joseph Harry Green (Magistrate, South Africa), Colonial Service. Major, Infantry. Served U.K., France, West Africa, Holland and Germany 1939-45. *Firms*—(1) Traquair, Dickson & MacLaren, then Cowan & Dalmahoy, latterly Lindsay Howe & Co. (after amalgamation); now Lindsays.

NOTMAN, JAMES HUME [12 March 1894]. Apprentice to John Milligan.—Son of William Notman, Architect, Newhaven Road, Edinburgh. *Born* 17 August 1858. *Married* 11 June 1896, Mary (*died* 19 November 1927), eldest surviving daughter of Robert Carfrae, Edinburgh. Assistant Clerk and Extractor, 1889-1904. Appointed Substitute Keeper of the Signet, 22 September 1904. Clerk to the Society, 11 October 1904. *Died* 29 April 1934. *Firm*—J. and J. Milligan.

NOTMAN, ROBERT CARFRAE, O.B.E., T.D., B.L. [17 December 1923]. Apprentice to James Watt and Another of Davidson & Syme.—Son of James Hume Notman, W.S., Edinburgh. *Born* 4 March 1899. *Married* 26 December 1923, Mary Grace Rutherford, daughter of William James Cullen, The Hon. Lord Cullen, Senator of the College of Justice. First World War: R.M.A., Woolwich 1916-17; France, 1918; Germany, 1919. Second World War: Lt.-Colonel, R.A. Served U.K., France and North West Europe 1939-45. Assistant Clerk and Extractor to the Society 1931-52; Substitute Keeper and Clerk to the Society 1952-64. *Died* 16 October 1980. *Firms*—J. & J. Milligan; Morton, Smart, Macdonald & Milligan (after amalgamation)—now Morton, Fraser & Milligan. (Retired.)

OFFICER, JOHN LIDDELL, O.B.E., LL.B. [12 January 1891]. Apprentice to John Clark Junner.—Son of William Officer, S.S.C., Edinburgh. *Born* 16 May 1866. *Married* 6 June 1899, Adriana Moore (*died* 2 January 1954), second daughter of James Carmichael, F.R.C.P., M.D., Edinburgh. Clerk to the Convention of Royal Burghs of Scotland, 1906. *Died* 28 April 1945. *Firm*—W. and J. L. Officer.

OGILL, GEORGE [6 March 1650]. *Married* 2 June 1643, Margaret Guthrie.

OGILVIE, ALEXANDER [11 July 1905]. Apprentice to D. Smith Clark.—Son of Alexander Ogilvie, Farmer, Tillinaught, Portsoy, Banff. *Born* 18 April 1881. *Married* 16 June 1921, Effie Aird (*died* 13 January 1967), Ardross, Ross-shire. *Died* 15 December 1966. *Firm*—Gordon, Falconer & Fairweather.

OGILVIE, CHARLES MAXWELL, M.A., B.Com., LL.B. [28 April 1952]. Apprentice to Thomas Young of Gray, Muirhead & Carmichael. *Born* 27 January 1908. *Married* 2 September 1939, Elizabeth Campbell Ritchie. *Firm*—Gray, Muirhead & Carmichael. (Retired.)

OGILVIE, ROBERT GAVIN [20 November 1818]. Apprentice to Hugh Warrender.— Second son of Adam Ogilvie of Hartwoodmyres, Advocate. *Born* 1793. *Died* 14 July 1879, unmarried.

OGILVIE, WILLIAM ALEXANDER [19 July 1879]. Apprentice to Robert Burt Ranken.—Son of William Ogilvie, M.A., residing at Dyke, near Forres. *Born* 24 January 1851. *Died* 17 March 1884, unmarried.

OGILVIE-THOMSON, MICHAEL CLAUDE, B.A.(Cantab), LL.B. [23 July 1951]. Apprentice to Robert Francis Shepherd and Others of Shepherd & Wedderburn.—Son of Vice-Admiral E. C. Ogilvie-Thomson. *Born* 3 August 1921. *Married* 5 September 1959, Sara Jane, daughter of Major John Wilson. Served in R.A., in France and Italy. Second World War. *Died* 21 June 1967. *Firm*—Thorburn & Lyon, Peebles.

OGILVY, DAVID [26 June 1832]. Apprentice to Robert Macmillan.—Son of David Ogilvy, Painter in Edinburgh. *Born* 14 January 1805. *Married* 9 September 1841, Elizabeth Aitchison (*died* 26 November 1896), daughter of James Williamson of Trinity. Latterly a Solicitor in Melbourne. *Died* 17 July 1871.

OGILVY, ERIC STANLEY, M.A., LL.B. [25 April 1955]. Apprentice to Charles Ritchie Black and Another of Warden, Bruce & Co.—Son of William Ogilvy, S.S.C., Edinburgh. *Born* 29 January 1921. *Married* 13 October 1949, Agnes Lyall Gibb, daughter of Andrew Ednie Hall. 2nd Lieutenant, K.O.S.B., 1941-42. Served U.K. Ordinary Seaman, R.N., 1942-46. Coastal Forces, U.K. and N.W. Europe. *Firms*—(1) Warden, Bruce & Co.; (2) Stuart & Stuart (now Stuart & Stuart, Cairns & Co.).

OGILVY, Sir HERBERT KINNAIRD, of Inverquharity, Bart. [13 January 1891]. Apprentice to Alexander Howe and William MacGillivray.—Second son of Sir Reginald Howard Alexander Ogilvy of Inverquharity, Bart. *Born* 29 June 1865. *Married* 15 December 1904, the Lady Christian Augusta Bruce (*died* 12 September 1940), second daughter of Victor Alexander, Earl of Elgin and Kincardine, K.G. Succeeded his nephew as Baronet, November 1914. Deputy Lieutenant for the County of Angus. *Died* 1 March 1956. *Firm*—Shiell and Small, Dundee.

OLIPHANT, ÆNEAS, of Balgonie [4 April 1707]. Apprentice to James Menzies.—Son of —— Oliphant of Condie. *Died* 23 February 1716.

OLIPHANT, CHARLES [4 December 1794]. Apprentice to William Balderston.—Son of Charles Oliphant, Merchant in Edinburgh. *Born* 1771. *Married* 2 July 1830, Eleanor (*died* 20 March 1847), daughter of Sir James Campbell of Aberuchill, Bart., and widow of Dr John Barclay. *Died* 28 October 1852.

OLIPHANT, COLIN PILKINGTON LYLE, B.A.(Oxon), LL.B. [2 December 1974]. Apprentice to James Todd Black of John Dickson & Son, Huntly, Aberdeenshire.— Son of Morton Duff Oliphant, Sugar Refiner, London. *Born* 5 January 1948. *Married* 3 July 1971, Anne Meredith, daughter of Bernard Henry Fawcett. *Firm*—John Dickson & Son, Huntly.

OLIPHANT, HARRY [Before 1613]. *Married* (1) 1 May 1605, Margaret, daughter of James Bartone, Burgess, Edinburgh; and (2) 11 August 1614, Sarah Colvin. *Died* 2 September 1636.

OLIPHANT, KENNETH MORTON, M.C. [20 March 1922]. Apprentice to John Henry Sang and Alan Welwood Hog.—Son of James Oliphant, Headmaster Charlotte Square Institution, and later Inspector of Schools to University of London. *Born* 24 May 1885. *Married* 28 July 1911, Florence Agnes (*died* 23 November 1937), daughter of Abram Lyle, Sugar Refiner. Served in Great War, September 1914 to August 1919; M.C. and mentioned in Despatches. *Died* 14 February 1946. *Firm*—Pearson, Robertson, and Maconochie.

OLIPHANT, LAURENCE [23 February 1680]. Apprentice to William Lockhart.—Eldest son of Laurence Oliphant of Orchardmilne. *Married* (1) (contract, 24 April 1667), Catherine, daughter of Patrick Murray of Woodend; and (2) Margaret Hepburn (*died* 7 February 1696). Clerk to the Admission of Notaries. *Buried* 16 September 1690.

OLIPHANT, PATRICK JAMES, T.D., B.A.(Oxon), LL.B. [19 December 1938]. Apprentice to Sir Kenneth Murray and Others of Macandrew, Wright & Murray.—Son of Kenneth Morton Oliphant, M.C., W.S., Edinburgh. *Born* 19 March 1914. *Married* 9 August 1938, Margaret Kemp (*died* 23 October 1979), daughter of James Brown, Ironfounder. Lieutenant Colonel, R.A. Served U.K., Egypt, Libya, Tunisia, Sicily and Italy 1939-45. Wounded at Anzio, May 1944. Deputy Keeper of the Signet 1964-75. *Died* 1 January 1979. *Firm*—Pearson, Robertson & Maconochie.

OLIPHANT, ROBERT, of Rossie [14 November 1883]. Apprentice to Æneas Macbean.— Eldest son of Lieut.-Colonel James Stewart Oliphant of Rossie, Perthshire. *Born* 23 February 1810. *Married* 20 March 1836. Susan Mary Elizabeth (*died* 1878), only child of Thomas Tod, Judge of the Commissary Court. *Died* 14 November 1872.

OLIPHANT, STUART, OF ROSSIE [16 March 1896]. Apprentice to Alexander Howe, W. MacGillivray, A. Yeaman, and J. Brookman.—Eldest son of Thomas Truman Oliphant of Rossie. *Born* 12 June 1872. *Married* 3 June 1914, Yvonne Marie Frances (*died* 16 January 1957), daughter of R. W. Mansfield of H.B.M. Consular Service in China. *Killed* by fall from train near Hatfield, 18 September 1918. *Firm*—Oliphant & Murray.

OLIVER, CHARLES KEITH, LL.B. [8 December 1981*].—Son of R. R. Oliver, Company Director, North Berwick. *Born* 21 April 1952. *Firm*—Dundas & Wilson.

OLIVER, JAMES SCOTT [21 July 1924]. Apprentice to Hamilton Maxwell of Kinmont & Maxwell.—Son of James John Oliver, Solicitor, Hawick. *Born* 24 October 1900. *Married* 12 April 1951, Mary Elliot, daughter of Major Anthony Gilchrist McCall, I.C.S. *Died* 9 March 1977. *Firm*—George & James Oliver, Hawick.

OLIVER, JOHN ANTHONY LINDSAY [11 December 1979]. Apprentice to Michael Henry David Armstrong of George & James Oliver, Hawick.—Son of James Scott Oliver, W.S., Hawick. *Born* 18 September 1952. *Firm*—George & James Oliver, Hawick.

OLIVER, WILLIAM GEORGE BEAUCHAMP, LL.B. [17 December 1923]. Apprentice to Sir Colin G. Macrae, Robert J. R. Flett, and Norman S. Pringle-Pattison.—Son of James Oliver, J.P., Agent of the Commercial Bank of Scotland Ltd., at Leith. *Born* 13 January 1895. War Service: Recruiting Staff, Edinburgh District, 1916; 2nd Lieutenant H.L.I., 1917; France, 1918. *Died* 12 September 1967.

ORD, ALEXANDER [4 June 1674]. Apprentice to Richard Guthrie.—*Married* 28 August 1679, Agnes Gordon. *Buried* 23 December 1690.

O'RIORDAN, FREDERICK ERNEST, M.A., LL.B. [17 July 1939]. Apprentice to James Watt and Others of Davidson & Syme.—Son of Ernest Timothy O'Riordan, Officer, H.M. Customs and Excise, Edinburgh. *Born* 19 April 1911. *Married* 21 December 1940, Enid Olivia, daughter of Cyril Lewis Laurent, M.B., Ch.B. Flight Lieutenant, R.A.F. Served U.K. and Burma 1942-45 (Intelligence Officer). *Died* 12 April 1981. *Firm*—Davidson & Syme (1946-51).

ORME, ALEXANDER, OF MUGDRUM [3 February 1755]. Apprentice to Archibald Stuart.—Eldest son of Alexander Orme of Balvaird, Writer in Edinburgh. *Married* Helen (*died* 26 May 1815), daughter of Henry Sinclair of Swining, Shetland, Town Clerk of Musselburgh. Principal Clerk of Session, 14 November 1777 till death. *Died* 8 January 1789.

ORR, ALEXANDER, OF WATERSIDE [3 February 1755]. Apprentice to Robert Dalrymple.—Son of Mr Alexander Orr, Minister of Hoddam. *Born* 22 March 1725. *Married* July 1761, Elizabeth (*died* 18 March 1811), daughter of Ludovick Cant of Thurston, East Lothian. *Died* 27 November 1774.

ORR, CHARLES JAMES FOX, OF THORNLY PARK [14 June 1814]. Apprentice to Robert Hill.—Son of James Orr of Thornly Park, Renfrewshire. *Married* 15 October 1816, Elizabeth (*died* 27 November 1887), youngest daughter of Robert Orr, Paisley. *Died* 8 February 1849.

ORR, JAMES ALEXANDER MACCONNELL, M.A., LL.B. [3 January 1963]. Apprentice to A. J. R. Bisset and Others of Baillie & Gifford.—Son of J. MacConnell Orr, Solicitor, Oban. *Born* 4 June 1939. *Married* 26 January 1963, Helen Claire, daughter of David Band, Surgeon. *Firm*—Macarthur, Stewart & Orr, Oban, Lochgilphead and Edinburgh.

ORR, JOHN ROGER, C.B.E., B.L. [19 March 1923]. Apprentice to David W. Marwick.— Son of Charles Roger Orr, C.B.E., Engineer, Edinburgh. *Born* 20 August 1892, Rosamund Helen Shaen, younger daughter of Colonel Ottley Lane Perry, T.D., J.P., North Loyal Lancashire Regiment, of Roxwell, Northwood, Middlesex. *Died* 14 April 1973, at Lakefield, Ontario. *Firm*—Simpson and Marwick.

ORR, PATRICK [12 August 1799]. Apprentice to William Macfarlane.—Second son of Patrick Orr of Bridgeton, Kincardineshire. *Married* 25 December 1814, Margaret Caroline (*died* 4 August 1861), second daughter of Major Martin Lindsay, younger of Kilconquhar, Fife. Sheriff-Clerk of Forfarshire, 1812-48. *Died* 19 July 1848.

ORR EWING, RONALD JAMES, LL.B. [24 April 1972]. Apprentice to David Blyth Bogle and Others of Lindsays.—Son of Sir Ronald Orr Ewing, Bt., Landed Proprietor, Cardross, Kippen. *Born* 9 January 1948. *Firm*—J. C. & A. Steuart.

OSBURN, HARRY [Before 1627]. Apprentice to Patrick Bannatyne.—Commissioner, 1631. *Married* (1) ——; (2) Alison Flemyng; (3) 23 June 1642, Janet Blair. *Died* 22 May 1655.

OSWALD, ROGER [7 June 1705]. Apprentice to Thomas Aikman.—Son of Sir James Oswald of Fingalton. *Married* Helen Sydserff. *Died* 9 June 1729, aged 50.

OSWALD, WILLIAM [Before 1627]. Apprentice to Anthony Whyte. *Buried* in Canongate, January 1632.

PAGAN, CHARLES DAVID, O.B.E., B.L. [19 December 1932]. Apprentice to Sir William Stowell Haldane and Another of W. & F. Haldane.—Son of Robert Osborne Pagan, W.S., Cupar, Fife. *Born* 7 June 1907. *Married* 2 January 1932, Mary, daughter of F. Malcolm Garnham, Metal Merchant, London. Author of "Justices of the Peace Handbook" (1955). *Firm*—Pagan & Osborne, latterly Pagan, Osborne & Grace, Cupar and St Andrews. (Consultant.)

PAGAN, CHARLES WILLIAM, B.A.(Cantab), LL.B. [7 December 1970]. Apprentice to A. F. Stark and Others of Morton, Fraser & Milligan.—Son of Charles David Pagan, W.S., Cupar, Fife. *Born* 22 June 1943. *Married* 19 July 1974, Gillian Morag Drummond. *Firm*—Pagan, Osborne & Grace, Cupar and St Andrews.

PAGAN, GRAEME HENRY, B.L. [28 July 1958]. Apprentice to A. Logan McClure and Another of Mackenzie & Black.—Son of Charles D. Pagan, W.S., Cupar, Fife. *Born* 20 March 1936. *Married* (1) 14 September 1960, Margaret Maria Jardine (divorced); (2) 25 May 1974, Susan Fiona Ferguson. *Firm*—Hosack & Sutherland, Oban.

PAGAN, ROBERT OSBORNE [16 July 1888]. Apprentice to James H. Jameson.— Younger son of George Hair Pagan, Sheriff-Clerk of Fife, Cupar. *Born* 17 October 1865. *Married* 9 October 1890, Emy (*died* 9 June 1943), eldest daughter of John Young, M.D., Regius Professor of Natural History and Honeyman Gillespie Lecturer on Geology, Glasgow University. Clerk of the Peace of Fife, 22 June 1903. Provost of Cupar, 1921-25. Member of Royal Commission on Licensing, 1929-30. *Died* at Cupar, 8 May 1935. *Firm*—Pagan and Osborne, Cupar.

PAIP, JOHN [Before 1594]. Apprentice to John Hay. Signs Minute of 16 December 1594. *Married* 4 October 1598, Mariot Bassindyne.

PAID, JOHN [c. 1620-38].

PANTON, WILLIAM, OF BLACKHOUSE [9 December 1672]. Apprentice to James Cheyne.—Son of James Panton of Blackhouse, Aberdeenshire. *Married* (1) 5 January 1673, Marjorie Halliburton, widow of Patrick Watt, Writer, Edinburgh; and (2) Helen Edgar (*died* 1 December 1701). *Died* before 1713.

PARKER, JOHN JAMES [25 November 1852]. Apprentice to Richard and John Ord Mackenzie.—Fourth son of John Parker, Principal Extractor of the Court of Session. *Born* 1 October 1829. *Married* 31 July 1855, Hannah (*died* 16 January 1890), only child of James Spittal, Edinburgh. *Died* 22 March 1908.

PATERSON, ADAM, OF WHITELEE [12 November 1829]. Apprentice to John Tod.—Son of Adam Paterson, residing in Galashiels. *Born* 1 February 1799. *Married* 18 November 1835, Elizabeth (*died* 7 August 1871), fourth daughter of David Scott, Farmer at Northfield, Duddingston. *Died* 14 June 1875.

PATERSON, ARTHUR BOURNE, OF BIRTHWOOD [10 January 1887]. Apprentice to J. O. Mackenzie, Harry Cheyne, and John Kermack.—Son of Robert Paterson of Birthwood, Lanarkshire. *Born* 29 October 1860. *Married* 17 April 1902, Constance (*died* 10 January 1914), youngest daughter of Archibald Macinder, Montreal. *Died* 26 October 1907.

PATERSON, CHARLES JOHN, LL.B. [16 July 1928]. Apprentice to E. M. Wedderburn, R. F. Shepherd, and R. W. Cockburn.—Son of Charles Alfred Paterson, Advocate, Madras. *Born* 8 October 1892. *Married* 10 February 1917, Ada May (*died* 22 June 1973), daughter of Rev. Mungo Reid, D.D., Newton Mearns. Served in 1917-19 in Royal Flying Corps and Royal Air Force. *Died* 16 June 1971. *Firm*—Shepherd and Wedderburn.

PATERSON, HEW OR HUGH, OF BANNOCKBURN (?) [Before 1627]. Signs the Acts, 26 December 1627.

PATERSON, SIR HUGH, OF BANNOCKBURN, 1ST BART. [10 April 1661]. Apprentice to Richard Guthrie.—Son of Hugh Paterson of Bannockburn, Stirlingshire. *Married* 18 August 1654, Elizabeth (*died* January 1689), daughter of Sir Thomas Kerr of Fernyhurst. Deputy Keeper of the Signet, 28 September 1682. Created a Baronet, 29 March 1686. Lieutenant in College of Justice Company for Service against the Rebels, 1679. *Died* October 1696.

PATERSON, HUGH [29 September 1682]. Apprentice to Sir Hugh Paterson of Bannockburn, W.S.—*Married* 7 April 1675, Mary Scott (*died* 17 February 1689). *Died* 5 May 1690.

PATERSON, JAMES, OF WHITELEE [12 November 1868]. Apprentice to James Mackenzie, J. B. Innes, and C. B. Logan.—Only son of Adam Paterson of Whitelee, Roxburghshire, W.S. *Born* 1 April 1845. *Married* (1) 17 April 1872, Mary Frances Hester (*died* 1874), third daughter of Sir Edmund Samuel Hayes of Drumboe Castle, Donegal, Bart.; and (2) 16 November 1882, Mary Georgina (*died* 19 February 1945), youngest daughter of Thomas Hodgkinson of Elm Leigh, Havant, Captain, R.N. *Died* 7 December 1888.

PATERSON, JAMES DOUGLAS STEWART, M.A., LL.B. [14 December 1936]. Apprentice to Finlay Ramage and Another of Steedman, Ramage & Co.—Son of William L. H. Paterson, S.S.C., Edinburgh. *Born* 28 March 1912. *Married* 10 August 1940, Christina Laura, daughter of Doctor W. Carrick Anderson, D.Sc., Strathblane, Dunbartonshire. Major, R.A. Served U.K., France and N.W. Europe 1939-45. *Firm*—Robson, McLean & Paterson. (Retired 1978.)

PATERSON, JOHN GEORGE GRAHAM [8 July 1913]. Apprentice to C. C. Nisbet.—Son of Robert Paterson Paterson of Montgomerie, Tarbolton, Ayrshire. *Born* 16 August 1887. On Recruiting Staff: Lieutenant Territorial Force Reserve in Great War. *Died* 14 May 1935.

PATERSON, JOSEPH [23 May 1808]. Apprentice to George Robinson.—Youngest son of George Paterson, Merchant in East Sheen, Surrey. *Born* 1778. *Died* 16 February 1832, unmarried.

PATERSON, NEIL DOUGLAS STEWART, LL.B. [11 December 1979]. Apprentice to Norman Croumbie Macpherson and Others of Robson, McLean & Paterson—Son of James Douglas Stewart Paterson, W.S. *Born* 1 January 1950. *Married* 4 March 1978, Jane Stewart, daughter of Lt. Commander William McKee, R.N. (Retd.). *Firm*—Robson, McLean & Paterson.

PATERSON, ROBERT. *See* WALLACE, ROBERT PATERSON.

PATERSON, THOMAS [14 July 1859]. Apprentice to Adam Paterson.—Son of John Paterson, Agent Royal Bank of Scotland at Dalkeith. *Born* 11 July 1834. *Maried* (1) 16 July 1902, Mary Campbell Craig (*died* 8 May 1905); and (2) 30 January 1907, Alice (*died* 14 March 1923), third daughter of John Mortimer, Elland, Brodie, Forres. *Died* 13 May 1911.

PATERSON, TOM SMITH [12 March 1893]. Apprentice to A. W. Black and A. L. Menzies.—Son of John Thomas Scott Paterson, Farmer, Plean, Bannockburn. *Born* 23 July 1869. *Married* 21 July 1897, Madge Steedman, elder daughter of George Bogie, Solicitor and Banker, Kinross. Extractor of Court of Session, 24 November 1927. *Died* 28 November 1946.

PATERSON, WALTER [3 December 1632]. Apprentice to Anthony Whyte.—Son of Alexander Paterson, Apothecar-Burgess of Edinburgh. *Married* (1) 30 December 1634, Anne Inglis (*died* 1643); (2) Margaret, daughter of John Logan, Merchant, Edinburgh. Re-admitted, 21 November 1661. *Died* February 1662.

PATERSON, WILLIAM [8 March 1714]. Apprentice to John Cunningham,—Son of Sir Hugh Paterson of Bannockburn, Bart. *Died* April 1715.

PATERSON, WILLIAM [24 October 1892]. Apprentice to Alexander Howe, W. MacGillivray, and Alexander Yeaman.—Son of Charles Paterson, Melrose Bank, Laurencekirk. *Born* 2 December 1861. *Died* 15 August 1917.

PATISON, JOHN [10 July 1798]. Apprentice to Alexander Young of Harburn.—Son of John Patison, Town Clerk, Leith. *Born* 1773. *Married* 6 February 1801, Ann Ferguson (*died* 2 September 1829), daughter of Thomas Hill, Architect, Edinburgh. *Died* 9 May 1843.

PATISON, JOHN [21 December 1809]. Apprentice to Robert Boswell.—Eldest son of William Patison, Merchant in Edinburgh. *Born* 1784. *Married* 14 March 1815, Elizabeth (*died* 14 January 1863), eldest daughter of James Paterson, Merchant, Leith. *Died* 24 June 1832.

PATISON, JOHN [12 November 1835]. Apprentice to Alexander Dallas.—Son of John Patison, W.S. *Born* 19 October 1807. *Married* 11 April 1856, Frances Mackenzie (*died* 27 January 1892), daughter of Lieutenant William Marshall, R.N., Dunbar. *Died* 8 August 1871.

PATON, ROBERT [17 January 1822]. Apprentice to Walter Cook.—Son of Rev. John Paton, Minister of Lasswade. *Born* 2 January 1795. *Married* 26 September 1832, Isabella (*died* 17 October 1897), only daughter of Thomas Phipps, London. Procurator-Fiscal for Burgh of Selkirk. *Died* 25 January 1884.

PATON, VICTOR ALBERT NOEL [12 July 1887]. Apprentice to James Auldjo Jamieson, George Dalziel, James Craik, and John Wharton Tod.—Son of Sir Joseph Noel Paton, Kt., H.M. Limner for Scotland. *Born* 29 December 1862. *Married* 11 June 1901, Eva Jemima (*died* 6 December 1930), second daughter of John Wharton Tod, W.S. *Died* 6 April 1931. *Firm*—Gillespie and Paterson.

PATOUN, WILLIAM, OF PANHOLE [16 September 1681]. Apprentice to John Cuningham.—*Married* 30 December 1680, Ann Gray. Resigned his Commission, 2 February 1711. *Died* January 1715.

PATRICK, BRUCE ROBERTSON, B.A.(OXON), LL.B. [13 May 1980*].—Son of Francis Wheatly Patrick, Insurance Manager, Edinburgh. *Born* 26 November 1945. *Married* 9 February 1980, Hilary Jane, daughter of R. A. Sutton, Chartered Accountant, Bowden, Cheshire. *Firm*—Maclay, Murray & Spens.

PATRICK, SPENCER FRANCIS RODGER, LL.B. [13 May 1980*].—Son of Francis Wheatly Patrick, Insurance Manager, Edinburgh. *Born* 12 December 1943. *Married* 25 August 1967, Lilian Gail, Advocate, daughter of A. Findlay McFadzean, Solicitor, Glasgow. *Firm*—Maclay, Murray & Spens.

PATRICK, WILLIAM, OF ROUGHWOOD [28 June 1793]. Apprentice to David Stewart.—Third son of John Patrick of Treehorn, Ayrshire. *Died* 28 February 1861, aged 91, unmarried.

PATTEN, HUGH [30 May 1878]. Apprentice to (1) John Patten; and (2) John Cook.—Fourth son of John Patten, W.S. *Born* 7 July 1855. *Married* 3 September 1891, Mary Ellen (*died* 28 August 1957), younger daughter of James Hope, Eastbarns, East Lothian. *Died* 5 November 1924.

PATTEN, HUGO JOHN [24 March 1930]. Apprentice to William Babington, Joseph Inglis, and Joseph E. Inglis.—Son of Hugh Patten, W.S. *Born* 19 March 1906. *Married* 18 July 1940, Jean, widow of Lt.-Col. Noel Paton Cross, Edinburgh. Collector of the Widows' Fund 1950. *Died* 26 January 1956, as the result of a motor accident. *Firm*—W. and J. Cook.

PATTEN, JOHN [29 June 1827]. Apprentice to James Greig.—Fifth son of James Patten, Cashier of the Greenock Bank Company. *Born* 13 May 1805. *Married* 24 April 1848, Jane Maxwell Campbell (*died* 25 February 1891), daughter of Dugald MacDougall of Gallanach, Argyllshire. *Died* 9 March 1877.

PATTEN-MACDOUGALL, JOHN, OF GALLANACH [16 July 1873]. Apprentice to, and second son of, John Patten, W.S.—*Born* 2 October 1850. *Married* 7 October 1880, Helen Isabel (*died* 14 April 1939), daughter of James Johnston Grieve, M.P. for Greenock. *Died* 3 March 1928.

PATTISON, GILCHRIST GRAY [10 July 1899]. Apprentice to A. G. Muir.—Son of Gilchrist Gray Pattison, residing at Viewpark, Trinity, Edinburgh. *Born* 1 March 1875. *Married* 28 February 1914, Janet Fletcher, only daughter of John Dalziel Fairley, Lagos, Southern Nigeria. In Army Pay Corps, 1918-19. *Died* 29 May 1931.

PATTISON, JAMES [29 November 1820]. Apprentice to Peter Couper.—Son of Rev. James Pattison, Thornhill. *Born* 1794. *Married* 16 June 1829, Isobella (*died* 29 November 1863), youngest daughter of John Cockburn, Edinburgh. *Died* 24 June 1832.

PATTISON, WILLIAM RALPH [18 March 1869]. Apprentice to George Maclachan.— Son of George Handaside Pattison, Advocate, Sheriff of Roxburghshire. *Born* 12 July 1837. *Died* 26 March 1872, unmarried.

PATTON, JAMES MURRAY, OF GLENALMOND [8 February 1816]. Apprentice to (1) Robert Cathcart; and (2) James Dundas.—Son of James Patton, Sheriff-Clerk of Perthshire. *Born* 1792. *Married* —— (*died* 27 April 1877). Sheriff-Clerk of Perthshire, 1817-53. *Died* 25 December 1853.

PATTON, THOMAS, OF GLENALMOND [6 March 1817]. Apprentice to Alexander Young.— Son of James Patton, Sheriff-Clerk of Perthshire. *Died* 28 August 1866, aged 77, unmarried.

PATTULLO, COLIN ARTHUR, M.C., B.L. [15 December 1930]. Apprentice to John Patrick Pattullo, his brother.—Son of James A. Pattullo, S.S.C., Edinburgh. *Born* 22 November 1904. *Married* 19 November 1932, Elizabeth Mary (*died* 16 May 1952), daughter of Edward Bruce, D.L., Edinburgh. Major R.A. Service U.K. and France, North Africa and Italy 1939-44. *Died* of wounds in Italy 9 May 1944. *Firm*—M'Neill and Sime.

PATTULLO, DAVID PATRICK, M.A. [2 December 1974]. Apprenticed to (1) Lewis Neil Bilton and Another of Kilgour, McNeill & Sime; (2) Alan George Laurie Baxter and Another of Pagan, Osborne & Grace, Cupar.—Son of John Patrick Pattullo, W.S., Edinburgh. *Born* 27 November 1947. *Married* 24 July 1971, Sarah Elizabeth, daughter of Andrew L'Estrange Brownlow. *Firm*—Pagan, Osborne & Grace, Cupar and St Andrews.

PATTULLO, JOHN PATRICK, T.D. [17 December 1923]. Apprentice to William Constable Hunter of Bonar, Hunter & Johnstone.—Son of James Adam Pattullo, S.S.C., Edinburgh. *Born* 15 March 1900. *Married* 1 June 1929, Una Margaret, daughter of Alexander Campbell, Sheep Farmer, Patagonia. First World War: Served in R.A.F. 1918-19; Second World War: Major, Royal Scots. Served U.K. 1939-44. *Firm*— Kilgour, McNeill & Sime (previously McNeill & Sime). (Retired.)

PATTULLO, NORMAN ADAM, B.A.(OXON) [23 March 1931]. Apprentice to Alexander Stevenson Blair and Others of Strathern & Blair.—Son of Charles Morrison Pattullo, Papermaker. *Born* 29 November 1905. *Married* 9 June 1933, Elizabeth Catherine, daughter of Sir Robert Barclay Pearson, Stockbroker, London. Lieutenant, Lothian & Border Yeomanry. Served in France. Prisoner-of-War 1940-45. Member of Queen's Bodyguard for Scotland, Royal Company of Archers. *Died* 26 October 1975. *Firm*— Mackenzie & Kermack. (Retired.)

PAUL, SIR GEORGE MORISON [21 November 1867]. Apprentice to John Dundas, William Wilson, and Alexander Montgomerie Bell.—Son of Rev. William Paul, D.D., Minister of Banchory-Devenick. *Born* 18 August 1839. *Married* 28 August 1872, Mary (*died* 31 October 1914), third daughter of Alexander John Kinloch of Park, Aberdeenshire. Deputy Keeper of the Signet, June 1905 to December 1924. Knighted, 1911. *Died* 4 May 1926. *Firm*—Dundas and Wilson.

PAUL, ROBERT [10 July 1812]. Apprentice to Harry Davidson.—Fourth son of John Paul, Shoemaker and Trades Bailie in Glasgow. *Born* 1774. *Married* 5 August 1811, Catherine, daughter of David Geddes, Deputy Auditor of Excise. *Died* 30 January 1866.

PAUL, THOMSON [1 July 1828]. Apprentice to James Thomson.—Son of Andrew Paul, Brewer in Linlithgow. *Born* 1796. *Died* 12 November 1876, unmarried.

PAULIN, NEIL GODFREY, B.A.(OXON) [19 July 1920]. Apprentice to Sir Colin G. Macrae, H. R. Macrae, and R. J. R. Flett.—Son of Sir David Paulin, Manager, Scottish Life Assurance Co., Edinburgh. *Born* 18 December 1888. *Married* 4 February 1931, Dorothy Margaret, M.A., daughter of John M'Burnie, Sheriff-Clerk, Dumfries. Served in France, 1915-18, with Lowland Brigade R.F.A.(T.), Captain. *Died* 26 September 1948.

PEARSON, ALEXANDER [2 December 1794]. Apprentice to James Ferrier.—Second son of Adam Pearson, Secretary of Excise for Scotland. *Born* 10 March 1770. *Married* 16 February 1826, Catherine (*died* 15 September 1848), daughter of David Paterson, Banker, Edinburgh. *Died* 9 December 1853.

PEARSON, ALEXANDER [11 July 1837]. Apprentice to David Cleghorn.—Youngest son of David Pearson, Principal Clerk in the Excise Office, Edinburgh. *Born* 23 April 1811. *Married* 6 February 1856, Alexandrina (*died* 1862), daughter of John Mackenzie, Edinburgh. *Died* 20 April 1857.

PEARSON, ANDREW [17 January 1893]. Apprentice to G. Robertson and W. P. Robertson.—Son of David Alexander Pearson of Johnston, W.S. *Born* 12 August 1866. *Married* 28 October 1908, Mary Henrietta Dorothea (*died* 5 June 1968), elder daughter of the Rev. F. H. Bowden Smith of Careys, Brockenhurst, Hants. *Died* 12 April 1921.

PEARSON, ANDREW ADAM, OF LUCE [14 November 1851]. Apprentice to Alexander Pearson and William Robertson.—Elder son of Alexander Pearson, W.S. *Born* 30 May 1827. *Married* 19 April 1855, Octavia (*died* 28 August 1861), daughter of Alexander Gillespie of Sunnyside, Lanarkshire. *Died* 19 July 1861.

PEARSON, CLAUDE GEOFFRY [8 December 1908]. Apprentice to J. P. Wright and T. M. Murray.—Son of the Rt. Hon. Sir Charles John Pearson (Lord Pearson), one of the Senators of the College of Justice. *Born* 20 June 1881. *Married* 30 March 1910, Edith Frances (*died* 2 May 1977), third daughter of Rev. E. W. Lomax, Vicar of Yarnton, Oxford. *Died* 8 July 1912.

PEARSON, DALZIEL [7 June 1872]. Apprentice to John Brown Innes.—Youngest son of Charles Pearson, President of the Society of Chartered Accountants, Edinburgh. *Born* 21 January 1848. *Died* 25 February 1919, unmarried.

PEARSON, DAVID ALEXANDER, OF JOHNSTON [30 November 1850]. Apprentice to, and younger son of, Alexander Pearson, W.S.—*Born* 15 December 1828. *Married* 4 December 1860, Elizabeth Abercromby (*died* 11 November 1922), only child of Alexander Gibbon, of Johnston, Kincardineshire. *Died* 22 December 1905.

PEARSON, DAVID WILLIAM, M.A., LL.B. [11 December 1978]. Apprentice to John Young of Ketchen & Stevens.—Son of David Johnstone Pearson, Telecommunications Engineer, Melrose. *Born* 2 October 1946. *Married* September 1973, Jessica Mary, daughter of Doctor Donald MacDonald, Bradford. *Firm*—Ketchen & Stevens.

PEAT, THOMAS [7 July 1795]. Apprentice to Robert Brown.—Son of John Peat, Writer in Edinburgh. *Born* 1772. *Married*, proclaimed 18 March 1797, Hannah (*died* 2 November 1826), daughter of Edward Broughton, Accountant of Excise. *Died* 26 July 1836.

PEDDIE, ALEXANDER. *See* WADDELL, ALEXANDER PEDDIE.

PEDDIE, ALEXANDER LOUIS DICK [30 October 1893]. Apprentice to A. Peddie Waddell and Holmes Ivory.—Son of John Dick Peddie, R.S.A., Architect, Edinburgh. *Born* 10 September 1869. Assistant Clerk and Extractor, 1904. *Died* 5 February 1938. *Firm*—Waddell, M'Intosh, and Peddie.

PEDDIE, JAMES [30 November 1819]. Apprentice to James Greig.—Eldest son of Rev. James Peddie, Minister of the Associate Burgher Congregation, Bristo Street, Edinburgh. *Born* 1798. *Married* 23 August 1821, Margaret (*died* 29 March 1851), daughter of Rev. John Dick, D.D., Glasgow. *Died* 5 September 1885.

PEDDIE, JOHN ALEXANDER DICK. *See* DICK PEDDIE.

PEDEN, ROBERT THOMAS, B.L. [27 April 1964]. (By Rule IX(a).)—Son of Alexander Peden, Engineer. *Born* 22 December 1925. *Married* 3 June 1955, Margaret, daughter of Andrew Gibson, Engineer. Served in Royal Signals during Second World War. Served in India. *Died* in Majorca, 27 March 1976. *Firm*—(1) D. & J. H. Campbell; (2) Drummond & Co. (after amalgamation).

PEDIE, JAMES [6 July 1813]. Apprentice to James Grant of Burnhall.—Only son of William Pedie of Mains of Dollar. *Died* 16 July 1844, aged 60, unmarried.

PENN, ALEXANDER STRATHERN [14 December 1931]. Apprentice to Alexander Stevenson Blair and Another of Strathern & Blair.—Son of Charles James Penn, W.S., Edinburgh. *Born* 9 January 1908. *Died* 10 October 1978. *Firm*—Campbell, Middleton, Burnett & Dickson, Montrose. (Retired.)

PENN, CHARLES JAMES [16 March 1891]. Apprentice to Robert Strathern.—Youngest son of Alexander Johnstone Penn, Writer in Glasgow. *Born* 5 September 1865. *Married* 14 June 1898, Euphemia Watson (*died* 12 June 1959), daughter of George Smart, Manufacturer, Brechin. *Died* 4 June 1930.

PENTLAND, DAVID SIM WHITE, M.A., LL.B. [23 March 1925]. Apprentice to James Watt and Another of Davidson & Syme.—Son of David White Pentland, Wool Merchant, Edinburgh. *Born* 20 November 1900. *Married* 8 October 1927, Muriel Annette, daughter of Charles Taylor, D.C.S., Edinburgh. *Firm*—Pentland & Russell. (Retired.)

PERFECT, ALAN PETER GEORGE, B.L. [19 November 1951]. Apprentice to Alexander Harper and Another of Pearson, Robertson & Maconochie.—Son of Lieutenant Colonel Patrick Cassan Perfect. *Born* 12 February 1928. *Married* 26 March 1963, Evelyn Anne Carew, daughter of William Blacklaw Storey, Cattle Farmer, Argentina. *Died* 22 February 1969 as the result of a ski-ing accident in Glencoe. *Firm*—P. & J. Stormonth-Darling, Kelso (incorporated with Turnbull, Simson & Sturrock, Jedburgh).

PETER, JAMES, OF CHAPEL [7 March 1664]. Apprentice to William Hunter, James Cheyne, and Walter Henderson.—Son of David Peter, Commissary of Peebles. *Married* 11 March 1670, Agnes, daughter of Mr William Rigg, Minister of Inverarity. *Buried* 12 February 1691.

PETER, JOHN, OF WHITSLEAD [Before 1612]. Signs the Acts, 7 December 1612. *Married* (1) 19 October 1609, Janet (*died* 15 April 1635), daughter of Andrew Mylne, Surgeon, Linlithgow; (2) (contract, 22 December 1636), Margaret, daughter of Thomas Hunter of Halkburn. Commissary of Peebles. Admitted Advocate, 26 June 1642. *Died* May 1650.

PETERKIN, WILLIAM CONON GRANT, O.B.E. [17 December 1934]. Apprentice to Donald Somerled Macdonald and Another of Scott & Glover.—Son of Dr George G. Peterkin, M.D., D.P.H., Forfar. *Born* 8 April 1910. *Married* 24 November 1937, Rachel Mary, daughter of The Hon. Adam George Watson, W.S., Edinburgh. Lieutenant, R.A.C. Served U.K., France and Belgium 1939-40. Prisoner-of-War in Germany 1940-1945. Member of Queen's Bodyguard for Scotland, Royal Company of Archers. *Died* 12 September 1978. *Firm*—Pagan, Osborne & Grace (formerly Pagan & Osborne), Cupar and St Andrews.

PETRIE, ANTHONY EDWARD ROSS, M.A., LL.B. [28 April 1969]. Apprentice to Ivan L. Young and Another of Blair, Cadell & Macmillan.—Son of Edward James Petrie, C.A., C.M.G., Retired Colonial Servant, Edinburgh. *Born* 2 December 1938. *Married* 1 October 1965, Alison Margaret, daughter of Alexander Pinkerton Murray, C.A. *Firm*—Bonar Mackenzie.

PHILIP, ROBERT JAMES [7 December 1903]. Apprentice to A. D. Mutter-Napier.—Only son of Rev. Thomas Philip, Catrine. *Born* 3 June 1875. *Married* 15 October 1908, Jessie Burgess (*died* 5 December 1956), daughter of Peter Dalgleish. *Died* 19 October 1908.

PHILIPS, JOHN [16 January 1800]. Apprentice to John Macnab.—Son of John Philips, Merchant in Glasgow. *Married* Euphemia Brown (*died* 9 November 1836). *Died* 11 November 1836.

PHILIPS, JOHN [10 March 1842]. Apprentice to John Kermack.—Son of John Philips, residing in Edinburgh. *Born* 23 November 1801. *Married* 7 January 1834, Annie Gordon (*died* 28 February 1887), youngest daughter of Robert Richard Maitland, Edinburgh. *Died* 2 August 1873.

PHILLIP, ANDREW, M.A., LL.B. [19 December 1949]. Apprentice to Arthur Woodman Blair and Others of Strathern & Blair.—Son of George Jeffrey Phillip, Solicitor, Edinburgh. *Born* 1 May 1922. *Married* 21 February 1950, Christine Martin, daughter of Henry Flint, Accountant, Edinburgh. Captain, Gordon Highlanders (seconded Indian Army); Served Assam and Burma 1942-45. Mentioned in Despatches. *Firm*—Strathern & Blair.

PIA, PAUL DOMINIC, LL.B. [6 December 1971]. Apprentice to John Parker Watson and Others of Lindsays.—Son of Joseph Pia, Wholesale Confectioner, Edinburgh. *Born* 29 March 1947. *Married* 9 July 1977, Christine Anne Argent. *Firm*—W. & J. Burness.

PITCAIRN, ALEXANDER, OF WOODHOUSELEE [14 August 1714].—Son of David Pitcairn of Dreghorn, Mid-Lothian. *Born* 1698. *Married* 1718, Margaret (*died* 26 March 1741), daughter of James Deans of Woodhouselee. Resigned his Commission, October 1745.

PITCAIRN, ALEXANDER YOUNG [5 December 1861]. Apprentice to Robert Haldane.—Only surviving son of Rev. Thomas Pitcairn, Free Church Minister at Cockpen. *Born* 5 April 1837. *Married* 18 August 1863, Helen (*died* 21 January 1932), daughter of John Wyld, Banker, Glasgow. *Died* 16 January 1921. *Firm*—Pitcairn & Mathers.

PITCAIRN, ARCHIBALD [3 August 1723]. Apprentice to Alexander Pitcairn.

PITCAIRN, JOHN WYLD [26 March 1900]. Apprentice to E. D. Young and James F. Roxburgh.—Son of Alexander Y. Pitcairn, W.S. *Born* 15 April 1869. Settled in Tobago, B.W.I. *Died* 1 August 1951.

PITCAIRN, PATRICK, OF DREGHORN [10 November 1704]. Eldest son of David Pitcairn of Dreghorn, Mid-Lothian. *Died* February 1734.

PITCAIRN, ROBERT [21 November 1815]. Apprentice to William Patrick.—Second son of Robert Pitcairn, Writer in Edinburgh. *Born* 1793. *Married* 4 September 1839, Hester Hine (*died* 7 April 1903, aged 100), daughter of Henry Hunt, Merchant, London. Author of *Ancient Criminal Trials in Scotland*, 1829-33, and other works. *Died* suddenly, 11 July 1855.

PITCAIRN, WILLIAM FETTES [15 November 1827]. Apprentice to (1) George Veitch; and (2) Matthew N. Macdonald Hume.—Son of Alexander Pitcairn, Merchant, Edinburgh. *Born* 14 October 1803. *Married* 29 March 1831, Agnes Campbell (*died* 6 July 1887), daughter of John Osburn Brown, W.S. *Died* 25 September 1891.

PITMAN, ARCHIBALD ROBERT CRAUFURD [19 April 1881]. Apprentice to, and eldest son of, Frederick Pitman, W.S.—*Born* 7 October 1858. *Married* 7 February 1920, Evelyn Mary Hay (*died* 6 March 1955), widow of Major-General A. A. Wolfe Murray, C.B., and daughter of Colin Mackenzie of Portmore. *Died* at Glencorse, 23 July 1924. *Firm*—J. and F. Anderson.

PITMAN, FREDERICK [4 June 1857]. Apprentice to John Anderson, his uncle.—Eldest son of Major-General Robert Pitman of the Hon. East India Company's Service. *Born* 26 September 1832. *Married* 17 November 1857, Anna Sitwell (*died* 6 September 1910), eldest daughter of John Tait, Advocate, Sheriff of Clackmannan and Kinross. *Died* at Polton House, 7 September 1896. *Firm*—J. and F. Anderson.

PITMAN, FREDERICK ISLAY [29 October 1888]. Apprentice to F. Pitman, J. R. Anderson, W. H. Murray, and A. R. C. Pitman.—Third son of Frederick Pitman, W.S. *Born* 18 April 1863. *Married* 2 July 1890, Helen Isabel (*died* 24 September 1944), younger daughter of James Auldjo Jamieson, W.S. B.A. Cambridge, 1885; M.A. 1888. Member of the London Stock Exchange, 1894. *Died* 22 January 1942.

PITMAN, IAN ROBERT, B.A.(OXON), LL.B. [11 July 1932]. Apprentice to John Sitwell Pitman and Others of J. & F. Anderson.—Son of Robert Octavius Pitman, W.S., Edinburgh. *Born* 28 October 1906. *Married* (1) 26 April 1935, Helen Anne (*died* 1939), daughter of James Low of Laws, Berwickshire, and (2) 22 October 1945, Katherine, daughter of Alastair Graham of Leckie. Lieutenant, Lothian & Border Yeomanry. Prisoner-of-War at St Valery, 1940. Mentioned in Despatches 1945 for service in France 1940. *Firm*—J. & F. Anderson. (Consultant.)

PITMAN, JOHN [24 March 1929]. Apprentice to John S. Pitman and Others of J. & F. Anderson.—Son of John Sitwell Pitman, W.S., Edinburgh. *Born* 30 March 1904. *Married* 12 June 1929, Christian Blanchette, daughter of James Curle, W.S. Flight Lieutenant, R.A.F. (Administrative Branch). Served U.K. 1941-45. Mentioned in Despatches 1946. Member of Queen's Bodyguard for Scotland, Royal Company of Archers. *Firm*—J. & F. Anderson. (Retired.)

PITMAN, JOHN SITWELL [19 October 1885]. Apprentice to F. Pitman, A. B. Macallan, J. R. Anderson, and W. H. Murray.—Second son of Frederick Pitman, W.S. *Born* 27 June 1860. *Married* 15 September 1888, Miriam Mabel Thornburgh (*died* 16 January 1942), only daughter of Captain Edward Thornburgh Parsons, R.N. Solicitor to the Post Office in Scotland, June 1892 to July 1932. *Died* 18 May 1938. *Firm*—J. & F. Anderson.

PITMAN, ROBERT OCTAVIUS, B.A.(Oxon) [7 December 1903]. Apprentice to J. R. Anderson, W. H. Murray, and A. R. C. Pitman.—Eighth son of Frederick Pitman, W.S. *Born* 17 July 1876. *Married* 17 October 1904, Beatrix (*died* 19 November 1950), third daughter of Arthur Sanderson, Wine Merchant, Edinburgh. Served from 1915 to 1918 with 11th Hussars and as A.D.C. to G.O.C., 2nd Cavalry Division. *Died* 19 October 1938. *Firm*—J. & F. Anderson.

PITTILLO [Before 1498].

PLENDERLEITH, JOHN [6 July 1691]. Apprentice to John Frank.—Brother to David Plenderleith of Byth. *Married* Margaret Douglas, relict of John Hunter, Merchant, Edinburgh. *Died* May 1728.

POLLEXFEN, JOHN RIDDOCH, OF CAIRSTON [10 March 1836]. Apprentice to William Stewart.—Son of Thomas Pollexfen of Cairston, Orkney. *Born* 22 October 1811. *Died* 18 November 1878, unmarried.

POLLOCK, NIGEL JAMES, LL.B. [28 April 1975]. Apprentice to Patrick Murray and Others of Murray, Beith & Murray.—Son of George Angus Pollock, F.R.C.S.E., Orthopaedic Consultant, Melrose. *Born* 12 February 1948. *Married* 8 October 1977, Anne Elizabeth, daughter of Denis James Clure, Civil Servant, Aberdeen. *Firm*—Murray, Beith & Murray.

POLLOK, JOHN, OF LOGIEGREEN [16 June 1807]. Apprentice to John Campbell. *Born* 18 January 1775.—Fifth son of Allan Pollok, Merchant in Glasgow. First Manager of the Commercial Bank of Scotland. *Died* in Virginia, U.S.A., April 1817.

PONTON, MUNGO [8 December 1825]. Apprentice to (1) James Balfour; and (2) William Scott and G. L. Finlay.—Only son of John Ponton, Farmer at Balgreen. *Born* 23 November 1802. *Married* (1) 24 June 1830, Helen Scott (*died* 7 August 1842), youngest daughter of Archibald Campbell, Edinburgh; (2) 1843, Margaret, daughter of Alexander Ponton, Procurator-Fiscal, Edinburgh; and (3) 1 August 1871, Jane (*died* 24 January 1910), eldest surviving daughter of Dougald M'Lean, Merchant, Edinburgh. Resident Law Officer and Secretary of National Bank of Scotland (1838). *Died* 3 August 1880. *Firm*—Goldie & Ponton.

POOLE, LAWRENCE NISBET BRUCE, M.A., LL.B. [12 July 1948]. Apprentice to George Francis Dalziel and Others of Tods, Murray & Jamieson.—Son of Major General Leopold Thomas Poole, C.B., D.S.O., M.C., Jedburgh. *Born* 11 December 1922. *Married* 8 August 1947, Hester Mary Campbell, daughter of John Douglas Hamilton Dickson, W.S., Edinburgh. *Died* 11 March 1953. *Firm*—Tods, Murray & Jamieson.

PORTEOUS, JOHN, OF SPITTLEHAUGH [20 May 1800]. Apprentice to James Walker.—Only son of William Porteous of Carmacoup, Lanarkshire. *Died* 9 January 1812.

PORTER, DAVID [10 July 1916]. Apprentice to James Watt, William Blair, and A. Blair.—Son of George Porter, Linen Yarn Bleacher, Claverhouse, near Dundee. *Born* 2 May 1876. *Married* 30 June 1908, Alice Mary (*died* 14 June 1967), younger daughter of William Cousland, G.P.O., Edinburgh. *Died* 4 May 1970. *Firm*—Davidson and Syme.

POTT, JAMES, OF POTBURN [20 November 1818]. Apprentice to James Mackenzie and William Innes.—Second son of Gideon Pott of Dod, Roxburghshire. *Born* 1792. *Married* 27 March 1839, Jane (*died* 9 August 1844), second daughter of Peter Brown of Rawflat, Roxburghshire. *Die* 6 November 1852.

POTTER, WILLIAM MISKIN [15 March 1920]. Apprentice to William Gibson and John D. Boswell.—Son of Frank Miskin Potter, Wine Merchant, Edinburgh. *Born* 3 August 1889. *Married* 10 April 1923, Alison Hunter, daughter of John Henderson, Solicitor, Dumfries. Captain 8th Seaforth Highlanders, 1915-19. Wounded and gassed, 1916. *Died* 23 October 1955 predeceased by his wife.

PRESSLIE, GEORGE WILLIAM SUTHER, B.L. [25 November 1963]. Apprentice to Charles Snow Campbell of Alex. Morison & Co.—Son of William Suther Presslie, Tea Planter. *Born* 24 March 1937. *Married* 15 August 1964, Dagny Ingela Gunnarsdotter, daughter of Doctor Gunnar Sigard Walter Jakobsson, Kristiehamn, Sweden. *Firm*—Alex. Morison & Co. (Retired on appointment to the Shrieval Bench, 1979.)

PRESTON, ALEXANDER [26 December 1773]. Apprentice to (1) George Turnbull; and (2) Walter Scott.—Only son of Rev. George Preston, Minister of Markinch. *Born* 29 December 1742. *Died* 4 November 1775.

PRESTON, JAMES [20 July 1731]. Apprentice to Hugh Somerville.—*Died* March 1738.

PRESTON, WILLIAM [3 December 1722]. Apprentice to Robert Hepburn.—*Married* April 1740, Helen Cumming, relict of William Carss of Tollcross. Resigned his Commission, 31 January 1750. Author of *A Poem to the Divine Majesty*. *Died* May 1752.

PRIMROSE, JAMES [1602].—Second son of David Primrose in Culross. *Married* (1) Sibylla Miller; and (2) Katherine (*died* 1651), daughter of Richard Lawson, Bookseller Burgess, Edinburgh. Commissioner, 18 October 1631. Clerk to the Privy Council, 1 February 1598-99. Clerk to Council of Prince's Revenue, 17 August 1623. Ancestor of Earls of Rosebery. Portrait in Parliament House. *Died* 21 February 1640.

PRINGLE, FRANCIS [26 February 1753]. Apprentice to James Pringle.—Youngest son of Sir Robert Pringle of Stichell, Roxburghshire. *Baptized* 24 May 1729. *Died* 15 April 1760, unmarried.

PRINGLE, JAMES, OF BOWLAND [14 July 1735]. Apprentice to James Home.—Son of James Pringle of Torwoodlee, Selkirkshire. *Married* 18 September 1749, Elizabeth (*died* 22 February 1799), daughter of James Nimmo, Receiver-General of Excise Duties for Scotland. Principal Clerk of Session, 13 December 1748 till death. *Died* 10 April 1776.

PRINGLE, JOHN [8 June 1741]. Apprentice to, and second son of, Thomas Pringle, W.S.—*Married* Mary (*died* 9 April 1804), sixth daughter of James Drummond of Blair-Drummond, Perthshire. *Died* 18 September 1784.

PRINGLE, JOHN [13 July 1811]. Apprentice to George Steuart.—Son of Dunbar Pringle, Merchant in Edinburgh. *Married* 24 July 1815, Margaret (*died* 16 April 1844), daughter of Thomas Wallace of Stockbridge. Sheriff-Substitute at Banff, 1821-53. *Died* 3 December 1853, aged 63.

PRINGLE, ROBERT, OF TEMPLEHALL AND WOODHEAD [Before 1615]. Apprentice to John Easton.—Eldest son of William Pringle, in Milton, Pencaitland. *Married* Violet Cant. Commissioner, 26 December 1627. *Died* April 1652.

PRINGLE, ROBERT, OF DEWAR [7 December 1655].—Son of Robert Pringle, W.S. *Married* (contract, 5 December 1657), Margaret, daughter of John Kerr in Bowden. Joint Fiscal, 1697-99.

PRINGLE, ROBERT, OF SYMINGTON [9 December 1830]. Apprentice to John Tait.—Only son of Lieut.-Colonel John Pringle of Symington, Mid-Lothian. *Born* 1803. *Married* (1) 17 June 1835, Mary (*died* 22 May 1838), eldest daughter of Major F. A. S. Knox, Royal Artillery; and (2) 15 October 1839, Eliza (*died* 16 September 1866), eldest daughter of James M'Farlane, Surgeon, 93rd Regiment. *Died* 21 April 1868.

PRINGLE, ROBERT [14 March 1872]. Apprentice to James Hope and Robert Mackay.—Son of Robert Pringle of Symington, W.S. *Born* 28 January 1845. *Married* 12 April 1870, Catherine (*died* 15 February 1908), only daughter of Robert William Jamieson, W.S. *Died* 18 March 1930. *Firm*—Pringle & Clay.

PRINGLE, ROBERT KEITH [27 July 1881]. Apprentice to D. Scott Moncrieff and J. P. Wood.—Son of Robert Keith Pringle of Broadmeadows, Selkirkshire. *Born* 22 April 1854. District Commissioner, Gold Coast. *Died* 13 January 1898, unmarried.

PRINGLE, ROBERT SHAUN, LL.B. [12 December 1977]. Apprentice to (1) Roy Alexander Wilson and Another of Allan McNeill & Son, and (2) David Andrew Bennett of A. C. Bennett & Son.—Son of Dr R. W. Pringle, O.B.E., Nuclear Physicist. *Born* 8 April 1953.

PRINGLE, THOMAS [10 May 1693]. Apprentice to John Macfarlane.—Fourth son of Sir Robert Pringle of Stichell, Roxburghshire. *Baptized* 24 March 1667. *Married* June 1700, Rebecca, daughter of Thomas Hay, Clerk of Session. Treasurer, 1697-98. Clerk of Privy Council, 24 November 1702. Deputy Keeper of the Signet, 1716-25. Father of Robert Pringle, Lord Edgefield. *Died* December 1735.

PRINGLE-PATTISON, NORMAN SETH, LL.B. [12 December 1911]. Apprentice to William Babington and Joseph Inglis.—Eldest son of Professor Andrew Seth Pringle-Pattison of The Haining, Selkirkshire. *Born* 27 July 1888. *Married* 25 June 1915, Doris Grey (*died* 4 December 1969), younger daughter of David Tweedie, Woodcroft, Edinburgh. Captain in Royal Scots; served in Gallipoli and France, 1915-18. *Died* 22 May 1974. *Firm*—Macrae, Flett, and Rennie.

PROCTOR, ROBERT [30 June 1801]. Apprentice to James Dundas.—Son of Patrick Proctor, Writer at Glamis Castle, Forfarshire. *Died* 5 January 1823.

PROSSER, DAVID GRIFFITHS, M.C., M.A., LL.B. [31 July 1922]. Apprentice to Sir John Prosser and Others of Morton, Smart, Macdonald & Prosser.—Son of Sir John Prosser, C.V.O., LL.D., W.S. *Born* 30 May 1896. *Married* 12 June 1928, Edith Mary Dallas, daughter of Dr William Paterson, Leith. First World War: Captain, Argyll & Sutherland Highlanders 1915-19; Second World War: Major, Argyll & Sutherland Highlanders. Served U.K. 1940-45. *Died* 17 June 1977. *Firm*—Morton, Smart, Macdonald & Prosser.

PROSSER, SIR JOHN, C.V.O., LL.D. [29 March 1898]. Apprentice to Andrew Gray Muir.—Son of David Prosser, Excise Officer at Bridge of Cally, Perthshire. *Born* 9 April 1857. *Married* 30 September 1886, Mary Anne (*died* 8 July 1915), daughter of John Taylor, Merchant, Elgin. S.S.C., 1883. Crown Agent and Prison Commissioner for Scotland, 1919-29. Knighted, 1927. C.V.O., 1928. LL.D., 1932. *Died* 16 June 1945. *Firm*—Morton, Smart, Macdonald, and Prosser.

PROSSER, JOHN [8 July 1913]. Apprentice to Ralph Dundas, W. J. Dundas, R. N. Dundas, and R. W. Dundas.—Son of Sir John Prosser, W.S. *Born* 1 April 1889. *Killed* in action, 28 September 1918. Lieutenant Black Watch (Royal Highlanders).

PURVES, ALEXANDER PATERSON [22 January 1874]. Apprentice to William Forbes Skene.—Eldest surviving son of William Brown Purves, Physician and Surgeon in Edinburgh. *Born* 11 September 1840. *Married* 22 December 1875, Sara Elizabeth (*died* 1 October 1923), eldest daughter of Charles Turner of the Royal Nurseries, Slough, Windsor. *Died* at London, 28 February 1897.

PURVES, JAMES PHILIP [8 July 1901]. Apprentice to Hamilton Maxwell.—Son of William Purves, Farmer, Thurdistoft, Thurso. *Born* 25 March 1877. *Married* 22 October 1912, Gladys Lizzie Leach (*died* 15 October 1964), Lieutenant Argyll and Sutherland Highlanders, and served in France. *Killed* in action, 11 April 1918.

PURVES, JAMES [3 August 1742]. Apprentice to James Ramsay.—Second son of Sir William Purves of that Ilk, Bart. *Baptized* 23 July 1709. Resigned his Commission, 16 February 1769. Commissary Depute of Lauder. *Died* 8 June 1770.

PURVES, JOHN DOVE [11 December 1899]. Apprentice to A. Wylie, J. L. Robertson, and W. B. Rankin.—Son of Dr Henry Black Purves, Howrah, Bengal. *Born* 1 October 1876. *Married* 16 June 1901, Adelaide (*died* 24 December 1967), second daughter of William Kinnaird Rose, Advocate, Edinburgh. *Died* 17 July 1939.

PURVES, WILLIAM [20 October 1890]. Apprentice to A. Howe, W. MacGillivray, and A. Yeaman.—Son of Robert Purves, Accountant, Glasgow. *Born* 24 October 1862. *Married* 14 July 1897, Mildred Graham (*died* 4 February 1953), third daughter of Sir John Sibbald, M.D., H.M. Commissioner in Lunacy for Scotland. *Died* suddenly in Court, 21 June 1923. *Firm*—W. & F. Haldane.

PURVES, WILLIAM GEORGE, O.B.E. [26 March 1928]. Apprentice to James Watt and Others of Davidson & Syme.—Son of William Purves, W.S., Edinburgh. *Born* 3 March 1904. *Married* 13 June 1940, Eva Graham Dundas, daughter of Paget Dundas Minchin, L.R.C.P. Captain, Royal Scots (Claims Commission); Served U.K. 1940-45. Sheriff Clerk of Chancery in Scotland 1932-74; Hon. Sherriff of The Lothians & Peebles, 1969. *Died* 15 December 1976. *Firm*—Campbell, Smith, Mathison & Oliphant (now Campbell, Smith & Co.).

PYLE, DEREK COLIN WILSON, LL.B. [9 December 1980*].—Son of Colin Lawson Pyle, Terminals Officer (British Rail), Edinburgh. *Born* 15 October 1952. *Married* 21 June 1980, Jean Blackwood Baillie May. *Firms*—(1) Dove, Lockhart, (2) Wilson Pyle & Co.

QUERELAND, WILLIAM [About 1478].

QUIGLEY, IAN SPIERS, LL.B. [13 May 1980*].—Son of John Spiers Quigley, Insurance Manager, Ayr. *Born* 29 November 1946. *Married* 6 July 1873, Elizabeth Ann, daughter of Tom Lindsay, Lenzie. *Firm*—Maclay, Murray & Spens.

RAE, SCOTT ALEXANDER, LL.B. [2 December 1968]. Apprentice to Douglas George Tweedie and Others of Fraser, Stodart & Ballingall.—Son of William Rae, Pharmaceutical Chemist. *Born* 17 December 1944. *Married* 9 September 1865, Annabella Georgina Ross, daughter of Alexander Hay Riach. *Firm*—Morton, Fraser & Milligan.

RAFFERTY, JOHN CAMPBELL, LL.B. [9 December 1980*].—Son of George Rafferty, Veterinary Surgeon, Grantown-on-Spey, Inverness-shire. *Born* 30 June 1951. *Firm*—W. & J. Burness.

RAINNIE, WILLIAM ROLLAND [15 December 1919]. Apprentice to A. T. S. Scott and John Glover.—Son of William Bowack Rainnie, S.S.C., Edinburgh. *Born* 13 March 1892. *Married* 18 February 1937, Isobel Wenley, daughter of William Baird Laing, Edinburgh. Lieutenant R.E. (Signal Service), 1915; served in France, 1917-19. *Died* 5 June 1960.

RAINY, JOHN BALFOUR [11 July 1892]. Apprentice to James Balfour, J. H. Balfour, and L. M. Balfour.—Younger son of George Rainy, M.D., Glasgow. *Born* 28 July 1866. *Married* 15 August 1899, Jessie (*died* 29 June 1950), eldest daughter of C. S. Goodchild of Great Wrothing Hall, Suffolk. *Died* 27 November 1929.

RALSTON, CLAUDE LYON [14 December 1896]. Apprentice to George Dunlop.—Son of Andrew Ralston, Factor, Glamis, Forfar. *Born* 6 December 1867. *Died* at Glamis, 6 October 1928, unmarried.

RAMAGE, ALEXANDER LISTON [16 August 1799]. Apprentice to Robert Boswell.— Fourth son of Alexander Ramage, Shoremaster of Leith. Lyon Clerk Depute, 13 September 1796. *Died* 28 February 1815, unmarried.

RAMAGE, FINLAY, LL.B. [10 July 1933]. Apprentice to George F. Dalziel and J. D. H. Dickson.—Son of Finlay Ramage, S.S.C., Edinburgh. *Born* 17 July 1907. *Died* 1 September 1938. *Firm*—Steedman and Ramage.

RAMSAY, DAVID, OF LETHAINE [7 August 1695]. Apprentice to Andrew Young.—Son of William Ramsay of Murthly. *Married* (1) 20 April 1692, Jean (*died* 26 May 1696), daughter of Mungo Campbell of Burnbank; and (2) 30 June 1699, Euphan, daughter of Michael Elphinstone of Quarrel, Stirlingshire. Treasurer, 1698-99. *Died* before 1736.

RAMSAY, DAVID, OF GRIMMET [6 March 1810]. Apprentice to John Campbell.—Eldest son of Rev. John Ramsay, Minister of Kirkmichael, Ayrshire. *Born* 19 August 1784. *Married* 20 April 1814, Helen (*died* 1877), only daughter of John Shaw of the Castle, Maybole. *Died* 30 April 1828.

RAMSAY, JAMES, OF AUCHTERTYRE [25 February 1723]. Apprentice to Alexander Glass. Brother of Robert Ramsay, Inspector of Customs. *Married* March 1734, Ann, daughter of Ralph Dundas of Manor, Perthshire. *Died* of apoplexy, 2 November 1748.

RAMSAY, JAMES [22 February 1793]. Apprentice to Walter Scott.—Son of James Ramsay, Architect in Edinburgh. *Died* 28 October 1798.

RAMSAY, NORMAN JAMES GEMMILL, M.A., LL.B. [17 July 1939]. Apprentice to William Leslie Christie of Cairns, McIntosh & Morton.—Son of James Ramsay, Engineering Contractor, Buenos Aires, Argentina. *Born* 26 August 1916. *Married* 5 January 1952, Rachael Mary Berkeley, daughter of Sir Herbert Charles Fahie Cox, formerly Chief Justice, Northern Rhodesia, Tanganyika and High Commission Territories. Lieutenant, Royal Navy. Served mainly with Eastern Fleet and East Indies Station, 1940-46. Served with Colonial Legal Service, Northern Rhodesia; latterly Puisne Judge of High Court of Northern Rhodesia (later Zambia). Retired 1968. Admitted to Faculty of Advocates 1956. Sheriff Principal of Dumfries and Galloway 1971.

RAMSAY, ROBERT [23 May 1820]. Apprentice to John Tod.—Second son of William Ramsay, Banker in Edinburgh. *Died* 19 November 1829.

RAMSAY, SIR WILLIAM, OF BAMFF, BART. [19 July 1779]. Apprentice to Alexander Duncan.—Third son of Sir James Ramsay of Bamff, Bart. *Married* 5 August 1796, Agnata Frances, daughter of John Hilton Biscoe of Hookwood, Surrey. Succeeded his brother as seventh Baronet on 16 April 1790. *Died* 17 February 1807, aged 52.

RANKEN, ROBERT BURT [25 March 1869]. Apprentice to (1) John Ord Mackenzie; and (2) Frederick Pitman.—Son of Thomas Ranken, S.S.C. *Born* 24 February 1840. *Married* 30 June 1874, Mary Witherington (*died* 12 April 1901), daughter of Charles Tennant Dunlop, Merchant, Glasgow. *Died* 4 August 1902.

RANKEN, THOMAS, T.D. [7 July 1902]. Apprentice to, and son of, R. B. Ranken, W.S.— *Born* 18 May 1875. *Married* 19 April 1920, Marion (*died* 25 March 1966), second daughter of the Hon. Frederick John Bruce of Seaton House, Arbroath. Major 8th Royal Scots and attached General Staff in Great War. *Died* 27 April 1950. *Firm*—T. and R. B. Ranken.

RANKIN, GEORGE, B.L. [28 October 1881]. Apprentice to T. G. Murray and J. A. Jamieson.—Son of Rev. William Thomson Rankin, Brechin. *Born* 15 July 1852. *Married* (1) 13 April 1887, Annie Cosens (*died* 27 August 1914), second daughter of Robert Romanes, Solicitor in Lauder; and (2) 6 July 1918, Christina Janet (*died* 11 May 1946), daughter of John Elder, Innerleithen. *Died* 9 June 1928.

RANKIN, WILLIAM BLACK, OF DARNGAVIL [14 January 1889]. Apprentice to Alexander Wylie.—Second son of Patrick Rankin of Cleddans and Auchengray, Lanarkshire. *Born* 16 February 1866. Major, 4th H.L.I.; served in India. *Died* 27 March 1944. *Firm*—W. B. Rankin & Nimmo.

RANKINE, CHARLES SIMSON. *See* SIMSON, CHARLES SIMSON RANKINE.

RANKINE, GILBERT DAVID, LL.B. [13 May 1980*].—Son of Harry Rankine, Solicitor, Alloa. *Born* 24 May 1953. *Married* 21 August 1976, Lilian Alice, daughter of John Moffat, Teacher, Kinross. *Firm*—Skene, Edwards & Garson.

RATTRAY, DAVID GRANT, LL.B. [13 May 1980]. Apprentice to Kenneth Alasdair MacKinnon of D. M. MacKinnon & Co., Oban.—Son of David James Campbell Rattray, Schoolmaster, Falkirk. *Born* 25 March 1956.

RATTRAY, ROBERT, OF BLACKCRAIG [12 November 1799]. Apprentice to Andrew Steuart.—Youngest son of James Rattray, residing at Bridgeness. *Born* 1773. *Married* (1) 4 October 1805, Rachel (*died* 5 September 1817), daughter of Thomas Milne, Merchant in Edinburgh; and (2) 16 July 1821, Dorothea (*died* 6 December 1864), daughter of James Dagnia, Durham. *Died* 6 May 1846.

RAWSOUN, ROBERT [Before 1606].—Son of Mr Alexander Rawsoun, Minister of Spynie. *Married* 31 December 1606, Margaret Wylie. *Died* 22 August 1623.

READMAN, GEORGE [30 March 1908]. Apprentice to W. J. Kirk and J. A. Hope.—Son of George Readman, Advocate. *Born* 17 February 1882. *Died* 24 August 1936.

REDDIE, JAMES CAMPBELL [10 December 1829]. Apprentice to David Cleghorn.—Son of James Reddie, Advocate. *Born* 26 November 1807. Wrote under the *nom de plume* of "James Campbell." *Died* 4 July 1878, unmarried.

REID, ALEXANDER [Before 1586].—Son of Adam Reid, Burgess, Edinburgh. *Married* Marion Johnston. Commissioner, 16 December 1594. *Died* before 1603.

REID, CHARLES GREENSHIELDS, OF GRANGEHILL [12 November 1840]. Apprentice to John Russell.—Son of Captain Charles Hope Reid of Grangehill, Ayrshire, R.N. *Born* 13 October 1814. *Married* 22 January 1850, Georgina, daughter of John Jardine, Advocate, Sheriff of Ross and Cromarty. *Died* 12 February 1897.

REID, CHARLES THOMSON, M.A., LL.B. [17 December 1934]. Apprentice to Mackenzie Smith Shaw of Thomson, Dickson & Shaw.—Son of Charles Edward Reid, Printer, Edinburgh. *Born* 3 August 1910. *Married* 18 November 1939, Marjorie Helen Ligertwood, daughter of Thomas Byers Tainsh, House Furnisher, Edinburgh. *Firms*— Thomson, Dickson & Shaw and J. A. Campbell & Lamond (now Thomson & Baxter). (Retired.)

REID, DAVID, LL.B. [13 May 1980*].—Son of Peter Galloway Reid, Retired Post Master, North Berwick. *Born* 6 September 1948. *Married* 23 March 1974, Sandra Mary, daughter of Alexander MacKenzie, Lairg, Sutherland. *Firm*—Thomson & Baxter.

REID, DAVID RONALD, M.A., LL.B. [27 April 1965]. Apprentice to Sir Peter George Macdonald and Others of W. & J. Burness.—Son of David Ronald Reid, Electrical Engineer, Falkirk. *Born* 23 June 1937. *Married* (1) 6 October 1965, Louise Ann, daughter of David Cross, Meat Merchant, and (2) 23 December 1980, Ruth Edith Wakeford or MacKintosh, daughter of Walter Wakeford, Forfar. *Firm*—W. & J. Burness.

REID, DAVID STUART, LL.B. [6 December 1971]. Apprentice to Ian Dalrymple Ross and Another of Thomson & Baxter.—Son of Hugh Reid, University Administrator, Edinburgh. *Born* 3 February 1947. *Married* 25 July 1970, Christine Elizabeth, daughter of James McCaul Findlay. *Firm*—Guild & Guild.

REID, DEREK JAMES, LL.B., B.SC. [25 April 1977]. Apprentice to Alexander John McDonald and Others of Thorntons & Dickies, Dundee.—Son of Kenneth Cathro Reid, Industrial Chemist, Eskbank, Midlothian. *Born* 8 September 1948. *Married* 30 July 1971, Sara Jean, daughter of David Charles Davies, Chief Telecommunications Officer (Scotland) N.A.T.S. *Firm*—Thorntons & Dickies (formerly Dickie, Gray, McDonald & Fair), Dundee.

REID, DONALD ALEXANDER, LL.B. [4 December 1967]. Apprentice to Arthur Henry Cecil Hope and Others of Gillespie & Paterson.—Son of Charles Thomson Reid, W.S., Appin, Argyllshire. *Born* 14 February 1945. *Married* (1) 6 September 1968, Patricia May, daughter of Andrew Haddon, Solicitor, Hawick, and (2) 13 October 1979, Shirley Alyson Hands. *Firms*—(1) Thomson & Baxter; (2) Morton, Fraser & Milligan.

REID, JAMES [28 July 1882]. Apprentice to Archibald Steuart.—Son of Walter Reid, Drem, East Lothian. *Born* 19 March 1855. *Married* 5 January 1888, Kate (*died* 26 May 1946), only daughter of William Scott, Calcutta. *Died* 17 April 1912.

REID, Sir JOHN [Before 1460]. Rector of Kirkchrist. A poet, "The gud gentill Stobo" (*William Dunbar*). Pensioned by King James III. in 1474. *Died* before 13 July 1505.

REID, JOHN MAY, M.A., LL.B. [28 April 1975]. Apprentice to F. H. Simpson and Another of Fyfe, Ireland & Co.—Son of John Reid, Solicitor. *Born* 25 April 1931. *Married* 25 March 1970, Patricia Ann, daughter of R. D. Thomson, Manufacturer. *Firms*—(1) Farquharson, Craig & Co.; (2) Strathern & Blair.

REID, ROBERT [3 April 1749]. Apprentice to Robert Fullarton.—Son of Mr William Reid, Minister of Stevenston. *Married* 23 March 1746, Ann (*died* 18 June 1782), daughter of James Grant, Stationer, Edinburgh. *Died* 10 March 1766.

REID, SYLVESTER [27 June 1822]. Apprentice to John Campbell.—Son of James Reid, Office of Excise at Huntly. *Born* 1780. *Married* 8 July 1822, Georgina (*died* 1849), daughter of Alexander Kidd, Writer in Edinburgh. Accountant and Depute Clerk of Teinds, 1818-39. Clerk, 1839-41. *Died* 8 May 1842.

REID, THOMAS LAURENCE GRAHAME, LL.B. [19 July 1926]. Apprentice to (1) Robert Beveridge Smith; and (2) H. E. Richardson, J. Carr, G. Lees, and Robert M'Cosh.—Son of William J. Reid, Yarn Dyer, Glasgow. *Born* 17 August 1899. *Married* 23 August 1934, May Emmeline, daughter of J. E. Gordon, Braeside, Dixie, Ontario. Held War Commission in R.G.A. *Died* 12 January 1969. *Firm*—Hill and Hoggan, Glasgow.

REID, WALTER MACARTHUR, B.A.(Oxon), LL.B. [1 December 1969]. Apprentice to Robert Scott and Others of Hagart & Burn-Murdoch.—Son of R. Macarthur Reid, S.S.C., Paisley. *Born* 6 August 1944. *Married* 29 July 1970, Janet, daughter of Duncan McPherson, F.I.C.E. *Firm*—T. F. Reid & Donaldson, Paisley.

REID, WILLIAM [27 November 1862]. Apprentice to Edmund Baxter.—Son of William Reid, Writer in Dundee. *Born* 28 October 1838. *Married* 23 May 1867, Elizabeth Geddes (*died* 12 October 1900), daughter of James Walker of Ravensby, Flax-spinner in Dundee. *Died* 8 September 1885.

REID, WILLIAM THOMAS, LL.B. [12 May 1981*].—Son of Thomas H. Reid, Schoolmaster, Grantown-on-Spey. *Born* 5 December 1944. *Married* 24 July 1971, Catriona Mary, daughter of John Gray Houston, Accommodation Officer, Dundee. *Firm*—Blair, Cadell & Macmillan.

REITH, DAVID STEWART, LL.B. [15 December 1975]. Apprentice to J. P. Watson and Others of Lindsays.—Son of Douglas Reith, Q.C., National Insurance Commissioner, Edinburgh. *Born* 15 April 1951. *Married* 12 May 1979, Fiona Lennox Munro, W.S. *Firm*—Lindsays.

REITH, FIONA LENNOX, LL.B. [8 December 1981*].—Daughter of P. D. M. Munro, Farmer and Hotelier, Birnam, Perthshire. *Born* 17 July 1955. *Married* 12 May 1979, David S. Reith, W.S., son of Douglas Reith, Q.C.

RENNIE, IAN SCOTT, M.A., LL.B. [29 April 1974*]. Son of Peter Bruce Rennie, Bus Conductor, Edinburgh. *Born* 24 December 1931. *Married* 3 September 1970, Marjorie Hope, daughter of James Samson Brand, Company Director. *Firm*—Cornillon Craig & Co. (formerly Cornillon Craig & Thomas).

RENNY, THOMAS. *See* STRACHAN, THOMAS RENNY.

RENNY, WILLIAM [16 May 1815]. Apprentice to George Robinson.—Third son of George Renny of Birkhill, Kirkcudbrightshire. *Born* 1788. *Married* 23 August 1819, Margaret (*died* 23 February 1832), second daughter of John Napier of Mollance, Kirkcudbrightshire. Solicitor for Inland Revenue. *Died* 11 February 1846.

RENNY, WILLIAM JOHN, OF DANEVALE PARK [14 November 1844]. Apprentice to, and eldest son of, William Renny, W.S.—*Born* 4 December 1822. *Married* (1) 19 July 1847, Julia Isobella (*died* September 1867), daughter of Arthur John Robertson of Inshes, Inverness-shire; and (2) 17 July 1873, Margaret Forbes (*died* November 1929), daughter of John Angus, Advocate and Town Clerk of Aberdeen. *Died* 25 January 1879.

RENTON, JOHN [16 January 1800]. Apprentice to John Home.—Eldest son of James Renton, Merchant in Berwick. *Born* 25 May 1779. *Married* 12 September 1803, Ann (*died* 12 August 1829), second daughter of Rev. Matthew Murray, Minister of North Berwick. *Died* 3 October 1838.

RENTONE, GEORGE [16 November 1702]. Apprentice to Alexander Home.—*Married* (contract, 14 October 1697), Helen Douglas. *Died* 17 December 1703, aged 29.

RHIND, WILLIAMSON [16 November 1831]. Apprentice to (1) Francis Wilson; and (2) Sir H. Jardine, G. T. Stodart, and William Fraser.—Son of John Rhind, Cashier of the Edinburgh Friendly Insurance Company. *Born* 11 June 1809. *Died* 22 April 1847, unmarried.

RICHARDSON, ANDREW [29 June 1827]. Apprentice to (1) Hay Donaldson; and (2) John Gibson, Jun.—Only son of Kerr Richardson, Farmer in Ardgilzean, Perthshire. *Born* 1804. *Married* (1) 16 March 1831, Jean Thomson (*died* 5 May 1833), daughter of William Blair; and (2) 28 March 1837, Charlotte (*died* 10 August 1893), daughter of David Davidson, Salton Mains, Haddington. *Died* 28 August 1885.

RICHARDSON, ARTHUR ROSS, B.L. [18 December 1950]. Apprentice to A. Logan McLure of Mackenzie & Black.—Son of Major General David Turnbull Richardson, Gairloch, Ross-shire. *Born* 10 March 1924. *Married* 12 March 1957, Sheila, daughter of Arthur Colebrook, Company Director. Lieutenant, R.N.V.R. Served Atlantic, Mediterranean, Far East and D-Day Landings. *Firm*—Scott Moncrieff & Trail.

RICHARDSON, HENRY EDWARD, OF BROADSHAW [13 July 1885]. Apprentice to J. A. Jamieson, J. W. Tod, and James Craik.—Son of Henry Cockburn Richardson, of the Indian Civil Service. *Born* 28 June 1862. *Married* 11 October 1900, Alison (*died* 21 July 1970), youngest daughter of George Miller Cunningham, C.E. of Leithenhopes, Peeblesshire. *Died* 9 May 1931.

RICHARDSON, JOHN [19 June 1823]. Apprentice to William Inglis.—Eldest son of William Richardson, residing in Edinburgh. *Born* 1799. *Married* (1) September 1819, Lewis Judith Hatley (*died* 19 October 1831), fifth daughter of Lieut.-Colonel Lewis Hay, R.E.; (2) 24 February 1857, Martha (*died* 14 February 1884), daughter of Peter Trezevant, London. Substitute Keeper, 1867-76. *Died* 17 December 1876.

RICHARDSON, JOHN, OF KIRKLANDS [13 November 1827]. Apprentice to Thomas Scotland.—Son of John Richardson, Farmer in Gilmerton. *Born* 9 May 1780. *Married* 5 August 1811, Elizabeth (*died* 26 November 1836), daughter of Laurence Hill, W.S. A close friend of Sir Walter Scott, who confided to him the secret of the authorship of the Waverley Novels. *Died* 4 October 1864.

RICHARDSON, JOHN [20 December 1921]. Apprentice to William C. M'Ewen.—Son of James Turnbull Richardson, M.D. *Born* 13 September 1882. *Married* 16 October 1917, Doris (*died* 23 June 1963), daughter of Arthur Thomson, Professor of Anatomy, University of Oxford. Solicitor in Scotland to H.M. Postmaster-General. Captain in Royal Scots, and served in France in Great War. *Died* 7 November 1962. *Firm*—Scott Moncrieff and Trail.

RICHARDSON, JOHN HERBERT [14 December 1925]. Apprentice to H. E. Richardson, V. A. Noel Paton, J. Carr G. Lees, G. L. D. Hole, and Robert M'Cosh.—Son of Brigadier-General Herbert Lance Richardson, Indian Army (retired). *Born* 28 September 1900. *Married* 28 April 1927, Margaret Joan, only child of Charles Lyall Dalziel, C.A., London. Major, General Service: served U.K. 1939-42. *Died* at Cape Town 26 October 1966. *Firm*—Dundas and Wilson.

RICHARDSON, RALPH [12 November 1869]. Apprentice to George Maclachlan and William Ivory.—Son of James Richardson, Merchant in Edinburgh. *Born* 22 November 1845. *Married* 15 October 1879, Melville Elizabeth (*died* 18 June 1947), daughter of Andrew Fleming, M.D., Deputy Surgeon-General, Bengal Army. Commissary Clerk of Edinburgh, 1883. Author of several books. *Died* 26 June 1933.

RICHARDSON, ROBERT [18 December 1676]. Apprentice to Sir Hugh Paterson.— *Married* (1) 24 November 1670, Margaret Cunningham, widow of Rev. Alexander Kinnear, Minister of Hawick; (2) 30 August 1678, Margaret, daughter of Walter Law of Conland. *Buried* 17 October 1699.

RICHARDSON, THOMAS [25 May 1814]. Apprentice to David Wemyss.—Only son of Robert Richardson, Secretary to the British Linen Company. *Married* 19 September 1818, Isabella (*died* 22 February 1866), daughter of James Heggie, younger of Pitlessie, Fife. *Died* 18 June 1853, aged 64.

RICHARDSON, WILLIAM MILNE, B.L. [15 December 1947]. Apprentice to James Falconer Fairweather and Others of Gordon, Falconer & Fairweather.—Son of William Alexander Richardson, Solicitor, Edinburgh. *Born* 11 September 1920. *Married* 24 September 1949, Catherine Hamilton Wilson, daughter of William Paterson. Sergeant, Lothian & Border Horse. Served U.K., North Africa, Italy and Austria 1939-46. *Firm*—Tods, Murray & Jamieson (prior to amalgamation, Tait & Crichton).

RIDDELL, Rev. HENRY SCOTT [15 November 1811]. Apprentice to James Thomson.— Second son of Henry Riddell, Merchant in Glasgow. *Born* 23 May 1789. *Married* (1) 2 October 1818, Agnes (*died* 22 February 1825), daughter of Archibald Gilchrist, Merchant, Edinburgh; and (2) 29 November 1831, Elizabeth (*died* 27 September 1885), youngest daughter of John Horne of Stirkoke, Caithness. Resigned his Commission, 12 May 1825. Licensed by the Presbytery of Selkirk, 7 July 1829. Ordained Minister of Longformacus, 6 September 1830. Translated to Duns, 6 October 1843. *Died* 15 April 1862.

RIDDELL, JOHN, OF GRANTON [20 March 1739]. Apprentice to Ronald Dunbar.—Eldest son of John Riddell, Physician in Edinburgh. *Born* 1713. *Married* 19 April 1741, Christian, daughter of Sir John Nisbet of Dean, Bart. *Died* 20 December 1745.

RIDDELL, JOHN RUGNIGALD, OF KINHARVIE [10 July 1798]. Apprentice to William Riddell.—Second son of Robert Riddell of Carzield, Dumfriesshire. *Married* March 1804, a daughter (*died* 8 July 1805) of David Crawford of Carronbank. *Died* 5 May 1849.

RIDDELL, STEPHEN PATERSON, M.A., LL.B. [8 May 1967]. Apprentice to Charles Ritchie Black and Another of Warden, Bruce & Co.—Son of Stephen Riddell, Sales Manager, Dumfries. *Born* 10 March 1933. *Married* 22 July 1961, Audrey Reid, daughter of John Brown, Marine Underwriter, Edinburgh. *Firm*—Melville & Lindesay.

RIDDELL, THOMAS, YOUNGER OF CAMIESTON [19 November 1805]. Apprentice to, and eldest son of, William Riddell, W.S.—*Born* 23 August 1777. *Married* 31 January 1805, Jane (*died* 11 January 1833), daughter of Walter Ferrier of Glenferrier, Stirlingshire. *Died* 18 April 1826.

RIDDELL, WALTER, OF NEWHOUSE [13 December 1708]. Apprentice to John Wilkie.—Son of Walter Riddell of Newhouse. *Married* Jean Pringle. *Died* December 1742.

RIDDELL, WILLIAM, OF CAMIESTON [3 July 1770]. Apprentice to Thomas Cockburn.—Eldest son of Thomas Riddell of Camieston, Roxburghshire. *Born* 1746. *Married* 12 January 1776, Elizabeth, only surviving daughter of John Carre of Cavers Carre, Roxburghshire. *Died* 23 November 1829.

RIGG, DUNCAN McKENZIE, LL.B. [12 May 1981*].—Son of Duncan McKenzie Rigg, Company Secretary, Falkirk. *Born* 24 December 1947. *Married* 23 December 1972, Shelagh Elizabeth, daughter of Graham Macdonald, Electrician. *Firm*—J. & F. Anderson.

RITCHIE, ALEXANDER [12 March 1795]. Apprentice to John Campbell.—Only son of Alexander Ritchie, Merchant in Edinburgh. *Died* 15 March 1816.

RITCHIE, ALEXANDER DAVID, LL.B. [9 December 1980*].—Son of William Ritchie, Solicitor, Dundee. *Born* 20 August 1955. *Firm*—Ogilvie, Cowan & Co., Dundee.

RITCHIE, BRUCE ALEXANDER, LL.B. [26 April 1976]. Apprentice to Lawrence Falconer McLaren and Others of Haldanes, McLaren & Scott.—Son of David Ritchie, Managing Director, Brown & Glegg Ltd., Edinburgh. *Born* 2 April 1948. *Married* 22 July 1972, Dorothy Ann, daughter of William Duncan Alexander Chisholm, Edinburgh. *Firm*—(1) Haldanes, McLaren & Scott; (2) Ballantyne & Copland.

RITCHIE, CHARLES RONALD, OF KILMUX [27 March 1911]. Apprentice to A. H. M‘Lean.—Son of Charles Ritchie, S.S.C. *Born* 27 January 1884. *Married* 21 July 1913, Mary (*died* 29 November 1960), daughter of William Henry Watson, Farmer, Coldstream. During Great War held Commission in Lowland Mounted Brigade R.A.S.C. Twice mentioned in Despatches. Received Greek Order of the Redeemer and Greek Medal of Military Merit. *Died* 17 April 1944. *Firm*—Ronald & Ritchie.

RITCHIE, DAVID [12 January 1891]. Apprentice to George Dunlop.—Son of William Ritchie of Dunottar, near Stonehaven. *Born* 17 March 1864. *Married* 10 March 1898, Georgina Hay (*died* 4 July 1959), youngest daughter of Daniel Davidson, Arran. *Died* 12 July 1935.

RITCHIE, GEORGE [2 July 1829]. Apprentice to John Renton and Joseph Grant.—Fourth son of George Ritchie of Hill of Ruthven, Perthshire. *Born* 1807. *Married* 8 June 1841, Euphemia (*died* 5 November 1889), only daughter of Andrew Scales of Blackburn. *Died* 30 November 1843.

RITCHIE, IAN SMAIL, M.A., LL.B. [14 December 1936]. Apprentice to David Sharpe of Mackenzie & Wylie.—Son of John Richard Smail Ritchie, S.S.C., Edinburgh. *Born* 24 August 1910. *Married* 11 September 1943, Mary Hargreaves Smail, daughter of Frederick John Palmer Fisher. Wing Commander, Royal Auxiliary Air Force. Served as Fighter Pilot in No. 603 (City of Edinburgh) Squadron (Flying Officer) 1937-41. Formed and commanded St Andrews University Air Squadron 1941-45. High Constable of Holyrood House (1957). *Firm*—Mackay & Young (after amalgamation, Dove, Lockhart, Mackay & Young).

RITCHIE, JAMES [Before 1586]. *Died* before 1594.

RITCHIE, JAMES STEWART, B.L. [18 December 1950]. Apprentice to James Campbell Walker and Another of Steedman, Ramage & Co.—Son of John Ritchie, Solicitor, Kilmarnock. *Born* 30 January 1917. *Married* 6 November 1964, Dorothy Magdalen, daughter of Dr Hugh G. Morris-Jones, Medical Practitioner, Llangollen, Denbighshire. Captain, Cameronians. Served Europe and East Africa 1939-46. *Firm*—W. & J. Burness.

RITCHIE, ROBERT GELLATLY, M.A., LL.B. [30 April 1962]. Apprentice to (1) Alastair Campbell Blair and Others of Davidson & Syme; (2) Charles Alexander of Auld & Macdonald.—Son of John Miller Ritchie, Draper, Edinburgh. *Born* 8 June 1930. *Married* (1) Lizzy Van der Pas (*died* 24 December 1964); (2) 24 September 1965, Agnes, daughter of James Dickie, Builder, Turriff, Aberdeenshire. *Firm*—Drummond & Co. (formerly Robert White & Co. prior to amalgamation).

RITCHIE, WILLIAM [Before 1541].

ROBB, GEORGE ALAN, M.A., LL.B. [2 December 1968]. Apprentice to Alastair C. Blair and Others of Davidson & Syme.—Son of G. Robb, Advocate in Aberdeen. *Born* 20 May 1942. *Married* 3 August 1973, Moira, daughter of Sidney M. Clark, Development Executive of Grampian Television. *Firm*—Brander & Cruickshank, Aberdeen.

ROBB, KENNETH MONTGOMERY, M.A., LL.B. [22 July 1963]. Apprentice to Charles Stewart Henderson and Another of Patrick & James.—Son of William Cuthbert Robb, Schoolmaster, Hawick. *Born* 20 August 1933. *Married* 26 June 1965, Ruth Irene, daughter of Donald Atherton, Company Director, Glasgow. *Firms*—(1) Patrick & James; (2) Haldanes, McLaren & Scott.

ROBERTON, WILLIAM [22 December 1698]. Apprentice to William Stirling.—Youngest son of Archibald Roberton of Bedlay, Lanarkshire. *Died* January 1757, unmarried.

ROBERTSON, ALEXANDER, OF PARSON'S GREEN [14 March 1744]. Apprentice to (1) Harry Maule; and (2) David Maule.—Son of George Robertson, Writer in Edinburgh. *Married,* proclaimed 8 July 1764, Jean (*died* 30 November 1821), third daughter of James Hay of Pitfour, Perthshire. Principal Clerk of Session, 12 June 1776 till death. *Died* 22 January 1788.

ROBERTSON, ALEXANDER FREDERICK, B.A.(OXON) [28 March 1927]. Apprentice to John Sitwell Pitman and Others of J. & F. Anderson.—Son of William Hope Robertson, W.S., Edinburgh. *Born* 30 September 1901. *Married* (1) 6 February 1928, Charlotte Susan Whitney (*died* 7 October 1957), daughter of Frank Roswell McMullin, U.S.A., and (2) 29 December 1958, Edith, daughter of William Rowe Linton, Edinburgh. 2nd Lieutenant Royal Scots. Served U.K. 1940-41. *Died* 17 July 1978. *Firm*—J. & F. Anderson.

ROBERTSON, ALEXANDER LAMBIE [18 November 1817]. Apprentice to (1) James Horne; and (2) Patrick Wishart.—Third son of Alexander Robertson of Prenderguest, Berwickshire. *Born* 11 June 1794. *Married* 16 August 1821, Katherine (*died* 1 November 1867), daughter of John Alison of Wellbank, Forfarshire. Lyon Clerk Depute, 30 July 1812-19. *Died* 22 December 1868.

ROBERTSON, ANDREW GIFFORD [29 April 1881]. Apprentice to A. Hamilton, G. T. Kinnear, and R. Beatson.—Son of Andrew Robertson, North British and Mercantile Insurance Co., Edinburgh. *Born* 29 April 1855. *Died* 7 February 1926, unmarried.

ROBERTSON, BARTHOLOMEW [1 November 1658]. Apprentice to Alexander Hamilton.

ROBERTSON, DAPHNE JEAN BLACK, M.A., LL.B. [12 December 1977]. (By Rule IX(a).)—Daughter of the Rev. Robert Black Kincaid, Wishaw. *Born* 31 March 1937. *Married* 26 August 1965, Donald Buchanan Robertson, Q.C., son of Donald Robertson, Yacht Builder, Sandbank. *Firm*—J. & R. A. Robertson. (Retired October 1979, after appointment to the Shrieval Bench.)

ROBERTSON, EAIN BLACKLAW, B.L. [27 April 1959]. Apprentice to Charles Law Forbes of Aitken, Methuen & Aikman.—Son of John Robertson, Marine Engineer, Dunfermline. *Born* 9 October 1923. *Married* 14 October 1950, Katherine Sinclair, daughter of James Colquhoun. Lieutenant, R.N.V.R. Served in Western Approaches, 2nd Escort Group. *Firm*—Aitken, Kinnear & Co. (formerly Aitken, Methuen & Aikman).

ROBERTSON, EUAN BARCLAY [28 March 1904]. Apprentice to Robert Fleming Johnston and Another of J. & R. A. Robertson.—Son of Robert Augustus Robertson, S.S.C., D.L., Edinburgh. *Born* 6 April 1880. *Married* 16 June 1908, Helen Macdonald (*died* 10 October 1975), daughter of Edward Hewetson, late of Indian Police. Served with R.A.S.C. in France 1915-19. *Died* 18 March 1975. *Firm*—J. & R. A. Robertson.

ROBERTSON, FIONA JANET, LL.B. [9 December 1980]. Apprentice to David Birrell and Others of Dundas & Wilson.—Daughter of Thomas Young, Farmer, Dumfries. *Born* 11 March 1956. *Married* 27 September 1980, Andrew John Robertson, son of Colin John Trevelyan Robertson, Company Director, Bridge of Allan.

ROBERTSON, FRANCIS JAMES [4 April 1884]. Apprentice to Anthony Murray. Third son of George Robertson of Hedderwick, Forfarshire, C.E. *Born* 8 December 1858. *Married* 18 December 1884, Elizabeth (*died* 7 August 1940), youngest daughter of Rev. John Caldwell Brown of Carbeth-Guthrie, Minister of Ceres, Fife. *Died* at Arundel, Sussex, 17 August 1922.

ROBERTSON, GEORGE [25 June 1819]. Apprentice to Archibald Hotchkis.—Sheriff-Substitute at Portree, 1829-44. *Died* 24 September 1844, aged 51, unmarried.

ROBERTSON, GEORGE [16 March 1891]. Apprenticed to Sir John Gillespie.—Son of George Brown Robertson, W.S., Deputy Keeper of the Records of Scotland. *Born* 6 October 1868. *Married* 8 October 1902, Alison Rose Lulworth (*died* 3 April 1964), daughter of Major Henderson, 77th Regiment. *Died* 2 May 1928.

ROBERTSON, GEORGE [18 November 1848]. Apprentice to William Robertson.—Son of William Robertson of the Island of Malta. *Born* 20 August 1820. *Married* 27 March 1856, Harriette Caroline Emily, youngest daughter of William Macbean, Leghorn. *Died* 27 September 1895.

ROBERTSON, GEORGE BROWN [24 June 1841]. Apprentice to Hugh Tod—Son of George Robertson, Deputy Keeper of the Records. *Born* 10 January 1819. *Married* 14 August 1867, Christina (*died* 14 September 1912), daughter of William Rose, Sheriffston, Elginshire. Deputy Keeper of the Records, 7 December 1853-73. *Died* 26 November 1873.

ROBERTSON, HUGH [6 December 1791]. Apprentice to David Erskine.—Second son of David Robertson of Loretto, Mid-Lothian. *Married* 3 November 1795, Barbara, second daughter of Alexander Hamilton of Gilkerscleugh. Lanarkshire. *Died* 21 January 1800.

ROBERTSON, IAN MACDONALD, T.D., B.A.(OxON), LL.B. [20 December 1937]. Apprentice to R. F. Shepherd and Others of Shepherd & Wedderburn.—Son of James Robertson, Jute Merchant, Edinburgh. *Born* 30 October 1912. *Married* 28 December 1938, Anna Love, daughter of James Fulton Glen, Judge of Supreme Court, Florida, U.S.A. Captain, Royal Scots. Staff Officer 15th Scottish Division. Served Normandy and N.W. Europe 1944-45. Mentioned in Despatches. Resigned Commission on admission to Faculty of Advocates, 1939. Q.C., 1954; Sheriff of Ayr and Bute 1961; Sheriff of Perth and Angus 1966. Senator of the College of Justice, October 1966, with judicial title of Lord Robertson.

ROBERTSON, JAMES. *See* BARCLAY, JAMES ROBERTSON.

ROBERTSON, JAMES [26 June 1789]. Apprentice to David Erskine.—Eldest son of Patrick Robertson, Writer in Glasgow. *Died* in Jamaica, April 1794.

ROBERTSON, JAMES [1 June 1795]. Apprentice to James Saunders.—Third son of Patrick Robertson, Schoolmaster at Bellie, Banffshire. *Born* 1760. *Married* 22 August 1788 (proclaimed 5 September 1785) Mary (*died* 21 September 1837), daughter of James Saunders, W.S. *Died* 15 April 1820.

ROBERTSON, JAMES [1 June 1820]. Apprentice to James Little.—Youngest son of Rev. Patrick Robertson, D.D., Minister of Eddleston. *Born* 22 July 1796. Crown Agent, 1858-59. *Died* 25 June 1864, unmarried.

ROBERTSON, JAMES ANGUS MACKIE. *See* MACKIE-ROBERTSON.

ROBERTSON, JAMES BRIGHT [29 November 1960]. (By Rule IX(a).)—Son of James Robertson, Dunfermline. *Born* 22 October 1906. *Married* 29 October 1930, Roberta, daughter of Robert Jeffrey, Superintendent with Prudential Assurance Company. Sergeant, R.A. 86th H.A.A. (H.A.C.), 1942-46. *Firm*—J. C. & A. Steuart. (Consultant.)

ROBERTSON, JAMES ROCHSOLES, T.D., M.A., LL.B. [24 December 1940]. Apprentice to Robert Nevill Dundas and Others of Dundas & Wilson.—Son of David Robertson, S.S.C., J.P., Town Clerk of Edinburgh. *Born* 27 August 1917. *Married* 6 December 1941, Joan, daughter of Wing Commander Harold Hillier, D.F.C. Major, R.A. Served U.K. and North West Europe 1939-45. Mentioned in Despatches 1945. *Firm*—Robertson & Wilson (formerly H. Brougham Paterson & Co.). (Retired 1978.)

ROBERTSON, JAMES SAUNDERS [10 March 1812]. Apprentice to, and eldest son of, James Robertson, W.S.—*Born* 17 August 1789. *Married* 16 April 1816, Sarah (*died* 2 February 1860), eldest daughter of Rev. Alexander Weir of Boghead, Linlithgowshire. *Died* 20 August 1856.

ROBERTSON, JAMES STEWART, OF EDRADYNATE [12 November 1846]. Apprentice to Alexander Pearson and William Robertson.—Son of James Stewart Robertson of Edradynate, Perthshire. *Born* 15 May 1823. *Married* 27 April 1852, Mary Jane Campbell, daughter of Robert Cuningham of Bandalloch, Stirlingshire and Ballanorris, Isle of Man. *Died* at Edradynate, 3 August 1896.

ROBERTSON, JOHN, OF DUNCANZIEMUIR [11 July 1817]. Apprentice to James Robertson.—Son of Robert Robertson, Writer in Ayr. *Died* 19 July 1859, aged 67, unmarried.

ROBERTSON, JOHN [11 December 1899]. Apprentice to George Dalziel.—Son of James Robertson, Surgeon, Bannockburn. *Born* 1 July 1858. *Died* 28 February 1919, unmarried.

ROBERTSON, JOHN [13 December 1926]. Apprentice to Francis G. Haldane and William Purves.—Son of John Robertson, Solicitor, Edinburgh. *Born* 15 July 1903. *Married* 6 September 1933, Elphingstone Margaret, daughter of James Herriot, Solicitor, Duns. Resigned Commission 16 October 1939.

ROBERTSON, JOHN ANDERSON [25 May 1826]. Apprentice to James Saunders Robertson.—Fourth surviving son of James Robertson, W.S. *Born* 4 November 1802. *Married* 13 September 1826, Isabella Eleanor (*died* 1864), daughter of Captain Johnston, R.E., and widow of James Errol Gray, Surgeon, Inverness. Stipendiary Magistrate at Sydney, New South Wales. *Died* 9 December 1862.

ROBERTSON, JOHN LOGIE [8 October 1883]. Apprentice to Alexander Wylie.—Son of William Robertson, Milnathort, Kinross-shire. *Born* 9 August 1859. *Married* 3 January 1899, Margaret Joanna (*died* 25 March 1906), second daughter of Peter Simpson, S.S.C., Edinburgh. *Drowned* at Granton, 23 June 1908.

ROBERTSON, JOHN RONALDSON [8 July 1831]. Apprentice to John Archibald Campbell.—Eldest son of Edward Robertson, Secretary to the Commercial Banking Company. *Born* 22 May 1807. *Died* 11 May 1872, unmarried.

ROBERTSON, NICOL. *Married* Margaret Forrester. *Died* before 1578.

ROBERTSON, PATRICK [1 July 1791]. Apprentice to David Erskine.—Eldest son of Patrick Robertson, Writer in Glasgow. *Died* 31 March 1795.

ROBERTSON, ROBERT [13 July 1780]. Apprentice to David Erskine.—Second son of James Robertson Barclay of Keavil, Fife, W.S. *Died* 11 June 1784.

ROBERTSON, ROBERT JAMES [31 May 1860]. Apprentice to James Robertson.—Son of Rev. Patrick Robertson, Minister of Eddleston. *Born* 17 March 1834. *Married* 3 April 1861, Harriott Margaret (*died* 1 April 1908), daughter of William Henry Holms of Manor House, Kilrea. *Died* 1 May 1867.

ROBERTSON, RONALD MACDONALD [20 July 1925]. Apprentice to George M. Wood.—Son of R. Macdonald Robertson, M.D., Edinburgh. *Born* 20 January 1899. *Married* 6 June 1932, Lucie Jessie, youngest daughter of Robert Laird, Pinkhill, Corstorphine. Lieutenant in Royal Artillery during Great War. *Died* 18 March 1968. *Firm*—Weir and Robertson.

ROBERTSON, RONALD WILLIAM MACPHERSON, B.L. [30 November 1959]. Apprentice to Edmund Menzies and Others of Allan, Dawson, Simpson & Hampton.—Son of Alexander Macpherson Robertson, Medical Practitioner, Comrie, Perthshire. *Born* 31 May 1936. *Married* 8 June 1968, Margaret McLaren Lamont, daughter of Stewart McFeat.

ROBERTSON, THOMAS ROBERT, OF GORGIE LODGE [21 November 1820]. Apprentice to John Campbell of Annfield.—Son of John Robertson, Wine Merchant in Edinburgh. *Born* 1796. *Married* (1) 9 June 1825, Helen (*died* 14 July 1833), second daughter of John Elder, Depute Clerk of Session; and (2) 5 August 1839, Jane Maria Sophia (*died* 17 April 1889), daughter of Alexander Smith of Land, Dumfriesshire. Was also a Stockbroker. *Died* 25 August 1873.

ROBERTSON, WILLIAM [11 December 1788]. Apprentice to George Cuming.— Youngest son of James Robertson Barclay of Keavil, Fife, W.S. *Died* 2 December 1839.

ROBERTSON, WILLIAM [26 November 1829]. Apprentice to Alexander Pearson.—Son of George Robertson Scott of Benholm, Kincardineshire. *Died* 8 May 1850, aged 49, unmarried.

ROBERTSON, WILLIAM DINWOODIE [15 January 1894]. Apprentice to James Burness.—Son of James Robertson, Wine Merchant, 4 Laverockbank Terrace, Leith. *Born* 3 October 1870. *Died* at Winnipeg, Canada, 18 August 1920.

ROBERTSON, WILLIAM HOPE [15 January 1894]. Apprentice to John Cowan and J. A. Dalmahoy.—Son of Alexander Robertson, Sheriff-Substitute of Forfar. *Born* 26 August 1868. *Married* (1) 15 March 1898, Alice Susan (*died* 11 January 1929), youngest daughter of Frederick Pitman, W.S.; and (2) 3 June 1930, Ernestine Mary Parker (*died* 20 July 1962), Stronvar, Strathyre. Retired, 1928. *Died* 11 May 1958. *Firm*—W. and J. Cook.

ROBERTSON, WILLIAM PEMBERTON [28 July 1882]. Apprentice to George Robertson and John Hope Finlay.—Son of George Robertson, W.S. *Born* 25 July 1859. *Married* 18 December 1889, Augusta (*died* 11 July 1947), eldest daughter of Lieut.-Colonel Babington of Brooklands, Hampshire. *Died* at St Boswells, 14 June 1915.

ROBERTSON-DURHAM, WILLIAM HUGH [10 December 1912]. Apprentice to W. H. Murray, John S. Pitman, and R. O. Pitman.—Son of James Alexander Robertson-Durham of Boghead, C.A. *Born* 17 February 1889. Captain, Scottish Rifles. *Killed* in action in France on 25/27 September 1915.

ROBINSON, GEORGE, OF CLERMISTON [22 June 1784]. Apprentice to Samuel Mitchelson.—Second son of William Robinson, Merchant in Banff. *Born* 15 November 1758. *Married*, proclaimed 10 March 1781, Elizabeth (*died* 19 March 1822), daughter of John Innes of Edingight, and widow of Thomas Innes of Monellie, W.S. Lord Treasurer's Remembrancer, 1815-25. *Died* 6 May 1825.

ROBINSON, JONATHAN ROGER EDWARD, M.A., LL.B. [4 December 1967]. Apprentice to A. M. Hodge and Another of Cowan & Stewart.—Son of Lt.-Colonel R. E. R. Robinson, O.B.E., Mosta, Malta, G.C. *Born* 24 December 1942. *Married* 20 November 1965, Rosemary, daughter of W. L. Thomson. *Firms*—(1) A. B. & A. Matthews, Newton Stewart; (2) J. R. E. Robinson & Co., Balerno.

ROBINSON, WILLIAM. *See* SMITH, WILLIAM ROBINSON.

ROBISON, CHARLES KNOWLES [10 July 1812]. Apprentice to Richard Hotchkis.— Second son of John Robison, Professor of Natural Philosophy in the University of Edinburgh. *Born* 1781. *Married* 8 July 1822, Elizabeth Carr. Magistrate of Police, Calcutta. *Died* at Calcutta, April 1846.

ROBSON, CHARLES MACLAREN [14 July 1890]. Apprentice to T. E. O. Horne, T. Horne, and David Lyell.—Son of James Curle Robson, Procurator-Fiscal of Berwickshire. *Born* 30 March 1863. *Died* 25 December 1890, unmarried.

ROBSON, JOHN ALEXANDER, LL.B. [26 March 1901]. Apprentice to A. H. M'Lean.—Son of the Rev. George Robson, D.D., Perth. *Born* 7 July 1871. *Married* 26 August 1902, Annie May (*died* 20 May 1909), younger daughter of James Ritchie, C.E., Birkhill, Stirling. *Died* 9 August 1903.

RODGER, MATHEW FREER, LL.B. [12 December 1911]. Apprentice to R. R. Simpson, Alexander P. Melville, and A. R. Simpson.—Son of Campbell Rodger, Fireclay Manufacturer, Helensburgh. *Born* 5 November 1885. *Married* (decree of declarator, 11 December 1917) Helen Esson. Lieutenant Scottish Rifles. *Killed* in action on 23 October 1916.

RODMAN, WILLIAM CURRIE [16 April 1947]. Apprentice to Thomas Mackintosh of Mackintosh & Boyd.—Son of John Rodman, Company Director and Engineer. *Born* 29 May 1905. *Married* (1) 6 June 1936, Elisabeth Ward (*died* 16 December 1939), daughter of Alexander Stewart Henderson, Engineer; (2) 21 January 1942, Frances Christian, daughter of John Christian Livingston, W.S., Edinburgh. *Firm*—Stuart & Stuart (now Stuart & Stuart, Cairns & Co.). (Retired.)

ROGER, GEORGE ALEXANDER, M.A., LL.B. [31 July 1922]. Apprentice to R. W. Cockburn of Guild & Shepherd.—Son of William Wood Roger, Provision Merchant, Dunblane. *Born* 28 July 1892. *Married* 18 September 1924, Mary Helen Caie, daughter of Robert Freer Myles, Solicitor, Forfar. Served as Wireless Telegraphist in Royal Naval Air Service, 1915-19. *Firm*—W. H. Mill, McLeod & Rose (formerly McLeod & Rose).

ROLLAND, ADAM, OF GASK [6 March 1787]. Apprentice to John Gordon.—Second son of Rev. Robert Rolland, Minister of Culross. *Born* 17 July 1763. *Married* 10 October 1796, Ann (*died* 1 January 1837), daughter of James Newbigging, residing in Whitehouse. Crown Agent, 1820-28. Principal Clerk of Session from 26 November 1828 till death. *Died* 31 March 1837.

ROLLAND, ADAM, OF GASK [25 June 1824]. Apprentice to Sir Frances Walker Drummond.—Eldest son of Adam Rolland, W.S. *Born* 5 July 1801. *Married* 5 September 1832, Charlotte (*died* 10 May 1880), daughter of John Craigie of Quebec, and niece of Laurence Craigie of Kilgraston, Perthshire. *Died* 18 October 1890.

ROLLAND, JAMES [7 July 1829]. Apprentice to, and second son of, Adam Rolland, W.S.—*Born* 24 November 1802. *Married* 21 April 1840, Maria Rebecca (*died* 3 March 1861), eldest daughter of William Stothert of Cargen, Kirkcudbrightshire. *Died* 20 November 1889.

ROLLO, DAVID BRUCE MACINTOSH, LL.B. [28 April 1975]. Apprentice to Ian Grant Smith and Others of Brodies.—Son of Thomas Landale Rollo, Solicitor, Cupar. *Born* 25 January 1946. *Married* 8 September 1972, Lesley, daughter of Victor Bellinger. *Firms*—(1) Brodies; (2) Rollo & Davidson, Cupar.

ROLLO, HUGH JAMES [10 March 1806]. Apprentice to Vans Hathorn.—Third son of Hugh James Paterson Rollo of Bannockburn. *Born* 4 February 1783. *Married* 12 July 1813, Jane Hathorn (*died* 27 August 1849), eldest daughter of William Richardson of Keithock, Brechin. *Drowned* on board steamer *Comet* off Gourock, 21 October 1825.

ROLLO, HUGH JAMES [20 May 1847]. Apprentice to John Richardson.—Son of Hugh James Rollo, W.S. *Born* 16 June 1818. *Married* (1) 30 November 1865, Mary (*died* 20 July 1875), daughter of Alexander Stuart of Inchbreck, Kincardineshire; and (2) 15 January 1880, Mary Dealtry (*died* 5 August 1905), daughter of Rev. John Hutton Pollexfen of Cairston, Orkney, Vicar of Middleton Tyas, Yorkshire. *Died* 28 February 1890.

ROMANES, CHARLES JAMES LORIMER [12 December 1911]. Apprentice to Andrew Wishart and Kenneth Sanderson.—Son of Charles Simson Romanes, C.A., Edinburgh. *Born* 23 July 1888. *Married* 6 July 1917, Frances Florence (*died* 26 November 1976), youngest daughter of Major A. Baird, A.V.S., Coveyheugh, Berwickshire. Clerk of Peace for Berwickshire, 1931. *Died* 12 January 1949. *Firm*—Tweedie and Romanes, Duns.

ROMANES, JOHN HYSLOP [29 October 1894]. Apprentice to Charles Morton.—Son of James Romanes, C.A., Edinburgh. *Born* 27 June 1870. *Married* 3 September 1913, Lucy (*died* 5 November 1962), youngest daughter of James Thomas, M.D., Selkirk. Served in Ireland as Lieutenant Royal Defence Corps in Great War. Author of *The Economic Studies of a Lawyer*, 1930. *Died* 2 April 1947.

RONALD, DUNCAN [23 June 1691]. Apprentice to John Campbell of Succoth.—*Married* (1) Euphan (*died* 14 July 1698), daughter of Patrick Scott of Langshaw; and (2) Ann Murray. Director Depute of the Chancellary. *Buried* 29 August 1700.

RORIE, JAMES [16 July 1889]. Apprentice to W. T. Dickson, T. S. Maclaren, and W. Traquair, Jun.—Eldest son of George Livingstone Rorie, Secretary, National Bank of Scotland, Edinburgh. *Born* 27 December 1864. *Died* 30 October 1908, unmarried.

ROS, WILLIAM [29 June 1661]. Apprentice to Hew Rose.—*Married* Marion Grier, widow of John M'Clure, Doctor of Physic. Fiscal, 1657-66. *Died* April 1668.

ROSE, HEW [1627]. *Married* 14 August 1623, Sara (*died* 31 October 1665), daughter of John Armour, Merchant Burgess of Edinburgh. Fiscal, 1627-51. *Died* 1651.

ROSE, JAMES [1 July 1824]. Apprentice to Walter Dickson.—Son of James Rose, Depute Clerk of Session. *Married* 16 June 1830, Susan Brabazon (*died* 8 February 1861), daughter of Lieut.-Colonel Wight of Largnean. *Died* 1 December 1864, aged 68.

ROSE, JAMES [9 July 1894]. Apprentice to R. L. Stuart and J. G. Stuart.—Son of the Rev. William Rose, Minister of the Parish of Sandsting in Shetland. *Born* 9 June 1866. *Married* 20 June 1917, Margaret (*died* 15 February 1954), third daughter of William Jackson, London. *Died* 7 March 1941.

ROSE, NORMAN HUNTER, LL.B. [4 December 1972]. Apprentice to R. MacDuff Urquhart of A. & W. M. Urquhart.—Son of David Douglas Rose, Civil Servant, Edinburgh. *Born* 11 March 1949.

ROSS, ALEXANDER [1627]. Signs the Acts, 26 December 1627.

ROSS, ALEXANDER, OF LITTLE DAAN [14 July 1718]. Apprentice to James Baird.—Son of Alexander Ross of Easter Fearn, Ross-shire. Commissary of Moray, 9 July 1724. *Died* 4 March 1753.

ROSS, DONALD STEWART, T.D., B.A.(OXON), LL.B. [15 July 1946]. Apprentice to Robert Kerr Blair and Others of Blair & Cadell.—Son of James Ross, Solicitor, Eskbank, Midlothian. *Born* 18 May 1914. *Married* 2 October 1940, Margery Evelyn, daughter of Dr T. R. Matson, D.S.O., Melbourne, Australia. Major, R.A. Served North Africa, Sicily, Italy and Gibraltar 1939-45. *Firm*—Cowan & Stewart.

ROSS, HUGH, OF KNOCKBRAKE [5 June 1845]. Apprentice to Joseph Gordon.—Son of Hugh Ross of Knockbrake, Ross-shire. *Born* 12 January 1820. *Married* 25 June 1845, Anne (*died* 9 November 1882), youngest daughter of Thomas Houstoun, Kintradwell, Sutherland. Sheriff-Substitute at Tobermory, 1865-85. *Died* 25 February 1889.

ROSS, IAN DALRYMPLE, B.A.(CANTAB), LL.B [7 September 1948]. Apprentice to Mackenzie Smith Shaw and Another of Thomson, Dickson & Shaw.—Son of Stewart Ker Ross, Solicitor, Edinburgh. *Born* 13 October 1919. *Married* 26 May 1946, Artemisia, daughter of Colonel Stavros Kalfakakou, Greece. Major, Cameronians (Scottish Rifles). Served S.O.E. (Greece 1944-45 and Malaya 1945). Mentioned in Despatches 1945. Honorary Vice Consul for Greece. *Firm*—Thomson & Baxter (previously Thomson, Dickson & Shaw, incorporating J. A. Campbell & Lamond).

ROSS, JAMES HECTOR [28 April 1958]. Apprentice to Ronald Macdonald Robertson of Weir & Robertson. *Born* 17 June 1916. Resigned Commission, 1968. *Firm*—T. F. Weir & Robertson.

ROSS, JAMES HUNTER [27 June 1820]. Apprentice to William Dallas.—Third son of William Ross, Collector of Customs, Stranraer. *Married* (1) 26 August 1816, Margaret (*died* 10 April 1827), daughter of —— Johnstone, Castle-Douglas; and (2) 1 June 1833, Margaret Penelope, youngest daughter of James Foulis, Wheatfield, Ayr. Latterly a Solicitor in Melbourne. *Died* 18 September 1865, aged 73.

ROSS, JAMES PAULL [12 July 1909]. Apprentice to William John Kirk and James A. Hope.—Son of the Rev. George Ross, Minister of the Parish of Hoddam. *Born* 7 April 1881. *Married* 2 June 1923, Catherine Birnie (*died* 26 July 1964), daughter of William Birnie Rhind, R.S.A. Assistant District Commissioner, Gold Coast, 1913. District Commissioner, 1916. Senior Assistant Colonial Secretary, 1921. Principal Assistant Colonial Secretary, Gold Coast, 1930. Author of *The Census Report of the Gold Coast, Ashanti, the Northern Territories and the Mandated Area of Togoland*, 1921. *Died* 10 May 1953.

ROSS, JOHN [1609]. Apprentice to John Paip.—*Married* (1) 7 September 1602, Janet Kellie; and (2) (contract, 20 February 1610), Helen, daughter of John Cunyngham in Leith. *Died* February 1621.

ROSS, JOHN, OF NUICK [23 October 1704]. Apprentice to William Thomson.—Son of Andrew Ross of Nuick. *Married* Jean Ross. *Died* 1740.

ROSS, JOHN [30 January 1797]. Apprentice to (1) Walter Ross; and (2) Robert Dundas.—Third son of Walter Ross, W.S. *Born* 17 October 1766. *Married* 20 September 1805, Christina (*died* 23 January 1846), daughter of John Moncrieff of Sauchopewood, Fife. *Died* 11 December 1817.

ROSS, JOHN [28 January 1876]. Apprentice to Robert Dobbie Ross, his brother.—Son of John Ross, S.S.C. *Born* 11 August 1850. *Married* 24 April 1879, Julia Ann (*died* 20 November 1916), widow of Robert Beckwith Towse, London. *Died* 5 November 1932.

ROSS, JOHN LEITH, OF ARNAGE [27 January 1801]. Apprentice to Craufurd Tait.—Second son of Alexander Leith of Freefield, Aberdeenshire. *Born* 29 September 1777. *Married* 7 January 1807, Elizabeth (*died* 3 June 1852), daughter of William Young of Theddocksley, Provost of Aberdeen. *Died* 15 May 1839.

ROSS, KENNETH HARRISON, B.A.(OXON), LL.B. [13 May 1963]. Apprentice to the Hon. D. A. Balfour and Others of Shepherd & Wedderburn.—Son of Stanley Solari Ross, C.A., Edinburgh. *Born* 18 June 1936.

ROSS, KENNETH MCLEAN, LL.B. [28 May 1979] (By Rule IX(a)). *Born* 1 March 1947.

ROSS, PETER MORISON [9 July 1895]. Apprentice to J. R. M. Wedderburn and G. G. Watson.—Son of the Rev. Robert Ross, Forfar. *Born* 24 December 1870. *Died* at Gin Gin, Queensland, 25 December 1926.

ROSS, ROBERT [21 November 1790]. Apprentice to John Innes.—Only son of Daniel Ross of Binns. *Died* 1825.

ROSS, ROBERT DOBBIE [31 December 1867]. Apprentice to James Duncan.—Son of John Ross, S.S.C. *Born* 1 March 1841. *Died* 1 October 1877, unmarried.

ROSS, SINCLAIR ALEXANDER, M.A.(CANTAB), LL.B. [3 December 1965]. Apprentice to A. J. R. Bisset and Others of Baillie & Gifford.—Son of Thomas Alexander Ross, Ph.D., Solicitor, Falkirk. *Born* 7 January 1938. *Married* 3 April 1965, Lorna Ann, daughter of Alexander McLaren, Tea Planter, Ceylon. *Firm*—Russel & Aitken, Falkirk and Edinburgh.

ROSS, WALTER [25 June 1764]. Apprentice to John Russell of Roseburne.—Son of Charles Ross, Merchant in Edinburgh. *Born* 28 September 1738. *Married* Margaret, daughter of John Moubray of the Cockairny family. Author of *Lectures on the Practice of the Law of Scotland*, 1792, and other legal works. *Died* suddenly 11 March 1789, and interred in lower part of a tower built by him at St Bernard's, Stockbridge. His remains were later buried in St Cuthbert's Churchyard, 1818.

ROSS, WILLIAM CRAIG [15 July 1949]. Apprentice to James Campbell Walker of Steedman, Ramage & Co.—Son of William Melvin Ross, S.S.C. and Auditor of Court of Session. *Born* 31 January 1920. *Married* 28 August 1948, Eirly Gwyneth, daughter of Dr H. G. Morris-Jones, Llangollen, Denbighshire. Lieutenant, Royal Scots. Served Gibraltar and Italy. *Firm*—J. & A. Hastie.

ROUGHEAD, WILLIAM [10 July 1893]. Apprentice to T. S. Maclaren and William Traquair, Jun.—Son of John Carfrae Roughead, Merchant in Edinburgh. *Born* 13 February 1870. *Married* 18 July 1900, Janey (*died* 24 January 1940), elder daughter of Francis More, C.A., Edinburgh. Author of *The Riddle of the Ruthvens, Malice Domestic, Bad Companions*, and other works dealing with aspects of crime, and editor of several volumes in Notable British Trials Series. *Died* 11 May 1952.

ROW, CHARLES, OF INNERALLAN [5 April 1688]. Apprentice to Sir Hugh Paterson of Bannockburn.—Son of Archibald Row of Innerallan. *Married* 1 July 1685 Christian Anderson. *Died* 5 March 1709.

ROWAN, JOHN [2 September 1648]. Apprentice to Archibald Gibson.—Son of —— Rowan; cousin of Andrew Rowan of Gask. Re-admitted, 21 November 1661. *Buried* 14 January 1663.

ROWAN, JOHN [13 February 1744]. Apprentice to Robert Wallace.—Son of James Rowan of Hethryhall. *Married* 1740, Janet, daughter of John Paterson, Merchant, Glasgow. *Died* April 1750.

ROXBURGH, JAMES FINDLAY [19 October 1891]. Apprentice to E. Denholm Young.—Son of John Roxburgh, 15 Lynedoch Crescent, Glasgow. *Born* 7 July 1856. *Died* 6 April 1918, unmarried. *Firm*—Young and Roxburgh.

ROY, FREDERICK LEWIS, OF NENTHORN [4 July 1823]. Apprentice to James Heriot.—Second son of William Roy of Nenthorn, Berwickshire. *Born* 1800. *Married* (1) 5 June 1827, Margaret Louisa (*died* 1848), daughter of Charles Maitland Makgill of Rankeillour; and (2) 26 October 1853, Mary Catherine (*died* 25 October 1898), daughter of Alexander Boswell, W.S. *Died* 15 February 1868.

ROY, JAMES [25 May 1826]. Apprentice to James Thomson.—Son of James Roy, residing in Perth. *Married* 10 May 1864, Anne (*died* 1 June 1910), youngest daughter of John Robertson, Invercomrie, Perthshire. *Died* 11 November 1881.

ROY, ROBERT, OF RIROY [7 February 1822]. Apprentice to Æneas Macbean.—Son of James Roy, Surgeon to the Forces at Fort George. *Born* 1796. *Married* 5 June 1867, Mary (*died* 31 October 1900), daughter of William Dean, Solicitor, London. *Died* 10 September 1873.

RUSSEL, GEORGE [17 February 1800]. Apprentice to James Watson.—Third son of Alexander Russel of Montcoffer, Aberdeenshire. *Married* 13 March 1804, his cousin, Catherine, eldest daughter of Thomas Russel of Rathen. *Died* at Skelmuir, 3 October 1826.

RUSSELL, ALEXANDER JAMES [16 November 1837]. Apprentice to, and second son of, John Russell, W.S.—*Born* 21 June 1814. *Married* (1) 9 January 1839, Magdalene (*died* 9 June 1857), daughter of Andrew Stein of Wester Greenyards; and (2) 13 April 1861, Elizabeth Anne (*died* 1 May 1903), youngest daughter of Samuel Lancaster, Wateringbury Place, Kent. *Died* 8 January 1887. *Firm*—Russell and Dunlop.

RUSSELL, ARTHUR WALKER, O.B.E. [28 March 1899]. Apprentice to David Shaw.—Son of Arthur Russell, Banker. Cupar, Fife. *Born* 6 July 1873. *Married* 19 March 1903, Barbara Stuart (*died* 6 May 1965), eldest daughter of Colin M'Cuaig, Actuary, Edinburgh. Served in France, Captain A. and S. Highlanders, in Great War. *Died* 15 December 1967. *Firm*—Strathern and Blair.

RUSSELL, GEORGE, OF INCH [16 January 1798]. Apprentice to John Anderson of Inchyra.—Eldest son of James Russell of South Inch. *Married* 11 November 1798, Jane (*died* 17 April 1836), daughter of William Simpson of Ogil. *Died* 1 April 1826.

RUSSELL, GEORGE RUTHERFORD, LL.B. [30 April 1973]. Apprentice to Patrick Murray and Others of Murray, Beith & Murray.—Son of George Stuart Russell, W.S., Edinburgh. *Born* 26 September 1946. *Married* 19 April 1974, Mary Ellen, daughter of Jay H. Rose, Executive with Exxon, Texas, U.S.A. *Firm*—Strathern & Blair.

RUSSELL, GEORGE STUART, O.B.E., T.D., B.L., C.A. [8 October 1941]. Apprentice to Arthur Woodman Blair and Others of Strathern & Blair.—Son of Arthur Walker Russell, O.B.E., W.S., Edinburgh. *Born* 21 January 1914. *Married* 29 April 1939, Nicholas Mary, daughter of Rutherfurd Clerk Gillespie, W.S., Castle Douglas. Lieutenant Colonel, Army Staff. Served U.K. and N.W. Europe 1939-45. Awarded Golden Cross of Merit (Poland) with Swords 1944. Fiscal of the Society 1974-80. *Firm*—Strathern & Blair.

RUSSELL, HAMILTON [13 November 1834]. Apprentice to James Gillespie Davidson.—Son of Adam Russell, Architect in Edinburgh. *Born* 22 September 1801. *Married* 29 April 1839, Mary (*died* 23 April 1883), daughter of Rev. T. B. Blackburn, Durham. Sheriff-Substitute at Wick, 1849-80. *Died* 18 June 1881.

RUSSELL, JAMES [30 January 1840]. Apprentice to John Tweedie.—Fourth son of Alexander Russell, Coachbuilder in Edinburgh. *Born* 16 June 1811. *Married* 1846, Isabella (*died* 24 November 1894), daughter of Charles Wildgoose, Captain in the Merchant Service. *Died* 7 February 1846.

RUSSELL, JOHN, OF BRAIDSHAW [16 November 1711]. Apprentice to James Anderson.— Fourth son of James Russell of Slipperfield, Peeblesshire. *Born* 3 December 1672. *Married* (1) 29 August 1698, Maria, third daughter of Andrew Russell, Merchant, Rotterdam; (2) 20 October 1706, Ursula (*died* 1717), daughter of Claud Alexander of Newton; and (3) 15 October 1719, Mary, daughter of Rev. John Anderson, Minister of West Calder. *Died* 27 January 1759.

RUSSELL, JOHN, OF ROSEBURNE [3 April 1749]. Apprentice to, and eldest son of, John Russell of Braidshaw, Mid-Lothian, W.S. *Born* 12 December 1710. *Married* 17 October 1751, Bethia (*died* December 1810), daughter of Daniel Campbell of Greenyards, Stirlingshire. Secretary to the Royal Bank of Scotland. *Died* May 1796.

RUSSELL, JOHN [24 June 1774]. Apprentice to, and eldest son of, John Russell of Roseburne, W.S.—*Born* 22 January 1753. *Married* 8 June 1778, Eleanor (*died* 17 January 1837), daughter of Rev. William Robertson, D.D., Principal of Edinburgh University. *Died* 2 December 1792.

RUSSELL, JOHN [8 March 1803]. Apprentice to James Dundas.—Only son of John Russell, W.S. *Born* 22 February 1780. *Married* 10 June 1810, Cecilia (*died* 1 June 1833), only daughter of Lieut.-Col. John Murray of Stewarthall, son of William Murray of Touchadam, Stirlingshire. Third Clerk to Jury Court, 1815-30. Principal Clerk of Session, 9 May 1842-58. *Died* 30 January 1862.

RUSSELL, PATRICK, OF KELLERSTAIN [24 February 1794]. Apprentice to John Russell, Sen., and John Russell, Jun.—Fifth son of John Russell, W.S. *Born* 1771. *Married* 28 December 1799, Rebecca Thomas, daughter of Michael Carmichael of Hazelhead. Fiscal, 1807-20. *Died* 9 April 1835.

RUSSELL, WILLIAM [30 November 1675]. Apprentice to Alexander Leslie.—*Married* 13 October 1668, Catherine, daughter of Alexander Leslie, W.S., and widow of John Ellis, Writer, Edinburgh. *Buried* 20 May 1684.

RUTHERFOORD, JOHN, OF KNOWSOUTH [31 July 1798]. Apprentice to William Riddell.—Eldest son of Thomas Rutherfoord of Knowsouth, Roxburghshire. *Died* 7 April 1801, unmarried.

RUTHERFORD, ANDREW [8 August 1649]. Apprentice to Adam Watt and Alexander Douglas.—Re-admitted, 21 November 1661.

RUTHERFORD, ARCHIBALD COCHRANE, O.B.E., T.D. [17 December 1928]. Apprentice to John Cowan and Others of Cowan & Dalmahoy.—Son of William Rutherford, Writer, Galashiels. *Born* 3 January 1904. *Married* (1) 16 January 1930, Christine Helen, daughter of Frank Greig Bucher, Electrical Engineer, Edinburgh, (divorced), and (2) 6 March 1947, Argot Marie Maien Berg, Oslo, Norway. Captain, R.A. Served U.K. and France 1939-45. *Died* 9 July 1980. *Firm*—W. A. & F. Rutherford, Galashiels. (Retired.)

RUTHERFORD, GEORGE, OF FAIRNINGTON [29 June 1759]. Apprentice to Samuel Mitchelson.—Son of George Rutherford of Fairnington, Roxburghshire. *Married* August 1757, Mary (*died* 1796), daughter of Strother Ker of Littledean, Roxburghshire. *Died* 27 October 1774.

RUTHERFORD, IAN CHARLES, B.A., LL.B. [13 December 1926]. Apprentice to Patrick Murray, William C. Johnston, D.K.S., William B. Wilson, Charles E. Stewart, and D. B. Sinclair.—Son of Robert S. Rutherford, Solicitor, Edinburgh. *Born* 10 May 1902. *Married* 31 July 1934. Alexandra Mary Morrison (*died* 22 March 1981). Served R.A.F.V.R. Squadron Leader (Intelligence and Photographic), in U.K., India and S.E. Asia 1939-45. Mentioned in Despatches 1944. *Died* 14 August 1967. *Firm*—Beveridge & Co., Leith.

RUTHERFORD, JAMES, OF ASHINTULLY [5 August 1777]. Apprentice to James Ramsay.—Third son of Andrew Rutherford, Tanner, Kirkcaldy. *Born* 1729. *Married* Elizabeth Wardlaw. *Died* 18 May 1817.

RUTHERFORD, JAMES [7 February 1822]. Apprentice to James Wright.—Son of James Rutherford, Merchant in Edinburgh. *Married* 27 December 1822, Susannah (*died* 24 January 1837), daughter of Michael Hardcastle of Haughton, Durham. *Died* 3 September 1843, aged 47.

RUTHERFORD, JAMES WIGHT, T.D. [19 December 1932]. Apprentice to James Murray Cooper of Macpherson & Mackay.—Son of Walter Carter Rutherford, S.S.C., Edinburgh. *Born* 2 September 1908. *Married* 30 August 1947, Doris, daughter of Alfred Shirt. Captain and Paymaster, Royal Army Pay Corps. Served U.K. and West Africa 1939-45. *Died* 20 April 1978. *Firm*—Dove, Lockhart, Mackay & Young. (Retired.)

RUTHERFORD, JOHN [14 November 1800]. Apprentice to Robert Trotter.—Eldest son of John Rutherford of Mossburn, Roxburghshire. *Married* —— (*died* 16 March 1839). *Died* 1822.

RUTHERFORD, JOHN DOUGLAS [11 July 1910]. Apprentice to W. Stuart Fraser.—Son of John Rutherford, Ancrum Craig, Roxburghshire. *Born* 18 March 1885. *Married* 27 October 1917, Elizabeth Olive (*died* 15 June 1967), daughter of George G. Mackay, Mellness, Hoylake. Captain R.A.S.C., 1915-17. *Died* 17 September 1952.

RUTHERFORD, ROBERT [7 March 1815]. Apprentice to Thomas Cranston.—Second son of Dr Daniel Rutherford, Physician in Edinburgh. *Born* 22 February 1790. Deputy Keeper of the Abbey of Holyrood. *Died* 6 June 1866, unmarried.

RUTHERFURD, JAMES HUNTER [10 January 1887]. Apprentice to George Dalziel.—Eldest son of Andrew Rutherfurd, Advocate, Sheriff-Substitute of Mid-Lothian. *Born* 13 June 1864. M.F.H. *Died* 7 October 1927, unmarried. *Firm*—Rutherfurd and Don Wauchope.

RUTHERFURD, JOHN [26 November 1829]. Apprentice to William Bell.—Son of John Rutherfurd, Saddler in Jedburgh. *Born* 20 December 1803. *Married* 23 February 1836, Cassandra (*died* 23 November 1882), daughter of Adam Scott Elliot of Arkleton, Dumfriesshire. *Died* 29 November 1865.

RUTHERFURD, JOHN [22 March 1866]. Apprentice to, and son of, John Rutherfurd, W.S.—*Born* 3 February 1841. *Died* 27 December 1920, unmarried.

RYDEN, NICHOLAS CHARLES, LL.B. [6 December 1976]. Apprentice to The Lord Kinross and Others of Shepherd & Wedderburn.—Son of Kenneth Ryden, M.C., Estate Agent, Edinburgh. *Born* 20 March 1953. *Firm*—Shepherd & Wedderburn.

RYDEN, PETER ANTHONY, LL.B. [9 December 1980]. Apprentice to Ian Temple Johnstone and Others of Biggart, Baillie & Gifford.—Son of Kenneth Ryden, Estate Agent, Edinburgh. *Born* 16 September 1956.

RYDER, ELIZABETH JANE, M.A.(St Andrews) [8 December 1981]. Apprentice to Robert Knox and Others of Boyd, Jameson & Young.—Daughter of James G. Ryder, Company Director, Wallingford, Oxfordshire. *Born* 27 January 1952.

RYMER, JOHN [9 June 1825]. Apprentice to John Mowbray.—Son of Henry Rymer, Merchant in Bo'ness. *Born* 1800. *Married* 1 October 1834, Christian (*died* 8 April 1862), only daughter of Lieut.-Colonel John Dalgleish of West Grange, Perthshire. *Died* 3 August 1837.

SADLER, DAVID GERALD, B.A.(Oxon) [28 November 1966]. Apprentice to Michael Lorimer of Henderson & Jackson.—Son of David W. Sadler, Soap Manufacturer, Coulter, by Biggar. *Born* 29 October 1931. *Married* 20 April 1956, Valerie Ann Victoria, daughter of Victor Donaldson, Timber Importer, Lundin Links, Fife. *Firm*—D. Gerald Sadler, Castle Douglas.

ST JOHN, EDMUND OLIVER, B.L. [17 November 1952]. Apprentice to Edward John McCandlish and Others of Cowan & Dalmahoy.—Son of Colonel Edmund Farquhar St John, North Berwick. *Born* 13 October 1927. *Married* 17 April 1959, Elizabeth Frances, daughter of Colonel H. R. Nicholl, Haydon Bridge, Northumberland. *Firm*— Cowan & Dalmahoy (1953-64, thereafter on amalgamation, Lindsays).

SANDEMAN, DAVID CHISHOLM, of Kirkwood [13 November 1828]. Apprentice to William Mackenzie.—Third son of David George Sandeman of Springland, Perthshire. *Born* 24 March 1806. *Married* 4 April 1843, Julia, only daughter of John Robertson of Foveran, Aberdeenshire. *Died* 13 November 1852.

SANDERSON, KENNETH [13 July 1891]. Apprentice to James Bruce and Thomas Kerr.—Son of Robert Sanderson, Manufacturer, Knowe Park, Galashiels. *Born* 1 July 1868. *Died* 16 October 1943. *Firm*—Wishart and Sanderson.

SANDERSON, ROBERT KENNETH [19 March 1934]. Apprentice to Robert Kerr Blair and Others of Blair & Cadell.—Son of Major Harry Sanderson, Manufacturer, Galashiels, Selkirkshire. *Born* 31 December 1908. Second World War, Royal Navy. Served in Bermuda, Caribbean, Malaya, India, Singapore and Java. Secretary and Treasurer of John Watson's School, Edinburgh. *Died* 11 March 1977. *Firm*—Wishart & Sanderson.

SANDERSON, WILLIAM [11 December 1828]. Apprentice to James Greig.—Second son of John Sanderson, Lapidary in Edinburgh. *Born* 1805. *Died* 25 June 1836, unmarried.

SANDILANDS, GEORGE ANTHONY MACPHERSON, M.A., LL.B. [20 July 1976]. Apprentice to (1) G. M. Shearer of Hunter, Harvey, Webster & Will; (2) J. P. Herd of Beveridge, Herd & Sandilands, Kirkcaldy.—Son of George Sandilands, Solicitor, Kirkcaldy. *Born* 29 August 1949. *Married* 16 December 1972, Jennifer Anne, daughter of James Paton. *Firm*—Beveridge, Herd & Sandilands (formerly Beveridge, Herd & Whyte), Kirkcaldy.

SANDILANDS, MATTHEW, of Couston [2 December 1779]. Apprentice to (1) James Home; and (2) Walter Scott.—Only son of Rev. Matthew Sandilands, Minister of Eccles. *Died* 3 August 1821.

SANDILANDS, ROBERT [26 May 1818]. Apprentice to John Tod.—Fourth son of George Sandilands of Nuthill, Fife. *Born* 1790. *Married* 14 July 1829, Mary, youngest daughter of Sir Charles Style, Bart., of Wateringbury, Kent. Assistant Judge at Nassau, New Providence, U.S.A. *Died* 20 May 1872.

SANDS, WARREN HASTINGS [25 May 1814]. Apprentice to James Thomson.—Second son of William Sands, Major in the service of the Hon. East India Company. *Born* 1791. *Married* 5 June 1820, Harrietta Lindesay, youngest daughter of Henry Bethune of Kilconquhar, Fife. Agent to Teind Court, 1825. *Died* 1 February 1874.

SANDS, WILLIAM, OF LANGSIDE [25 November 1780]. Apprentice to William Macdonald.—Third son of William Sands of Langside. *Died* 20 June 1783.

SANDS, WILLIAM JOHN [22 May 1845]. Apprentice to, and eldest son of, Warren Hastings Sands, W.S.—*Born* 9 July 1821. *Married* 8 June 1852, Augusta Sophia (*died* 14 February 1906), daughter of Major-General Wemyss of Green Park, Bath. *Died* 11 April 1879.

SANDY, GEORGE [10 July 1798]. Apprentice to Anthony Barclay.—Son of George Sandy, Writer in Edinburgh, and Substitute Keeper of the Signet. *Born* 29 May 1772. Catalogued the books in the Library, 1805. Secretary to the Bank of Scotland. The Manuscript of his diary is in the Signet Library (*see also* Book of the Old Edinburgh Club, Vol. XXIV, p. 1). *Died* 8 April 1853.

SANG, DAVID [13 July 1871]. Apprentice to Alexander Forsyth Adam.—Son of John Sang, S.S.C. *Born* 27 January 1838. *Died* 27 May 1883, unmarried.

SANG, GEORGE [28 March 1899]. Apprentice to J. H. Sang.—Son of George Sang, S.S.C. *Born* 11 March 1875. *Married* 28 August 1901, Florence (*died* 2 February 1970), daughter of Walter Sang, Liverpool. *Died* 6 November 1930.

SANG, JOHN HENRY, LL.B., OF WESTBROOK [20 October 1884]. Apprentice to (1) Robert Blair Maconochie; and (2) Andrew Forrester.—Son of George Sang, S.S.C. *Born* 26 May 1861. *Married* 21 July 1896, Helen Mary (*died* 21 June 1937), youngest daughter of James Meikle, F.I.A., Edinburgh. *Died* 2 March 1936. *Firm*—Pearson, Robertson, and Maconochie.

SANGSTER, MICHAEL FARQUHAR, LL.B. [3 December 1973]. Apprentice to (1) Norman Angus Miller Mackay and Another of Baillie & Gifford; (2) The Hon. David Andrew Balfour and Others of Shepherd & Wedderburn.—Son of Alfred James Sangster, Radiologist, Inverness. *Born* 8 November 1949. *Married* 1 June 1974, Anne Veronica McAvoy. *Firm*—Anderson, Shaw & Gilbert, Inverness.

SAUNDERS, JAMES [10 August 1775]. Apprentice to Charles Gordon.—*Married* Margaret (*died* 7 August 1809), daughter of Joseph Williamson, Advocate. *Died* 16 May 1795.

SCARTH, PILLANS [10 March 1825]. Apprentice to Walter Dickson.—Son of James Scarth, Merchant in Leith. *Married* 5 June 1828, Cecilia (*died* 30 May 1882), daughter of Rev. Thomas Scott, Minister of Newton, Mid-Lothian. *Died* 24 October 1881.

SCHAW MILLER, ROBERT GRANT, B.A.(CANTAB), LL.B. [19 November 1951]. Apprentice to Euan Barclay Robertson and Another of J. & R. A. Robertson.—Son of Alexander Grant Schaw Miller, W.S., Edinburgh. *Born* 10 November 1925. *Married* 7 October 1961, Jean Clare, daughter of Major Stephen G. Squires. Lieutenant (Acting Captain) Royal Artillery. Served in India and Malaya. Former Governor of John Watson's School. *Firm*—Hamilton, Kinnear & Beatson (now Aitken, Kinnear & Co.).

SCHENIMAN, HOPE [4 June 1829]. Apprentice to (1) Robert Y. Anderson; (2) Archibald Crawford; and (3) R. Y. Anderson.—Youngest son of Ferdinand Scheniman, Accountant in Edinburgh. *Died* 28 November 1858, aged 54, unmarried.

SCHOIR, OR SCHYR, ADAM [Before 1586]. Signs Minute of 16 December 1594.

SCOTLAND, JOHN, OF GLENDOUGLAS [7 July 1815]. Apprentice to (1) Charles Innes; and (2) William Handyside.—Son of Thomas Scotland, W.S. *Married* (1) 24 April 1820, Mary (*died* 2 March 1849), daughter of Robert Burn, Architect, Edinburgh; and (2) 26 June 1851, Anne Catherine (*died* 1 February 1880), daughter of Browne Roberts of Ravensbourne Park, Lewisham. *Died* at Kenilworth, 14 October 1860, aged 69.

SCOTLAND, THOMAS, OF WESTER LUSCAR [12 July 1791]. Apprentice to James Buchan.—Son of John Scotland, Merchant in Perth. *Married*, proclaimed 19 July 1790, Rachel (*died* 1843), youngest daughter of Walter Orrock. *Died* 26 November 1824.

SCOTT, ALEXANDER, OF TRINITY [27 February 1817]. Apprentice to Joseph Cauvin.— Eldest son of William Scott, Solicitor-at-Law. *Born* 1792. *Married* (1) 3 August 1819, Helen Sutherland, only daughter of Ebenezer Marshall Gardiner of Hillcairny; and (2) 5 August 1823, Magdalene (*died* March 1867), second daughter of William Blair of Blair, Ayrshire. *Died* at Melbourne, 22 May 1840.

SCOTT, ANDREW [8 July 1823]. Apprentice to (1) Joseph Cauvin; and (2) James Carnegie.—Eldest son of David Scott, Farmer at Northfield, Duddingston. *Born* 1798. *Married* (1) 31 October 1827, Mary Ann (*died* 3 July 1843), daughter of William Affleck, Liverpool; and (2) 29 June 1847, Marion S. (*died* 7 April 1886), daughter of James Lidderdale, Lochbank, Castle-Douglas. *Died* 31 October 1874.

SCOTT, ANDREW [18 November 1861]. Apprentice to James Peddie.—Son of Andrew Scott, W.S. *Born* 26 November 1834. *Married* 21 March 1870, Barbara Jennison (*died* 8 August 1918), eldest daughter of Thomas Beamish of Cashelmore, Co. Cork, and widow of Alfred Henry Hannay. *Died* 31 October 1870.

SCOTT, ANDREW GEDDES [19 October 1885]. Apprentice to Robert Burt Ranken.— Son of William David Scott, S.S.C. *Born* 8 March 1861. *Married* 1 June 1892, Mary Agnes (*died* 17 December 1934), younger daughter of John Usher Somner, Brewer, Jedburgh. *Died* 22 September 1938.

SCOTT, ANDREW HAMILTON, LL.B. [29 March 1909]. Apprentice to R. Strathern and A. S. Blair.—Only son of Adam Cunningham Scott, Merchant and Insurance Agent, Glasgow. *Born* 4 June 1881. Lieutenant K.O.S.B. Officially believed *killed* in action near Arras on 3 May 1917.

SCOTT, ANDREW THOMAS STEELE, OF CROSSWOODHILL [21 April 1875]. Apprentice to John Cook.—Son of Archibald Scott, Solicitor in Edinburgh. *Born* 30 September 1851. *Married* 15 April 1879, Anna Euphemia (*died* 7 March 1940), daughter of John Menzies Baillie of Culterallers, Lanarkshire. *Died* 10 December 1931.

SCOTT, CHARLES BALFOUR [10 March 1806]. Apprentice to Archibald Gibson.— Second son of Charles Scott of Woll, Roxburghshire. *Born* 1782. *Married* 9 November 1818, Eliza (*died* 1870), second daughter of Rev. Alexander Ker, Minister of Stobo. *Died* 3 February 1838.

SCOTT, CHARLES FRANCIS [14 July 1890]. Apprentice to F. Pitman, J. R. Anderson, W. H. Murray, and A. Pitman.—Only surviving son of George Ferme Scott, S.S.C. *Born* 20 December 1866. *Died* 30 April 1931, unmarried. *Firms*—(1) Balfour & Scott; (2) Hope, Todd & Kirk.

SCOTT, DAVID, OF SIBMISTER [15 May 1817]. Apprentice to Henry Moncrieff.—Son of Andrew Scott, Watchmaker in Dingwall. *Married* 14 December 1821, Theodosia, youngest daughter of Robert Anderson, Edinburgh. *Died* suddenly 22 January 1839, aged 48.

SCOTT, GEORGE [24 May 1827]. Apprentice to John K. Campbell and Andrew Clason.—Son of William Scott, Brewer in Leith. *Born* 1804. *Died* 12 May 1833, unmarried.

SCOTT, HARRY BELL- [26 March 1900]. Apprentice to R. Dundas, W. J. Dundas, G. M. Paul, and R. N. Dundas.—Son of Adam Bell Scott, Strowan Lodge, Morningside, Edinburgh. *Born* 12 September 1874. *Married* 6 March 1912, Buckie (*died* 19 November 1935), youngest daughter of Peter Morison, S.S.C., Edinburgh. *Died* 25 February 1946. *Firm*—P. Morison and Son.

SCOTT, HERCULES, OF BROTHERTON [19 March 1719]. Apprentice to Thomas Pringle.—Son of Hercules Scott of Brotherton, Kincardineshire. *Born* 1659. *Married* 1707, Helen, eldest daughter of Sir Charles Ramsay of Balmain, Bart. Substitute Keeper of the Signet, 1719-25. *Died* March 1725.

SCOTT, JAMES [Before 1552].

SCOTT, JAMES [1606]. *Married* Euphan Inglis. Signs Minute of 17 January 1606. *Died* 1628.

SCOTT, JAMES, OF SCOTSLOCH [20 December 1672]. Apprentice to James Allan.—Third son of Sir William Scott of Clerkington, East Lothian, Senator of the College of Justice (Lord Clerkington). *Born* 28 December 1642. *Married* Margaret Boyd (*died* 14 December 1712). *Buried* 8 May 1693.

SCOTT, JAMES [9 January 1738]. Apprentice to Robert Dalrymple.—Son of James Scott of Howden, Writer in Edinburgh. *Married* Margaret (*died* 27 December 1787), daughter of Andrew Marjoribanks of that Ilk. *Died* 12 December 1792.

SCOTT, JAMES, OF BROTHERTON [18 June 1802]. Apprentice to Charles Innes.—Son of David Scott of Netherholm, Kincardineshire. *Born* 1776. *Died* 22 September 1844, unmarried.

SCOTT, JOHN, OF GLENORMISTON [26 February 1784]. Apprentice to Cornelius Elliot.—Youngest son of William Scott of Woll, Roxburghshire. *Married*, proclaimed 4 March 1783, Beatrice (*died* 11 March 1787), daughter of Thomas Caverhill, Merchant, Jedburgh. *Died* 24 March 1803.

SCOTT, JOHN, OF TEVIOTBANK [15 November 1832]. Apprentice to Gilbert Laurie Finlay.—Son of William Scott of Teviotbank, Roxburghshire, W.S. *Born* 2 October 1809. *Married* 2 October 1850, Anne (*died* 9 December 1891), second daughter of Henry Singleton of Belpatrick, Co. Louth. *Died* 16 July 1867.

SCOTT, JOHN, LL.B. [19 October 1885]. Apprentice to Robert Craigie Bell.—Son of William Scott, residing at Coaltown of Balgonie, Markinch. *Born* 21 March 1861. *Died* 7 February 1944. *Firm*—R. C. Bell and J. Scott.

SCOTT, JOHN MENZIES BAILLIE, O.B.E., T.D., J.P. [27 March 1911]. Apprentice to (1) Charles Cook; and (2) A. T. Steele Scott and John Glover.—Son of A. T. Steele Scott, W.S. *Born* 6 October 1887. *Married* 21 January 1915, Alice Nicholson, elder daughter of W. N. Turner, 4 Mossley Hill Drive, Liverpool. Major R.F.A.(T.F.); wounded in France. Mentioned in Despatches. Served U.K. 1939-45. (Colonel, General list T.A.) *Died* 14 January 1967.

SCOTT, PATRICK [5 December 1699]. Apprentice to Robert Innes.—Brother of Hercules Scott, Merchant, Edinburgh. *Married* 24 December 1700, Elizabeth, daughter of George Cunningham of Blairquhosh. *Died* August 1711.

SCOTT, ROBERT [Before 1552]. Clerk of the College of Justice (Clerk of Session). *Married* Elizabeth Scott (*died* 24 February 1592). *Died* 27 March 1592.

SCOTT, ROBERT, B.L. [15 March 1948]. Apprentice to Alexander Burn-Murdoch of Hagart & Burn-Murdoch. *Born* 2 January 1906. *Married* 3 September 1938, Doris Mary Blakey. *Firm*—Hagart & Burn-Murdoch. (Retired.)

SCOTT, ROBERT GREIG [13 July 1891]. Apprentice to Henry Cook and Charles Cook.— Only son of the Rev. Archibald Scott, D.D., Minister of the Parish of St George's, Edinburgh. *Born* 25 September 1867. *Died* 12 September 1911, unmarried.

SCOTT, THOMAS [4 August 1777]. Apprentice to Leonard Urquhart.—Seventh son of Archibald Scott of Rossie, Fife. *Died* 24 June 1794.

SCOTT, THOMAS [19 November 1797]. Apprentice to George Johnston.—Eighth son of Walter Scott, W.S. *Born* 1774. *Married* 16 December 1799, Elizabeth (*died* April 1848), third daughter of David M'Culloch of Ardwall, Kirkcudbrightshire. Extractor of Court of Session, 1810. Officer of Manx Fencibles. Paymaster of the 70th Regiment, Major Huxley of the same being married to his eldest daughter. *Died* in Canada, 14 February 1823.

SCOTT, THOMAS GRAY [27 June 1833]. Apprentice to Walter Dickson and James Steuart.—Son of Archibald Scott, Solicitor-at-Law, Edinburgh, and Procurator-Fiscal for Mid-Lothian. *Born* 29 August 1811. *Married* 11 April 1844, Ellinor (*died* 20 August 1888), daughter of Samuel Cooper of Failford, Ayrshire. *Died* at Funchal, Madeira, 15 January 1856.

SCOTT, THOMAS MACMILLAN, OF WAUCHOPE [22 November 1838]. Apprentice to Laurence Davidson and Thomas Syme.—Eldest son of Walter Scott of Wauchope, Roxburghshire. *Born* 13 February 1816. *Married* 10 April 1844, Catherine Jane (*died* 4 April 1913), daughter of Captain Browne Roberts of Ravensbourne Park, Kent. *Died* 10 June 1862.

SCOTT, WALTER [13 January 1755]. Apprentice to (1) James Pringle; and (2) Thomas Cockburn.—Son of Robert Scott in Sandyknowes, Roxburghshire. *Born* 11 May 1729. *Married* (contract, 25 April 1758), Anne (*died* 24 December 1819), eldest daughter of John Rutherford, M.D., Professor of Medicine in the University of Edinburgh. Father of Sir Walter Scott, Bart., "the Wizard of the North." *Died* 12 April 1799.

SCOTT, SIR WILLIAM, OF ELIE [Before 1586]. Commissioner, 16 December 1594. Son of John Scott of Orchardfield, Edinburgh. *Married* (1) Elizabeth (*died* June 1590), daughter of Thomas Hamilton of Priestfield; (2) Isobel (*died* January 1594), daughter of David Durie of that Ilk; and (3) 7 May 1595, Jean (*died* March 1639), daughter of Sir John Skene, Clerk Register. Director in Chancery, 1592. Clerk of Session. *Died* 1628, aged 82.

SCOTT, SIR WILLIAM, OF CLERKINGTON [Before 1631].—Son of Lawrence Scott of Clerkington, Advocate. *Married* (1) 4 October 1621, Catherine, daughter of John Monson of Prestongrange; (2) Barbara, eldest daughter of Sir John Dalmahoy of that Ilk. Commissioner, 18 October 1631. Clerk of Council and Session. Appointed one of the Senators of the College of Justice (Lord Clerkington), 8 June 1649. *Died* 23 December 1656.

SCOTT, WILLIAM, OF TEVIOTBANK [23 May 1808]. Apprentice to William Riddell.—Only son of John Scott of Glenmoriston, Peeblesshire, W.S. *Born* 1782. *Married* (1) 2 September 1808, Miss Jordan of Edinburgh; (2) 9 October 1816, Margaret (*died* 13 March 1852), second daughter of Dr Andrew Duncan, Professor of Theory of Medicine, Edinburgh. *Died* 18 August 1841.

SCOTT, WILLIAM ISAAC HAIG, M.C. [7 December 1914]. Apprentice to William Davidson.—Only son of William Isaac Haig Scott, S.S.C., Leith. *Born* 25 October 1891. *Married* 9 November 1921, Edith, younger surviving daughter of Captain G. M. Telford, Edinburgh. In Great War, Captain R.F.A.; twice wounded. Awarded Military Cross and mentioned in Despatches. *Died* at Southampton, 29 May 1922.

SCOTT-DEMPSTER, RONALD, B.L. [19 March 1923]. Apprentice to William Thomson and Another of Menzies, Bruce-Low & Thomson.—Son of Thomas Dempster, Solicitor, and Lord Provost of Perth. *Born* 8 May 1898. *Married* 5 September 1933, Ann, daughter of the Rt. Rev. Edward Thomas Scott Reid, D.D., Bishop of St Andrews, Dunkeld and Dunblane. First World War, Lieutenant R.F.A. 1917-19. Wounded at Ypres 1917; Second World War, Lieutenant Colonel, General List. *Firm*—Robertson, Dempster & Co., Perth. (Retired.)

SCOTT DOUGLAS, DUNCAN, B.A.(CANTAB), LL.B. [26 November 1956]. Apprentice to David Blyth Bogle and Others of Lindsay, Howe & Co.—Son of William Alexander Scott Douglas, W.S., Edinburgh. *Born* 3 May 1931. *Married* 10 September 1955, Patience Mary, daughter of Charles Lindsay Saul. *Firms*—(1) Boyd, Jameson & Young; (2) Bonar Mackenzie & Kermack (formerly Mackenzie & Kermack). (Retired.)

SCOTT DOUGLAS, HUGH, M.A.(OXON), LL.B. [28 November 1955]. Apprentice to Gilbert Lindsay Douglas Hole and Others of Gillespie and Paterson.—Son of William Alexander Scott Douglas, W.S., Edinburgh. *Born* 19 May 1929. *Married* 19 December 1955, Shirley Margaret Chegwidden, Penarth, Wales. Barrister-at-Law in Calgary, Alberta, Canada. *Died* as a result of a road accident 16 April 1979.

SCOTT DOUGLAS, WILLIAM ALEXANDER, LL.B. [7 December 1914]. Apprentice to T. J. Carlyle Gifford.—Son of John Gordon Douglas, West Indian Merchant, Edinburgh. *Born* 7 March 1883. *Married* 20 November 1926, Isobel Frances, daughter of Rev. James Ewing Somerville, D.D., Mentone and Crieff. *Died* 21 March 1965. *Firm*—Baillie and Gifford.

SCOTT-MONCRIEFF, DAVID CHARLES, C.V.O., T.D., B.L. [3 June 1946]. Apprentice to William Babington and Others of Melville & Lindesay.—Son of John Irving Scott Monrieff, M.R.C.V.S. *Born* 2 July 1915. *Married* 28 September 1948, Ann Pamela, daughter of Sir Kenneth Murray, W.S. Captain, Royal Scots. Served U.K. and N.W. Europe 1939-45. Wounded at Hubermont, Ardennes, January 1945. Awarded Cross of Valour (Poland) May 1945; Mentioned in Despatches May 1945. Bailie of Holyrood since 1957; Purse Bearer to Lord High Commissioner to the General Assembly of the Church of Scotland 1959 and 1960. *Firm*—Tods, Murray & Jameson. (Consultant.)

SCOTT-MONCRIEFF, JOHN KENNETH, LL.B. [6 December 1976]. Apprentice to (1) Francis John Stewart and Others of Murray, Beith & Murray; (2) John Stewart Macfie and Others of Tods, Murray & Jamieson.—Son of David Charles Scott-Moncrieff, W.S., Edinburgh. *Born* 9 February 1951. *Firm*—Murray, Beith & Murray.

SCRIMGEOUR, HENRY, OF WEST LOCHGELLY [9 February 1702]. Apprentice to John Montgomery.—Son of Mr James Scrimgeour, Minister of Currie. *Married* 23 February 1704, Agnes, daughter of Uthred Macdougall of Hagburn. *Died* 9 October 1731.

SCRIMGEOUR, HENRY [14 July 1735]. Apprentice to Charles Farquharson.—Son of Henry Scrimgeour of Wester Lochgelly, Fife, W.S. *Married* 12 June 1743, Margaret (*died* 10 June 1787), daughter of George Cruickshanks of Banchory. *Died* 29 March 1778.

SEAMAN, STEPHEN MICHAEL, M.A., LL.B. [23 July 1956]. Apprentice to James Campbell Walker and Another of Steedman, Ramage & Co.—Son of Stephen Treviss Seaman, Civil Servant, Dundee. *Born* 20 October 1932. *Married* 27 April 1957, Marjory Elizabeth, daughter of Colonel Allan Stewart Fortune, C.B.E., T.D. *Firm*—Archibald Campbell & Harley (previously Whigham & Macleod).

SELLAR, JAMES TYRRELL [16 January 1879]. Apprentice to T. G. Murray and J. A. Jamieson.—Eldest son of Rev. James Annand Sellar, Incumbent of St Peter's Episcopal Church, Edinburgh. *Born* 3 June 1854. *Married* 21 October 1885, Eliza (*died* 26 May 1944), daughter of John Granger of Pitcur, Forfarshire. *Died* 14 January 1940.

SELLAR, THOMAS HARPER, LL.B. [20 January 1975]. Apprentice to Maurice Graham Kidd of Maurice Kidd & Co.—Son of Dr Thomas McCall Sellar, Medical Practitioner, Juniper Green, Midlothian. *Born* 7 December 1942. *Married* 5 April 1967, Irene, daughter of Henry Hardie Stewart, Publican. *Firm*—Maurice Kidd & Co.

SEMPLE, ALEXANDER [Before 1628]. *Died* 1628.

SEMPLE, JOHN, OF BALGONE [28 August 1635]. Apprentice to Harry Veache.—Son of John Semple of Close of Dumbarton, and brother of Mr James Semple, Minister of Carmichael. *Married* (1) Margaret Lewis; (2) 16 June 1653, Anna, second daughter of Sir Archibald Sydserff, Bailie of Edinburgh. *Died* 20 June 1662.

SEMPLE, JOHN, OF BALGONE [23 July 1674]. Apprentice to (1) John Semple, his uncle; and (2) Walter Ewing.—*Died* 1680.

SETON, WILLIAM [6 December 1707]. Apprentice to Arthur Forbes.—Son of Robert Seton of Scotsmilne. *Married* Anne, daughter of Adam Gordon of Invermay. *Died* 18 August 1747.

SHAND, DAVID LISTER [25 November 1869]. Apprentice to John Cook.—Son of John Shand, W.S. *Born* 31 July 1839. *Married* 23 July 1873, Angelica Manning (*died* 13 November 1904), daughter of John Inglis Harvey of Kinnettles, Forfarshire, Accountant-General, Bengal. *Died* 28 February 1895.

SHAND, JOHN [4 December 1823]. Apprentice to Hugh Macqueen.—Son of Rev. James Shand, Minister of Marykirk. *Born* 6 January 1801. *Married* 4 September 1827, Isobel (*died* 30 September 1878), only daughter of David Lister of Kininmonth, Fife, W.S. *Died* 26 October 1876.

SHAND, JOHN BATTY [26 November 1829]. Apprentice to William Bell.—Second son of John Shand of the Burn, Kincardineshire. *Born* 1803. *Died* 1 August 1877, aged 74, unmarried.

SHAND, JOHN HARVEY [11 July 1904]. Apprentice to Andrew Wishart and Kenneth Sanderson.—Son of David Lister Shand, W.S. *Born* 17 February 1879. *Died* 18 November 1942.

SHARPE, DAVID, T.D. [13 December 1926]. Apprentice to Henry Inglis Lindsay and Others of J. K. & W. P. Lindsay.—Son of Robert Scott Sharpe, Solicitor, Dunbar. *Born* 28 June 1902. *Married* (1) 8 October 1932, Mary, daughter of John Forsyth, Sorbie, Wigtownshire (divorced 1945); (2) 6 April 1946, Margaret Edith Mary, daughter of Percy Hunter Hutchinson, Chemist. Lieutenant Colonel, R.A.O.C. Served U.K. and India 1939-45. *Died* 14 July 1981. *Firm*—J. K. & W. P.Lindsay. (Retired 1939.)

SHARPE, WILLIAM, OF HODDAM [10 July 1820]. Apprentice to John Forman.—Son of Charles Sharpe of Hoddam, Dumfriesshire. *Born* 1791. *Died* 18 December 1875, unmarried.

SHAW, CHARLES [11 December 1834]. Apprentice to William Mackenzie.—Son of Duncan Shaw, residing at Nunton, Benbecula. *Born* 1 March 1812. *Married* 4 August 1842, Ann Margaret (*died* 21 December 1891), eldest daughter of James Thomas Macdonald of Balranald, North Uist. Sheriff-Substitute at Lochmaddy, 1843-81. *Died* 10 September 1885.

SHAW, DAVID [21 May 1812]. Apprentice to Craufurd Tait.—Eldest son of Charles Shaw, Writer in Ayr. *Born* 5 November 1788. *Married* 1 November 1826, Glencairn Dalrymple, eldest daughter of John Armstrong, Cherry Vale, Co. Antrim. *Died* 9 October 1870.

SHAW, DAVID OF AUCHENLEISH [27 June 1872]. Apprentice to Thomas Thomson and David Scot Dickson.—Son of Thomas Shaw of Shawfield and Dalrulzean. *Born* 14 June 1835. *Died* 12 March 1921, unmarried.

SHAW, DOUGLAS WILLIAM DAVID, B.A.(CANTAB), LL.D., B.D. [19 November 1951]. Apprentice to William Blair and Others of Davidson & Syme.—Son of William David Shaw, Whisky Blender and Wine Merchant. *Born* 25 June 1928. Ordained Minister of the Church of Scotland 1961. *Firm*—Davidson & Syme (1951-57).

SHAW, DUNCAN [21 January 1874]. Apprentice to Colin Mackenzie and A. D. M. Black.—Son of Charles Shaw, W.S. *Born* 7 October 1850. *Married* 15 January 1889, Elizabeth (*died* 6 December 1946), third daughter of George Gordon, Aberdeen. *Died* at Inverness, 11 August 1923. *Firm*—Anderson & Shaw, Inverness.

SHAW, MACKENZIE SMITH, OF AUCHENLEISH AND FORTER [28 March 1899]. Apprentice to David Shaw and David S. Dickson.—Fourth son of William Shaw of Milton, and Westertown of Blacklunans. *Born* 27 August 1875. Edited *The Family Papers of the Hunters of Hunterstoun. Died* 30 May 1948. *Firm*—Thomson, Dickson, and Shaw.

SHEARER, GEORGE MILLER, B.L. [15 July 1949]. Apprentice to George Waddell Harvey of Hunter, Harvey, Webster & Will.—Son of George Shearer, Nurseryman. *Born* 13 February 1906. *Married* 10 August 1940, Margaret Vida, daughter of David Aitken Robertson. *Died* 15 April 1978. *Firms*—(1) Hunter, Harvey, Webster & Will (formerly E. A. & F. Hunter & Harvey); (2) Weir & Macgregor.

SHEARER, ROY GALLOWAY, M.A., LL.B. [17 July 1972]. Apprentice to John Parker Watson and Others of Lindsays.—Son of James Galloway Shearer, General Practitioner. *Born* 2 February 1943. *Married* 29 July 1969, Margaret Ann, daughter of James Borthwick. *Firm*—Lindsays.

SHEDDEN, WILLIAM, B.L. [15 July 1949]. Apprentice to Sir Charles Gibson Connell of Connell & Connell.—Son of Alfred Henry Wathan Sheddon, Mechanical Engineer, Leith. *Born* 12 June 1904. *Married* 20 August 1938, Catherine Jamieson (*died* 25 August 1975), daughter of James Graham Crawford Allister, Mercantile Office Manager. *Died* 27 October 1979. *Firm*—Connell & Connell. (Consultant.)

SHELDON, FIONA JEAN RICHMOND, M.A., LL.B. [11 December 1979]. Apprentice to John McVie of Anderson & McVie, Haddington.—Daughter of John McVie, W.S., Haddington. *Born* 9 July 1948. *Married* 26 July 1972, John Clifford, son of Clifford Samuel Sheldon, Farmer. *Firm*—Anderson & McVie, Haddington.

SHEPHERD, ALFRED [11 April 1887]. Apprentice to James Hotchkis Jameson.—Son of David Shepherd, Property Agent, Dundee. *Born* 6 June 1857. *Married* 12 May 1891, Mary Blair, eldest daughter of Robert Hunter, Edinburgh. *Died* 26 July 1940. *Firm*—Shepherd and Wedderburn.

SHEPHERD, JAMES [10 March 1817]. Apprentice to George Dunlop.—Son of Rev. Robert Shepherd, Minister of Daviot. *Born* 6 February 1790. *Married* 2 May 1848, Marion Scott (*died* 23 February 1885), daughter of William Handyside, W.S. *Died* 4 December 1857.

SHEPHERD, JOHN DOUGLAS, B.A.(Oxon), LL.B. [17 November 1952]. Apprentice to Alastair Campbell Blair and Others of Davidson & Syme.—Son of John Maclagan Shepherd, Pharmacist, Broughty Ferry. *Born* 21 August 1924. *Married* 26 April 1961, Joyce McQueen, daughter of Oliver Howie, Post Office Official. Petty Officer, Royal Navy 1943-46.

SHEPHERD, ROBERT FRANCIS [11 July 1905]. Apprentice to Alfred Shepherd.—Son of Robert Shepherd, Bank Accountant, Dundee. *Born* 29 August 1882. *Married* 3 June 1909, Mabel Bedford (*died* 29 November 1960), youngest daughter of William Wilson, M.A., Headmaster, Morgan Hospital, Dundee, and granddaughter of Frederick W. Bedford, LL.D., D.C.L., Edinburgh. Captain R.G.A. in Great War. *Died* 24 April 1955. *Firm*—Shepherd and Wedderburn.

SHEPHERD, ROBERT JOHN, T.D., B.A.(Cantab), LL.B. [16 December 1946]. Apprentice to Robert Nevill Dundas and Others of Dundas & Wilson.—Son of Robert Francis Shepherd, W.S., Edinburgh. *Born* 13 October 1915. *Married* 23 June 1948, Helen Rhoda Laura, daughter of D. Alan Stevenson, Civil Engineer, Edinburgh. Captain, R.A. Served North Africa, Italy and N.W. Europe 1939-45. *Firm*—Shepherd & Wedderburn.

SHEPHERD, WILLIAM HERBERT, M.A., LL.B. [2 May 1966]. Apprentice to Andrew White Young and Another of J. & R. A. Robertson.—Son of David Arthur Shepherd, Teacher of Classics, Kilmarnock. *Born* 8 September 1934. *Married* 29 March 1980, Catherine Craig Turner. *Firm*—J. & R. A. Robertson.

SHIACH, GORDON LESLIE KEMP, LL.B. [27 November 1940]. Apprentice to James L. Mounsey and Others of John C. Brodie & Sons.—Son of Allan S. Shiach, Dental Surgeon, Elgin. *Born* 31 August 1913. *Married* 20 September 1938, Lucie Sybil Moore or de Freitar. Captain, Intelligence Corps. Served U.K. and North West Europe 1939-45. *Died* as the result of a road accident 30 December 1948. *Firm*—Allan, Black & McCaskie, Elgin.

SIBBALD, CHARLES [22 November 1776]. Apprentice to John Bell.—Son of William Sibbald, Tailor, Edinburgh. *Died* 11 October 1777.

SIBBALD, DAVID, OF ABDEN [2 June 1809]. Apprentice to Edward Bruce.—Son of John Sibbald of Abden, Fife. *Died* 23 February 1815.

SIBBALD, GEORGE [18 January 1656]. Apprentice to John Learmonth.—Son of James Sibbald in Drumgay. *Married* Janet Learmonth. Re-admitted, 14 January 1662. *Buried* 19 March 1668.

SIBBALD, HENRY [27 February 1819]. Apprentice to James Gibson.—Ninth son of William Sibbald of Gladswood, Merchant in Leith. *Born* 1793. *Married* 3 October 1821, Agnes (*died* 1874), only child of James Edmund, Glasgow. *Died* 13 August 1837.

SIBBALD, WILLIAM GRAHAM [14 July 1890]. Apprentice to Henry Cook and Charles Cook.—Son of Sir John Sibbald, M.D., Edinburgh, H.M. Commissioner in Lunacy. *Born* 25 October 1866. *Married* 17 July 1918, Emily Florence (*died* 8 September 1933), youngest daughter of late Thomas Bell, M.A.(Oxon), London. *Died* at London, 18 May 1929. *Firm*—Sibbald & Mackenzie.

SIEVWRIGHT, WILLIAM ARTHUR [11 July 1910]. Apprentice to James Mylne and A. B. Campbell.—Son of John Lornie Sievwright, Stockbroker, Dundee. *Born* 31 March 1884. *Married* 15 April 1914, Muriel Beatrice, eldest daughter of Andrew Melville Paterson, Professor of Anatomy, 21 Abercrombie Square, Liverpool. Served as Lieutenant R.F.C. during Great War. *Died* 24 April 1962.

SIME, THOMAS [19 March 1917]. Apprentice to John Ewart.—Son of Thomas Sime, Schoolmaster, Kilconquhar, Fife. *Born* 23 April 1872. *Married* 20 July 1915, Adelaide Grace (*died* 23 June 1968), daughter of John Biggam, Physician and Surgeon, Prospect House, Upper Cornal, Cornwall. *Died* 20 December 1930. *Firm*—J. & J. Turnbull.

SIMMONS, ERIC BARRIE, LL.B. [8 December 1981*].—Son of George Herbert Simmons, Sales Manager, Glasgow. *Born* 23 July 1946. *Married* 30 July 1970, Eleanor, daughter of John D. Boog, Security Officer, North Berwick. *Firm*—Barlas & Sharp, Dunbar.

SIMPSON, ALEXANDER PETRIE, O.B.E. [12 March 1894]. Apprentice to R. R. Simpson.—Son of John Simpson of the firm of Messrs. Duncan Flockhart and Co., Chemists, Edinburgh. *Born* 28 September 1867. *Married* (1) 4 January 1898, Nellie (*died* 22 November 1919), fifth daughter of Alexander Brown, Accountant, Edinburgh; (2) 1 February 1922, Janie (*died* 9 February 1973), third daughter of Robert Mickel, Rivaldo, Linlithgow. Sheriff-Clerk of West Lothian, 4 April 1908. Lieutenant-Colonel Royal Scots. World War I. Deputy-Lieutenant for County of West Lothian 1941. *Died* 2 April 1961.

SIMPSON, ALEXANDER RUSSELL [29 March 1905]. Apprentice to D. Wardlaw and J. L. Mounsey.—Son of Sir R. R. Simpson, W.S. *Born* 13 December 1879. *Married* 14 October 1913, Dorothy (*died* 1 November 1974), eldest daughter of William Duncan Lowe, W.S. During Great War was Captain R.G.A. *Died* 19 May 1928. *Firm*—R. R. Simpson & Lawson.

SIMPSON, DANIEL [26 July 1695]. Apprentice to George Mackenzie.—*Married* June 1698, Jean, daughter of Robert Aitchison of Sydserff, East Lothian. *Died* 28 January 1715.

SIMPSON, DAVID FRANCIS, B.L. [15 December 1947]. Apprentice to Hugh W. Eaton and Another of J. & R. A. Robertson.—Son of John Francis Simpson, Music Seller. *Born* 6 April 1919. *Married* 18 March 1943, Jessie Ogilvie Steel, daughter of James Dickie. Major, Cameronians (Scottish Rifles). Served U.K. and North West Europe 1939-45. Wounded in Germany, March 1945. *Firm*—Drummond, Johnstone & Grosset, Cupar.

SIMPSON, FRANCIS HUGH, T.D., B.L. [16 December 1935]. Apprentice to William Leslie Christie of Cairns, McIntosh & Morton.—Son of Francis Hugh Simpson, Manufacturer, Edinburgh. *Born* 16 January 1912. *Married* 14 May 1943, Molly Beal Colville, daughter of Robert Welsh, Civil Servant (Customs and Excise). Major, R.A. Served U.K. and India 1939-45. *Firm*—Fyfe, Ireland & Co. (formerly partner of Paterson, Davidson & Cowie, prior to amalgamation).

SIMPSON, JOHN [1727]. Apprentice to Alexander Mitchell of Craigend.—*Died* before 1733.

SIMPSON, MICHAEL JOHN RUSSELL, B.A.(Oxon), LL.B. [4 December 1967]. Apprentice to David Blyth Bogle and Others of Lindsays.—Son of R. J. B. Simpson, W.S., Edinburgh. *Born* 30 October 1941. *Married* 4 July 1967, Lesley, daughter of G. F. H. Walker. *Firm*—Tods, Murray & Jamieson.

SIMPSON, PETER JOHN HUGH, LL.B. [1 December 1969]. Apprentice to Alastair C. Blair and Others of Davidson & Syme.—Son of Francis Hugh Simpson, W.S., Edinburgh. *Born* 24 April 1945. *Married* 4 July 1969, Sheena Margaret, daughter of Colonel A. Gordon-Rogers.

SIMPSON, ROBERT JOHN BLANTYRE, M.B.E.(Mil), T.D., M.A.(Oxon), LL.B. [19 December 1938]. Apprentice to Adam West Gifford and Others of Mackenzie & Black.—Son of Alexander Russell Simpson, W.S., Edinburgh. *Born* 28 August 1914. *Married* (1) 7 October 1939, Helen Mary Radmore, daughter of William Percival Miller, Engineer; (2) 2 April 1962, Barbara Helen, daughter of John MacRobert, Solicitor, Paisley. Lieutenant Colonel, Royal Scots (The Royal Regiment). Served U.K., Gibraltar and N.W. Europe 1939-46. Awarded the Croix Militaire (Belgium) 1946. *Firms*—(1) Simpson Kinmont & Maxwell (1939-52); (2) A. G. Cairns & Simpson.

SIMPSON, SIR ROBERT RUSSELL [12 November 1869]. Apprentice to Thomas Dawson Brodie.—Fourth son of Alexander Simpson, Banker in Bathgate, and nephew of Sir James Young Simpson, Bart. *Born* 31 December 1840. *Married* 26 December 1877, Helen Dymock (*died* 28 January 1923), eldest daughter of Samuel Raleigh, Manager, Scottish Widows' Fund, Edinburgh. Knighted, January 1917. *Died* 14 December 1923. *Firm*—R. R. Simpson & Lawson.

SIMPSON, SAMUEL RALEIGH [2 April 1906]. Apprentice to A. D. M. Black, A. W. Gifford, and C. M. Black.—Son of Sir Robert Russell Simpson, W.S. *Born* 6 April 1882. Enlisted in Army Service Corps in 1916. Received Commission in Labour Corps, December 1917, and served in France. Author of *The Gleam on the Hill, Tall Tales and Small Tales, etc. Died* 6 December 1961. *Firm*—R. R. Simpson and Lawson.

SIMSON, CHARLES SIMSON RANKINE, OF THREEPWOOD [14 March 1872]. Apprentice to John and James Turnbull.—Second son of Rev. John Rankine, D.D., Minister of Sorn. *Born* 15 October 1847. Assumed name of Simson on succeeding to estate of Threepwood. *Died* 19 November 1911, unmarried.

SIMSON, HARRY MACDONALD [29 March 1905]. Apprentice to J. R. M. Wedderburn and G. G. Watson.—Son of James Simson of the Bengal Civil Service, 51 Manor Place, Edinburgh. *Born* 11 November 1878. *Married* 18 October 1921, Isobel (*died* 8 November 1971), eldest daughter of Henry Moubray Cadell of Grange. Captain 52nd Lowland Divisional Train; served in Servia, Macedonia, Palestine, and Egypt, 1915-19. *Died* 19 December 1965. *Firm*—Greig and Simson.

SIMSON, JOHN THOMAS [31 May 1860]. Apprentice to James Shepherd, T. M. Grant, and William Cuthbertson.—Son of Rev. Henry Simson, Minister of Chapel of Garioch, Aberdeenshire. *Born* 26 May 1837. *Died* 9 November 1865, unmarried.

SIMSON, ROBERT, O.B.E. [29 October 1894]. Apprentice to J. P. Wright and T. M. Murray.—Second son of David Simson of Bonaly in the County of Edinburgh. *Born* 5 February 1872. *Married* 22 June 1905, Mabel Fraser (*died* 12 November 1943), daughter of Captain Abel Henry Chapman, 19th Hussars, of Gateshead-on-Tyne, and of Mrs Chapman, Redhall, Slateford. Commandant Infantry Base Depot, 1917. Lieut.-Colonel; mentioned in Despatches. *Died* 20 October 1926.

SINCLAIR, DONALD BOASE, O.B.E., LL.B. [12 December 1911]. Apprentice to Harry Cheyne, F. J. G. Borthwick, Ian MacIntyre, and J. G. Kirkpatrick.—Son of Robert Sinclair, M.D., Dundee. *Born* 16 May 1886. *Married* 6 September 1917, Margaret Richardson (*died* 13 April 1978), eldest daughter of Colonel James Arnott, M.D., I.M.S., of 8 Rothesay Place, Edinburgh and Wyseby, Kirtlebridge. Captain in 9th Royal Scots, 1914-19. *Died* 21 November 1972. *Firm*—Murray, Beith, and Murray.

SINCLAIR, GEORGE [4 August 1777]. Apprentice to Leonard Urquhart.—Third son of James Sinclair of Durran, Caithness. *Baptized* 11 February 1749. *Married* 19 September 1775, Elizabeth, daughter of John Sutherland of Forss, Caithness. *Died* 6 December 1779.

SINCLAIR, GEORGE LEWIS, OF DALREOCH [23 November 1827]. Apprentice to William Renny.—Second son of James Sinclair of Forss, Caithness. *Born* 1803. *Married* 11 February 1830, Frances Ann (*died* 2 June 1875), second daughter of John Boazman of Acornbank, Westmorland. *Died* 22 October 1878.

SINCAIR, GEORGE SUTHERLAND [12 November 1829]. Apprentice to James and Charles Nairne.—Son of Lieut.-Colonel John Sutherland Sinclair, R.A. *Born* 2 November 1803. *Died* 16 January 1834, unmarried.

SINCLAIR, JOHN, OF BALGRIGIE [28 June 1736]. Apprentice to James Graham.—Only son of George Ross, Advocate. *Married* 25 October 1753, Rachel, daughter of John Moncrieff, Merchant, Perth. Admitted Advocate, 11 June 1748. *Died* 26 October 1784.

SINCLAIR, PETER [18 June 1739]. Apprentice to Robert Hepburn.—Son of Sir John Sinclair of Stevenston, Bart. Fiscal, 1755-63. *Died* 8 July 1763.

SINCLAIR, ROBERT [Before 1575]. Writer to the Privy Seal. *Died* 30 November 1594.

SINCLAIR, ROBERT [31 December 1708]. Apprentice to John Macfarlane.—*Married* 18 January 1711, Lilias, daughter of John Anderson, Coppersmith in Edinburgh. *Died* 11 April 1715, aged 30.

SINCLAIR, THOMAS [Before 1552]. *Married* Alison Foulis. *Died* November 1571.

SINCLAIR, WILLIAM [8 August 1785]. Apprentice to Francis Anderson.—Youngest son of Alexander Sinclair of Barrock, Caithness. Commissary of Caithness. *Died* 7 July 1799, unmarried.

SINCLAIR, WILLIAM HUGH MACKAY, B.A., B.L. [8 December 1981*].—Son of Dr William Wells, Consultant Psychiatrist, Edinburgh. *Born* 22 December 1954.

SINGER, JAMES [12 December 1822]. Apprentice to Robert Ainslie.—Son of the Rev. William Singer, D.D., Minister of Kirkpatrick-Juxta. *Born* 26 September 1797. *Died* 1 February 1836, unmarried.

SKELTON, JAMES [12 February 1824]. Apprentice to Robert Fleeming.—Son of John Skelton, Sheriff-Substitute at Kinross. *Born* 1799. *Married* 11 October 1830, Margaret Marjory (*died* 3 October 1878), eldest daughter of Thomas Kinnear of Kinloch, Fife. Sheriff-Substitute at Peterhead, 1829-70. *Died* 14 May 1882.

SKENE, JAMES [Before 1611]. Mentioned, 16 May 1611. *Died* before 1632.

SKENE, JOHN, OF HALLYARDS [Before 1631]. Commissioner, 18 October 1631.—Second son of Sir John Skene of Curriehill, Lord Register. *Married* 29 June 1603, Alison, sister of William Rigg of Athernie, Fife. Clerk of the Bills, 1614. Clerk of Session. *Died* December 1644.

SKENE, THOMAS [Before 1564].

SKENE, WILLIAM FORBES, D.C.L., LL.D. [16 November 1831]. Apprentice to (1) Francis Wilson; and (2) Sir H. Jardine, G. T. Stodart, and William Fraser.—Second son of James Skene of Rubislaw, Aberdeen, Advocate. *Born* 7 June 1809. Author of *The Highlanders of Scotland, their Origin, History, and Antiquities*, 1837, *Celtic Scotland*, and other works. Depute Clerk of Session, 1 November 1853-67. Historiographer-Royal for Scotland, 1881-92. *Died* 29 August 1892, unmarried.

SKINNER, JOHN ROBERT [6 July 1813]. Apprentice to Alexander Youngson.—Son of James Skinner, Writer in Edinburgh. *Born* 1786. *Married* 21 April 1814, Ann (*died* 14 May 1869), daughter of William Black, Writer in Brechin. *Died* 13 September 1849.

SKINNER, WILLIAM, OF CORRA [16 November 1848]. Apprentice to John Hunter, Auditor of Court.—Eldest surviving son of John Robert Skinner, W.S. *Born* 24 July 1823. *Married* (1) 18 June 1850, John Ann Farish (*died* 21 May 1866), only surviving child of Robert Kirk of Drumstenchill, Kirkcudbrightshire; and (2) 25 November 1880, Charlotte Eremengarde (*died* 21 March 1931), youngest daughter of Charles Warren of Longford and Market-Drayton. Town Clerk of Edinburgh, 1874-95. *Died* 4 May 1901.

SLIGO, GEORGE, OF AULDHAME [23 June 1820]. Apprentice to William Dallas.—Youngest son of John Sligo, Merchant in Leith. *Born* 1797. *Married* 4 June 1822, Anna Sita (*died* 26 November 1875), eldest daughter of Benjamin Outram of Butterly Hall, Derbyshire. *Died* 3 December 1847.

SLOAN, STANLEY WILLIAM GRAY, LL.B. [24 March 1930]. Apprentice to Robert O. Pitman and Patrick C. Smythe.—Son of Rev. Andrew D. Sloan, D.D., Minister of Hope Park Church, St Andrews. *Born* 9 January 1904. *Married* 19 April 1942, Freyda Averil Moir-Gray, daughter of Surgeon-Lieutenant Moir-Gray, St Andrews. Squadron Leader R.A.F.V.R. 1940-45. *Died* 17 July 1970. *Firm*—Miller, Thompson, Henderson & Co., Glasgow.

SMAIL, ANDREW JAMES, B.L. [15 July 1949]. Apprentice to Gavin Leith Allardyce and Another of J. C. & A. Steuart.—Son of Robert Smail, Banker, Bathgate, West Lothian. *Born* 20 March 1920. *Married* 12 January 1946, Joan Bowring, daughter of Andrew Romilly Langlands, Comptroller of Military Accounts, Burma. *Firm*—Cairns, McIntosh & Morton. (Resigned 1969.)

SMALL, ALEXANDER MURISON, V.D. [27 June 1878]. Apprentice to Robert and James Alexander Haldane.—Son of James Small, Accountant, Calcutta, and grandson of Rev. Alexander Small, D.D., Stirling. *Born* 26 July 1854. *Married* 3 April 1875, Marion (*died* 15 July 1950), youngest daughter of Surgeon-General George Bidie, I.M.S., C.I.E., K.H.S., Madras Army. Chevalier of the Crown of Italy. Town Clerk of Melrose, 2 June 1908; District Clerk, Melrose, 15 May 1893. *Died* 27 March 1939. *Firm*—Small and Macpherson, Melrose.

SMALL, J. [Before 1606]. Signs Minute of 17 January 1606.

SMALL, PATRICK [Before 1608]. Mentioned, 20 January 1608. *Married* 9 August 1598, Isabella Coult.

SMALL, THOMAS [5 March 1801]. Apprentice to William Dunbar.—Only son of Charles Small, Wigmaker in Edinburgh. *Married* (1) Mary Hatley; and (2) 27 April 1829, Margaret (*died* 10 January 1877), daughter of Colin Clark, Edinburgh. Marchmont Herald, 1801-30. Officiated as Deputy Lord Lyon at Coronation of King George IV. *Died* 1 October 1830.

SMALL, WILLIAM DOUGLAS, LL.B. [2 December 1974]. Apprentice to (1) Walter Nigel Jamieson Thomson of Kilgour, McNeill & Sime, and (2) Francis Ernest Harris Snell of Snell & Co.—Son of W. P. Small, F.R.C.S., Surgeon, Edinburgh. *Born* 20 January 1950. *Married* 26 June 1971, Judith Lilian May, daughter of William Hamilton Lee, Liverpool.

SMART, JOHN, LL.B. [8 July 1901]. Apprentice to John P. Wood and William Babington.—Son of John Smart, S.S.C., Edinburgh. *Born* 6 October 1876. *Married* 8 February 1905, Janet Aird (*died* 23 September 1974), eldest daughter of James Buchanan, Wholesale Chemist, 3 Oswald Road, Edinburgh. *Died* 26 August 1920. *Firm*—Morton, Smart, Macdonald & Prosser.

SMITH, ADAM [31 March 1707]. Apprentice to William Thomson.—*Married* (1) 14 November 1710, Lilias, eldest daughter of Sir George Drummond of Milnab, Lord Provost of Edinburgh; (2) (contract, 17 November 1720), Margaret (*died* 23 May 1784), daughter of John Douglas of Strathendry, by whom he had a posthumous son, Adam Smith, Author of *The Wealth of Nations*. Adam Smith, W.S., afterwards was Comptroller of the Customs at Kirkcaldy and Judge-Advocate for Scotland. *Died* April 1723.

SMITH, ALEXANDER [23 February 1816]. Apprentice to John Smith, his brother.—Son of Thomas Smith, one of the Principal Clerks of the Bills. *Married* (1) 1 June 1830, Mary (*died* 12 August 1841), eldest daughter of James Christie of Durie, Fife; (2) 27 July 1842, Margaret Louisa (*died* 10 January 1876), daughter of Henry Wedderburn of Wedderburn. *Died* 3 August 1868, aged 82.

SMITH, ALEXANDER ROSS, M.A., LL.B. [26 November 1962]. Apprentice to Andrew White Young and Another of J. & R. A. Robertson.—Son of Alexander Smith, Company Director, Edinburgh. *Born* 28 September 1935. *Married* 14 October 1964, Elizabeth Gall, daughter of Alexander Glen Green, Company Director, Falkirk. *Firm*—Allan, Dawson, Simpson & Hampton.

SMITH, ANDREW [6 July 1813]. Apprentice to John Campbell of Annfield.—Eldest son of John Smith, Farmer at Law, Linlithgowshire. *Died* 17 December 1861, aged 77, unmarried.

SMITH, ANDREW [11 December 1899]. Apprentice to T. J. Gordon and James Falconer.—Son of Joseph Smith, Merchant in Perth. *Born* 2 November 1874. *Married* 28 August 1903, Jessie Elizabeth Agnes (*died* 9 February 1962), second daughter of James Wright, Murrayville, Perth. *Died* 4 September 1905.

SMITH, ANDREW JAMES NIMMO. *See* NIMMO-SMITH.

SMITH, CHILTON LIND ADDISON, C.B.E. *See* ADDISON-SMITH, CHILTON LIND.

SMITH, DAVID [30 November 1826]. Apprentice to James Greig.—Second son of Alexander Smith, Banker in Edinburgh. *Born* 13 January 1803. *Married* (1) 14 September 1830, Harriet Elizabeth (*died* 27 June 1838), daughter of Thomas Allan of Lauriston; and (2) 22 February 1849, Charlotte Eliza (*died* 11 February 1884), second daughter of Charles William Bigge of Linden, Northumberland. *Died* 18 December 1880.

SMITH, DAVID ALEXANDER, LL.B. [4 December 1972]. Apprentice to The Hon. D. A. Balfour and Others of Shepherd & Wedderburn.—Son of William Duncan Smith, Depute County Clerk, Edinburgh. *Born* 17 November 1947. *Married* 22 September 1979, Anne Hamilton-Douglas. *Firm*—Shepherd & Wedderburn.

SMITH, DONALD M'CALLUM [16 July 1888]. Apprentice to James Burness.—Son of Alexander Bell Smith, LL.D., Edinburgh. *Born* 23 July 1863. *Died* 23 February 1950. *Firm*—W. and J. Burness.

SMITH, FRANCIS CLEMENT NIMMO [10 July 1911]. Apprentice to W. H. Murray and R. O. Pitman.—Son of Rev. Robert Nimmo Smith, LL.D., Edinburgh. *Born* 10 October 1884. *Married* 22 August 1917, Elinor Elizabeth (*died* 7 January 1972), younger daughter of Professor Andrew Seth Pringle-Pattison of The Haining, Selkirkshire. Served in Belgium, France, and Macedonia with Royal Scots; severely wounded, 1916. *Died* 30 July 1939. *Firm*—Kinmont & Maxwell.

SMITH, GEORGE FREDERICK GRAHAM [9 December 1907]. Apprentice to W. Stuart Fraser.—Son of David Smith, 12 Belgrave Place, Edinburgh. *Born* 24 March 1884. *Married* 17 July 1915, Isabella Alice (*died* 30 June 1916), only daughter of Charles Stuart Robertson, St Anne's, Lasswade. Lieutenant Scottish Horse during Great War. *Died* 19 May 1938. *Firm*—Kessen & Smith.

SMITH, HARRY [25 November 1852]. Apprentice to John and John Robert Tod.—Fifth son of Alexander Smith, Advocate in Aberdeen. *Born* 12 August 1829. *Married* 6 August 1861, Julia Medina (*died* 21 December 1914), daughter of Colonel Rice Jones, K.H., Royal Engineers. Admitted Advocate, 6 June 1857. Sheriff-Substitute at Greenock, 1874-85. M.P. for Falkirk Burghs, 1892-95. *Died* 27 September 1910.

SMITH, HARRY WEDDERSPOON [16 January 1894]. Apprentice to David Turnbull.—Son of Henry Smith, Merchant, Dundee. *Born* 4 July 1865. *Married* 12 December 1895, Eleanor (*died* 17 January 1944), youngest daughter of Rev. James Whyte, D.D., Minister of Methlick Parish, Aberdeenshire. *Died* 7 August 1928.

SMITH, HECTOR WALLACE [16 March 1896]. Apprentice to (1) Sir R. R. Simpson; (2) John Macpherson; and (3) J. F. Mackay.—Son of James Duncan Smith, S.S.C. *Born* 27 November 1865. *Married* 14 July 1897, Lillias Mary (*died* 11 June 1937), only daughter of David Mason, Edinburgh. *Died* 2 May 1923.

SMITH, HENRY [14 December 1896]. Apprentice to David Turnbull.—Son of John Smith, residing at Saline, Fifeshire. *Born* 25 April 1853. *Married* 31 March 1882, Christina Moir Barrowman (*died* 7 August 1939). Solicitor to Board of Trade. *Died* 1 November 1937. *Firm*—H. and J. Smith.

SMITH, IAIN ROBERT, B.L. [19 December 1938]. Apprentice to (1) Sir William Stowell Haldane and Another of W. & F. Haldane; (2) Archibald Cochrane Rutherford of W. A. & F. Rutherford, Galashiels.—Son of John Smith, Solicitor, Galashiels. *Born* 23 April 1915. *Married* (1) 15 August 1940, Helen Smith (*died* 4 August 1943), daughter of Robert Smith Wyllie, Insurance Cashier; (2) 15 February 1945. Marion McCuthcheon (*divorced* 1952), daughter of John Laidlaw, Forester; (3) 29 May 1968, Mary Elizabeth, daughter of John Dalgliesh, Post Office Engineer. Observer Lieutenant, Royal Observer Corps. Served U.K. 1939-45. *Died* 14 March 1982. *Firm*—Iain Smith & Partners (formerly W. A. & F. Rutherford) Galashiels.

SMITH, IAN GRANT, T.D., B.A.(Cantab), LL.B. [25 January 1941]. Apprentice to Evan James Cuthbertson and Others of Mackenzie, Innes & Logan.—Son of Lieutenant Colonel John Grant Smith, Estate Factor, Grantown-on-Spey. *Born* 3 August 1910. *Married* 9 November 1939, Ruth, daughter of George Samuel Crawford, Northwich, Cheshire. Major, Infantry. Served U.K.; France and South East Asia Command 1939-1945. *Firms*—(1) Mackenzie, Innes & Logan (dissolved 1955); (2) Cuthbertson & Watson (later Brodie, Cuthbertson & Watson, latterly Brodies). (Retired.)

SMITH, JAMES IAN HAY, M.A., LL.B. [17 November 1952]. Apprentice to Ranald Ker Cuthbertson and Others of Mackenzie, Innes & Logan.—Son of John Hay Smith, W.S., Edinburgh. *Born* 29 July 1927. *Married* 2 September 1960, Valerie Anne, daughter of John Meurice Henshaw, Lieutenant, R.A. Served mainly in Singapore, 1945-48. *Firm*—Bell and Scott, Bruce & Kerr (formerly R. C. Bell and J. Scott).

SMITH, JOHN [23 July 1628]. Apprentice to George Mack.—*Married* (1) 11 March 1622, Jean, daughter of James Brown, Surgeon, Edinburgh; (2) (contract, 12 September 1634), Jean, daughter of John Morison, Citizen of Dunblane.

SMITH, JOHN. *See* Cunningham, John Smith.

SMITH, JOHN, of Brousterland [21 December 1730]. Sheriff-Clerk of Lanarkshire, 1743. Fiscal, 1763-77. Resigned his Commission, 14 July 1778.

SMITH, JOHN [18 December 1922]. Apprentice to, and son of, Henry Smith, W.S.—*Born* 24 April 1884. Held temporary Commission in Cavalry, September 1914. Served in France with 2nd Life Guards, 1915-19; mentioned in Despatches. *Died* 4 January 1959. *Firm*—H. and J. Smith.

SMITH, JOHN FAIRFULL, of Westfield [19 November 1829]. Apprentice to William Bell.—Son of Captain John Wilson Smith of the 33rd Regiment. *Married* (1) 12 June 1830, Caroline (*died* 2 January 1849), third daughter of Dutton Smith Turner of Clarendon, Jamaica; and (2) 10 January 1850, Alexandrina (*died* 23 April 1913), second daughter of William Thomson, Dumfries. *Died* 7 January 1868, aged 62.

SMITH, JOHN HAY [15 December 1930]. Apprentice to John Scott.—Son of James Smith, Auctioneer, Peebles. *Born* 5 June 1891. *Married* 16 September 1925, Gertrude Kathleen Janet (*died* 8 March 1981), younger daughter of James Gibson, S.S.C., Edinburgh. *Died* 27 December 1961. *Firm*—R. C. Bell and J. Scott.

SMITH, JOHN MITCHELL MELVIN, B.L. [26 November 1956]. Apprentice to James Robert Leslie Cruickshank and Another of Menzies & White.—Son of John Mitchell Smith, Farmer, St Boswells. *Born* 5 July 1930. *Married* 9 August 1958, Elizabeth Marion, daughter of Mark Slight, Farmer, Ormiston, East Lothian. *Firm*—Masson & Glennie, Peterhead.

SMITH, JOHN ROBERT, LL.B. [6 December 1971]. Apprentice to N. A. M. MacDonald and Others of Baillie & Gifford.—Son of Iain Robert Smith, W.S., Melrose. *Born* 27 April 1948. *Married* 5 November 1976, Ruth Helen Mackay Gate. *Firm*—Iain Smith & Partners (formerly W. A. & F. Rutherford), Galashiels.

SMITH, KATHRYN ELIZABETH, LL.B. [11 December 1979]. Apprentice to Eric Ian Cuthbertson and Another of Russel & Aitken, Edinburgh.—Daughter of John McCulloch Smith, Bank Manager, North Berwick. *Born* 15 March 1948. *Firm*—Russell & Aitken.

SMITH, NORMAN, B.L. [23 November 1953]. Apprentice to Ranald Ker Cuthbertson and Another of Mackenzie, Innes & Logan.—Son of John Hunter Smith, Builder, Leith. *Born* 23 June 1914. *Married* 13 September 1939, Anne Johnstone, daughter of William Johnstone Meikle. Captain/Adjutant, R.A.O.C., 3rd Battalion R.A.O.C. (Ammunition). Served U.K. Second World War. *Firms*—(1) Mackenzie, Innes & Logan (dissolved 1955); (2) Cuthbertson & Watson, later Brodie, Cuthbertson & Watson. (Resigned 1965.)

SMITH, RALPH COLLEY, M.C., LL.B. [14 July 1919]. Apprentice to David Shaw and Mackenzie S. Shaw.—Son of Patrick Smith, Advocate, Sheriff-Substitute of Selkirkshire. *Born* 2 March 1891. *Married* 31 January 1928, Jessie Elizabeth (*died* 24 February 1977), only daughter of Philip B. Cousland, M.B., Ch.B., LL.D., Shanghai, Medical Missionary in China. War Service: Captain Northumbrian Territorial Artillery; severely wounded in France, 1915. *Died* 12 July 1957. *Firm*—Fraser, Stodart, and Ballingall.

SMITH, RICHARD BAIRD [12 January 1891]. Apprentice to William H. Murray and Archibald R. C. Pitman.—Eldest son of John Young Smith, M.D., and Deputy Inspector-General, Bombay Army. *Born* 14 June 1865. *Died* 21 September 1930, unmarried.

SMITH, ROBERT BEVERIDGE [13 December 1910]. Apprentice to W. H. Murray and R. O. Pitman.—Son of Robert Smith, S.S.C., Leith. *Born* 14 October 1886. *Married* 1 March 1926, Elmine Jean (*died* 25 January 1941), daughter of William Laird, Kingston, Jamaica. Captain Seaforth Highlanders; severely wounded, 1916. Mentioned in Despatches. *Died* 29 July 1953. *Firm*—Beveridge, Sutherland, and Smith.

SMITH, ROBERT GIBSON HAY, B.L. [17 November 1952]. Apprentice to Ralph Colley Smith and Others of Fraser, Stodart & Ballingall.—Son of John Hay Smith, W.S., Edinburgh. *Born* 30 July 1929. *Married* 4 March 1966, Valerie Christine, daughter of William Gray Miller, S.S.C., Edinburgh. *Firm*—Gillespie, McAndrew & Co. (formerly Gillespie & Paterson).

SMITH, THOMAS STODART WHYTE [11 December 1906]. Apprentice to Sir R. R. Simpson and Alex. P. Melville.—Son of Rev. William Whyte Smith, Newington U.F. Church, Edinburgh. *Born* 6 March 1883. *Married* 7 June 1922, Jean Witherow (*died* 22 March 1969), elder daughter of the Rev. Andrew Gilchrist, B.A., Minister of Newington U.F. Church. War Service: with Royal Scots at home and King's African Rifles in Nyasaland, Captain, 1919; Acting Assistant Land Officer and Assistant Crown Solicitor, Hong-Kong, 1924; Acting Land Officer and Registrar of Marriages there, 1934. *Died* 15 November 1950.

SMITH, WILLIAM [29 May 1878]. Apprentice to James Peddie and Alexander Peddie Waddell.—Son of William Smith, Writer in Edinburgh. *Born* 20 May 1855. *Married* (1) 7 February 1882, Elizabeth Mary (*died* 22 October 1896), eldest daughter of Jackson Coward Robinson, Ambleside; (2) 13 April 1898, Martha Elizabeth Mary (*died* 5 December 1951), daughter of Rev. John Garson of Bea and Garson, Free Church Minister at Birsay, Orkney. *Died* 5 November 1934.

SMITH, WILLIAM DONALD NIAL, M.A., LL.B. [26 November 1962]. Apprentice to Charles Edward Stewart and Others of Murray, Beith & Murray.—Son of A. G. Smith, Professor of Anatomy, University of Ibadan, Nigeria. *Born* 15 July 1937. *Married* 10 July 1965, Sheena, daughter of George James McClymont, Tighnabruaich. *Firm*— Alex. Morison & Co.

SMITH, WILLIAM ROBINSON [29 March 1909]. Apprentice to, and son of, William Smith.—*Born* 18 November 1882. *Married* 14 July 1910, Jane Thomson Doctor (*died* 24 January 1966), granddaughter of Mrs Thomson, Dunearn, Newport, Fife (latterly known as William Robinson). *Died* 4 June 1937, at Toronto.

SMITH, WILLIAM RUFUS [16 March 1936]. Apprentice to Robert Nevill Dundas and Others of Dundas & Wilson.—Son of William Smith, Indian Civil Servant. *Born* 13 July 1912. *Married* 20 July 1938, Elspeth Nanette, daughter of Dr G. A. Strain, M.D. 1977-1982 Auditor of the Court of Session. *Firms*—(1) Dundas & Wilson; (2) Macpherson & Mackay; (3) Shepherd & Wedderburn.

SMYTH, JAMES, OF BALHARRY [5 April 1742]. Apprentice to James Graham.—Son of John Smyth of Leitfie, Writer in Alyth. *Married* (contract, 3 and 4 January 1743), Cecil, eldest daughter of Dr John Kinloch of Clasbinny. *Died* 1781.

SMYTH, JAMES [10 December 1789]. Apprentice to Thomas Adair.—Son of Robert Smyth, Schoolmaster in Paisley. *Born* 1759. *Married* 23 March 1798, Barbara (*died* 15 March 1839), daughter of John Barbour of Laws, Renfrewshire. *Died* 28 June 1827.

SMYTH, JOHN, OF BALHARRY [12 July 1779]. Apprentice to, and only son of, James Smyth, W.S.—*Married* (1) 8 June 1766, Agatha, fourth daughter of Sir John Wedderburn, third Baronet of Blackness; and (2) (contract, 17 May 1796), Joanna (*died* 10 May 1823), daughter of Robert Gray, Writer in Edinburgh. *Died* 7 February 1809.

SMYTH, ROBERT, OF BALHARRY [2 June 1809]. Apprentice to, and second son of, John Smyth, W.S.—*Died* 6 October 1855, aged 73, unmarried.

SMYTH, ROBERT GILLESPIE, OF GIBLISTON [18 June 1802]. Apprentice to John Campbell (1785).—Son of Dr James Gillespie, Principal of St Mary's College, St Andrews. *Born* 4 February 1777. *Married* 8 November 1806, Amelia, daughter of Sir Robert Murray Keith, Bart. Assumed name of Smyth on succeeding to Estate of Gibliston, Fife. *Died* 10 November 1855.

SMYTHE, PATRICK CECIL, O.B.E., B.A.(Oxon) [15 March 1920]. Apprentice to William Hugh Murray and John S. Pitman.—Son of Very Rev. Patrick Murray Smythe, Provost of St Ninian's Cathedral, Perth. *Born* 3 September 1888. *Married* 21 July 1922, Ysenda Mabel, daughter of James Maxtone Graham of Cultoquhey and Redgorton, C.A. In Great War held Commission in 2/6th Black Watch, and served in France. O.B.E.(Mil.). Mentioned in Despatches. *Died* 28 March 1969. *Firm*—J. and F. Anderson.

SMYTHE, PATRICK MUNGO, B.L. [28 April 1958]. Apprentice to Patrick Cecil Smythe and Others of J. & F. Anderson.—Son of Patrick Cecil Smythe, W.S., Edinburgh. *Born* 2 May 1923. *Married* 13 January 1960, Heather Evelyn, daughter of Rambert Standring. Flight Lieutenant, R.A.F. Night Fighter Command, 169 Squadron. Second World War. *Firm*—J. & F. Anderson (resigned).

SNEDDON, ROBERT RAYMOND OVENS, LL.B. [6 December 1971]. Apprentice to W. G. Moodie of Keir, Moodie & Co.—Son of Robert O. Sneddon, Civil Servant, Edinburgh. *Born* 13 October 1948. *Married* 21 April 1974, Alexandra Niven, daughter of W. N. McGarry, Dental Technician, Edinburgh. *Firm*—John Laurie & Co., Aberdeen (and at Keith, Aberlour and Dufftown).

SNELL, FRANCIS ERNEST HARRIS, M.A., LL.B. [28 November 1966]. Apprentice to Alexander Harper and Others of Pearson, Robertson & Maconochie.—Son of Ernest James Snell, Company Director, Barnstaple, Devon. *Born* 18 February 1926. *Married* 9 April 1949, Betty Irene, daughter of Rowland Harold Ordish, Accountant, sometime of Tientsin, China and Richmond, Surrey. Served in Royal Navy 1944-46.

SNODGRASS, FRANCIS [10 March 1803]. Apprentice to Thomas Gordon.—Son of Hugh Snodgrass, Writer in Paisley. Resigned his Commission, 24 November 1823. *Married* —— (*died* in 1847). *Died* 1824.

SOMERVELL, GRAHAM CHARLES [16 January 1879]. Apprentice to Charles Morton and John Neilson.—Third son of Graham Somervell of Sorn Castle, Ayrshire. *Born* 13 July 1854. *Died* 3 February 1889, unmarried.

SOMERVILLE, DAVID KENNETH, M.A., LL.B. [28 May 1979]. Apprentice to Kenneth Macrae and Others of Murray, Beith & Murray and John Alexander Spens and Another of Maclay, Murray & Spens.—Son of Dr David K. Somerville, Headmaster (retired), Edinburgh. *Born* 10 July 1952.

SOMERVILLE, GEORGE IAIN LIVINGSTON, B.A.(Cantab), LL.B. [20 December 1948]. Apprentice to Robert Somerville and Others of Fraser, Stodart & Ballingall.— Son of Robert Somerville, W.S., Edinburgh. *Born* 18 August 1919. *Married* 8 July 1948, Eleanore, daughter of Sir Alexander B. King, C.B.E., D.L., LL.D., J.P. Captain, R.I.A.S.C. Served India and Malaya 1939-45. *Died* 29 August 1974. *Firm*—Graham, Johnston & Fleming.

SOMERVILLE, HUGH, of Inverteil [1 June 1696]. Apprentice to Robert Carstairs.— Second son of James Somerville of Corehouse, Lanarkshire, Commission of H.M. Forces in Scotland. *Born* 13 December 1670. *Married* 1708 Agnes (*died* 1716), third daughter of Sir Alexander Gibson of Pentland, P.C.S. *Died* 29 May 1739.

SOMERVILLE, JAMES ALAN WALKER, B.L. [12 July 1948]. Apprentice to Sir John Ireland Falconer and Another of Fyfe, Ireland & Co.—Son of the Rev. David Somerville, Glasgow. *Born* 15 April 1922. *Married* 16 September 1953, Elizabeth Margaret Tennant, daughter of Frank Henry Normand Walker, Investment Trust Manager. Sergeant, R.A.F. 1942-46. *Firms*—(1) Lewis & Somerville (1949-50); (2) Lindsay, Howe & Co. (now Lindsays).

SOMERVILLE, JAMES WALKER, LL.B. [12 December 1904]. Apprentice to Horatius Bonar and W. C. Hunter.—Son of the Rev. David Somerville, D.D., Roseburn Free Church, Edinburgh. *Born* 9 December 1879. *Married* 1 June 1918, Lucy Ada (*died* 21 July 1965), daughter of James Cochrane, Galashiels. Sergeant Royal Scots in Great War. *Died* 7 July 1950. *Firm*—Lewis and Somerville, latterly A. & A. S. Gordon.

SOMERVILLE, JOHN [27 February 1650]. *Married* Barbara Boog. *Buried* 2 June 1661.

SOMERVILLE, ROBERT [26 June 1845]. Apprentice to James Macallan.—Son of Rev. James Somerville, Minister of Drumelzier. *Born* 20 April 1814. *Died* 5 February 1857, unmarried.

SOMERVILLE, ROBERT [2 April 1906]. Apprentice to William Morton.—Elder son of George Somerville, Procurator-Fiscal, Edinburgh. *Born* 21 February 1882. *Married* 27 June 1917, Norah Campbell (*died* 26 June 1968), daughter of John M'Nab of Swinton, Berwickshire. Lieutenant Lowland Heavy Battery R.G.A.(T.). Served 1915-18. *Died* 11 December 1950. *Firm*—Graham, Johnston, and Fleming.

SOMERVILLE, SAMUEL CHARTERS, OF LOWOOD [29 January 1802]. Apprentice to John Tait.—Second son of Rev. Thomas Somerville, D.D., Minister of Jedburgh, author of *The Reign of Queen Anne*, etc., referred to by Sir Walter Scott as "one of the oldest of the literary Brotherhood." *Born* 1776. *Married* 15 July 1807, Ann Charlotte (*died* 1862), eldest daughter of Robert Low of Clatto, Fife. *Died* at Wimbledon, 18 June 1823.

SOOTE, GEORGE GIBSON, OF WOODLEY [15 November 1872]. Apprentice to James Mackenzie, J. B. Innes, and C. B. Logan.—Son of James Soote, Merchant and Shipowner in Dundee. *Born* 13 March 1849. *Married* 17 April 1886, Alice Victoria (*died* 25 December 1939), youngest daughter of Lieut.-General Edward Patrick Lynch of Partry House, Ballenrobe, Co. Mayo. *Died* at Farnborough, Hants, 19 January 1925.

SORLIE, KATHLEEN HELEN, LL.B. [13 May 1980*].—Daughter of Daniel Sorlie, Grocer, Perth. *Born* 10 September 1952. *Firm*—Maurice Kidd & Co.

SOUTER, JAMES, OF KINMINITIES [11 March 1830]. Apprentice to William Inglis.—Son of Stewart Souter of Melrose, Banffshire. *Born* 1806. *Married* 5 April 1831, Anne (*died* 31 January 1870), daughter of Patrick Carnegy of Lour, Forfarshire. *Died* 18 July 1858.

SPALDING, THOMAS [21 March 1865]. Apprentice to Thomas M. Grant and William Cuthbertson.—Only son of William Spalding, Professor of Logic and Metaphysics in the University of St Andrews. *Born* 31 December 1840. *Died* 4 March 1878, unmarried.

SPALDING, WILLIAM MELLIS [21 November 1833]. Apprentice to William Fettes Pitcairn.—Son of William Spalding of Glennebray. *Born* 9 February 1811. *Married* 30 April 1846, Jane (*died* 6 June 1898), daughter of William Gordon of Hallmyre, Peeblesshire. *Died* 4 September 1857.

SPEID, JAMES, OF FORNETH [21 April 1875]. Apprentice to J. O. Mackenzie, W. R. Kermack, and George Mackenzie.—Son of William Speid, Forneth, Blairgowrie. *Born* 22 August 1849. *Married* 24 November 1898, Margaret (*died* 15 September 1954), younger daughter of Charles Kinloch, Harrow. *Died* 8 November 1936.

SPEID, JOHN, OF ARDOVIE [4 March 1841]. Apprentice to William Murray.—Second son of Robert Speid of Ardovie, Forfarshire, W.S. *Born* 26 June 1814. *Died* 16 May 1861, unmarried.

SPEID, ROBERT, OF ARDOVIE [20 June 1793]. Apprentice to William Leslie.—Only son of Robert Speid, Merchant in Dundee. *Married* 23 November 1801, Isabella (*died* 11 May 1856), daughter of James Hall of Millholm, Renfrewshire. *Died* 20 December 1846, aged 82.

SPEIR, WILLIAM [Before 1586]. Signs the Acts, 4 April 1607.

SPENCE, JAMES [6 March 1828]. Apprentice to William Dallas.—Second son of Alexander Spence, Goldsmith in Edinburgh. *Married* 23 September 1834, Jemima Grace, youngest daughter of James Hall, Major, 83rd Regiment, Gibraltar. *Died* 15 September 1856, aged 68.

SPENS, DAVID [15 June 1730]. Apprentice to James Armour.—Brother of Walter Spens, Writer, Rutherglen. *Married* 10 August 1735, Elizabeth (*died* 23 June 1787), daughter of Rev. Lawrence Johnstone, Minister of Duns, and widow of Lieutenant Alexander Spittal, 2nd Dragoons (Scots Greys). *Died* 6 February 1771.

SPENS, HENRY GLASSFORD BELL [13 December 1909]. Apprentice to A. G. Brown.—Son of Walter Cook Spens, Advocate, Sheriff-Substitute of Lanarkshire. *Born* 15 May 1886. Resigned, April 1911, to go to the Bar. *Died* 29 June 1911.

SPENS, JOHN ALEXANDER, R.D., B.A.(CANTAB), LL.B. [12 December 1977]. Apprentice to and son of Thomas Patrick Spens, W.S., of Maclay, Murray & Spens, Glasgow. *Born* 7 June 1933. *Married* 14 October 1961, Finella Jane, daughter of Donald Duff Gilroy, Stockbroker. Carrick Pursuivant. *Firm*—Maclay, Murray & Spens.

SPENS, NATHANIEL, OF CRAIGSANQUHAR [25 November 1830]. Apprentice to James Hope.—Eldest son of Colonel James Spens of Craigsanquhar, Fife. *Born* 18 February 1805. *Married* 23 January 1840, Janet Law (*died* 24 June 1889), second daughter of George Guild. *Died* 22 November 1869.

SPENS, REGINALD HOPE [21 April 1875]. Apprentice to Colin Mackenzie and A. D. M. Black.—Fourth son of Archibald Spens of Lathallan, Stirlingshire. *Born* 6 November 1850. *Married* 18 April 1876, Mary Elizabeth (*died* 20 June 1920), elder daughter of Francis Anderson, W.S. *Died* at Walton-on-Thames, 4 December 1919.

SPENS, THOMAS PATRICK, O.B.E., M.C., M.A.(CANTAB), HON. LL.D. [20 December 1921]. Apprentice to Sir George Paul and Others of Dundas & Wilson.—Son of John Alexander Spens, LL.D., Solicitor, Glasgow. *Born* 10 July 1894. *Married* 2 September 1924, Nancy Farie, daughter of James Farie Anderson, Solicitor, Glasgow. First World War—Served with B.E.F. in France, 1914-16, Lieutenant, 5th Scottish Rifles (T.A.) until wounded in 1916; Served U.K. 1917-18. Second World War—Lieutenant Colonel, General Staff; Served U.K. and Norway 1939-45; O.B.E. 1942; U.S.A. Bronze Star Medal 1945; Norway Freedom Cross 1945. Chancellor of the Dioceses of Glasgow and Galloway (from 1933); St Andrews, Dunkeld and Dunblane (from 1938), Aberdeen and Orkney (from 1972). *Died* 25 April 1980. *Firm*—Maclay, Murray & Spens. (Retired 1971.)

SPIERS, WILLIAM FULTON [7 July 1902]. Apprentice to Robert Strathern.—Son of Fulton Spiers, Banker, Dundee. *Born* 6 December 1876. *Died* 27 May 1959.

SPOTTISWOODE, DAVID [20 June 1793]. Apprentice to Cornelius Elliot.—Sixth son of James Spottiswoode of Dunipace, Stirlingshire. *Died* 8 March 1807.

SPROT, THOMAS [12 June 1823]. Apprentice to James Renton.—Youngest son of Alexander Sprot, residing in Edinburgh. *Born* 27 January 1800. *Married* 3 August 1874, Margaret Morrison Malcolm (*died* 7 September 1892). *Died* at Buxton, 23 July 1880.

STARK, ALAN FORREST, M.B.E., B.L. [20 December 1948]. Apprentice to T. J. Carlyle Gifford and Another of Baillie & Gifford.—Son of John Forrest Stark, Timber Merchant, Perth. *Born* 8 December 1909. *Married* 18 January 1940, Marjorie Jean, daughter of W. Thow Munro, O.B.E., Woollen Manufacturer. *Died* 9 April 1982. *Firm*—Morton, Fraser & Milligan (formerly Morton, Smart, Macdonald & Prosser and Morton, Smart, Macdonald & Milligan). (Retired 1975.)

STARK, WILLIAM [1612].—Son of Robert Stark, Merchant Burgess, Edinburgh. *Married* 14 August 1606, Margaret Douglas. Signs the Acts, 7 December 1612. *Died* 23 November 1614.

STEEDMAN, WILLIAM KERR [30 October 1893]. Apprentice to Charles Baxter.—Son of William Steedman, Merchant, Edinburgh. *Born* 18 November 1871. *Married* (1) 17 April 1901, Mrs Anna Brandon (*died* 16 February 1907), daughter of Julius Adler, Kongen's Nytorv, Copenhagen; and (2) 22 April 1921, Jeanne (*died* 30 November 1964), daughter of Claude Brenot, Distillery Manager. *Died* 16 January 1937, at Monte Carlo. *Firm*—Steedman, Ramage and Co.

STEEL, WILLIAM MACPHERSON, B.L. [20 July 1950]. Apprentice to John Douglas Hamilton Dickson and Others of Tods, Murray & Jamieson.—Son of Dr James Kenneth Steel. *Born* 4 August 1922. *Married* 24 June 1961, Jean, daughter of Dr Alan Gordon Ogilvie. Flight Lieutenant, R.A.F. Served in Bomber Command U.K. *Firm*— Aitken, Kinnear & Co. (formerly Hamilton, Kinnear & Beatson).

STEELE, ANDREW, OF CROSSWOODHILL [18 March 1788]. Apprentice to Alexander Cunningham.—Only surviving son of James Steele, Merchant in Edinburgh. *Born* 5 January 1759. *Married* 15 August 1810, Marion (*died* 23 November 1824), eldest daughter of Thomas Bell of Nether Horsburgh, Peeblesshire. Deputy Keeper of Register of Sasines, 1788. *Died* 5 November 1832.

STEIN, ANDREW [8 July 1847]. Apprentice to Henry Inglis.—Fourth son of Robert Stein of Kilbagie, Clackmannanshire. *Born* 31 July 1824. *Married* 6 August 1856, Margaret Haig (*died* 20 August 1903), daughter of Francis Stupart, Major in 2nd Dragoons (Scots Greys). *Died* at Farnborough, 17 August 1899.

STENHOUSE, ALEXANDER THOMSON [14 April 1884]. Apprentice to James Peddie, A. Peddie Waddell, and H. Ivory.—Son of James Stenhouse of North Fod, Dunfermline. *Born* 28 December 1858. *Married* 16 October 1889, Mary Johnston (*died* 10 October 1945), elder daughter of Arthur Colville, Edinburgh. *Died* at Burnside, Manitoba, 6 November 1903.

STENHOUSE, JOHN [19 June 1812]. Apprentice to Alex. Pearson.—Youngest son of James Stenhouse, Farmer at Grange. *Died* 6 February 1821.

STEPHEN, CHARLES CAMPBELL [10 January 1887]. Apprentice to Charles Patrick Finlay.—Son of Rev. Thomas Stephen, Minister of Kinloss, Morayshire. *Born* 14 April 1862. *Died* 29 October 1897, unmarried.

STEUART, ALEXANDER, OF EDINGLASSIE [26 July 1727]. Apprentice to Andrew Hay of Montblairie. *Born* 1700. *Married* Margaret (*died* 22 June 1752), only child of Colonel Cranston of Glen, Peeblesshire. *Died* 19 September 1787.

STEUART, ANDREW, OF AUCHLUNKART [15 July 1763]. Apprentice to Alexander Steuart.—Third son of George Steuart of Tannachy, Banffshire. *Married* December 1778, Harriet (*died* 10 September 1814), daughter of James Gordon of Cocklarachy, Aberdeenshire. *Died* 10 October 1798.

STEUART, ARCHIBALD [23 June 1853]. Apprentice to, and second son of, James Steuart, W.S.—*Born* 25 July 1829. *Married* 21 March 1859, Christian (*died* 8 May 1871), third daughter of George Graham Bell of Crurie, Dumfriesshire, Advocate. *Died* 29 July 1900.

STEUART, CHARLES [21 December 1786]. Apprentice to William Dick.—Second son of James Steuart, Writer in Edinburgh. *Born* 19 September 1760. *Married* (1) 13 April 1795, Mary, daughter of William Gordon, Bookseller in Edinburgh; and (2) 27 October 1801, Margaret (*died* 20 November 1857), daughter of James Lindesay, Merchant, Leith. *Died* 6 February 1821.

STEUART, CHARLES [15 November 1832]. Apprentice to James and Charles Nairne.—Second son of Charles Steuart, W.S. *Born* 1 April 1804. *Died* 14 June 1899, unmarried.

STEUART, CHARLES [14 November 1851]. Apprentice to, and eldest son of, James Steuart, W.S.—*Born* 7 December 1827. *Died* 9 May 1888, unmarried.

STEUART, GEORGE, OF TANNACHY [20 December 1791]. Apprentice to Andrew Steuart, his uncle.—Eldest son of Patrick Steuart of Tannachy, Banffshire. *Died* 25 October 1814, aged 45.

STEUART, GEORGE GRAHAM BELL [13 January 1891]. Apprentice to, and second son of, Archibald Steuart, W.S.—*Born* 28 March 1866. *Died* 19 August 1939. *Firm*—J. C. and A. Steuart.

STEUART, GEORGE MACKENZIE [17 March 1890]. Apprentice to R. L. and J. G. Stuart.—Son of George Steuart, Accountant to the Commissioners of Northern Lighthouses, Edinburgh. *Born* 10 December 1866. *Married* 24 April 1919, Mary Dorothea (*died* 4 January 1981), daughter of Rear-Admiral F. S. Clayton of Wyelands, Ross-on-Wye. Served wilth Red Cross during Great War. *Died* 20 March 1942.

STEUART, JAMES [8 July 1763]. Apprentice to James Pringle.—Third son of Charles Steuart of Ballechin, Perthshire. *Died* 16 September 1779, unmarried.

STEUART, JAMES [20 May 1794]. Apprentice to James Walker.—Fourth son of Robert Steuart of Ballechin, Perthshire. *Born* 22 May 1767. *Died* 4 August 1803, unmarried.

STEUART, JAMES [22 December 1825]. Apprentice to (1) Charles Steuart; and (2) Francis Walker.—Eldest son of Charles Steuart, W.S. *Born* 1 October 1802. *Married* 27 February 1827, Elizabeth Brand (*died* 8 November 1836), eldest daughter of Archibald Scott, Solicitor, Edinburgh, and Procurator-Fiscal of Mid-Lothian. *Died* 21 September 1886.

STEUART, JAMES, O.B.E. [15 July 1884]. Apprentice to, and eldest son of, Archibald Steuart, W.S.—*Born* 7 September 1860. *Married* 15 January 1890, Agatha (*died* 27 October 1938), youngest daughter of Rev. Francis Coulman Royds, Rector of Coddington, Cheshire, and Canon of Chester. Commanded City of Edinburgh Special Constables during War period. Published Works: *Sketching in Water Colours*; *Sketching Ways and Sketching Days*; *The Bell Family in Dumfriesshire*, etc. Member of the King's Bodyguard for Scotland, Royal Company of Archers, 1888. *Died* 27 September 1938. *Firm*—J. C. and A. Steuart.

STEUART, JOHN [17 November 1701]. Apprentice to Daniel Simpson.—Son of Charles Steuart of Ballechin, Perthshire. *Married* Helen Steuart. Commissary of Inverness, 1709. Commissary of Moray. Fiscal, 1717-22. Treasurer. Resigned his Commission, 1 August 1747. *Died* December 1750.

STEUART, JOHN, OF DALGUISE [7 June 1825]. Apprentice to Harry Davidson.—Eldest son of Charles Steuart of Dalguise, Perthshire. *Born* 7 August 1799. *Married* 6 August 1829, the Hon. Janet Oliphant Murray (*died* 9 August 1871), eldest daughter of Alexander, eighth Lord Elibank. High Sheriff of Cape Colony, 1829. Master of Supreme Court, 1848-76. *Died* at Wynberg, South Africa, 29 December 1881.

STEVEN, CHARLES BANNATYNE [19 March 1888]. Apprentice to Robert Burt Ranken.—Son of Charles Bannatyne Steven, Writer in Edinburgh. *Born* 8 September 1864. *Married* 20 September 1927, Mary (*died* 11 February 1965), second daughter of John Mackenzie. *Died* 11 September 1947.

STEVEN, ROBERT [12 November 1869]. Apprentice to John Beatson Bell.—Son of Alexander Steven, Glasgow. *Born* 31 July 1839. *Married* 22 September 1870, Jessie (*died* 29 July 1917), younger daughter of James Maxwell, Crossmichael. *Died* 3 June 1918.

STEVEN, ROBERT CLEMENT, M.A., LL.B. [27 April 1953]. Apprentice to Ranald Ker Cuthbertson and Others of Mackenzie, Innes & Logan.—Son of H. M. Steven, Professor of Forestry, Aberdeen. *Born* 20 May 1924. *Married* 30 January 1965, Judith Clare, daughter of James William Dunbar Locker, H.M. Colonial Service. Captain, Royal Signals; Served India and Malaya 1943-46.

STEVENS, EDWIN THOMSON, M.A., LL.B. [15 December 1930]. Apprentice to James Miller Thomson of J. Miller Thomson & Co.—Son of Alfred Richard Stevens, Billiard Table Manufacturer (Master), London. *Born* 28 July 1907. *Married* 30 September 1938, Joan Mary Spotswood. *Died* 28 September 1964. *Firm*—J. Miller Thomson & Co.

STEVENS, ERNEST HILDEBRAND, O.B.E., LL.B. [20 December 1937]. Apprentice to W. J. Guild of Guild & Guild.—Son of Ernest John Carwithin Stevens, Accountant, Bedford. *Born* 2 June 1909. Group Captain, Auxiliary Air Force. Served U.K. 1939-45. Command of 603 Squadron (City of Edinburgh) Auxiliary Air Force 1939-40, Deputy Commander, Allied Air Forces, Norway 1945. Mentioned in Despatches 1940 and 1942. Awarded Norway Freedom Cross 1945. *Died* 22 January 1949. *Firm*—Guild & Guild.

STEVENSON, ALEXANDER [22 December 1686]. Apprentice to James Johnston.—Son of Rev. Alexander Stevenson, Minister of Dalmellington. *Married* 22 October 1676, Janet, fourth daughter of Quentin Hamilton of Barncluith, Lanarkshire. Commissary Clerk of Glasgow, 12 March 1692. *Died* before 1698.

STEVENSON, ALEXANDER, OF MONTGREENAN [11 March 1712]. Apprentice to Thomas Pringle.—Son of Hugh Stevenson of Montgreenan, Ayrshire. *Married* 19 December 1711, Ann (*died* 4 January 1754), third daughter of Sir Archibald Hope of Rankeillor, one of the Lords of Session (Lord Rankeillor). Treasurer of the Society, 1722 and 1746-1755. *Died* 25 February 1755.

STEVENSON, ALEXANDER [28 January 1803]. Apprentice to Alexander Duncan.—Second son of Alexander Stevenson, Depute Clerk of Session. *Died* 6 July 1805 on his passage from London to Leith.

STEVENSON, ALEXANDER [7 July 1807]. Apprentice to John Campbell.—Son of Hugh Stevenson, Merchant in Oban. *Married* 29 August 1811, Martha, youngest daughter of James Pollock, Campbeltown. *Died* 30 September 1815.

STEVENSON, ALEXANDER [23 November 1819]. Apprentice to John Forman.—Son of Thomas Stevenson, Farmer at ¦Gilmerton. *Born* 1794. *Married* 17 August 1824, Catherine (*died* 2 November 1853), second daughter of Andrew White, Glasgow. *Died* 7 April 1877.

STEVENSON, ARCHIBALD, OF MONTGREENAN [17 July 1755]. Apprentice to, and eldest son of, Alexander Stevenson of Montgreenan, Ayrshire, W.S.—*Died* 13 July 1791.

STEVENSON, ERIC JOHN POTT [18 December 1922]. Apprentice to David Shaw and Mackenzie S. Shaw.—Son of Alexander Pott Stevenson, Writer, Kelso. *Born* 21 December 1891. *Married* 2 August 1928, Vera, only daughter of A. B. Tully, The Priory, Kelso. In Great War, Lieutenant R.F.A. in France and Italy; mentioned in Despatches. *Died* 16 April 1936. *Firm*—Alex. and E. J. Stevenson, Kelso.

STEVENSON, HENRY JAMES [17 January 1893]. Apprentice to J. P. Wood and W. Babington.—Son of Rev. Robert Horne Stevenson, D.D., Minister of the Parish of St George's, Edinburgh. *Born* 12 July 1867. *Married* 3 August 1911, Mary Elizabeth (*died* 16 January 1961), youngest daughter of William Scott-Kerr of Chatto and Sunlaws, Roxburghshire. Secretary, North British and Mercantile Insurance Co., 1894-1926; Manager, 1926-31. Served during Great War with Lowland Mounted Brigade; Brigade-Major. Twice mentioned in Despatches, and received a Brevet. *Died* 8 August 1945.

STEVENSON, JAMES REID, LL.B. [3 December 1973]. Apprentice to Ian Dalrymple Ross and Others of Thomson & Baxter.—Son of William Reid Stevenson, Marine Engineer, Clydebank. *Born* 1 June 1949.

STEVENSON, JOHN WALTER [11 July 1904]. Apprentice to William Thomson.—Son of James Stevenson, J.P., Northwood, Lauder Road, Edinburgh. *Born* 28 October 1880. *Married* 2 October 1909, Georgina, youngest daughter of George Pringle, Eccles, Manchester, and of Mrs Pringle, 1 Dick Place, Edinburgh. *Died* 6 June 1922.

STEVENSON, LOUIS, M.A., LL.B., J.D.(CHICAGO) [24 April 1961]. Apprentice to Sir Charles Connell of Connell & Connell.—Son of Thomas Stevenson, Farmer, Kirkcaldy. *Born* 17 April 1936. *Married* 31 July 1965, Rebecca Nelson.

STEWART, ADRIAN ARTHUR MACGREGOR, LL.B. [28 April 1969]. Apprentice to Alexander John McDonald of Dickie, Gray, McDonald & Fair.—Son of Ian Macgregor Stewart, Grocer, Dundee. *Born* 22 September 1942. *Married* 5 September 1966, Lilian Turner, daughter of David K. Whyte. *Firm*—Thorntons & Dickies, Dundee (formerly Dickie, Gray, McDonald & Fair).

STEWART, ALAN EDWARD JAMES, LL.B. [11 December 1979*].—Son of Francis John Stewart, W.S., Edinburgh. *Born* 12 July 1950.

STEWART, ALEXANDER [5 April 1715]. Apprentice to Thomas Boyes.—*Died* before 1733.

STEWART, ALEXANDER DONALD, B.A.(Oxon), LL.B. [26 July 1960]. Apprentice to A. J. Ambrose and Others of Macandrew, Wright & Murray.—Son of John Stewart of Ardvorlich, Farmer and Landowner, Ardvorlich, Lochearnhead, Perthshire. *Born* 18 June 1933. *Married* 4 December 1970, Virginia Mary, daughter of Peter Washington, Farmer. *Firm*—Moncrieff, Warren, Paterson & Co., Glasgow.

STEWART, ALEXANDER JAMES [10 March 1842]. Apprentice to John Bowie.—Son of Joseph Stewart Menzies of Foss, Perthshire. *Born* 13 November 1820. *Died* 8 March 1873, unmarried.

STEWART, ARTHUR NEIL [16 January 1894]. Apprentice to J. R. M. Wedderburn and G. G. Watson.—Son of Captain Daniel Shaw Stewart of West Park, St Andrews. *Born* 26 October 1866. *Died* 11 October 1901, unmarried.

STEWART, CHARLES [19 April 1876]. Apprentice to J. O. Mackenzie and W. R. Kermack.—Eldest son of John Stewart of Eskgrove, Mid-Lothian, W.S. *Born* 22 September 1852. *Died* 27 July 1927, unmarried.

STEWART, CHARLES CAMPBELL [23 June 1817]. Apprentice to John Ferrier.—Second son of Alexander Stewart, Surgeon at Gogar. *Born* 1794. *Married* 10 March 1826, Mary Henrietta (*died* 4 December 1888), daughter of Andrew Wood, Surgeon in Edinburgh. *Died* 13 August 1836.

STEWART, CHARLES EDWARD [12 July 1909]. Apprentice to William Babington and Joseph Inglis.—Son of William Stewart of Shambellie, Kirkcudbrightshire, formerly Captain, 83rd Regiment (Royal Irish Rifles). *Born* 4 January 1885. *Married* 26 February 1916, Anne Laurie (*died* 19 May 1969), youngest daughter of Holmes Ivory, W.S. *Died* 8 March 1967. *Firm*—Murray, Beith, and Murray.

STEWART, CHARLES EDWARD, B.A., M.C. [10 December 1912]. Apprentice to Sir John Prosser, A. G. Muir, John Smart, and J. H. Macdonald.—Son of John George Stewart, Carpet Manufacturer, Lasswade. *Born* 22 June 1887. Captain Durham Light Infantry. *Died* of wounds receive in action, 10 April 1917.

STEWART, DAVID, OF STEWARTHALL [6 July 1768]. Apprentice to Samuel Mitchelson.—Youngest son of Archibald Stewart of Stewarthall, Stirlingshire. *Born* 1744. *Married* April 1722, Margaret (*died* 15 September 1806), daughter of Robert Ramsay of Cammo and Arthurstone, Forfarshire. *Died* 2 May 1823.

STEWART, DAVID LOGAN, B.A.(Cantab), LL.B. [21 July 1970]. Apprentice to H. A. Nicolson and Others of Morton, Fraser & Milligan.—Son of A. M. Stewart, Consultant Radiologist, Aberdeen. *Born* 18 March 1942. *Married* 26 August 1967, Elisabeth, daughter of Einar Hogfors, Civil Engineer, Malmo, Sweden. *Firm*—Morton, Fraser & Milligan (formerly Morton, Smart, Macdonald & Milligan).

STEWART, DOUGLAS FLEMING, M.A., LL.B. [27 November 1961]. Apprentice to Arthur Woodman Blair and Others of Strathern & Blair.—Son of James Wilson Stewart, Civil Servant, Edinburgh. *Born* 22 May 1927. *Married* 7 June 1952, Catherine, daughter of Frank Edward Coleman. Solicitor to Crown Estate Commissioners in Scotland (1970). *Firm*—J. & F. Anderson.

STEWART, FRANCIS [16 February 1826]. Apprentice to (1) Walter Dickson and George Dunlop; and (2) George Dunlop.—Son of General Francis Stewart King of Lesmurdie, Banffshire. *Born* 1801. *Died* at Paris, 23 September 1833, unmarried.

STEWART, FRANCIS JOHN, T.D., M.A.(Oxon), LL.B. [15 December 1947]. Apprentice to C. E. Stewart and Others of Murray, Beith & Murray.—Son of C. E. Stewart, W.S., Edinburgh. *Born* 11 May 1917. *Married* 28 November 1946, Olga Margaret, daughter of James Little Mounsey, W.S., Edinburgh. Lieutenant, R.A.C. Lothian & Border Yeomanry. Served U.K. and France 1939-40. Prisoner-of-War in Germany and Poland 1940-45. Member of Queen's Bodyguard for Scotland, Royal Company of Archers. Hon. Consul for Principality of Monaco in Edinburgh. *Firm*—Murray, Beith & Murray.

STEWART, GEORGE ROBERT GORDON, M.A., LL.B. [19 December 1949]. Apprentice to John Donaldson Lownie of H. Brougham Paterson & Co.—Son of David Gordon Stewart, Insurance Manager, Edinburgh. *Born* 13 October 1924. *Married* 11 October 1952, Rachel Jean, daughter of John Baxter Morrison, Land Agent. Private, Royal Scots 1942; Captain, Royal Signals, S.E.A.C. 1943-46. *Firm*—Melville & Lindesay. (Resigned 1959.)

STEWART, IAN CHARLES LINDSAY [15 July 1889]. Apprentice to Alexander Howe and William MacGillivray.—Son of Colonel Duncan Stewart, 92nd Highlanders. *Born* 8 September 1865. *Died* 18 July 1945.

STEWART, JAMES [25 November 1672]. Apprentice to William Guthrie.—Son of John Stewart of Fungorth, youngest son of Sir William Stewart of Grandtully, Perthshire.

STEWART, JAMES, B.L. [19 December 1938]. Apprentice to James Falconer Fairweather and Another of Gordon Falconer & Fairweather.—Son of George William Stewart, Banker. *Born* 4 March 1914. *Married* 25 April 1961, Stella Mary, daughter of Thomas Williams, Bournemouth and Rio de Janeiro. Captain, Intelligence Corps. Served U.K. and West Africa (G.H.Q.); War Office (M.I.5). *Firms*—(1) Macpherson & Mackay; (2) Shepherd & Wedderburn; (3) Bonar Mackenzie & Kermack (now Bonar Mackenzie).

STEWART, JAMES [10 July 1978]. (By Rule IX(a).)—Son of Adam Stewart, Prison Officer, Edinburgh. *Born* 10 November 1919. *Married* 3 March 1942, Margaret, daughter of Arthur Blacon, Bathing Master, Heysham, Lancashire. Captain, Royal Scots and Cameronians; served Burma and India. Second World War. *Firm*—A. C. Bennett & Fairweather (formerly A. C. Bennett & Son).

STEWART, JAMES DALRYMPLE HAY [6 July 1896]. Apprentice to Horatius Bonar.— Son of James Stewart, 9 North Mansionhouse Road, Edinburgh. *Born* 12 August 1862. *Died* 29 December 1945.

STEWART, JOHN [29 January 1705]. Apprentice to William Dallas.—Second son of Robert Stewart of Inverichatt. *Married* 6 April 1707, Janet, daughter of Sir Robert Blackwood, Dean of Guild, Edinburgh. *Died* 12 August 1731.

STEWART, JOHN, of Eskgrove [29 June 1837]. Apprentice to John Ker and Henry Gordon Dickson.—Youngest son of Charles Stewart, Captain of the *Airly Castle*, East Indiaman. *Born* 21 November 1813. *Married* 21 November 1851, Isabella (*died* 28 July 1857), eldest daughter of James Hunter of Thurston, East Lothian. *Died* 1 July 1890.

STEWART, JOHN ANDERSON, M.A., LL.B. [21 March 1932]. Apprentice to E. M. Wedderburn and Others of Shepherd & Wedderburn.—Son of John A. Stewart, Solicitor, Perth. *Born* 10 October 1907. *Married* 25 June 1936, Margaret Enid, daughter of Alexander Crichton Mitchell, D.Sc., Edinburgh. *Firm*—Kippen, Campbell & Burt, Perth.

STEWART, JOHN DORSEY, LL.B. [6 December 1976]. Apprentice to (1) Alexander Jackson Ambrose and Others of Macandrew Wright & Murray; (2) Andrew McGregor Young and Another of J. & R. A. Robertson.—Son of A. I. B. Stewart, O.B.E., Solicitor, Campbeltown, Argyll. *Born* 16 March 1951. *Married* 17 July 1976, Alison Jane, daughter of Daniel McLellan Lean, Company Director, Bearsden, Glasgow. *Firm*—Stewart, Balfour & Sutherland, Campbeltown (and also at Lochgilphead, Ardrishaig and Tarbert).

STEWART, JOHN WALCOT, M.C. [29 March 1909]. Apprentice to James Burness.—Son of Robert Stewart, S.S.C. *Born* 2 October 1885. Held Commission in Royal Scots. Wounded, February 1916. *Killed* in action, 21 March 1918.

STEWART, PATRICK LOUDON McIAIN, LL.B. [28 April 1969]. Apprentice to the Hon. D. A. Balfour and Others of Shepherd & Wedderburn.—Son of A. I. B. Stewart, O.B.E., Solicitor, Campbeltown. *Born* 25 July 1945. *Married* 25 October 1969, Mary Anne, daughter of Dr Malcolm McLellan. *Firm*—Stewart, Balfour & Sutherland, Campbeltown (and also at Lochgilphead, Ardrishaig and Tarbert).

STEWART, QUINTIN KENNEDY, B.L. [29 April 1974]. (By Rule IX(a).)—Son of Kennedy Stewart, Producer, B.B.C., Edinburgh. *Born* 12 October 1939. *Married* 12 September 1964, Rosemary Jean, daughter of W. A. M. B. Stewart, Royal Air Force. *Firm*—Simpson & Marwick. (Resigned.)

STEWART, ROBERT [Before 1594].—Son of William Stewart, Writer, Rutherglen. Signs Minute of 16 December 1594. Macer.

STEWART, ROBERT, OF ARDVORLICH [27 June 1822]. Apprentice to James Dundas.— Eldest son of William Stewart of Ardvorlich, Perthshire. *Born* 25 August 1799. *Died* 16 July 1854, unmarried.

STEWART, ROBERT, OF CARPHIN [27 June 1823]. Apprentice to John Donaldson.—Son of James Stewart of Carphin, Lanarkshire. *Born* 25 July 1797. *Married* (1) 14 September 1826, Elizabeth, daughter of Andrew Pringle of Kersmains; and (2) 1 July 1841, Agnes (*died* 2 December 1883), daughter of James Jeffrey, M.D., Professor of Anatomy in the University of Glasgow. *Died* 25 May 1868.

STEWART, WALTER [16 July 1661]. Apprentice to William Henderson.—Son of John Stewart of Newhalls, Linlithgowshire. *Married* 28 July 1653, Helen Dowie (*died* 1713). *Died* before 1711.

STEWART, WILLIAM [21 March 1865]. Apprentice to James Steuart.—Son of William John Stewart, W.S. *Born* 25 June 1840. *Married* 1 June 1875, Mary Harriet Binns (*died* 14 February 1942), daughter of George Greaves. Father of Society. *Died* at Wimbledon, 13 October 1930.

STEWART, WILLIAM JOHN [12 December 1822]. Apprentice to John Irving.—Fourth son of William Stewart of Hillhead. *Born* 10 December 1798. *Married* 28 July 1835, Alison (*died* 4 December 1893), daughter of Charles Steuart, W.S. *Died* 13 February 1842.

STIMPSON, ROBIN MACKAY, LL.B. [11 July 1977]. Apprentice to George Stuart Russell and Others of Strathern & Blair.—Son of David E. Stimpson, C.B.E., Principal, Dundee College of Education, Dundee. *Born* 1 August 1947. *Married* 4 August 1973, Fiona Elizabeth, daughter of the Rev. George T. Poustie, Boyndie, near Banff. *Firms*— (1) Farquharson, Craig & Co. (1973-74); (2) Strathern & Blair.

STIRLING, JAMES, OF HORNEHILL [18 November 1841]. Apprentice to John Dundas and William Wilson.—Only son of William Stirling, Architect in Dunblane. *Born* 27 May 1816. *Married* 23 January 1844, Christian (*died* 1871), daughter of David Erskine of Elambazar, Bengal. *Died* 31 August 1866.

STIRLING, JAMES [14 December 1925]. Apprentice to Laurence M'Laren.—Son of Rev. Alexander Stirling, Minister of Original Secession Church, Arbroath. *Born* 10 July 1884. Lieutenant R.G.A.; served in France during Great War. *Died* 9 February 1946. *Firm*—L. and J. M'Laren.

STIRLING, JOHN SCOTT, B.L. [20 July 1950]. Apprentice to James Miller Thomson and Another of J. Miller Thomson & Co.—Son of John Scott Stirling, Law Cashier, Edinburgh. *Born* 10 September 1918. *Married* 20 August 1949, Ida Kathleen Henderson, daughter of James Nelson Beazley. Flight Lieutenant, R.A.F.V.R. Coastal Command. Served Atlantic, Mediterranean, India and Ceylon. *Firm*—Miller Thomson & Robertson (formerly John F. Robertson & Co.).

STIRLING, WILLIAM [23 February 1680]. Apprentice to James Cunningham.—Son of George Stirling, Indweller in Glasgow. *Married* (1) Elizabeth, daughter of John Watson of Damhead; and (2) April 1704, Margaret (*died* December 1726), sister of Robert Cathcart of Drumjoan, Ayrshire, and widow of Robert Crawfurd of Crawfurdtoun, W.S. Fiscal, 1686-90. *Died* 21 February 1726.

STIRLING-AIRD, PATRICK KENNETH, LL.B. [2 December 1968]. Apprentice to John Parker Watson and Others of Lindsays.—Son of Peter Douglas Miller Stirling-Aird, Company Director, Baslow, Derbyshire. *Born* 10 August 1943. *Married* 12 May 1973, Elizabeth Susan, daughter of Group Captain Frederick Wakeham. *Firm*—Brodies.

STIRLING-GRAHAM, WILLIAM, OF DUNTRUNE [12 June 1818]. Apprentice to Andrew Storie.—Only son of Patrick Stirling of Pittendreich, Merchant in Dundee. *Born* 12 June 1794. Admitted Advocate, 5 December 1823. Assumed name of Graham. *Died* 19 December 1844, unmarried.

STODART, DAVID RIDDLE [21 February 1856]. Apprentice to, and second son of, John Riddle Stodart, W.S.—*Born* 12 October 1832. *Married* 2 April 1861, Louisa Flora Wilhelmina (*died* 22 June 1908), daughter of Peter Shepherd, Merchant, Quebec. *Died* at Staten Island, New York, 14 November 1893.

STODART, GEORGE TWEEDIE, OF OLIVER AND HOLMESHAW [2 December 1824]. Apprentice to Francis Wilson.—Son of Thomas Stodart, Biggarshiels, Lanarkshire. *Born* 13 October 1799. *Married* 4 June 1833, Mary Wilson (*died* 9 October 1844), daughter of Alexander Paul, Merchant in Birmingham. *Died* 26 August 1869.

STODART, GEORGE TWEEDIE [14 March 1867]. Apprentice to, and third son of, George Tweedie Stodart, W.S.—*Born* 18 January 1841. *Died* 23 May 1882, unmarried.

STODART, JOHN RIDDLE [7 July 1815]. Apprentice to Andrew Storie.—Fifth son of Robert Stodart of Kailzie, Peeblesshire. *Married* 5 July 1826, Jemima Henrietta (*died* 29 September 1865), seventh daughter of David Brown of Greenknowe, Stirlingshire. *Died* 5 February 1871.

STODDART, SHEILA GRAHAME, LL.B. [9 December 1980]. Apprentice to Thomas Munro Hunter and Others of Allan, Dawson, Simpson & Hampton.—Daughter of Grahame Stoddart, Writer, Ayton, Berwickshire. *Born* 20 November 1943.

STORIE, ANDREW [2 December 1794]. Apprentice to Alexander Duncan.—Only son of Andrew Storie, Candlemaker in Edinburgh. *Born* 14 March 1767. *Married* 3 February 1803, Penelope (*died* 31 October 1840), daughter of Barclay Fyfe, Merchant in Leith. Treasurer, 1828-62. *Died* 10 May 1862.

STORMONTH DARLING, JAMES, OF LEDNATHIE [24 January 1822]. Apprentice to (1) William Balderston; and (2) William Scott.—Son of James Darling, Writer in Kelso. *Born* 9 February 1799. *Married* 19 July 1825, Elizabeth Moir (*died* 1872), only surviving daughter of James Tod of Deanstoun. *Died* 12 August 1866.

STORMONTH DARLING, JAMES, OF LEDNATHIE [29 November 1855]. Apprentice to Alexander and Christopher Douglas.—Son of James Stormonth Darling, W.S. *Born* 4 October 1830. *Died* 8 January 1881, unmarried.

STORMONTH DARLING, JAMES, B.A.(OXON) [24 March 1902]. Apprentice to John R. Anderson, W. H. Murray, and A. R. C. Pitman.—Son of Patrick Stormonth Darling of Lednathie, Angus, Writer and Banker, Kelso. *Born* 31 January 1876. Joint County Clerk of Roxburghshire, 1905-16. County Clerk of Roxburghshire, 1916-30. Clerk of Lieutenancy, Roxburghshire. Member of the King's Bodyguard for Scotland, Royal Company of Archers, 1905. *Died* 8 September 1956. *Firm*—P. and J. Stormonth Darling, Kelso.

STORMONTH DARLING, JAMES CARLISLE, C.B.E., M.C., T.D., M.A.(OXON), LL.B. [15 July 1949]. Apprentice to William Fraser and Others of Fraser, Stodart & Ballingall.—Son of Robert Stormonth Darling, W.S., Kelso. *Born* 18 July 1918. *Married* 29 July 1948, Mary Finella, daughter of Lieutenant General Sir James Gammell, Alrick, Glenisla. Served with King's Own Scottish Rifles and Lieutenant Colonel commanding 52(L) Division Reconnaissance Regiment, R.A.C. Director of The National Trust for Scotland since 1949.

STORMONTH DARLING, ROBERT, B.A.(OXON) [8 July 1907]. Apprentice to George Dunlop, J. A. S. Millar, and J. H. Guild.—Son of Patrick Stormonth Darling of Lednathie, Angus. *Born* 6 June 1880. *Married* 7 June 1911, Beryl Madeline, younger daughter of Alfred Leighton Sayer of Westfield, Battle, Sussex. War Service: Major 2/1st Lothian and Border Horse; A.D.C. to G.O.C. 51st (Highland) Division. *Died* 20 May 1956. *Firm*—P. and J. Stormonth Darling, Kelso.

STRACHAN, FRANCIS [24 November 1766]. Apprentice to David Anderson.—Son of Arthur Strachan, Writer in Edinburgh. *Born* 6 September 1734. *Married*, proclaimed 17 March 1771, Katherine, daughter of William Hutton, Merchant in Edinburgh. *Died* 20 December 1798.

STRACHAN, GEORGE SMITH GOODALL [14 July 1919]. Apprentice to Thomas Ranken.—Son of Charles Souter Strachan, Mine Owner, of Gladstone, Kimberley, South Africa. *Born* 11 March 1878. *Married* (1) 9 October 1913, Blanche Watson; and (2) 10 September 1930, Jean Shearer Paul (*died* 17 January 1953), youngest daughter of Rev. John G. Dickson, D.D., Edinburgh. Served with Royal Scots as Lieutenant and Captain. Severely wounded, April 1917. *Died* 9 November 1942.

STRACHAN, JOHN, OF CRAIGCROOK [5 November 1683]. Apprentice to James Cheyne.— *Married* Jean Moodie. Fiscal, 1696-97. He mortified his lands of Craigcrook, Mid-Lothian, which he purchased in 1698, for certain charitable purposes. *Died* 22 April 1719.

STRACHAN, ROBERT [23 March 1796]. Apprentice to Robert Hotchkis.—Second son of John Strachan, Merchant in Edinburgh. *Born* 1773. *Married* 11 March 1806, Janet (*died* 16 January 1846), third daughter of Paul Darling of Bogangreen, Berwickshire. *Died* 23 April 1832.

STRACHAN, THOMAS RENNY, OF TARRIE [19 November 1782]. Apprentice to (1) Alexander Robertson; and (2) William Leslie.—Youngest son of Thomas Renny, Merchant in Montrose. *Married* 20 December 1796, Harriet (*died* 1853), daughter of Shadrach Moyse, Solicitor to the Board of Customs. Assume name of Strachan, 1808. *Died* 20 October 1823.

STRANG, WILLIAM [1627]. Signs the Acts, 26 December 1627. *Died* before 1646.

STRANG STEEL, MALCOLM GRAHAM, B.A.(CANTAB), LL.B. [30 April 1973]. Apprentice to Sir Alastair Campbell Blair and Others of Davidson & Syme.—Son of Jock Wykeham Strang Steel, Farmer, Kirriemuir, Angus. *Born* 24 November 1946. *Married* 21 October 1972, Margaret Philippa, daughter of William Patrick Scott, Distiller. *Firm*—W. & J. Burness.

STRATHAIRN, DONALD IAN CONSTABLE, LL.B. [11 December 1978]. Apprentice to William Milne Goodburn and Another of Blackwood & Smith, Peebles.—Son of Hubert William Strathairn, School Secretary, Crieff. *Born* 17 December 1950. *Married* 20 November 1976, Catriona Elizabeth, daughter of George Ronald Campbell Lumsden, M.B.E., Farmer, Brechin. *Firm*—Blackwood & Smith, Peebles.

STRATHERN, ROBERT [14 March 1872]. Apprentice to John and Henry Gordon Gibson.—Eldest son of Alexander Strathern, Sheriff-Substitute of Lanarkshire. *Born* 16 July 1839. *Married* 23 December 1867, Wilhelmina (*died* 29 November 1921), daughter of Daniel Brown, Shipowner. Liverpool. *Died* 2 October 1921. *Firm*—Gibson and Strathern, afterwards Strathern and Blair.

STRATOUN, ARTHUR.—Son of John Stratoun in Stratoun Mill. Commissioner, 1 June 1607. *Married* (1) Agnes, daughter of John Short in Canongate, widow of John Henderson, W.S.; (2) Margaret Irving; and (3) 11 November 1606. Margaret, daughter of Clement Kincaid of Coitts.

STRATOUN, ARTHUR, OF SNAWDOUN [15 May 1629]. Apprentice to James Stratoun.— Grandson of Arthur Stratoun of Kirksyde. Re-admitted, 21 November 1661. *Married* (1) 14 April 1630, Catherine Menteith; and (2) 26 April 1642, Bessie Purves. *Died* 1690.

STRATOUN, JAMES, OF STRATOUN [22 December 1610].—Son of John Stratoun in Stratoun Mill. Commissioner, 26 December 1627. *Married*. *Died* April 1647.

STRONG, THOMAS [26 March 1857]. Apprentice to (1) John Gibson; and (2) Andrew Storie.—Son of Thomas Strong, Merchant, Leith. *Born* 1 September 1819. *Died* 14 January 1881, unmarried.

STROYAN, COLIN STRATHEARN ROPNER, T.D., B.L. [25 April 1955]. Apprentice to C. T. Reid and Others of Thomson, Dickson & Shaw.—Son of Ronald Strathearn Stroyan, Landowner, Killin, Perthshire. *Born* 24 March 1927. *Married* 8 October 1959, Caroline Jane, daughter of Andrew L'Estrange Brownlow. *Firm*—Brodies (formerly John C. Brodie & Sons and Brodie, Cuthbertson & Watson).

STRUTHERS, JAMES [7 July 1807]. Apprentice to Thomas Adair.—Only son of John Struthers, Merchant in Strathaven. *Born* 1 July 1776. *Married* 12 November 1813, Marion (*died* 6 April 1844), youngest daughter of James Carmichael, Douglas, Lanarkshire. *Died* 3 February 1841.

STUART, ANDREW, OF CRAIGTHORN AND CASTLEMILK [10 August 1759]. Apprentice to, and second son of, Archibald Stuart of Torrance, Lanarkshire, W.S.—*Married* October 1790, Margaret (*died* 1 November 1849), fourth daughter of Sir William Stirling of Ardoch, Bart. Keeper of the Signet, 1777-79. Commissioner for Trade and Plantations, 1779. M.P. for Lanarkshire, 1777-84; Weymouth, 1790-1801. Keeper of the Register of Sasines, 1786-99; Joint Keeper of the Register of Sasines, 1800-1. Was Agent for Duke of Hamilton in the Douglas cause, and arising out of it he fought a duel with Edward, later Lord, Thurlow. Portrait by Reynolds was engraved by Thomas Watson. Author of *Genealogical History of the Stewarts*, 1798; and his *Letters to Lord Mansfield* were likened to those of Junius for their caustic wit. *Died* at London, 18 May 1801.

STUART, ARCHIBALD, OF TORRANCE [9 January 1723]. Apprentice to Hugh Somerville.—Seventh son of Alexander Stuart of Torrance, Lanarkshire. *Married* Elizabeth (*died* 12 January 1772), daughter of Sir Andrew Myreton, Bart. of Gogar, Mid-Lothian. *Died* November 1767.

STUART, DAVID, OF DUCHRA [2 March 1804]. Apprentice to John Hunter of Doonholm.—Son of Andrew Stuart, Maltster in Ayr. *Died* 11 March 1824.

STUART, FRANCIS BURNETT [24 March 1902]. Apprentice to John Cowan and J. A. Dalmahoy.—Son of Eustace Robertson Burnett Stuart, Crichie, Mintlaw, Aberdeenshire. *Born* 7 December 1877. *Married* 13 July 1912, Mary Campbell, daughter of Edward Martin and step-daughter of Mrs Hugh Lang, Brackley Lodge, Brackley, Northamptonshire. *Died* 26 April 1949.

STUART, GEORGE MALCOLM, B.A.(CANTAB) [24 October 1892]. Apprentice to R. L. Stuart and J. G. Stuart.—Son of R. L. Stuart, W.S. *Born* 26 August 1868. *Married* 2 September 1896, Mary Elizabeth (*died* 15 October 1961), daughter of John Scott Moncrieff, C.A., Edinburgh. Member of Town Council of Edinburgh, 1909-23. Clerk to George Heriot's Trust, 1924-34. *Died* 23 March 1952. *Firm*—Stuart and Stuart.

STUART, JAMES, YOUNGER OF DUNEARN [17 August 1798]. Apprentice to Hugh Robertson.—Eldest son of Dr Charles Stuart, Physician in Edinburgh. *Born* 1775. *Married* 29 April 1802, Eleanor Maria Anna (*died* 1868), only daughter of Dr Robert Moubray of Cockairnie, Fife. In 1822, having killed Sir Alexander Boswell of Auchinleck in a duel, he was tried for murder before the High Court of Justiciary, but was honourably acquitted. Afterwards Editor of *The Courier* newspaper, and Inspector of Factories. Collector of Widows' Fund, 1818-28. *Died* 3 November 1849.

STUART, JOHN, OF CASTLETON AND INCHBRECK [18 June 1802]. Apprentice to William Handyside.—Son of Dr David Stuart, Physician in Aberdeen. *Married* January 1800, Isabella, daughter of Charles Wright, younger of Phallope, Dean of Guild, Edinburgh. *Died* 8 April 1815.

STUART, JOHN [12 November 1868]. Apprentice to (1) Edmund Baxter; and (2) Frederick Pitman.—Son of William Stuart, Attorney in Exchequer. *Born* 15 August 1844. *Married* 28 September 1875, Jessie Warren (*died* 9 June 1923), eldest daughter of Rev. Thomas Mitchell, Minister of Oldhamstocks. *Died* 24 April 1895.

STUART, JOSEPH GORDON, LL.D. [21 July 1875]. Apprentice to Robert L. Stuart and Harry Cheyne.—Son of Joseph Gordon Stuart, Manufacturer, Balgonie, Fife. *Born* 31 December 1849. *Married* 6 June 1877, Moncrieff (*died* 25 May 1913), only daughter of the Very Rev. Principal William Leitch, Queen's College, Kingston, Canada. *Died* 14 December 1925.

STUART, LYALL DUNCAN, B.L. [27 April 1965]. Apprentice to Henry Maurice Braine and Others of Gordon, Falconer & Fairweather. *Born* 24 July 1932. *Firm*—A. C. Bennett & Fairweather (formerly Gordon, Falconer & Fairweather).

STUART, MISS PATRICIA MAIR [6 December 1976]. (By Rule IX(a).)—Daughter of Ludovic Mair Stuart, Solicitor. *Born* 9 July 1939. The first woman to be admitted to membership of the Society. *Firm*—Haldanes, McLaren & Scott.

STUART, ROBERT LAIDLAW [13 November 1856]. Apprentice to Henry Cheyne.—Youngest son of Alexander Stuart, Circuit Clerk of Justiciary. *Born* 16 February 1832. *Married* (1) 15 October 1861, Maria Campbell Hill (*died* 8 November 1881), daughter of Rev. George Anstey, Richmond, Surrey; and (2) 12 December 1887, Marie Louise (*died* 25 December 1937), only daughter of Thomas Treloar of Plymouth. Circuit Clerk of Justiciary, 1863-69. Procurator-Fiscal for Mid-Lothian, 1869. Fiscal of the Society, 13 June 1892-99. *Died* 2 October 1899.

STUART, ROBERT LAURENCE [26 December 1933]. Apprentice to George Malcolm Stuart and William L. Stuart.—Son of George Malcolm Stuart, W.S. *Born* 5 February 1900. *Married* (1) 19 November 1924, Barbara (*died* 28 November 1947), daughter of Harold M. Milward, Architect, and (2) 3 July 1952, Mary Purves Miller or Wilson. Lieutenant-Commander, R.N. Served Royal Navy 1914-18; Baltic 1919; and with Army of Occupation, Germany 1921-22; Served U.K. 1939-44. *Died* 23 August 1980. *Firm*—Stuart & Stuart. (Retired.)

STUART, WILLIAM [10 March 1836]. Apprentice to Thomas Corrie and David Welsh.—Son of Robert Stuart, Deputy Presenter of Signatures in Exchequer. *Born* 12 October 1810. *Married* (1) 13 July 1830, Charlotte (*died* 3 January 1853), youngest daughter of William Douglas, Edinburgh; (2) 21 June 1860, Isabella Rachel (*died* 17 January 1863), youngest daughter of John Scotland, W.S.; and (3) 31 March 1864, Helen (*died* 29 December 1932), daughter of Peter Scott, Banker, and widow of John Erkine of Venlaw, Peeblesshire. Sheriff-Clerk of Peeblesshire, 1843. *Died* 10 April 1881.

STUART, WILLIAM LEITCH [17 March 1919]. Apprentice to Joseph Gordon Stuart, his father, and G. M. Stuart.—*Born* 22 September 1889. *Married* 18 December 1915, Betty Goodall, daughter of Peter Herd, Coalmaster. War Service: Lieutenant in Black Watch (Royal Highlanders); served in France, May 1915 to November 1917, when invalided home. *Died* 10 May 1967. *Firm*—Stuart and Stuart.

STURROCK, ALEXANDER MONRO, M.A., LL.B. [13 July 1936]. Apprentice to Charles Law Forbes of Aitken, Methuen & Aikman.—Son of the Rev. Thomas Chapman Sturrock, B.D., Edzell, Angus. *Born* 13 May 1909. *Married* 10 April 1939, Ann Millicent, daughter of John Bolam Johnson, C.A. Lieutenant, R.A. Served U.K. and North West Europe 1939-45. Also Deputy Assistant Judge Advocate General, Allied Forces, South East Asia; President No. 4 Military Court, Rangoon, for trial of War Criminals 1946 (A/Lieutenant Colonel). Appointed Secretary Scottish Provident Institution, 1960. *Firm*—Aitken, Methuen & Aitken (1936-38).

STURROCK, ALEXANDER MUIR, T.D., B.A.(Oxon), M.B.E. [21 December 1939]. Apprentice to George Murray Lawson and Another of Murray, Lawson & Macdonald.—Son of David Muir Sturrock, Solicitor, Jedburgh. *Born* 21 September 1913. *Married* 17 December 1938, Mary Percival, daughter of Andrew Walsh, Solicitor, Oxford. Major, K.O.S.B. Served U.K. and North West Europe 1939-45. Wounded at Gheel, Belgium, September 1944. Mentioned in Despatches, February 1945; Awarded Croix de Guerre (French) with Gilt Star, February 1945. Honorary Sheriff, Jedburgh Sheriff Court (District of Roxburgh). *Firm*—Turnbull, Simson & Sturrock, Jedburgh (incorporating P. & J. Stormonth Darling, Kelso, and Lang & Steedman, Selkirk).

STURROCK, DAVID PERCIVAL, T.D., LL.B. [28 November 1966]. Apprentice to Alexander Jackson Ambrose and Others of Macandrew, Wright & Murray.—Son of Alexander Muir Sturrock, W.S., Jedburgh. *Born* 16 March 1943. *Married* 4 June 1966, Pamela Ann, daughter of the Rev. Alexander Hunter Wray. *Firm*—Turnbull, Simson & Sturrock, Jedburgh (incorporating P. & J. Stormonth Darling, Kelso, and Lang & Steedman, Selkirk).

STURROCK, JAMES SILVESTER [9 July 1883]. Apprentice to (1) J. O. Mackenzie, W. R. and John Kermack; and (2) John Philp Wood.—Second son of Robert Sturrock, Banker, Dundee. *Born* 31 October 1853. *Married* 8 August 1881, Josephine Lucy Florence (*died* 3 October 1928), second daughter of Lieutenant Benjamin Woolley, R.N. *Died* 12 August 1934.

SUTHERLAND, ALEXANDER GORDON [19 November 1829]. Apprentice to Alexander Blair.—Son of Neil Sutherland, M.D., Aberdeen. *Born* 16 January 1804. *Died* 25 October 1869, unmarried.

SUTHERLAND, ALFRED [12 April 1886]. Apprentice to Henry Tod.—Fifth son of George Sutherland of Forss, Caithness. *Born* 4 February 1862. *Married* 26 August 1890, Helen Barbara (*died* 12 April 1935), eldest daughter of D. R. Crawford. *Died* 24 November 1895.

SUTHERLAND, ALISTER MACDONALD, M.A., LL.B. [25 April 1960]. Apprentice to Arthur Woodman Blair and Others of Strathern & Blair.—Son of Alister Sutherland, Medical Practitioner, Peebles. *Born* 11 July 1934. *Married* 5 October 1963, Victoria Anne Boswell, daughter of Baron Erik Ivel-Brockdorff. *Firms*—(1) John C. Brodie & Sons (later John C. Brodie, Cuthbertson & Watson, and Brodie, Cuthbertson & Watson); (2) McGrigor, Donald & Co., Glasgow.

SUTHERLAND, ANDREW, of Pitgrudie [6 December 1699]. Apprentice to Robert Watson.—Son of Andrew Sutherland of Pitgrudie. *Married* 24 October 1702, Barbara, daughter of John Guthrie, W.S. *Died* before 1715.

SUTHERLAND, FRANCIS GILLIES [25 March 1912]. Apprentice to William Garson and James Garson.—Son of Rev. George Stewart Sutherland, Minister of Free St Paul's, Montrose. *Born* 13 November 1874. *Married* 1 October 1907, Gertrude Emily Maconochie (*died* 28 March 1955). *Died* 4 March 1951. *Firm*—Tods, Murray and Jamieson.

SUTHERLAND, JAMES CUBBISTON [3 July 1820]. Apprentice to (1) A. L. Ramage and John Blair; and (2) James Dundas.—Only son of Arthur Sutherland of the Island of Jamaica. Went to Australia—not known when he died. Struck off Roll, December 1893.

SUTHERLAND, LINDSAY ROBERTSON, M.A., LL.B. [14 December 1931]. Apprentice to F. G. Borthwick and Others of Mackenzie & Kermack.—Son of Hector Sutherland, Solicitor and Town Clerk of Wick. *Born* 18 December 1905. *Married* 7 April 1959, Maria Manuela, daughter of Manuel Seixas, Coffee Broker, Lisbon, Portugal.

SUTHERLAND, ROBERT, M.A., LL.B. [25 November 1963]. Apprentice to Archibald Campbell and Others of Archibald Campbell & Harley.—Son of Robert Sutherland, Civil Servant, Aberdour, Fife. *Born* 9 September 1926. Lieutenant, The Assam Regiment (Indian Army) 1944-47. Contributed various reviews and articles on legal topics and memoranda on constitutional matters. *Firm*—Stuart & Stuart (afterwards Stuart & Stuart Cairns & Co.) 1955-73.

SUTHERLAND, THOMAS CUNNINGHAM [18 July 1927]. Apprentice to Adam W. Gifford and Another of Mackenzie & Black.—Son of Symon Flett Sutherland, S.S.C., Edinburgh. *Born* 8 December 1901. *Married* 25 August 1937, Frances Mary (*died* 21 August 1963), daughter of Colonel J. J. Chevers, Connaught Rangers, Deputy Lieutenant of County of Galway. At one time Managing Director of Indian Trans-Continental Airways Ltd. and associated with Vickers-Armstrong during Second World War.

SUTHERLAND, WILLIAM [3 July 1828]. Apprentice to Adam Gib Ellis.—Son of Josiah Sutherland, Merchant in Wick. *Died* 12 October 1853, aged 53, unmarried.

SUTHERLAND, WILLIAM MILNE [24 March 1924]. Apprentice to James Watt and William Blair.—Son of Angus Sutherland, Hotelkeeper. *Born* 6 December 1874. *Married* 14 September 1908, Isabella Kerr, daughter of James M'Leish of Bellfield, Strathmiglo, Farmer. Admitted C.A., 22 July 1904. *Died* 27 July 1953. *Firm*—Davidson and Syme.

SUTTIE, GEORGE [11 December 1699]. Apprentice to John Cunningham.—*Died* March 1701.

SUTTIE, JOHN [30 June 1741]. Apprentice to Hew Crawford.—Second son of Sir James Suttie of Balgone, East Lothian, Bart. *Died* 23 August 1764.

SWAN, JAMES [3 July 1806]. Apprentice to Hamilton Bell.—Son of George Swan, Merchant in Edinburgh. *Married* 27 April 1807, Sarah (*died* 23 April 1834), daughter of Benjamin Bartlet, Storekeeper, Edinburgh Castle, and widow of William Buchanan of Auchmar, Stirlingshire. *Died* 1841, aged 58.

SWAN, WILLIAM [Before 1606]. Apprentice to William Kellie.—Son of George Swan, Burgess of Dunbar. *Married* 29 April 1604, Marion, daughter of James Ritchie, Commissary Clerk of Edinburgh. *Died* 15 April 1623.

SWINTON, ARCHIBALD [1 August 1788]. Apprentice to Samuel Mitchelson, Sen.—Third son of John Swinton of Swinton, Berwickshire, one of the Senators of the College of Justice (Lord Swinton). *Born* 1762. Reporter of Cases before High Court of Justiciary, 1835-40. *Died* 22 April 1840, unmarried.

SYDSERFF, JOHN, OF QUARLEDGESTEID [14 January 1634]. Apprentice to James Kinnear.—Son of William Sydserff of Ruchlaw. *Died* 1638.

SYM, JAMES PITCAIRN [24 January 1878]. Apprentice to (1) Robert Dobbie Ross; and (2) John Ross.—Son of William Sym, residing in Edinburgh. *Born* 1 June 1853. *Married* 2 August 1883, Elizabeth Leslie (*died* 20 April 1944), only daughter of Rev. John Watt, Minister of Fetteresso. *Died* 13 March 1931.

SYM, ROBERT [30 November 1775]. Apprentice to Robert Syme, his uncle.—Second son of Andrew Sym, Merchant in Glasgow. *Born* 29 February 1752. Was a Member of the Judicature Commission of which Sir Walter Scott was Clerk. On retiral from practice he wrote articles under the pseudonym "Timothy Tickler" for Blackwood's Magazine. See "Noctes Ambrosianae" ("Christopher North"). Was in the Royal Edinburgh Volunteers. "One of the handsomest men of Modern Athens." *Died* 2 April 1845, unmarried, the oldest member of the Society but one.

SYME, JAMES GORDON [8 October 1883]. Apprentice to (1) Charles Morton and John Neilson; and (2) T. D. Brodie and J. G. C. Brodie.—Son of James Syme, Merchant in Edinburgh. *Born* 10 July 1854. *Married* 20 October 1887, Nellie (*died* 18 May 1891), second daughter of Donald Macgregor of Ardgartan, Argyllshire. Struck off the List of the Society on 19 October 1891. *Died* January 1908.

SYME, JOHN, OF BARNCAILZIE [31 January 1750]. Apprentice to Thomas Goldie.—Only son of Alexander Syme, Writer in Edinburgh. *Married* (1) ——; (2) March 1748, Mary (*died* 18 July 1779), daughter of John Ravenscroft of Foulpark. Depute Writer to the Privy Seal, 1754. *Died* 6 June 1790.

SYME, JOHN, OF CARTMORE [10 July 1794]. Apprentice to Samuel Mitchelson, Jun.— Eldest son of David Syme of Cartmore. *Married* 20 October 1795, Barbara (*died* 14 October 1835), daughter of James Spottiswoode of Dunipace, Stirlingshire. *Died* 19 June 1821.

SYME, ROBERT [4 August 1735]. Apprentice to Hew Crawford.—Third son of John Syme, Merchant in Glasgow. *Died* 21 November 1780.

SYME, THOMAS [23 June 1820]. Apprentice to Harry Davidson.—Son of James Syme of Northfield, East Lothian. *Born* 5 November 1795. Solicitor to Bank of Scotland from 1837. *Died* 28 November 1869, unmarried. *Firm*—Davidson & Syme.

SYMON, GORDON DAVID, LL.B. [12 December 1977]. Apprentice to John McVie of Anderson & McVie, Haddington.—Son of Alexander John Symon, Agricultural Adviser, Edinburgh. *Born* 20 December 1951. *Married* 10 February 1979, Jane Maxwell Robertson. *Firms*—(1) Anderson & McVie, Haddington; (2) J. Paris Steele & Co., North Berwick.

TAIT, ADAM DUNCAN [15 July 1889]. Apprentice to John Kirk.—Son of Rev. Walter Tait, Minister of St Madoes. *Born* 20 December 1863. *Married* 6 June 1901, Evelyn (*died* 21 August 1946), second daughter of Rev. Richard Ford Heath, M.A., Vicar of Bishopswood, Staffordshire. *Died* 4 November 1946.

TAIT, ALEXANDER [9 July 1756]. Apprentice to (1) John Hay; and (2) George Balfour.— Son of Alexander Tait, Merchant in Edinburgh. *Married* Janet (*died* 17 January 1805), third daughter of William Blair of that Ilk. Substitute Keeper, 1744-62. Principal Clerk of Session, 13 November 1760 till death. *Died* at Restalrig, 8 July 1781.

TAIT, CRAUFURD, OF HARVIESTON [10 December 1789]. Apprentice to, and son of, John Tait of Harvieston, Clackmannanshire.—*Born* 8 April 1766. *Married* 17 June 1796, Susan (*died* 3 January 1814), fourth daughter of Sir Ilay Campbell of Succoth, Bart., Lord President of the Court of Session. Father of His Grace Archibald Campbell Tait, Archbishop of Canterbury. *Died* 2 May 1832.

TAIT, CRAUFURD, OF HARVIESTON [10 December 1789]. Apprentice to, and son of, John Tait of Harvieston, Clackmannanshire.—*Born* 8 April 1766. *Married* 17 June 1796, Susan (*died* 3 January 1814), fourth daughter of Sir Ilay Campbell of Succoth, Bart., Lord President of the Court of Session. Father of His Grace Archibald Campbell Tait, Archbishop of Canterbury. *Died* 2 May 1832.

TAIT, DAVID WARDLAW BROWN, OF LANGRIGG [24 October 1879]. Apprentice to Sir John Gillespie and Thomas Paterson.—Son of James Tait of Langrigg, Berwickshire, W.S. *Born* 21 October 1855. *Died* at Kelso, 9 November 1925.

TAIT, GEORGE WILLIAM, M.A., LL.B. [26 November 1962]. Apprentice to G. L. F. Henry and Others of Shepherd & Wedderburn.—Son of Haldane Philp Tait, Principal Medical Officer, Edinburgh. *Born* 9 September 1940. *Married* 7 September 1963, Kathleen Alison, daughter of James Cowie Johnston, Bank Manager. *Firm*—G. W. Tait & Sons.

TAIT, JAMES, OF LANGRIGG [14 November 1839]. Apprentice to George Turnbull.—Son of James Tait of Edenside, Kelso. *Born* 3 June 1816. *Married* 24 April 1849, Elizabeth Moir (*died* 9 March 1863), daughter of James Stormonth Darling of Lednathie, Forfarshire, W.S. *Died* 21 October 1899.

TAIT, JAMES [17 November 1859]. Apprentice to John Gibson.—Second son of John Renny Tait, Baker in Edinburgh. *Born* 16 November 1836. *Died* at Cameron Emporium, U.S.A., 16 March 1873, unmarried.

TAIT, JAMES CAMPBELL [27 June 1823]. Apprentice to, and second son of, Craufurd Tait of Harvieston, W.S.—*Born* 1 November 1798. *Died* 17 January 1879, unmarried.

TAIT, JOHN, OF HARVIESTON [8 March 1763]. Apprentice to William Fraser of Ford.—Eldest son of Thomas Tait of Buthlaw, Mason in Manderston, Aberdeenshire. *Born* 1727. *Married* March 1764, Charles (*died* 25 March 1784), youngest daughter of Thomas Murdoch of Cumloden, Kirkcudbrightshire. His portrait was painted by Raeburn. *Died* 11 March 1802.

TAIT, JOHN [16 November 1781]. Apprentice to John Tait.—Son of George Tait, Tenant in Redbog, Aberdeenshire. *Born* 1748. *Married* 16 September 1782, Margaret (*died* 24 April 1810), daughter of Peter Edgar of Bridgelands, Mid-Lothian. Judge of Police, 1805-12. *Died* 29 July 1817.

TAIT, JOHN, OF PIRN [7 July 1808]. Apprentice to Archibald Gibson.—Eldest son of William Tait of Pirn, Mid-Lothian. *Born* 1783. *Married* 23 March 1819, Harriet (*died* 1 November 1819), eldest daughter of Archibald Hepburn Mitchelson of Middleton, Mid-Lothian. *Died* 12 December 1838.

TAIT, JOHN, *tertius* [17 May 1811]. Apprentice to, and son of, John Tait, W.S.—*Born* 1786. *Died* 29 March 1832, unmarried.

TAIT, JOHN CRAUFURD [19 July 1855]. Apprentice to James Campbell Tait.—Eldest son of John Tait, Advocate, Sheriff of Clackmannan and Kinross. *Born* 31 August 1825. *Married* 7 December 1863, Maria Louisa Mann (*died* 27 January 1915). *Died* at Epping, 14 June 1901.

TARBERT, JAMES [Before 1586].—Son of James Tarbert, Edinburgh.

TARBERT, JOHN [Before 1606].—Son of James Tarbert, W.S.

TAWSE, ANDREW, OF NETHER LEASTON [22 June 1819]. Apprentice to Charles Tawse, his brother.—Youngest son of John Tawse, Writer in Edinburgh. *Born* 22 October 1788. *Married* 28 March 1822, Margaret (*died* 25 February 1869), fourth daughter of Alexander Bonar of Ratho, Mid-Lothian. *Died* 13 July 1851.

TAWSE, CHARLES [7 July 1808]. Apprentice to Alexander Duncan.—Eldest son of John Tawse, Writer in Edinburgh. *Born* 1785. *Married* 16 September 1817, Sarah Harriet (*died* 1875), only daughter of John Connell of Carlisle. *Died* 22 October 1826.

TAWSE, JOHN, OF NETHER LEASTON [13 November 1849]. Apprentice to Walter and John Cook.—Eldest son of Andrew Tawse of Nether Leaston, East Lothian, W.S. *Born* 20 April 1824. *Died* 29 October 1892, unmarried.

TAWSE, JOHN WARDROBE, OF STOBSHIEL [22 November 1838]. Apprentice to Andrew Tawse.—Eldest son of John Tawse of Stobshiel, East Lothian, Advocate. *Born* 21 September 1813. *Died* 9 July 1887, unmarried.

TAYLOR, ANGUS GRAEME, M.A., LL.B. [28 November 1955]. Apprentice to Ranald Ker Cuthbertson and Others of Mackenzie, Innes & Logan.—Son of John Gow Taylor, Textile Executive, Monifieth, Angus. *Born* 20 March 1930. *Married* 21 January 1956, Gloria June, daughter of Major George William Powell, Royal Signals. Resident in Ontario, Canada.

TAYLOR, GEORGE [26 June 1832]. Apprentice to James Macdonell.—Son of Alexander Taylor, Writer in Tain. *Born* 20 October 1808. *Married* 3 August 1841, Robina (*died* 11 June 1879), daughter of Alexander Smart of Cononsyth, Forfarshire. Editor *Montrose Standard*, 1838-44. Deputy Assistant Registrar of Joint Stock Companies, London, 1847. Registrar, 1857-64. *Died* 1 October 1864.

TAYLOR, JAMES, OF PITCAIRLIE [9 June 1698]. Apprentice to John Cunningham.— *Married* 6 March 1701, Catherine (*died* 24 December 1762), daughter of John Menzies of Cammo, Mid-Lothian, Advocate. Commissary of Dunblane, 20 August 1701. *Died* 10 December 1735.

TAYLOR, JAMES, OF PITCAIRLIE [4 August 1731]. Apprentice to, and son of, James Taylor of Pitcairlie, Fife.—*Married* (1) July 1751, Margaret Balfour (*died* 6 February 1770), relict of James Callander, Writer, Edinburgh; (2) Marion Anstruther. Resigned his Commission, 5 August 1778. *Died* 1784.

TAYLOR, JAMES PRINGLE [12 January 1885]. Apprentice to Donald Beith and Andrew Forrester.—Son of Rev. James Taylor, D.D. *Born* 6 September 1851. *Married* 11 February 1886, Annie (*died* 13 November 1920), youngest daughter of Charles Thornton, Leeds. *Died* 15 September 1910.

TAYLOR, JAMES WILSON, B.L. [23 July 1973]. Apprentice to George W. Wallace and Another of Ferguson, Wallace & Gardner.—Son of George Swan Taylor, A.R.I.B.A., Architect, Edinburgh. *Born* 30 May 1935. *Married* 29 July 1961, Ann Frances Sheila, daughter of Lachlan Donald Macmillan, A.R.I.C.S. *Firm*—Graham & Finlayson, Crieff.

TAYLOR, JOHN, OF BLACKHOUSE [20 July 1775]. Apprentice to Alexander Mackenzie.— Son of Rev. William Taylor, Minister of New Deer. *Born* 5 November 1744. *Died* 30 January 1810.

TAYLOR, WILLIAM [5 March 1840]. Apprentice to William Scott, W. C. Balderston, and John Scott.—Son of Robert Taylor of Broomlands. *Born* 28 July 1817. *Died* 2 July 1888, unmarried.

TEDCASTLE, ROBERT, M.C. [20 December 1921]. Apprentice to James and G. G. B. Steuart.—Eldest son of Joseph Studholme Tedcastle, Portarlington, Ireland. *Born* 10 October 1889. *Married* 9 October 1926, Alice Mary, youngest daughter of John Maclennan, Inverness. Enlisted in Scots Guards in Great War. Captain Cheshire Regiment: twice wounded in France. Awarded M.C. *Died* at Montana, Switzerland, 26 December 1932.

TEMPLETON, ROGER EDGAR, LL.B. [30 April 1970]. Apprentice to William George Moodie of Keir, Moodie & Co.—Son of George Roger Templeton, Edinburgh. *Born* 30 December 1940. *Married* 4 November 1968, Jennifer Ann, daughter of Jack Lister. *Firm*—Malcolm, Jack & Matheson, Dunfermline.

TENNENT, PATRICK [23 May 1808]. Apprentice to Archibald Gibson.—Third son of Robert Tennent, Brewer in Glasgow. *Born* 1782. *Married* 27 April 1812, Margaret Rodger (*died* 11 January 1867), youngest daughter of Hugh Lyon of Wester Ogle, Forfarshire. *Died* 18 December 1872.

THAIN, JOHN WILLIAM [8 July 1895]. Apprentice to J. H. Sang.—Son of Herbert William Thain, Merchant, Dundee. *Born* 20 April 1866. *Married* 4 April 1925, Madeline Clair, youngest daughter of Brigade Surgeon Francis Parsons, I.M.S. *Died* 24 September 1948.

THAIN, LESLIE ALISTER, M.A., LL.B. [2 December 1968]. Apprentice to William Cumming and Others of W. & J. Burness.—Son of Alexander Simpson Thain, Building Company Director, Edinburgh. *Born* 22 August 1939. *Married* 24 February 1968, Katherine Mary Hudson. *Firm*—Bell & Scott, Bruce & Kerr.

THOMAS, ALFRED PATRICK MACTHOMAS, OF ABERLEMNO [13 July 1903]. Apprentice to William J. Gordon.—Son of Thomas Watt Thoms of Craigfold, Dundee. *Born* 6 July 1871. *Married* 6 October 1908, Evelyn Charteris (*died* 22 July 1968), only daughter of James Buyers Black, 1 Florentine Gardens, Glasgow. *Died* 17 May 1958.

THOMSON, ALEXANDER, OF WHITRIG [26 May 1818]. Apprentice to David Thomson and Robert Fleming.—Son of David Thomson, W.S. *Born* 1794. *Married* (1) 12 July 1819, Ann (*died* 13 December 1828), eldest daughter of Charles Hay, Edinburgh; and (2) 24 December 1832, Eliza (*died* 1879), daughter of Robert Burn, Architect in Edinburgh. *Died* at Tillicoultry, 10 October 1867.

THOMSON, ALEXANDER [21 July 1924]. Apprentice to James Murray Cooper of Macpherson & Mackay.—Son of Sir William Brown Thomson, Solicitor, Wishaw. *Born* 26 August 1895. *Married* 6 October 1936, Marjorie Marchbank, daughter of Sir William Marchbank Marshall, Solicitor, Motherwell. Served with H.L.I. to September 1914, when commissioned, thereafter with Border and York, and Lancaster Regiments until 1919. Wounded at Arras, April 1917. Assistant Solicitor (later Solicitor) to Department of Health for Scotland. Deputy Solicitor to Secretary of State for Scotland from 1946-60. *Died* 16 February 1978.

THOMSON, ALEXANDER, M.A., LL.B. [27 April 1965]. Apprentice to Alexander James Ramsay Bisset and Others of Baillie & Gifford.—Son of James Thomson, Manager, Glasgow. *Born* 16 August 1933. *Married* 30 July 1960, Helen Mairi, daughter of James Steele, Headmaster. *Firm*—Biggart, Baillie & Gifford (formerly Baillie & Gifford).

THOMSON, ALAN GRAHAM, B.A. [10 December 1907]. Apprentice to Sir John Prosser, A. G. Muir, and John Smart.—Son of Andrew Thomson, Timber Merchant, Edinburgh. *Born* 5 May 1882. *Married* 25 April 1914, Alice (*died* 21 March 1937), youngest daughter of Robert Weir, 6 Oswald Road, Edinburgh. Captain Royal Scots. *Killed* in action, 26 September 1917. *Firm*—Mitchell and Baxter.

THOMSON, ANDREW, OF KINLOCH [2 June 1809]. Apprentice to Robert Hill.—Son of Andrew Thomson of Kinloch, Fife. *Married* 20 February 1818, Barbara (*died* 8 February 1835, youngest daughter of James Hunter of Seaside and Glencarse, Perthshire. *Died* at Saratoga, U.S.A., 19 August 1831.

THOMSON, ANDREW [23 June 1820]. Apprentice to John Russell.—Son of John Thomson of Priorletham, Fife. *Died* in Florida, 14 July 1841, aged 52, unmarried.

THOMSON, DAVID [12 March 1788]. Apprentice to John Syme.—Son of Alexander Thomson, Accountant of Excise. *Married*, proclaimed 21 September 1790, Margaret (*died* 7 December 1812), daughter of Adam Keir, Baker, Edinburgh. *Died* 28 February 1837, aged 73.

THOMSON, DAVID, OF HOLEKETTLE AND ORKIE [19 June 1812]. Apprentice to Robert Hill.—Son of John Thomson of Holekettle, Fife. *Born* 1784. *Married* 25 May 1829, Lilias, eldest daughter of —— Milner, Boghall. *Died* at Alnwick, 12 January 1853.

THOMSON, DUNCAN WISHART, LL.B. [11 December 1978]. Apprentice to (1) George Stuart Russell and Others of Strathern & Blair and (2) Douglas Andrew and Another of Morton, Fraser & Milligan.—Son of James Thomson, F.R.C.S., Edinburgh. *Born* 23 October 1954.

THOMSON, EDWARD PETER [20 October 1885]. Apprentice to Robert Russell Simpson.—Son of Rev. Edward Anderson Thomson, Minister of Free St Stephen's Church, Edinburgh. *Born* 8 June 1861. *Married* 31 January 1889, Mary Lamond Haig (*died* 25 May 1934), second daughter of William Lindsay Christie, Assistant Keeper General Register of Sasines, Edinburgh. Principal Extractor of the Court of Session, September 1906-26. *Died* at Arosa, Switzerland, 29 January 1926.

THOMSON, FRANCIS [16 August 1671]. Apprentice to William Thomson, his brother.—Son of William Thomson of Angustoun.

THOMSON, FRANCIS HAY LOCKHART [16 March 1896]. Apprentice to Sir T. D. Brodie.—Son of Lockhart Thomson, S.S.C., Edinburgh. *Born* 31 July 1870. *Died* 10 July 1910, unmarried.

THOMSON, GEORGE [Before 1624].

THOMSON, GEORGE MONRO, OF BERRYHILL, KINCARDINESHIRE [21 October 1874]. Apprentice to James Lindsay, Jun.—Son of Rev. John Thomson, Minister of Balmerino, Fife. *Born* 12 February 1851. *Died* 20 December 1904, unmarried.

THOMSON, IAN MACKENZIE, B.L. [31 March 1958]. Apprentice to William Watt and Others of Davidson & Syme.—Son of Donald Hugh Thomson, Mechanical Engineer and Company Director, Edinburgh. *Born* 16 February 1926. *Married* 18 October 1950, Elizabeth Marie, daughter of Walter Wallace. Rating Coder, Royal Navy, 1944-47. Served South East Asia Command. *Firm*—Davidson & Syme (then Dundas & Wilson, Davidson & Syme). (Resigned 1976.)

THOMSON, JAMES, OF WESTER BOGIE [21 November 1777]. Apprentice to James Chalmers.—Son of John Thomson, Merchant in Cupar. *Married* 24 July 1809, Helen (*died* 1 June 1851), daughter of Patrick Moncrieff of Reidie, Fife. *Died* 25 October 1831, aged 82.

THOMSON, JAMES, M.A., LL.B. [29 November 1960]. Apprentice to Francis Hugh Simpson and Another of Fyfe, Ireland & Co.—Son of Alexander Thomson, Solicitor. *Born* 15 December 1927. *Married* 7 March 1953, Annalise Iversen, daughter of Rudolph Svarrer, Accountant, Denmark. *Firm*—Fyfe, Ireland & Co. (Retired 1978.)

THOMSON, JAMES MILLER, M.A., LL.B. [6 July 1896]. Apprentice to James Young.—Son of William Thomson, Timber Merchant, Bo'ness. *Born* 10 February 1872. *Died* 15 August 1953. *Firm*—J. Miller Thomson and Co.

THOMSON, JOHN [Before 1606]. *Married* (1) 21 October 1601, Alison Drummond; (2) Elizabeth Hay. Signs the Acts, 26 December 1627.

THOMSON, JOHN, OF CHARLTON [15 October 1705]. Apprentice to Robert Carstairs.—Son of James Thomson, Merchant, Kirkcaldy. *Married* 28 January 1709, Rachel, daughter of John Brymer of Edrom, Berwickshire. *Died* December 1738.

THOMSON, JOHN SUTHERLAND, B.L. [1 December 1969]. Apprentice to Donald S. Macdonald of Scott & Glover.—Son of John Sutherland Thomson, H. M. Inspector of Taxes. *Born* 12 September 1925. *Married* 6 September 1958, Ruth, daughter of George Nicol. Flight Lieutenant, R.A.F.V.R. *Firm*—Malcolm, Jack & Matheson, Dunfermline.

THOMSON, NIGEL CAMPBELL, M.A., LL.B. [1 December 1969]. Apprentice to Sir Peter G. Macdonald and Others of W. & J. Burness.—Son of David Spalding Thomson, Brewer, Edinburgh. *Born* 27 May 1944. *Married* 1 March 1969, Margery Renwick, daughter of John M. Esslemont, Department of Agriculture and Fisheries in Scotland. *Firm*—W. & J. Burness.

THOMSON, ROBERT LEWIS MAITLAND BROWN [14 July 1891]. Apprentice to George Dunlop.—Son of William Thomson, residing at New Pentland, Loanhead. *Born* 2 September 1865. *Died* 19 March 1936 in British Columbia.

THOMSON, THOMAS [6 March 1834]. Apprentice to (1) Sir James Gibson-Craig; and (2) John Dundas and William Wilson.—Son of John Thomson, Cashier of the Royal Bank, Edinburgh. *Born* 11 June 1807. *Married* 8 July 1851, Elizabeth (*died* 18 September 1872), daughter of Alexander Cleghorn, Inspector of Imports and Exports for Scotland. *Died* 6 July 1877.

THOMSON, WALTER NIGEL JAMIESON, LL.B. [30 April 1970]. Apprentice to John Patrick Pattullo and Another of McNeill & Sime.—Son of Edward Christie Thomson, C.A., Edinburgh. *Born* 5 March 1944. *Married* 11 October 1969, Elizabeth, daughter of William Nelson, Blacksmith, Leyland. *Firm*—Kilgour, McNeill & Sime (formerly McNeill & Sime).

THOMSON, WILLIAM, OF FAIRLIEHOPE [29 June 1661]. Apprentice to Robert Alexander.—Son of William Thomson, Portioner of Angustoun. *Married* 7 November 1664, Margaret Young. Lyon Depute, 4 January 1666-87. *Died* March 1693.

THOMSON, WILLIAM [9 February 1681]. Apprentice to, and only son of, William Thomson, W.S.—*Married* September 1698, Jean, daughter of John Mason, Merchant, Edinburgh. *Died* 12 January 1708, aged 56.

THOMSON, WILLIAM [19 March 1888]. Apprentice to T. E. O. Horne, Thomas Horne, and David Lyell.—Son of Andrew Thomson of Mainhill, Roxburghshire. *Born* 19 May 1864. *Married* 12 June 1894, Mary Cramond (*died* 31 July 1951), fifth daughter of George Scott of Overwells, Roxburghshire. *Died* 14 May 1927. *Firm*—Menzies, Bruce-Low & Thomson.

THOMSON, WILLIAM GIBSON [20 December 1827]. Apprentice to Sir James Gibson-Craig.—Second son of John Thomson, Merchant in Edinburgh. *Died* 25 January 1832, aged 28, unmarried.

THORBURN, KENNETH MACKENZIE [18 June 1829]. Apprentice to Thomas Corrie and Thomas Welsh.—Son of Rev. William Thorburn, Minister of Troqueer. *Born* 13 May 1805. *Died* 17 June 1852, unmarried.

THORBURN, THOMAS [5 July 1821]. Apprentice to John Russell.—Son of Thomas Thorburn, Tanner in Dumfries. *Born* 1797. *Married* 7 May 1861, Margaret Johnston (*died* 30 September 1888). *Died* 30 July 1872.

THORNTON, GEORGE MUIR, LL.B. [10 December 1907]. Apprentice to William Thomson.—Eldest son of George Boyd Thornton of Feddal, Perthshire. *Born* 17 February 1882. Resigned his Commission, 3 March 1909. Admitted Advocate, 13 March 1910. Captain Seaforth Highlanders. *Killed* in action, 22 August 1917.

THORNTON, JAMES DAVID, M.A., LL.B. [15 December 1947]. Apprentice to James Milligan and Another of J. & J. Milligan.—Son of Robert Thornton, Farmer, North Pitkinnie, Cardenden, Fife. *Born* 21 May 1916. *Married* 4 September 1950, Marion Marshal Elliot. Captain, R.A. Served U.K., B.E.F., Persia, Iraq and Middle East, 1939-45. *Firm*—Macrae, Flett & Rennie.

THORNTON, PHILIP JOHN ROGER, M.A. [12 December 1977]. Apprentice to Eric Ian Cuthbertson and Another of Russel & Aitken.—Son of Arthur Roger Thornton, Buyer C.W.S., Manchester. *Born* 28 July 1947. *Married* 28 June 1969, Alexandra Janet, daughter of Joseph Taylor, Civil Servant, Helensburgh. *Firm*—Cuthbertson, Riddle & Graham (now Russel & Aitken).

THRESHIE, DAVID SCOTT [16 November 1819]. Apprentice to William Bell.—Son of Robert Threshie of Barnbarroch, Writer in Dumfries. *Born* 22 October 1796. *Married* (1) 1816, Jean, eldest daughter of John Crawford, Merchant in Leith; (2) 9 February 1829, Penelope Gordon of Aberlour (*died* 27 July 1853), widow of Patrick Duff of Carnoustie; and (3) 6 June 1854, Eliza Bird (*died* 10 November 1895), youngest daughter of Charles Ray Martin, Bengal Civil Service. *Died* 18 November 1878.

THURSTON SMITH, DIANA AGNES STEWART, LL.B. [11 December 1978]. Apprentice to Alexander James Ramsay Bisset and Others of Biggart, Baillie & Gifford. Daughter of the Rev. Andrew Stewart Todd, Old Aberdeen. *Born* 24 August 1955. *Married* 18 October 1980, Martin Howard Thurston Smith, W.S.

THURSTON SMITH, MARTIN HOWARD, B.A.(Cantab), LL.B. [11 December 1979]. Apprentice to John S. Macfie and Others of Tods, Murray & Jamieson.—Son of George William Smith, Civil Servant, Edinburgh. *Born* 20 November 1951. *Married* 18 October 1980, Diana Agnes Stewart Todd, W.S. *Firm*—Tods, Murray & Jamieson.

TINNING, JOHN [16 June 1796]. Apprentice to John Macnab.—Son of Francis Tinning, Tobacconist in Glasgow. *Died* 15 December 1808.

TOD, ALEXANDER [20 February 1834]. Apprentice to, and second son of, John Tod, W.S.—*Born* 23 June 1810. *Died* 8 November 1883, unmarried.

TOD, ARCHIBALD, OF DRYGRANGE [3 July 1781]. Apprentice to, and eldest son of, Thomas Tod, W.S.—*Born* 31 May 1758. *Married* 1 February 1802, Elizabeth (*died* October 1865), third daughter of Sir James Pringle of Stichell, Bart. *Died* 20 April 1816.

TOD, FREDERICK LEWIS MAITLAND, M.B.E. [10 December 1907]. Apprentice to James Burness.—Son of Henry Tod, W.S. *Born* 25 May 1884. Enlisted in 9th Royal Scot, 1914. Obtained a Commission and served in Egypt with Army Service Corps, afterwards in Servia, Macedonia, Palestine, and France. Wounded, 1918. *Died* 4 November 1962. *Firm*—H. and H. Tod.

TOD, GEORGE. *Married* Margaret Porterfield, who *died* about 1635. Clerk of Exchequer. *Died* 3 August 1615.

TOD, HENRY [11 December 1823]. Apprentice to John Campbell, Jun.—Son of Henry Tod, Merchant in Edinburgh. *Married* 4 June 1832, Isabella (*died* 28 September 1858), daughter of James Blyth. *Died* 31 October 1871, aged 73.

TOD, HENRY [17 January 1861]. Apprentice to, and son of, Henry Tod, W.S.—*Born* 19 March 1836. *Married* (1) 2 June 1869, Margaret, second daughter of Robert Walker, Hillside, Portlethen; and (2) 19 April 1877, Margaret Louisa (*died* 16 August 1929), daughter of John Moir, M.D., Edinburgh. *Died* 10 May 1896.

TOD, HENRY [17 January 1893]. Apprentice to W. Stewart Fraser.—Eldest son of Henry Tod, W.S. *Born* 3 July 1870. *Married* 11 June 1902, Elizabeth Knap (*died* 18 July 1940), second daughter of William Metcalf of Pittsburgh, Pennsylvania, U.S.A., Steel Manufacturer. *Died* 12 October 1954. *Firm*—H. and H. Tod.

TOD, HEW [Before 1622].—Son of George Tod, Writer. Mentioned, 15 November 1633.

TOD, HUGH [17 November 1814]. Apprentice to James Robertson.—Son of William Tod, Factor to the Duke of Gordon. *Born* 1784. *Died* 3 October 1857, unmarried.

TOD, JAMES, OF DEANSTON AND HOPE PARK [29 November 1820]. Apprentice to David Wemyss.—Son of James Tod, sometime Merchant at Bo'ness and afterwards at Hope Park, Edinburgh. *Married* 27 July 1830, Susan (*died* 2 July 1876), only daughter of James Mercer of Scotsbank, Selkirkshire. *Died* 26 March 1858.

TOD, JOHN [5 May 1796]. Apprentice to, and son of, Thomas Tod, W.S.—*Born* 9 March 1773. *Married* 9 April 1808, Helen (*died* 22 September 1873), daughter of Alexander Duff of Hatton, Aberdeenshire. *Died* 24 December 1856.

TOD, JOHN ROBERT [16 November 1837]. Apprentice to, and third son of, John Tod, W.S.—*Born* 14 February 1814. *Married* 17 August 1841, Jemima (*died* 5 July 1846), youngest daughter of Richard Wharton Duff of Orton, Elginshire. *Died* 29 July 1856.

TOD, JOHN WHARTON. *See* DUFF, JOHN WHARTON WHARTON-.

TOD, THOMAS, OF DRYGRANGE [3 February 1755]. Apprentice to Samuel Mitchelson.— Second son of Archibald Tod, Writer in Edinburgh. *Born* 6 December 1726. *Married* November 1755, Jean (*died* 5 November 1815), daughter of James Gartshore, W.S. *Died* 24 December 1800.

TOD, WILLIAM [20 December 1821]. Apprentice to Roger Aytoun.—Second son of William Tod, Surgeon in Lanark. *Died* 27 November 1866, aged 70, unmarried.

TODRICK, THOMAS [12 December 1904]. Apprentice to John Ewart.—Eldest son of Robert Todrick, Bank Agent, Haddington. *Born* 25 December 1879. *Married* 27 August 1910, Emma Brenda (*died* 15 February 1961), elder daughter of John List, M.I.C.E., and granddaughter of James R. Napier, F.A.S., Glasgow. Captain 8th Royal Scots. *Killed* in action on 15 December 1914.

TOWNER, DAVID HENRY, B.L. [28 November 1966]. (By Rule IX(a).)—Son of Robert Towner, Motor Engineer, Falkirk. *Born* 7 January 1933. *Married* 8 August 1958, Anne Knight, daughter of Charles Walker, Motor Engineer. *Firms*—(1) Ketchen & Stevens; (2) Archibald Campbell & Harley.

TOWSE, HAROLD BECKWITH [30 October 1893]. Apprentice to R. B. Ranken.—Son of Robert Beckwith Towse, Solicitor, London. *Born* 9 November 1866. *Married* 19 April 1909, Jane Haywood, daughter of Edward Collins of Kelvindale, Glasgow (*divorced* her for desertion, 19 July 1922). Captain in Scots Greys, 16 June 1902. Major (second in command) Royal Fusiliers, 1915. Served in East Africa, 1915-18. Promoted Lieut.-Colonel, served as D.A.Q.M.G. at G.H.Q., France, 1918-19. Three times mentioned in Despatches. *Died* at Kisuma, Kenya, 20 July 1923.

TRAIL, ANTHONY [7 July 1829]. Apprentice to John Irving.—Son of Thomas Trail, Merchant in Montrose. *Married* Hannah —— (*died* 29 December 1833). *Died* 27 September 1866, aged 64.

TRAIL, JOHN ARBUTHNOTT, LL.B., LL.D. [14 November 1872]. Apprentice to Patrick Dalmahoy and John Cowan.—Son of Rev. Samuel Trail, D.D., Minister of Harray and Birsay, afterwards Professor of Systematic Theology in the University of Aberdeen. *Born* 23 June 1846. *Married* 23 November 1892, Minnie (*died* 12 January 1920), youngest daughter of Rev. William Anderson, Parish of Walls and Flotta, Orkney. *Died* 11 June 1920.

TRAQUAIR, WILLIAM [13 November 1834]. Apprentice to James Peddie.—Son of William Traquair, Builder in Edinburgh. *Born* 1 May 1810. *Died* 7 April 1895, unmarried.

TRAQUAIR, WILLIAM [27 June 1878]. Apprentice to William Traquair, his uncle.—Son of Ramsay Heatley Traquair, Farmer at Colinton. *Born* 23 November 1851. *Married* 11 June 1884, Cecilia Ross (*died* 21 February 1947), only daughter of William Munro of Marchbank, Mid-Lothian. *Died* at Dunbar, 28 February 1923. *Firm*—Traquair, Dickson, and MacLaren.

TROTTER, GEORGE, OF CHARTERHALL [3 January 1634].—Third son of Robert Trotter of Catchelraw, but brought up by his uncle, John Trotter, First of Mortonhall and apprenticed to John Learmonth. *Born* circa 1590. *Married* (1) Jean, (*died* 1645), daughter of William King, Minister of Cramond, and (2) circa 1650, Margaret, daughter of Sir John Scot of Scotstarvit. *Died* April 1670. A monument displaying his Coat of Arms is in Fogo Kirk, near Duns, at the back of the Charterhall Gallery.

TROTTER, JOHN [10 March 1664]. Apprentice to George Trotter.—Youngest son of George Trotter of Prentannan. *Married* Margaret Anderson. *Died* May 1672.

TROTTER, ROBERT, OF CASTLELAW AND THE BUSH [8 August 1774]. Apprentice to John Syme.—Eldest son of Archibald Trotter, Merchant in Edinburgh. *Married* 16 August 1787, Ann, only daughter of John Trotter of Castleshiels, Berwickshire. Postmaster of Scotland, 1802-7. *Died* 3 July 1807.

TROTTER, THOMAS [26 June 1789]. Apprentice to David Steuart.—Fourth son of Thomas Trotter of Mortonhall, Mid-Lothian. *Died* 26 April 1837.

TROTTER-CRANSTOUN, THOMAS, OF DEWAR [18 December 1823]. Apprentice to William Bell.—Eldest son of Young Trotter of Broomhouse, Berwickshire. *Died* 16 December 1848, unmarried.

TURCAN, PATRICK WATSON, M.A.(Oxon), LL.B. [9 May 1938]. Apprentice to W. H. Fraser and Another of Fraser, Stodart & Ballingall.—Son of John Watson Turcan, Merchant, Leith, Edinburgh. *Born* 17 March 1913. *Married* 9 December 1939, Barbara Christian, daughter of Harry Cheyne, W.S. Captain, Royal Armoured Corps, Lothian and Border Yeomanry. Served U.K. and France 1940. Prisoner-of-War in Germany 1940-45. Mentioned in Despatches October 1945. *Firm*—Dundas & Wilson (formerly Dundas & Wilson, Davidson & Syme).

TURCAN, ROBERT CHEYNE, M.A.(Oxon), LL.B. [29 April 1974]. Apprentice to the Hon. D. A. Balfour and Others of Shepherd & Wedderburn.—Son of Henry Hutchison Turcan, Lindores House, Newburgh, Fife. *Born* 28 May 1947. *Married* 14 December 1974, Elizabeth Catherine Carslake. *Firm*—Dundas & Wilson.

TURNBULL, ALASTAIR JOHN, M.A., LL.B. [4 December 1967]. Apprentice to Sir Hugh Watson and Others of Dundas & Wilson.—Son of Dr Alexander Edward Turnbull, Medical Practitioner, Kirk Yetholm, by Kelso. *Born* 7 September 1941. *Married* 14 October 1967, Fiona Sybil, daughter of Dr A. Clarke, Northern Ireland. *Firm*—James & David W. B. Tait, Kelso.

TURNBULL, DAVID [24 February 1809]. Apprentice to Roger Aytoun.—Fifth son of Patrick Turnbull, Farmer in Myles. *Born* 1781. *Married* 27 September 1813, Elizabeth (*died* 7 July 1847), daughter of John Logan of New Edrom, Berwickshire. Clerk and Extractor to Dean of Guild Court. *Died* 21 September 1854.

TURNBULL, DAVID [19 July 1872]. Apprentice to Alexander Hamilton and George Thomas Kinnear.—Only son of Patrick Turnbull, W.S. *Born* 24 May 1847. *Married* (1) 1 December 1871, Mary, daughter of Allan Gilmour of Lundin and Montrave, Fife; (2) 2 May 1904, Marjory Janet (*died* 17 December 1933), second daughter of Thomas Gow of West Grange, Cambo, and Woodhall, Otterburn, Northumberland. *Died* 28 October 1910.

TURNBULL, GEORGE, of Balglassie [1 June 1696]. Apprentice to Henry Graham.— *Married* Catherine Garden. *Died* 11 January 1726.

TURNBULL, GEORGE, of Dalladies [25 June 1733]. Apprentice to Harry Maule.— *Married* Jean Turnbull (*died* 14 March 1807). *Died* 30 April 1760.

TURNBULL, GEORGE, of Abbey St Bathans [8 February 1816]. Apprentice to John Renton.—Eldest son of John Turnbull of Abbey St Bathans, Berwickshire. *Married* 15 August 1817, Grace (*died* 1868), youngest daughter of James Brunton of Lugton, Bridgend, Mid-Lothian. *Died* 26 February 1855, aged 62.

TURNBULL, GEORGE GILLON, of Abbey St Bathans [15 July 1885]. Apprentice to John Turnbull, his uncle.—Eldest son of James Turnbull, W.S. *Born* 6 September 1858. *Died* 16 July 1928, unmarried.

TURNBULL, JAMES [12 November 1857]. Apprentice to John Turnbull.—Second son of George Turnbull, W.S. *Born* 12 August 1828. *Married* (1) 17 November 1857, Mary Ann (*died* 10 September 1858), youngest daughter of William Downe Gillon of Wallhouse, Linlithgowshire; and (2) 29 January 1867, Jane (*died* 9 April 1919), daughter of John Corse Scott of Sinton, Roxburghshire. *Drowned* off Aberdour, 12 May 1887.

TURNBULL, JOHN, of Abbey St Bathans [18 November 1841]. Apprentice to, and eldest son of, George Turnbull, W.S.—*Born* 3 March 1820. *Died* 20 June 1891, unmarried.

TURNBULL, JOHN [12 July 1897]. Apprentice to John Rutherfurd.—Son of John Turnbull, Farmer, Lilburnhill, Wooler. *Born* 31 March 1864. *Married* 4 September 1888, Elizabeth White (*died* 2 October 1933), daughter of James Carmichael, Poulterer and Game Dealer, 60 Queen Street, Edinburgh. *Died* at Dunbar, 24 March 1929.

TURNBULL, JAMES, LL.B. [15 July 1975]. Apprentice to P. J. Oliphant and Others of Pearson, Robertson & Maconochie.—Son of Thomas Turnbull, Master Joiner, Philpstoun, by Linlithgow. *Born* 16 October 1943. *Married* 2 December 1967, Anne Naismith, daughter of Thomas Lawrie, Linlithgow. Clerk to West Lothian District Court. *Firm*—Peterkin & Kidd, Linlithgow.

TURNBULL, PATRICK [20 November 1845]. Apprentice to, and son of, David Turnbull, W.S.—*Born* 14 August 1815. *Married* 28 July 1846, Martha (*died* 11 May 1899), daughter of John Ord of Muirhouselaw. *Died* 12 January 1900.

TURNER, JOHN, OF TURNERHALL [9 July 1824]. Apprentice to Francis Brodie and George Imlach.—Eldest son of Keith Turner of Turnerhall, Aberdeenshire. *Born* 22 July 1796. *Married* 23 September 1820, Elizabeth Helen (*died* 5 January 1837), youngest daughter of Captain William Urquhart, 30th Regiment. *Died* 2 August 1834.

TWEEDIE, DOUGLAS GEORGE, T.D., M.A., LL.B., [12 July 1948]. Apprentice to A. F. Macpherson and Another of Fraser, Stodart & Ballingall.—Son of R. W. Tweedie, Landowner and Farmer. *Born* 14 March 1918. Captain, Royal Scots. *Firms*—(1) Fraser, Stodart & Ballingall; (2) Morton, Fraser & Milligan (after amalgamation). (Retired).

TWEEDIE, GILBERT [7 December 1903]. Apprentice to R. Pringle and A. T. Clay.—Son of Gilbert Tweedie of The Moat, Annan. *Born* 3 May 1876. Found *drowned* in River Eden at Newmills, Fife; missing since 22 March 1918, unmarried.

TWEEDIE, JOHN [23 November 1795]. Apprentice to Andrew Hamilton.—Son of James Tweedie, Tenant in Dreva, Peeblesshire. *Born* 20 August 1766. Keeper of the Minute Book of Court, 1830-47. *Died* 18 March 1847, unmarried.

TYNTO, JAMES [18 May 1649]. *Married* 15 August 1644, Catherine Dick. *Died* April 1655.

TYTLER, JAMES [24 November 1774]. Apprentice to, and second son of, William Tytler, W.S.—*Died* 20 July 1778.

TYTLER, JAMES, OF WOODHOUSELEE [8 March 1803]. Apprentice to Richard Hotchkis.— Second son of Alexander Fraser-Tytler of Woodhouselee, Mid-Lothian, one of the Senators of the College of Justice (Lord Woodhouselee). *Born* 9 October 1780. *Married* 12 August 1810, Elizabeth (*died* 19 February 1845), eldest daughter of Maurice Carmichael of Eastend, Lanarkshire. Lyon Depute, 2 June 1827. Crown Agent, 1829-1832, 1834-35, 1841-46, and 1852-53. *Died* 10 October 1862.

TYTLER, JAMES FRANCIS FRASER-, OF WOODHOUSELEE, B.A.(OXON), D.S.O., T.D. [27 March 1911]. Apprentice to (1) the Hon. J. W. Moncreiff, G. G. Soote, and Evan J. Cuthbertson; and (2) W. P. Robertson.—Son of James William Fraser-Tytler of Woodhouselee, W.S. *Born* 11 September 1884. *Married* 11 August 1911, Florence Helen (*died* 2 February 1946), only child of Henry Williams, Calcutta. Major in The Lovat Scouts, 1914-19. Served in Gallipoli, Egypt, Macedonia, and France. Awarded D.S.O., and mentioned in Despatches. *Died* 28 March 1969.

TYTLER, JAMES STUART FRASER-, OF WOODHOUSELEE, LL.D. [8 November 1849]. Apprentice to, and third but eldest surviving son of, James Tytler of Woodhouselee, W.S.—*Born* 5 August 1820. *Married* 8 August 1850, Mary Elizabeth (*died* 1857), only child of Alexander Blair, Treasurer of Bank of Scotland. Professor of Conveyancing in the University of Edinburgh, 28 May 1866. *Died* 26 November 1891.

TYTLER, JAMES WILLIAM FRASER-, OF WOODHOUSELEE [27 July 1881]. Apprentice to A. Howe, J. S. Tytler, and W. MacGillivray.—Only son of James Stuart Fraser-Tytler, W.S. *Born* 28 February 1854. *Married* 28 July 1883, Christian Alice Scott (*died* 21 September 1954), third daughter of William Scott-Kerr of Sunlaws and Chatto, Roxburghshire. *Died* at Cousta, Shetland, 14 August 1904.

TYTLER, WILLIAM, OF WOODHOUSELEE [5 October 1742]. Apprentice to William Forbes.—Son of Alexander Tytler, Writer in Edinburgh. *Born* 12 October 1711. *Married* September 1745, Anne (*died* 28 March 1783), daughter of James Craig of Costerton and Dalnair, Stirlingshire, W.S. Treasurer, 1788-92. Author of *An Inquiry, Historical and Critical, into the Evidence produced by the Earls of Moray and Morton against Mary Queen of Scots*, 1760, and other works. *Died* 12 September 1792.

URE, GEORGE INNES [1 July 1822]. Apprentice to Alexander Dallas.—Second son of James Ure, Collector of Customs at Alloa. *Born* 1796. *Died* 31 January 1843, unmarried.

URE, JAMES, OF SHIRGARTOUN [18 December 1701]. Apprentice to John Cuningham.—Son of James Ure of Shirgartoun, Perthshire, a noted Convenanter. *Married* Elizabeth Montgomery. *Died* before 1743.

URE, MASTERTON [2 July 1799]. Apprentice to J. A. Higgins.—Fourth son of Rev. Robert Ure, Minister of Airth. *Born* 3 April 1777. M.P. for Weymouth, 1813-32. *Died* 1863, unmarried.

URMSTON, CHARLES HANSON, OF GLENMORVEN [18 March 1889]. Apprentice to Matthew M. Bell.—Son of Captain William Brabazon Urmston, R.N. *Born* 1 May 1862. *Married* 29 October 1919, Mrs Maude Beatrice Ralph or Mason (*died* 16 January 1951). *Died* 11 February 1930. *Firm*—Hagart and Burn-Murdoch.

URQUHART, FRANCIS WILLIAM GEORGE [11 July 1910]. Apprentice to Sir W. S. Haldane, F. G. Haldane, and William Purves.—Eldest son of Alexander Reid Urquhart, M.D., LL.D., Perth. *Born* 3 June 1882. *Married* 28 August 1920, Gladys Muriel (*died* 25 February 1972), second daughter of Rev. William Veitch, M.A., Minister of St Margaret's, 12 Lennox Street, Edinburgh. Lieutenant R.A.S.C.; in France, 1914-18; mentioned in Despatches. *Died* 17 January 1962.

URQUHART, H. [1607]. Signs the Acts, 4 April 1607.

URQUHART, LEONARD [14 July 1735]. Apprentice to Robert Dalrymple of Dreghorn. *Died* 7 December 1786.

URQUHART OF RUCHLAW, RONALD MACDUFF, T.D., B.A.(OXON), LL.B. [28 July 1952]. Apprentice to the Hon. David Balfour and Another of Shepherd & Wedderburn.—Son of William Macduff Urquhart, S.S.C., Edinburgh. *Born* 28 December 1924. *Married* 12 May 1956, Rosemary Jean, daughter of Douglas Foulis, D.S.O., O.B.E., D.L. Major, Seaforth Highlanders, Served in India, Malaya and Java. *Firm*—A. & W. M. Urquhart (incorporating A. & A. S. Gordon and R. McLaren Henderson & Co.).

URQUHART, WILLIAM [19 December 1767]. Apprentice to, and son of, Leonard Urquhart, W.S. *Died* in Jamaica, January 1783.

USHER, JOHN [17 January 1822]. Apprentice to John Tod.—Eldest son of Thomas Usher, Farmer at Courthill, Roxburghshire. *Died* 29 March 1864, aged 70, unmarried.

VALLANCE, JOHN MILNE, LL.D. [9 December 1901]. Apprentice to James Balfour-Melville, James H. Balfour-Melville, L. M. Balfour-Melville, and Charles F. Scott.—Youngest son of William Vallance, Confectioner, Edinburgh. *Born* 20 May 1878. *Married* 8 September 1909, Marian (*died* 29 March 1947), eldest daughter of William Allison, M.D., Millfield, Killalo, Londonderry. Solicitor, Scottish Board of Health, 1919, and to Department of Health for Scotland, 1929. Assistant Secretary, Department of Health for Scotland, 1931. Author of Article on *National Health Insurance* in Green's *Encyclopaedia of Scots Law*. *Died* 4 September 1961.

VEACHE, OR WAITCHE, HARRY OR HENRY [1627]. Signs Acts, 26 December 1627. *Married* 30 January 1628, Geilles Archibald, who *died* 1 August 1630.

VEITCH, GEORGE, OF RATHO BANK [21 December 1809]. Apprentice to Thomas Cranston.—Only son of George Veitch, Architect in Edinburgh. *Born* 1787. *Married* 13 July 1811, Mary (*died* 6 November 1863), daughter of John Pitcairn of Pitcairns, Perthshire. *Died* at Ratho Bank, 16 October 1826.

VEITCH, GEORGE SCOTT, M.A., LL.B. [25 April 1977]. Apprentice to David Birrell and Others of Dundas & Wilson.—Son of David Young Veitch, Managing Director, Edinburgh. *Born* 4 February 1950. *Married* 20 January 1978, Irene Margaret, daughter of John Thomson. *Firm*—G. L. Sturrock & Armstrong.

VEITCH, JOHN [28 June 1827]. Apprentice to Thomas Richardson.—Third son of Henry Veitch of Eliock, Dumfriesshire, one of the Commissioners of H.M. Customs for Scotland. *Born* 12 September 1802. *Died* 12 March 1830, unmarried.

VEITCH, THOMAS LOUGHNAN [11 July 1833]. Apprentice to Alexander Hunter.—Fourth son of Henry Veitch of Eliock, Dumfriesshire, one of the Commissioners of H.M. Customs for Scotland. *Born* 29 July 1804. *Died* 6 February 1841, unmarried.

VEITCH, WILLIAM, OF ELIOCK [13 December 1723]. Apprentice to John Frank.—Son of Alexander Veitch of Lyne, Merchant and Burgess of Peebles. *Born* 2 January 1671. *Married* Christian, daughter of Gavin Thomson, Provost of Peebles. *Died* 25 October 1747.

WADDELL, ALEXANDER PEDDIE, OF BALQUHATSTON [18 December 1856]. Apprentice to, and son of, James Peddie, W.S. *Born* 19 August 1832. *Married* 6 September 1864, Georgina Catherine (*died* 7 May 1927), eldest daughter of George Waddell, W.S., of Balquhatston, Stirlingshire, whose name he assumed. *Died* 26 January 1917.

WADDELL, GEORGE, OF BALLOCHNIE AND BALQUHATSTON [17 November 1815]. Apprentice to (1) John Tinning; and (2) J. A. Higgins.—Eldest son of George Waddell of Ballochnie, Lanarkshire. *Married* 1 October 1844, Elizabeth Gaston (*died* 25 July 1883), eldest surviving daughter of John Brand Ralston of Glenellrigg, Stirlingshire. *Died* 10 March 1850, aged 62.

WADDELL, WILLIAM, OF EASTER MOFFAT [14 June 1814]. Apprentice to (1) John Tinning; and (2) Masterton Ure.—Youngest son of George Waddell of Ballochnie. *Born* 15 November 1788. *Married* 19 August 1829, Margaret (*died* 26 November 1867), eldest daughter of Archibald Campbell of Melfort, Argyllshire. Solicitor to Board of Ordnance. *Died* 14 March 1876.

WADDELL, WILLIAM N. [10 February 1825]. Apprentice to John K. Campbell and Andrew Clason.—Son of James Waddell, Writer in Edinburgh. Resident Magistrate at Albany, Cape Colony. *Died* 3 September 1834, aged 33, unmarried.

WAKELIN, HENRY, M.C. [11 July 1910]. Apprentice to William Gibson.—Son of Henry Wakelin, Solicitor, Edinburgh. *Born* 24 July 1885. *Married* 10 July 1915, Catherine Paton (*died* 7 January 1965), only daughter of Thomas Carmichael, S.S.C., Edinburgh. In Great War, Captain 2/10th Royal Scots. *Died* 11 March 1941. *Firm*—H. and H. Wakelin.

WALKER, CHARLES [19 October 1891]. Apprentice to Thomas Horne and David Lyell.—Son of John William Walker, 9 Mayfield Street, Edinburgh. *Born* 7 August 1865. *Married* 1 June 1904, Maud Isabel (*died* 22 July 1925), elder daughter of C. Harcourt Loraine, late 86th Regiment. *Died* at Boscombe, 27 May 1923. *Firm*—Calder Marshall and Walker.

WALKER, DOUGLAS STEWART, LL.B. [15 December 1930]. Apprentice to James Steuart, George G. B. Steuart, and Gavin L. Allardyce.—Son of George W. S. Walker, Solicitor, Aberdeen. *Born* 15 May 1898. *Married* 3 October 1927, Edythe Margaret, daughter of Charles Murray, C.M.G., LL.D., Civil Servant ("Hamewith"). Lieutenant R.F.A. Served in France and Belgium in Great War; wounded. *Died* 18 June 1963. *Firm*—J. C. and A. Steuart.

WALKER, ESME, M.A., LL.B. [11 December 1979]. Apprentice to A. S. Young and Others of J. & R. A. Robertson.—Daughter of David Burnett, S.S.C., Edinburgh. *Born* 7 January 1932. *Married* 17 March 1956, Ian Macfarlane Walker, W.S., son of James Walker.

WALKER, ERIC DUNWOODIE, B.L. [20 December 1948]. Apprentice to John Herbert Richardson and Others of Dundas & Wilson.—Son of George T. Walker, S.S.C., Edinburgh. *Born* 27 April 1921. *Married* 25 October 1951, Muriel Fraser Dalziel, daughter of Archibald Fyfe. Sergeant, R.A.F. Served India Command, Second World War. *Firm*—Campbell Smith & Co. (formerly Campbell Smith, Mathison & Oliphant).

WALKER, FRANCIS. *See* Drummond, Sir Francis Walker.

WALKER, GEORGE ROBERT, M.A., LL.B. [15 July 1940]. Apprentice to Samuel Kerr Gifford Kerr and Another of Bruce & Kerr.—Son of William Charles Walker, Draper, Edinburgh. *Born* 12 January 1906. *Married* 20 July 1939, Margaret McGregor, daughter of William Fleming Russell. *Firm*—Archibald Campbell & Harley. (Retired.)

WALKER, IAN MACFARLANE, B.A. [27 October 1975]. (By Rule IX(a).) *Born* 17 December 1924. *Firm*—Burnett, Walker & Reid.

WALKER, IAN NEIL DUNN, LL.B. [30 April 1970]. Apprentice to The Hon. David Andrew Balfour and Others of Shepherd & Wedderburn.—Son of William Lawson Walker, Schoolmaster. *Born* 3 January 1947. *Married* 4 October 1969, Ann Doreen, daughter of Donald Robertson Peatie, Assistant Keeper, H.M. Register House, Edinburgh. *Firm*—Patrick & James.

WALKER, JAMES, OF DALRY [2 July 1771]. Apprentice to Thomas Tod.—Third son of Francis Walker of Mainshill, East Lothian. *Married* (1) 13 July 1780, Jane Hay (*died* 7 January 1792), third daughter of Richard Newton of that Ilk; and (2) 21 October 1797, Marion Ann (*died* 6 July 1837), daughter of Dr John Hope, Professor of Botany in the University of Edinburgh. Principal Clerk of Session, 15 November 1803 till death. *Died* 9 May 1817. His son, Francis, on his marriage with the heiress of Hawthornden, assumed the name of Drummond.

WALKER, JAMES [7 July 1824]. Apprentice to John Tod.—Only son of Alexander Walker, Surgeon, H.E.I.C.S., residing in Edinburgh. *Married* 19 November 1838, Ann Sophia (*died* 3 July 1889), daughter of John Reade of Halbrooke House, Suffolk. *Died* 20 May 1881.

WALKER, JAMES [25 June 1829]. Apprentice to Alex. Hunter.—Eldest son of James Walker, Captain in the East India Company's Service. *Died* 8 February 1831.

WALKER, JOHN [29 June 1838]. Apprentice to William Scott, G. L. Finlay, and W. C. Balderston.—Second son of William Walker of Jamaica and Kelton Mains, Dumfriesshire. *Born* 12 November 1815. *Married* 9 June 1853, Margaret (*died* 18 December 1906), daughter of Francis Maxwell of Gribton, Dumfriesshire. *Died* 27 October 1879.

WALKER, JAMES CAMPBELL, M.M. [24 March 1941]. Apprentice to William Kerr Steedman and Others of Steedman, Ramage & Co.—Son of James Walker, Bank Agent, Dundee. *Born* 3 April 1895. *Married* 2 September 1929, Sophie Turnbull (*died* 11 March 1974), daughter of William Cram, North Queensferry. First World War, Gunner, Royal Field Artillery. Served in France and Belgium 1915-19. *Died* 13 October 1975. *Firm* Steedman, Ramage & Co.

WALKER, JAMES CAMPBELL, B.A.(OXON), LL.B. [30 November 1959]. Apprentice to William Watt and Others of Davidson & Syme.—Son of James Campbell Walker, W.S., Edinburgh. *Born* 2 August 1932. *Married* 10 August 1966, Sandra Georgette Smith, daughter of George Lumsden. *Firm*—Steedman, Ramage & Co.

WALKER, KENNETH MURRAY, T.D. (and Bar), M.A.(OXON), LL.B. [26 April 1957]. Apprentice to John Herbert Richardson and Others of Dundas & Wilson.—Son of Douglas Stewart Walker, W.S., Edinburgh. *Born* 8 April 1930. *Married* 20 February 1965, Rosemary Godela, daughter of Wilfrid N. S. Hoare, T.D., Headmaster of Strathallan School. *Firm*—J. C. & A. Steuart.

WALKER, ROBERT, OF WOODEN [28 June 1787]. Apprentice to Alexander Keith.—Eldest son of Adam Walker of Wooden, Roxburghshire. *Married*. *Died* 18 July 1825.

WALKER, RONALD GORDON, LL.B. [11 December 1979]. Apprentice to A. J. McDonald and Others of Thorntons & Dickies, Dundee.—Son of William Ronald Walker, Assurance Official, Dundee. *Born* 18 May 1952. *Married* 28 August 1973, Elizabeth Anne, daughter of Stanley Gordon Jones Clare, Lithographer, Dundee. *Firm*—Thorntons & Dickies.

WALKER, WILLIAM, OF DAFFMILN AND PITLAIR [23 November 1795]. Apprentice to Alexander Abercromby.—Son of James Walker of Daffmiln, Fife. *Married* 17 April 1798, Magdalen (*died* 20 November 1812), eldest daughter of Rev. William Walker, Minister of Collessie, Fife. *Died* 10 June 1845, aged 80.

WALKER, WILLIAM DONALD, LL.B. [9 December 1980*].—Son of William Walker, Bank Clerk, Edinburgh. *Born* 22 December 1952. *Married* 27 October 1979, Susan Margaret, daughter of James Forfar, Edinburgh.

WALLACE, ALEXANDER, OF WHITEHILL [10 July 1899]. Apprentice to L. A. Guthrie.— Son of David Wallace, Farmer, Balgrummo, Leven, Fife. *Born* 17 March 1860. *Married* 4 July 1901, Beatrice (*died* 13 March 1923), eldest daughter of Alexander Thomson, Wood Merchant, Edinburgh. *Died* 23 July 1942. *Firm*—Wallace and Guthrie.

WALLACE, ANDREW, OF WOOLMET [28 June 1736]. Apprentice to Robert Fullarton. *Married* 26 November 1758, Janet, daughter of James Law of Brunton. *Died* 10 October 1764.

WALLACE, ANDREW STARK, LL.B. [12 December 1977]. Apprentice to Thomas Alexander Crawford and Another of Courtney, Crawford & Co.—Son of Allan Wallace, Headmaster, Carluke, Lanarkshire. *Born* 15 November 1945. *Married* 18 August 1972, Jeanette Grace, daughter of Nicol Porteous Macmillan, M.I.P.M.

WALLACE, ARTHUR CHARLES [24 October 1879]. Apprentice to W. J. Menzies and H. J. Coventry.—Son of George Wallace, Solicitor in Fraserburgh. *Born* 18 May 1853. *Died* 5 January 1884, unmarried.

WALLACE, DAVID SWAN [20 March 1933]. Apprentice to Alexander Wallace and Another of Wallace & Guthrie.—Son of Sir David Wallace, K.B.E., C.M.G., D.L., LL.D., Surgeon, Edinburgh. *Born* 14 September 1906. *Married* 17 November 1945, Una Douglas, daughter of Douglas Strachan, H.R.S.A., LL.D., Stained Glass Artist, Pittendriech, Lasswade. Captain, R.A.O.C. Served U.K. and Middle East 1940-45. Member of the Queen's Bodyguard for Scotland, Royal Company of Archers. *Firm*— Wallace & Guthrie. (Retired.)

WALLACE, EBENEZER [11 July 1832]. Apprentice to John Renton and Joseph Grant.— Son of James Wallace, Gunmaker in Edinburgh. *Born* 9 April 1807. *Married* 2 December 1846, Isabella, youngest daughter of Ralph Hardie, Currie House, Borthwick. *Died* 31 July 1884.

WALLACE, EDWARD [17 January 1683]. Apprentice to John Alexander.—*Born* 1636. *Married* 19 April 1682, Euphan (*died* 30 October 1688), daughter of John Muir, W.S. *Died* 3 December 1736.

WALLACE, GEORGE WILLOUGHBY [15 December 1919]. Apprentice to W. Babington and Joseph Inglis.—Son of Robert Walker Wallace, W.S. *Born* 11 November 1888. *Married* 6 April 1921, Lilian Mabel, only daughter of Dr John Hancock Busteed, Bungay, Suffolk. Served in R.G.A.(T.), 1914-19, promoted from 2nd Lieutenant to Major. *Died* 4 September 1959. *Firm*—Wallace and Begg.

WALLACE, HORATIO [10 July 1893]. Apprentice to A. D. M. Black and J. M. Mackenzie.—Eldest son of Ebenezer Wallace, residing at 23 Saxe-Coburg Place, Edinburgh. *Born* 16 June 1866. *Married* 27 June 1908, Susanna Younghusband (who predeceased him). Author of *Poems and Songs of Life*. Resident in Victoria, British Columbia. *Died* 30 October 1954.

WALLACE, HOUSTON STEWART [29 March 1898]. Apprentice to G. Dunlop and J. A. S. Millar.—Son of Houston Stewart Wallace, Minden, Peebles. *Born* 18 March 1870. *Married* 28 November 1901, Phillis Rosamund (*died* 28 December 1940), youngest daughter of Very Rev. John Oakley, D.D., Dean of Manchester. *Died* at Littlehampton, 7 July 1929.

WALLACE, HUGH, OF INGLISTOUN [10 March 1664]. Apprentice to (1) John Rowan; and (2) William Hunter.—Son of William Wallace of Mainholm. *Born* 1640. *Married* (1) 4 August 1665, Margaret, daughter of Laurence Scott of Bavelaw, Mid-Lothian; and (2) Mary Syme. Fiscal, 1671-78. Council appointed him to be "the good town's writer in all their affairs," 1677. Aid-Lieutenant of the College of Justice Company that proceeded against the Rebels in the West. His Majesty's Cash Keeper. M.P. for Kirkcudbright Stewartry, 1685-86, and Burgh of Aberdeen, 1689-93. *Died* 4 February 1724.

WALLACE, JAMES CLERK [15 November 1838]. Apprentice to John and William Home.—Son of Alexander Wallace of Auchinvole, Dunbartonshire. *Born* 16 June 1813. *Married* 27 August 1839, Margaret Sommerville, third daughter of Marcus Smith, Surgeon, 51st Regiment. *Died* 23 March 1881.

WALLACE, JOHN [Before 1537]. *Married* Janet Marjoribanks. Clerk of Session. *Died* 1572.

WALLACE, JOHN WILLIAM M'NAIR, OF SHOESTANES [11 January 1892]. Apprentice to James Burness.—Son of Andrew Wallace, Solicitor, 11 Claremont Park, Leith. *Born* 16 September 1868. *Married* 14 June 1893, Jane Ann, third daughter of John Mitchell, 5 Rosslyn Street, Leith. *Died* 8 January 1947.

WALLACE, ROBERT [1627]. Signs the Acts, 26 December 1627. *Married* Katherine Henderson. *Buried* 6 January 1661.

WALLACE, ROBERT, OF HOLMSTONE [29 January 1701]. Apprentice to Robert Crawfurd of Crawfurdtoun.—Eldest son of John Wallace of Holmstone, Ayrshire. *Born* 19 June 1670. *Married* 17 January 1693, Elizabeth, daughter of William Crichton, Sheriff-Depute of Ayr. Commissary of Wigtown, 1720. Sheriff-Depute of Ayrshire, 1737. *Died* 24 March 1752.

WALLACE, ROBERT, OF SAUCHRIE [25 February 1723]. Apprentice to Robert Wallace of Holmstone.—Son of Robert Wallace of Cairnhill, Ayrshire. *Baptized* 9 February 1693. *Married* 4 April 1723, Anne, eldest daughter of Patrick Fullarton, younger of Fullarton, Ayrshire. Fiscal, 1729-32. *Died* February 1767.

WALLACE, ROBERT PATERSON, OF HOLMSTONE [30 August 1736]. Apprentice to Robert Wallace of Holmstone, his maternal uncle.—*Married*, proclaimed 2 November 1735, Elizabeth (*died* 14 January 1781), daughter of John Houston, Writer, Edinburgh. Assumed name of Wallace, 1752. *Died* 11 December 1779, aged 71.

WALLACE, ROBERT WALKER, OF HALBEATH [18 July 1877]. Apprentice to James Peddie and Alexander Peddie Waddell.—Son of Andrew Wallace, Coalmaster, Halbeath, Fife. *Born* 28 April 1853. *Married* 17 August 1881, Mary Parker (*died* 22 May 1943), only daughter of Rev. J. T. Willoughby of Leamington. Retired 1919. *Died* 21 January 1935. *Firm*—Wallace and Begg.

WALLACE, THOMAS WATT [21 July 1875]. Apprentice to Ebenezer Wallace, his uncle.—Son of George Wallace, Merchant in Leith. *Born* 19 December 1849. *Died* at Dunkeld, 13 October 1909, unmarried.

WALLACE, WILLIAM [8 December 1808]. Apprentice to Thomas Grierson.—Son of Captain Thomas Wallace of Newton, Ayrshire. *Married* 8 March 1824, Zelica Cheshire (*died* 6 September 1830), widow of Lieutenant Donald Grant. *Died* in St Cuthbert's Poorhouse, 22 February 1864, aged 79.

WALTON, JOHN WILLIAM JACKSON [11 April 1887]. Apprentice to George Dunlop.—Son of William Roger Walton, residing at Murraybank House, Murrayfield. *Born* 28 February 1863. *Married* 7 June 1895, Emily May (*died* 10 December 1938), eldest daughter of A. B. Jones, Regnella, Queensland, Australia. *Died* 23 January 1918.

WALMESLEY, JANE, LL.B. [9 December 1980]. Apprentice to Andrew Alexander Rose Carleton and Another of Pagan, Osborne & Grace, St Andrews.—Daughter of Roy Gerard Walmesley, Architect, Culross, by Dunfermline. *Born* 6 December 1955.

WARD, ROBERT [10 July 1911]. Apprentice to (1) John William M'Nair Wallace; and (2) John MacGregor.—Son of Henry Ward, Builder, Leith. *Born* 24 August 1885. *Died* 13 July 1959.

WARDLAW, DAVID [13 November 1856]. Apprentice to James Thomson Gibson-Craig.—Eldest son of David Brown Wardlaw of Gogarmount, Mid-Lothian, H.E.I.C.S. *Born* 15 June 1831. *Died* 6 November 1908.

WARDLAW, HENRY, OF KILLERNIE [Before 1555]. Natural son of Henry Wardlaw of Kilbaberton, legitimated, 19 August 1543. *Married* Marion Weir. *Died* before 6 July 1596.

WARDLAW, JOHN [Before 1586].—Son of Henry Wardlaw of Killernie, W.S. *Married* 1586, Elizabeth, daughter of William Cokkie, Goldsmith Burgess of Edinburgh. Commissioner, 16 December 1594. Master and Chaplain of the Hospital of St Leonard's, Edinburgh. *Died* before 1610.

WARDLAW, JOHN FLEMING [11 December 1828]. Apprentice to William Renny.—Son of David Wardlaw, Writer in Edinburgh. *Born* 1806. *Married* 27 November 1832, Ann Macnab (*died* 12 February 1891), eldest daughter of Andrew Stevens, S.S.C. Was a Clergyman in Cumberland. *Died* 4 May 1871.

WARDROP, JAMES CHARLES [14 July 1879]. Apprentice to William Wilson.—Eldest son of Maitland Wardrop, Architect in Edinburgh. *Born* 2 August 1854. *Married* (1) 19 December 1884, Elizabeth Evelyn (*died* 17 May 1888), second daughter of John Turner Hopwood, M.P., of Ketton Hall, Rutland; and (2) 7 June 1893, Mildred (*died* 7 June 1931), daughter of George Hanbury of Hitcham House, Burnham, Bucks. Associate of Institute of Actuaries, London, 1905. V.D. Commanded South Bucks National Reserve. *Died* 30 January 1939.

WARK, JOHN GRAHAM LEAN, M.A., LL.B. [16 December 1935]. Apprentice to J. Miller Thomson and Another of J. Miller Thomson & Co.—Son of John Lean Wark, The Hon. Lord Wark, Senator of the College of Justice. *Born* 4 February 1909. *Married* 28 September 1939, Maira Henderson, daughter of David Cargill Walker, Director of Music for Fife. During Second World War, District Commissioners Offices in Edinburgh and Glasgow. *Firm*—Breeze, Paterson & Chapman, Glasgow. (Retired.)

WARNER, GRAEME CHRISTOPHER, LL.B. [8 December 1975]. Apprentice to J. D. H. McIntosh and Others of Boyd, Jameson & Young.—Son of R. J. L. Warner, Company Director, Glasgow. *Born* 20 October 1948. *Married* 14 August 1976, Rachel Kidd, daughter of John Gear. *Firms*—(1) Boyd, Jameson & Young; (2) Graeme C. Warner & Co.

WARRENDER, HUGH [8 May 1798]. Apprentice to John Davidson.—Second son of George Warrender of Bruntsfield, Edinburgh. Deputy Keeper of the Signet, 1797-1820. He was appointed by the Rt. Hon. Henry Dundas—following the precedent of Alexander M'Millan of Dunmore—before he became W.S. Crown Agent, 1800-20. *Died* 8 June 1820.

WATERS, HENRY LETHBRIDGE [16 December 1935]. Apprentice to D. G. McGregor, Edinburgh.—Son of Donald Waters, Builder, Edinburgh. *Born* 20 February 1908. *Married* 18 April 1936, Jean Manson, daughter of James Alexander Manson Baxter, Architect. Captain, General Staff. Served U.K. and France, 1939-45. *Died* 5 January 1978. *Firm*—J. & A. Hastie.

WATERSON, WILLIAM GEORGE, LL.B. [4 December 1972]. Apprentice to F. H. Simpson and Others of Fyfe Ireland & Co.—Son of George Waterston, Ornithologist, Humbie, East Lothian. *Born* 2 February 1949. *Married* 20 September 1975, Andrea Lesley Bennet, Canada. *Firm*—Pearson, Robertson & Maconochie.

WATKINS, JOHN [23 January 1818]. Apprentice to Walter Cook.—Youngest son of Thomas Watkins, Merchant in Linlithgow. *Married* 23 March 1831, Isabella (*died* 1871), daughter of William Clark of East Woodside. *Died* 4 March 1858, aged 64.

WATSON, Hon. ADAM GEORGE [26 March 1901]. Apprentice to Sir Charles B. Logan, Hon. J. W. Moncreiff, and G. G. Soote.—Son of the Right Hon. William Watson, Baron Watson of Thankerton, one of Her late Majesty's Lords of Appeal in Ordinary. *Born* 15 August 1876. *Married* (1) 26 November 1904, Gwendoline Mary (*died* 16 November 1918), eldest daughter of Sir Richard Lodge, Professor of History in the University of Edinburgh; and (2) 2 December 1920, Ella Maud (*died* 1 March 1966), only daughter of George David Ballingall, W.S. Member of the King's Bodyguard for Scotland, Royal Company of Archers, 1910. In Great War, Captain Royal Scots; wounded. *Died* 30 May 1948. *Firm*—Mackenzie, Innes, and Logan.

WATSON, ANDREW, OF BRIDGECASTLE [30 January 1798]. Apprentice to (1) Robert Donaldson; and (2) Charles Young.—Only son of James Watson of Bridgecastle, Writer in Linlithgow. *Married* 7 August 1809, Harriet (*died* 1851), third daughter of Sir David Maxwell of Cardoness, Kirkcudbrightshire, first Bart. *Died* 27 October 1837, aged 68.

WATSON, ANDREW, OF TORSONCE [18 November 1858]. Apprentice to Adam Hay and Robert Pringle.—Son of Hugh Watson, W.S., of Torsonce, Mid-Lothian. *Born* 3 August 1830. *Married* 19 July 1853, Camilla Ottlie (*died* 13 February 1890), daughter of Henry Bate of Broomfield Place, Ealing, Middlesex. *Died* 21 January 1867.

WATSON, ARCHIBALD WATSON [29 March 1904]. Apprentice to W. Blair, James Watt, and John Blair.—Son of Archibald Watson, Stroquhan, Dunscore, Dumfries-shire. *Born* 13 November 1864. *Died* 20 March 1916, unmarried.

WATSON, DAVID, OF SAUGHTON [1 June 1655]. Apprentice to Harry Osburn.—Son of James Watson of Saughton, Mid-Lothian. *Married* 28 August 1652, Isabel, daughter of Adam Keltie, Clerk in Exchequer. Re-admitted, 15 February 1661. Treasurer, 1662-82. *Died* December 1685.

WATSON, GEORGE, OF NEWHALL [1627]. Apprentice to James Wynram.—*Married* 23 October 1628, Catherine (*died* 28 January 1677), daughter of John Nisbet, Merchant Burgess, Edinburgh. Lyon Clerk, 1630. *Buried* 9 October 1658.

WATSON, GEORGE [25 June 1829]. Apprentice to James Greig.—Son of George Watson, Merchant in Edinburgh. *Born* 17 September 1807. *Married* 14 September 1837, Ellen Mary (*died* 24 December 1899), daughter of Rev. Thomas Hattam Wilkinson, Clerk in Holy Orders. *Died* 24 April 1889.

WATSON, GEORGE JOHN EWEN [29 March 1904]. Apprentice to R. C. Bell and John Scott.—Son of the Rev. George Watson, Minister of the Parish of Hounam. *Born* 15 March 1880. *Died* 2 December 1943.

WATSON, GILBERT [17 August 1798]. Apprentice to James Hay and Thomas Manners.—Third son of David Watson, Banker, Glasgow. Banker in Glasgow. *Died* 1837.

WATSON, GRAHAM GILBERT [18 April 1877]. Apprentice to C. Mackenzie, A. D. M. Black, and J. M. Mackenzie.—Fifth son of James Watson, Manager of the Scottish Provident Institution. *Born* 20 September 1854. *Married* 5 December 1894, Mary Caroline (*died* 24 March 1933), eldest daughter of Matthew Wardrop, Architect, Edinburgh. *Died* 22 January 1929. *Firm*—Carment, Wedderburn & Watson.

WATSON, HUGH, OF TORSONCE [19 November 1797]. Apprentice to Allan MacDougall.— Eldest son of Samuel Watson, Writer in Edinburgh. *Married* (1) 19 April 1813, Mary Crichton (*died* 10 February 1821), only daughter of James Kyle, Architect, Edinburgh; and (2) 11 March 1825, Elizavetta Andrevna (*died* 28 May 1886, aged 86), only daughter of Andrew Watson of Petrosavodsk, Russia. *Died* at Leamington, 3 November 1834, aged 62.

WATSON, SIR HUGH, LL.B. [16 July 1928]. Apprentice to Robert William Dundas and Others of Dundas & Wilson.—Son of William John Watson, LL.D., Professor of Celtic Language, etc., Edinburgh University. *Born* 4 May, 1897. *Married* 14 July 1925, Winifred Margaret (*died* 4 December 1976), daughter of William Dawson Paterson, Deputy Chief Constable, Edinburgh. World War 1, 2nd Lieutenant 3rd Batt. Cameron Highlanders; Lieutenant 12th Batt. A. and S. Highlanders; served in Macedonia. Knighted 1957; Deputy Keeper on the Signet 1954-64; President of the Law Society of Scotland 1964-66. *Died* 16 October 1966. *Firm*—Dundas & Wilson.

WATSON, JAMES [26 November 1770]. Apprentice to Robert Jamieson.—Son of John Watson, Writer in Edinburgh. *Born* 28 June 1747. *Married* (1) 25 March 1788, Nicolas (*died* 19 April 1790), daughter of Thomas Buchan of Auchmacoy, Aberdeenshire; and (2) 13 June 1795, Isabella, daughter of Alexander Milne, Merchant in Leith. *Died* 30 September 1805.

WATSON, JAMES OF INCHYRA [10 December 1829]. Apprentice to Robert Ramsay.— Second son of James Watson, Merchant in Dundee. *Born* 2 May 1805. *Married* 14 November 1838, Helen (*died* 15 February 1900), eldest daughter of John Guthrie, Banker, Brechin. *Died* 30 August 1892.

WATSON, JAMES ARTHUR, B.A.(OXON) [7 December 1903]. Apprentice to R. Dundas, W. J. Dundas, G. M. Paul, and R. N. Dundas.—Son of George Watson, Advocate, Sheriff-Substitute of Dumfries and Galloway. *Born* 9 December 1876. *Married* 7 March 1910, Gwendoline Isabel (*died* 27 May 1970), elder daughter of T. P. Gillespie, Papermaker, Muiravonside House, Linlithgow. Town Clerk, Nairobi, Kenya Colony. *Died* 24 December 1967.

WATSON, JAMES STUART [18 March 1889]. Apprentice to Henry Tod.—Son of Rev. William Watson, U.P. Minister, Forres. *Born* 1 May 1861. *Married* 17 June 1911, Grace (*died* 11 February 1951), daughter of John S. Christie, Inverness. *Died* 26 November 1946. *Firm*—Macandrew and Jenkins, Inverness.

WATSON, JOHN [February 1739].—Son of David Watson, Writer in Edinburgh. *Married* November 1741, Isabel (*died* 10 June 1779), daughter of David Mudie, Merchant in Montrose. Substitute Keeper, 1746-62. He mortified his means and estates to charitable purposes, and from these funds the Institution in Belford Road, Edinburgh, called by his name, was erected in 1825-28 and endowed. *Died* 5 November 1762.

WATSON, JOHN DOUGLAS, LL.B. [8 July 1912]. Apprentice to P. Murray, W. C. Johnston, and A. E. Murray.—Son of the Rev. John Watson, at one time Minister of the North U.F. Church, Kelso, afterwards a Missionary of the English Presbyterian Church, Amoy, China. *Born* 3 October 1887. *Married* 16 December 1914, Margaret Louisa (*died* 24 December 1960), eldest daughter of Arthur A. Smart, Tullohill Lodge, Banchory-Devenick, Aberdeen. War Service: with 9th Gordon Highlanders. Presumed *killed* in action, 25 September 1915.

WATSON, JOHN NEIL, M.A., LL.B. [4 December 1967]. Apprentice to Eric David Buchanan and Another of Steedman, Ramage & Co.—Son of Neill Watson, C.B.E., S.S.C., Edinburgh. *Born* 17 August 1941. *Firm*—Cairns, McIntosh & Morton (now Stuart & Stuart, Cairns & Co.).

WATSON, JOHN PARKER [17 January 1893]. Apprentice to Henry Tod.—Son of David Matthew Watson, Papermaker, Bullionfield, Dundee. *Born* 28 December 1868. *Married* 20 April 1898, Rachael Watson (*died* 7 July 1946), second daughter of William Gavin Henderson, Manager, Liverpool Union Bank Ltd. *Died* 29 September 1956. *Firm*—Lindsay, Howe, and Co.

WATSON, JOHN PARKER, C.B.E., T.D., M.A.(Oxon), LL.B. [17 December 1934]. Apprentice to Robert Nevill Dundas and Others of Dundas & Wilson.—Son of John Parker Watson, W.S., Edinburgh. *Born* 22 August 1909. *Married* 25 April 1926, Barbara Parkin Wimperis. Lieutenant Colonel, R.A. Served U.K. and Middle East Forces 1939-45. President of the Law Society of Scotland 1970-72. Chairman of Solicitors' Discipline Tribunal 1974. *Firm*—Lindsays (formerly Lindsay, Howe & Co.). (Retired.)

WATSON, MICHAEL CHALMERS, B.L. [23 July 1956]. Apprentice to Stanley Whitton Fairweather and Others of Gordon, Falconer & Fairweather.—Son of David Scott Chalmers Watson, Solicitor, Leith, Edinburgh. *Born* 27 January 1932. *Married* 26 May 1956, Helen Hendry, daughter of William Smart. *Firm*—Beveridge, Philp & Ross (formerly Beveridge & Co.).

WATSON, PATRICK WIMPERIS GRANT, B.A.(Oxon) [24 April 1972]. Apprentice to (1) Thomas Patrick Spens and Another of Maclay, Murray & Spens, Glasgow, and (2) John Parker Watson and Others of Lindsays.—Son of John Parker Watson, W.S., Edinburgh. *Born* 22 May 1939.

WATSON, ROBERT, OF GRANGE [5 January 1678]. Apprentice to William Chieslie. *Married* (1) 12 October 1678, Margaret Peebles; and (2) 27 July 1683, Elizabeth Thomson. Under Keeper of the Signet, 20 February 1699. *Died* November 1699.

WATSON, RONALD KENNETH, M.C., T.D., B.L. [17 February 1942]. Apprentice to Evan James Cuthbertson and Others of Mackenzie, Innes & Logan.—Son of The Hon. Ronald Bannatyne Watson, Stockbroker, Edinburgh. *Born* 13 February 1914. *Married* 28 June 1941, Judith Cicely, daughter of Major General Sir Percival Spearman Wilkinson, K.C.B., D.S.O. Lieutenant Colonel, R.A.C. Lothains and Border Yeomanry. Served U.K., France and Germany 1939-45. *Firm*—Cuthbertson & Watson (later Brodie, Cuthbertson & Watson and Brodies).

WATSON, THOMAS [7 January 1734]. Apprentice to (1) John Inglis; and (2) John Stewart.—Son of John Watson, Jun., Merchant in Edinburgh. *Died* 14 January 1751.

WATSON, THOMAS WILLIAM, OF NEILSLAND [14 July 1890]. Apprentice to C. B. Logan, Hon. J. W. Moncreiff, and G. G. Soote.—Third son of Sir John Watson of Earnock, first Bart. *Born* 31 October 1864. *Married* 23 July 1891, Lucy (*died* 2 January 1947), daughter of William Henry Hamilton, Shenstone House, Broughton Park, Manchester. *Died* 23 March 1935.

WATSON, WILLIAM, OF PILMUIR [3 December 1729]. Apprentice to (1) John Inglis; and (2) John Lumsdaine. *Married* 11 January 1741, Isabella (*died* 3 June 1785), daughter of James Robertson, Merchant, Edinburgh. *Died* 18 October 1758.

WATSON, WILLIAM [10 July 1820]. Apprentice to Andrew Storie.—Son of William Watson, Farmer at Liberton Mains. *Born* 1795. *Married* 22 September 1830, Marion (*died* 2 May 1861), daughter of John Weir. Sheriff-Substitute at Aberdeen, 1829-66. *Died* 12 May 1887.

WATSON, HON. WILLIAM DOUGLAS [21 March 1932]. Apprentice to Adam W. Gifford, Colin M. Black and John R. Gifford.—Son of the Rt. Hon. William Watson, Lord Thankerton. *Born* 25 January 1905. *Married* 16 June 1934, Enid Agnes, daughter of Colin Ballantyne of The Kirna, Walkerburn. Lt. Col. R.A. Served U.K. and Western Desert 1939-45. Mentioned in Despatches 1942 and 1943. *Died* 11 November 1971. *Firm*—Fraser, Stodart & Ballingall (latterly Morton, Fraser & Milligan).

WATSON, WILLIAM NAIRN BOOG. *See* BOOG WATSON.

WATT, ADAM [27 May 1629]. Apprentice to David Anderson. Commissary of Kirkcudbright, 1641, and Peebles, 1649. *Died* 1 August 1662.

WATT, ALEXANDER STUART [12 July 1909]. Apprentice to Sir John Prosser, A. G. Muir, and John Smart.—Son of George Watt, Advocate, K.C., Edinburgh. *Born* 13 October 1884. *Married* 3 July 1920, Vera Stuart, only daughter of Alexander Moncur Prain, J.P., Eastwood, Colinton Road, Edinburgh. War Service mainly on Gold Coast and German East Africa, 1915-18. *Died* 7 November 1958.

WATT, ANDREW ROBIN, LL.B. [11 December 1979]. Apprentice to Edward Graham Marquis and Another of J. & F. Anderson.—Son of Andrew Watt, C.B.E., Commissioner of Forests, Edinburgh. *Born* 31 March 1949. *Married* 5 April 1975, Rosalind Jane, daughter of Dr Ronald Paley. *Firm*—J. & F. Anderson.

WATT, GEORGE [24 February 1825]. Apprentice to John and Alexander Smith.—Only son of George Watt, Surgeon, of Old Deer. *Died* 6 September 1832, aged 31, unmarried.

WATT, JAMES, LL.D. [6 July 1896]. Apprentice to John Blair. *Born* 21 March 1863. *Married* 7 June 1899, Menie (*died* 13 December 1957), elder daughter of Rev. William Cruickshank Eddie Jamieson, Tron Kirk, Edinburgh. F.F.A. Treasurer of the Society, 25 May 1925. *Died* 3 December 1945. *Firm*—Davidson and Syme.

WATT, JAMES PATERSON, B.Com., LL.B., LL.M.(HARVARD) [6 December 1976]. Apprentice to David Birrell and Others of Dundas & Wilson.—Son of James P. Watt, Engineer, Edinburgh. *Born* 19 April 1943. *Married* 31 December 1971, Hilary Anne, daughter of Matthew T. G. Cessford, Insurance Manager. *Firm*—Dundas & Wilson.

WATT, NIGEL GEORGE MORLEY, LL.B. [8 December 1975]. Apprentice to Allan Cameron Frazer and Others of Hagart & Burn-Murdoch.—Son of Alan C. R. Watt, Chairman of Industrial Tribunals, Skene, Aberdeenshire. *Born* 17 November 1950. *Firm*—Hagart & Burn-Murdoch.

WATT, RICHARD TYRRELL [13 July 1936]. Apprentice to William Alexander Macgillivray and Others of Lindsay, Howe & Co.—Son of The Rev. George Watt, B.D., Edinburgh. *Born* 16 May 1912. *Married* 11 March 1947, Ruth Goda, daughter of Lt. Colonel Cecil George de Pree. Major, Intelligence Corps. Served U.K. 1941-45. *Firms*—(1) Pitcairn & Mathers; (2) Pearson, Robertson & Maconochie (after amalgamation); (3) Pitcairns.

WATT, ROBERT JAMES GORDON, B.A.(CANTAB), LL.B., B.D. [23 April 1956]. Apprentice to James Harold Macdonald and Others of Morton, Smart, Macdonald & Prosser.—Son of Robert Cameron Watt, Schoolmaster, Edinburgh. *Born* 24 September 1930.

WATT, WILLIAM, B.L. [29 March 1926]. Apprentice to (1) James Garson of Skene, Edwards & Garson, and (2) Sir John Prosser and Others of Morton, Smart, Macdonald & Prosser.—Son of James Watt, LL.D., W.S. *Born* 4 December 1902. *Married* (1) 29 April 1930, Margaret Isobel (*died* 12 September 1935), daughter of James William Phillips, Nigg, Kincardineshire, Newspaper Editor, and (2) 16 December 1946, Ethel Elizabeth Mynors, daughter of James McIlwraith, Naval Architect, Collingwood, Ontario, Canada. Solicitor, Supreme Court of Judicature, England, 1929. Member of Queen's Bodyguard for Scotland, Royal Company of Archers. *Firm*—Davidson & Syme. (Retired.)

WAUCHOPE, ANDREW [14 November 1839]. Apprentice to Andrew Smith.—Eldest son of George Wauchope, Wine Merchant in Leith. *Born* 20 May 1817. *Married* 24 April 1844, Anne Montagu Scott (*died* 30 December 1892), daughter of John Boyd of Broadmeadows, Selkirkshire. *Died* 21 November 1890.

WAUCHOPE, JOHN [24 June 1774]. Apprentice to John Mackenzie of Delvine.— Youngest son of Andrew Wauchope of Niddry, Mid-Lothian. *Born* 1751. *Married*, proclaimed 18 August 1779, Ann Cockburn (*died* at Portobello on 31 October 1840, aged 85 years), daughter of Colonel Charles Craigie Halkett of the Dutch Service. *Died* 10 February 1828.

WAUCHOPE, PATRICK HAMILTON DON [29 October 1888]. Apprentice to George Dalziel.—Third son of Sir John Don Wauchope, Bart., of Edmonstone, Mid-Lothian. *Born* 1 May 1863. *Married* 10 June 1897, Georgiana Renira (*died* 5 May 1928), daughter of George Fitzjohn, Edinburgh, and widow of H. Buchan, Musselburgh. *Died* 9 January 1939.

WAUGH, JOHN JAMES, B.L. [28 October 1889]. Apprentice to J. O. Mackenzie, H. Cheyne, and John Kermack.—Son of Robert Somerville Waugh, Edinburgh. *Born* 4 March 1864. *Married* 11 January 1913, Rosina Gertrude Caroline (*died* 17 March 1955), younger daughter of Albert Stolz, Coal Exporter, Leith. Officier d'Académie (from French Government). *Died* 4 December 1940. *Firm* Burns and Waugh, till retiral.

WEBSTER, CHARLES RODNEY, B.L. [15 July 1949]. Apprentice to S. Raleigh Simpson and Others of R. R. Simpson & Lawson.—Son of Major Charles David Webster, Indian Army. *Born* 25 May 1918. *Married* 4 January 1946, Diana, Margaret Elizabeth, daughter of William Thomson Bottomley, A.R.T.C., A.M.I.E.E. Captain, General Staff. Served U.K., India and Burma 1940-45. *Died* 5 April 1972. *Firms*—(1) Simpson, Kinmont & Maxwell; (2) A. G. Cairns & Simpson.

WEBSTER, FRANCIS [18 November 1830]. Apprentice to Messrs. Campbell and Arnott.—Sixth son of Rev. John Webster, Minister of Inverarity. *Born* 4 November 1804. *Married* 27 November 1833, Jane, daughter of Captain E. H. Adams, 55th Regiment. *Died* 12 September 1888.

WEBSTER, GEORGE [29 November 1821]. Apprentice to John A. Campbell.—Son of Rev. John Webster, Minister of Inverarity. *Born* 28 March 1800. *Married* 20 September 1836, Margaret Isabella (*died* 3 April 1882), daughter of Alexander M'Callum of Hanover, Jamaica. Sheriff-Clerk at Forfar, 1854-82. *Died* 19 August 1882.

WEDDERBURN, ALEXANDER ARCHIBALD INNES, M.A., LL.B. [24 March 1930]. Apprentice to Archibald S. Leslie and Another of Alex. Morison & Co.—Son of Alexander John Forbes Wedderburn, S.S.C., Edinburgh. *Born* 18 December 1897. *Married* 29 July 1931, Ellen Innes, daughter of Allan Jeans, Newspaper Proprietor, Liverpool. In First World War, Munition Worker, National Service. Collector of Widows Fund 1950-51, when appointed Auditor of the Court of Session. Retired 1967. *Died* 16 April 1977. *Firm*—Alex. Morison & Co. (until 1951).

WEDDERBURN, ERNEST ALEXANDER MACLAGAN [14 December 1936]. Apprentice to Sir William Campbell Johnston and Others of Murray, Beith & Murray.—Son of Sir Ernest Maclagan Wedderburn, W.S., Edinburgh. *Born* 31 May 1912. *Married* 8 May 1937, Marjorie Felice Mainwaring (*died* 15 May 1952), daughter of Major Francis Brooks, Royal Scots. Major, Lovat Scouts (T.A.) Served U.K., France, Iceland, U.S.A., Canada, North Africa and Italy 1939-44. Accidentally killed at Aquila, Italy, 24 December 1944. *Firm*—Shepherd & Wedderburn.

WEDDERBURN, Sir ERNEST MACLAGAN, O.B.E., LL.D., LL.B., D.Sc. [10 December 1907]. Apprentice to H. E. Richardson, V. A. Noel Paton, and J. C. G. Lees.—Son of Alexander Stormonth Maclagan Wedderburn of Pearsie, Medical Officer of Health of the County of Forfar. *Born* 3 February 1884. *Married* 5 April 1911, Mary (*died* 28 January 1979), eldest daughter of the Rev. Thomas Smith Goldie, Minister of Granton. Professor of Coneyancing, 20 July 1922-35. Deputy Keeper of the Signet, 1935-53. Chairman of General Council of Solicitors, 1935; Statutory Chairman of the Law Society of Scotland, 1949-50; Author of *Conveyancing: Abridgement of Conveyancing Statutes.* In Great War served with Mediterranean Expeditionary Force as Meteorological Officer at G.H.Q. Afterwards in Salonica and France; awarded O.B.E.(Mil.); twice mentioned in Dispatches. Deputy Lieutenant for the County of the City of Edinburgh, 1947. Knighted 1942. *Died* 3 June 1958. *Firm*—Carment, Wedderburn, and Watson, afterwards Shepherd and Wedderburn

WEDDERBURN, GEORGE [30 January 1840]. Apprentice to Walter Cook—Second son of Right Hon. James Wedderburn, Solicitor-General for Scotland. *Born* 25 March 1817. *Died* 1 May 1865, unmarried.

WEDDERBURN, JOHN OGILVIE MACLAGAN [11 July 1892]. Apprentice to Charles Morton.—Eldest son of Alexander Stormonth Maclagan Wedderburn, M.D., Forfar. *Born* 10 April 1869. *Married* 2 June 1902, Margaret (*died* 11 April 1941), second daughter of John Duncan, M.D., F.R.C.S.E., of 8 Ainslie Place, Edinburgh. *Died* 11 September 1902.

WEDDERBURN, JOSEPH ROBERT MACLAGAN [18 October 1876]. Apprentice to Robert Craigie Bell.—Son of Rev. James Maclagan, D.D., Professor of Divinity in the Free Church College, Aberdeen, and Mrs Katherine Maclagan Wedderburn of Pearsie, Forfarshire. *Born* 16 October 1850. *Died* 17 May 1936. *Firm*—Carment, Wedderburn & Watson.

WEDDERBURN, THOMAS MACLAGAN, T.D., M.A.(CANTAB), C.A., F.T.I.I. [15 March 1948]. Apprentice to Robert William Cockburn and Another of Shepherd & Wedderburn.—Son of Sir Ernest Maclagan Wedderburn, W.S., Edinburgh. *Born* 19 May 1915. *Married* (1) 25 May 1940, Margaret Marshall, daughter of Dr Robert Scott (divorced 1965), and (2) 19 June 1965, Margaret Anne, daughter of James Neil, Civil Servant. Major, R.A. and later transferred to Special Air Service. Captured in Italy and spent the rest of Second World War as P.O.W. *Died* 2 January 1968. *Firm*—Shepherd & Wedderburn (1948-64).

WEIR, EVAN HUGH, B.A.(CANTAB), LL.B. [26 April 1954]. Apprentice to John Roger Orr and Another of Simpson & Marwick.—Son of Albert Jackson Weir, M.M., B.A., Ph.D., Schoolmaster, Edinburgh. *Born* 20 May 1926. *Married* 12 September 1953, Joan Patricia, daughter of Kenneth A. Woodward, Cheltenham. Served Royal Air Force 1944-48. *Firm*—Simpson & Marwick.

WEIR, JAMES [9 May 1668]. Apprentice to John Semple.—Son of James Weir, Tenementar Burgess of Hamilton. *Married* December 1671, Marjory Barclay. *Died* 1687.

WEIR, MATTHEW [9 July 1816]. Apprentice to William Inglis.—Eldest son of James Weir, Baker in Leith. *Married* 17 March 1823, Janet (*died* 3 December 1875), eldest daughter of William Spottiswoode, Claywhat, Perthshire. *Died* 27 August 1856, aged 68.

WEIR, MICHAEL ECKFORD LIND, M.A., LL.B., S.S.C. [17 July 1972]. Apprentice to J. R. L. Cruickshank and Another of Menzies & White.—Son of Norman James Lind Weir, M.B.E., J.P., S.S.C., Edinburgh. *Born* 5 May 1938. *Married* 12 June 1963, Hazel Dobson, daughter of Thomas Cunningham. *Firm*—Weir & Macgregor.

WEIR, ROBERT WILLIAM GRANT, B.L. [25 April 1955]. Apprentice to (1) A. J. Ambrose and Another of Macandrew, Wright & Murray, and (2) A. J. R. Bisset and Others of Baillie & Gifford.—Son of Robert Smellie Weir, Medical Practitioner, Dunfermline. *Born* 14 August 1928. *Married* 18 April 1959, Joan Miller, daughter of James Anderson, C.A. *Firm*—Pearson, Robertson & Maconochie.

WEIR, THOMAS [9 July 1818]. Apprentice to John Murray.—Second son of Thomas Weir, Writer in Edinburgh. *Married* 13 December 1822, Lilias Gray (*died* 23 February 1845), second daughter of John Orr, Edinburgh. *Died* 2 June 1849, aged 57.

WELSH, DAVID, OF COLLIN [31 January 1812]. Apprentice to James Gilchrist.—Son of Robert Welsh of Collin, Kirkcudbrightshire. *Born* 1789. *Married* 20th February 1824, Margaret (*died* 1867), daughter of Colonel Andrew Ross, 21st Regiment. *Died* 23 May 1857.

WELSH, HENRY [29 June 1786]. Apprentice to John Syme.—Son of John Welsh, Tenant in Morton Mains. *Died* 1821.

WELSH, JOHN [3 July 1770]. Apprentice to Andrew Stuart.—Only son of James Welsh, Goldsmith in Edinburgh. *Married* 23 April 1772, Primrose, only daughter of Woodroff Gascoigne. Resigned his Commission, 13 June 1779. *Died* in Calcutta, 1794.

WELSH, JOHN [16 November 1812]. Apprentice to John Tweedie.—Third son of William Welsh of Mossfennan, Peeblesshire. Sheriff-Clerk of Peeblesshire, 1820-43. *Died* 5 June 1843, aged 57, unmarried.

WELSH, THOMAS SCOTT [10 July 1899]. Apprentice to J. R. Anderson, and A. R. C. Pitman.—Younger son of John Welsh of Moredun, S.S.C., Edinburgh. *Born* 18 September 1875. *Married* 12 July 1904, Alice Cairns (*died* 14 July 1957), younger daughter of William Adams, 14 Lynedoch Place, Edinburgh, Antique Furniture Dealer. In R.A.S.C. during Great War. *Died* 8 July 1956. *Firm*—Welsh and Forbes.

WEMYSS, DAVID, of PITKENNY [21 June 1787]. Apprentice to James Walker.—Second son of Alexander Wemyss of Pitkenny, Physician in Kirkcaldy. *Married* 25 October 1799, Agnes, daughter of James Lindsay, Merchant in Leith. *Died* 14 May 1839.

WEMYSS, DAVID, of WEMYSS HALL [26 January 1854]. Apprentice to J. M. Melville, J. F. Walker Drummond, and James Lindesay.—Second son of James Wemyss Hall, Fife. *Born* 1st January 1830. *Married* 10 August 1859, Marie (*died* 6 January 1893), daughter of Colonel Gustav von Waldisch of Schaffhausen, Switzerland. *Died* 5 May 1907.

WEMYSS, SIR JAMES, of BOGIE, BART. [23 May 1820]. Apprentice to Robert Jamieson.—Eldest son of Rev. James Wemyss, Minister of Burntisland. *Born* 30 April 1795. Succeeded his kinsman as fourth Baronet. Depute Clerk of Session, 16 January 1844 till death. *Died* 31 December 1849, unmarried.

WEMYSS, WILLIAM [8 March 1763]. Apprentice to (1) Andrew Hay; and (2) Robert Grant.—Eldest son of John Wemyss, Tacksman of Mains of Aberdour. *Married* Robina (*died* 11 April 1794), daughter of James Hamilton of Olivestob, East Lothian. *Died* 29 April 1802.

WHIGHAM, DAVID, of CORNLEE [22 November 1827]. Apprentice to Alexander Goldie.—Son of Robert Whigham of Hallidayhill, Dumfriesshire. *Born* 1803. *Died* 16 October 1882, unmarried.

WHIGHAM, GEORGE, of HALLIDAYHILL [20 January 1825]. Apprentice to James Little.—Eldest son of Robert Whigham of Hallidayhill, Dumfriesshire. *Baptized* 29 April 1792. *Married* 5 August 1816, Jane (*died* 6 February 1854), daughter of Robert Anderson, Strawquhan, Dumfriesshire. *Died* 9 January 1842.

WHITE, ALEXANDER [3 April 1906]. Apprentice to David Shaw.—Son of Thomas White, S.S.C., Edinburgh. *Born* 20 May 1882. *Married* 11 October 1913, Winifred Caroline (*died* 3 December 1972), eldest daughter of Thomas William Leisk Spence, C.B., of Uyea, Shetland. Major 5th Royal Scots. *Died* 9 September 1915, of wounds received in action at the Dardanelles.

WHITE, ANDREW [14 January 1889]. Apprentice to Hew Hamilton Crichton.—Son of Andrew White, Solicitor, Cumnock. *Born* 10 March 1865. *Married* 20 June 1903, Helen (*died* 12 August 1930), fourth daughter of William Frederick Montague Wemberley, Harringay, Middlesex. *Died* at Cannes, 2 December 1951.

WHITE, JAMES TEMPLETON [12 July 1909]. Apprentice to William Gibson.—Son of John White, Builder, Edinburgh. *Born* 14 August 1880. *Died* 21 April 1951.

WHITE, JOHN [22 February 1813]. Apprentice to John Mowbray.—Son of Gilbert White, Tailor in Edinburgh. *Died* 25th April 1820, aged 34.

WHITE, JOHN WALTON, B.L. [19 December 1927]. Apprentice to John C. Strettell Miller.—Son of Thomas White, S.S.C., Edinburgh. *Born* 5 November 1892. *Married* 6 January 1932, Ethel Vera, daughter of J. Morison Inches, Brewer, Edinburgh. *Died* 2 May 1968. *Firm*—Thomas White & Park (latterly W. & J. Cook).

WHITE, MARY AINSLIE, M.A., LL.B. [9 December 1980*].—Daughter of Alexander George Stuart, Company Director, Insch, Aberdeenshire. *Born* 21 March 1954. *Married* 2 September 1977, John Howard White, son of James George Charles White, Investment Trust Manager, Edinburgh.

WHITE, RICHARD [3 April 1906]. Apprentice to (1) John Milligan; and (2) James H. Notman.—Son of William White, Tea Merchant, Edinburgh. *Born* 31 March 1882. *Married* 29 April 1919, Roberta McKinnel (*died* 7 October 1963), daughter of John Patrick Currie, Edinburgh. 2nd Lt. R.G.A. 1916-18. *Died* 13 August 1954. *Firm*—Menzies & White.

WHITE, ROBERT [13 December 1827]. Apprentice to William Young.—Sixth son of Adam White, of Fens, Roxburgh, Merchant in Leith. *Born* 16 August 1802. *Married* 3 June 1852, Anne Reid (*died* 23 October 1905), daughter of Thomas Macmillan Fogo, M.D. Author of *Treatise on the Knowledge Necessary to Amateurs in Pictures*, translated from the French, 1845, and other works. *Died* 9 June 1886.

WHITELAW, WILLIAM FREDERICK MARTIN, T.D., B.A.(Oxon), LL.B. [11 July 1932]. Apprentice to Robert Beveridge Smith of Beveridge, Sutherland & Smith.—Son of William Martin Whitelaw, S.S.C., Edinburgh. *Born* 16 June 1906. *Married* (1) 17 March 1950, Mary Kennedy, daughter of Frederick Cuthbert, Master Mariner, and (2) 24 November 1956, Frances Jean, daughter of Edward Whiting, Dental Surgeon. Major, R.A. Served U.K. and North West Europe 1939-45. Adjutant of Chemical Defence Experimental Station, Porton. *Died* 3 May 1982. *Firm*—Beveridge & Kellas (formerly Beveridge, Sutherland & Smith, and Beveridge & Co.).

WHITSON, DAVID SHIRESS [16 March 1896]. Apprentice to Sir T. Dawson Brodie.—Brother of Sir Thomas B. Whitson, C.A., sometime Lord Provost of Edinburgh. *Born* 10 January 1872. *Married* 22 August 1898, Jessie Borwick (*died* 10 December 1946), second daughter of James Mainland M'Beath, F.S.A.Scot., Lynnfield, Kirkwall. *Died* 1 January 1932.

WHYT, BAIN [10 March 1789]. Apprentice to Robert Jamieson.—Son of John Whyt, Maltster in Falkirk. *Baptized* 13 March 1748. Founder of the Wagering Club (1775), which still flourishes. Secretary to S.S.C. Society, 1784. Lieutenant and Adjutant, afterwards Major in the Royal Edinburgh Volunteers, 1794. Deputy Lieutenant for City of Edinburgh. *Died* (unmarried) 26 December 1818. His merit is handsomely acknowledged on his tombstone in the West Kirk Burying Ground.

WHYTE or QUHYTE, ANTHONY [Before 1607].—Brother of Robert Whyte of Dowald. Commissioner, 8 November 1609. *Married* (1) 23 July 1600, Agnes, daughter of William Tait, Burgess of Edinburgh; and (2) 7 September 1613, Katherine (*died* August 1645), daughter of David Kinloch, Burgess of Edinburgh, and widow of William Symson, Merchant Burgess, Edinburgh. Clerk to the Incorporation of Chirurgeons. Writer to the Prince, March 1620. *Died* 11 August 1634.

WHYTE, ERIC ANDREW, LL.B. [11 December 1978]. Apprentice to Ronald Kenneth Watson and Others of Brodies.—Son of Andrew Cuthbertson Whyte, Company Director, Motherwell. *Born* 9 May 1954.

WHYTE, NICHOLAS DOUGLAS, LL.B. (Edinburgh and London) [6 December 1976]. Apprentice to Campbell Young and Another of Gray, Muirhead & Carmichael.—Son of Douglas Noel Whyte, Solicitor, Forfar. *Born* 15 February 1951. *Married* 10 July 1971, Helen Mary, daughter of Ralph Chettle. *Firm*—MacHardy, Alexander & Whyte, Forfar.

WHYTE, WILLIAM GEORGE, B.L. [15 December 1947]. Apprentice to George W. Harvey of Hunter, Harvey, Webster & Will.—Son of Frederick John Whyte, Building Contractor, Edinburgh. *Born* 13 January 1919. *Married* 7 October 1954, Mary Cameron, daughter of Alexander Lewis Ross, Actuary, Edinburgh. Major, R.A. Served U.K., Middle East, Persia, Iraq and Italy, 1939-45. *Firms*—(1) Beveridge, Herd & Whyte, Kirkcaldy; (2) Biggart, Baillie & Gifford.

WIGHT, ALEXANDER [4 July 1783]. Apprentice to James Chalmers.—Son of James Wight, Farmer, Duncrahill, East Lothian. *Married* (1) 7 August 1781, Jane (*died* 15 February 1814), daughter of William Maconochie, Wright in Edinburgh; and (2) 22 September 1826, Catherine (*died* 17 February 1860), second daughter of Sir James Campbell of Aberuchill, Bart. *Died* 22 February 1829.

WIGHT, DAVID [2 July 1829]. Apprentice to Charles Campbell Stewart.—Second son of David Wight of Ormiston. *Died* 15 June 1860, unmarried.

WIGHT, JOHN [9 July 1819]. Apprentice to (1) John Dundas; and (2) Hugh James Rollo.— Son of Claud Wight, of the Customs, Leith. *Married* Helen —— (*died* 24 June 1836). *Died* 14 May 1836, aged 43.

WIGHTMAN, JAMES CULLEN SETON [21 July 1875]. Apprentice to John M. Lindesay and Alexander Howe.—Son of James Seton Wightman of Courance, Dumfriesshire. *Born* 6 December 1850. *Died* 10 March 1883, unmarried.

WIGHTMAN, ROBERT JOHNSON [15 December 1930]. Apprentice to Sir John Prosser, A. Gray Muir, J. Harold Macdonald, and David G. Prosser.—Son of John Wightman, Ironmonger, North Berwick. *Born* 21 October 1901. *Married* 6 January 1933, Edith Wilkinson, youngest daughter of William Laing, Ellonville, Clifford Road, North Berwick. *Died* 17 December 1971. *Firm*—Morton, Smart, Macdonald, and Prosser (then Morton, Smart, Macdonald and Milligan, latterly Morton, Fraser and Milligan).

WIGHTMAN, JOHN WATT, R.D., M.A., LL.B., [29 November 1960]. Apprentice to Alexander Jackson Ambrose and Another of Macandrew, Wright & Murray.—Son of Robert J. Wightman, W.S., Edinburgh. *Born* 20 November 1933. *Married* 24 February 1962, Isla Fraser, daughter of William McLeod. *Firm*—Morton, Fraser & Milligan (formerly Morton, Smart, Macdonald & Milligan).

WILKIE, GEORGE, OF BRIDGERHEUGH [7 March 1705]. Apprentice to John Wilkie, his brother.—Son of Rev. Thomas Wilkie, Minister of Lady Yester's, Edinburgh. *Married* 12 November 1708, Jean, daughter of Thomas Rutherford of that Ilk. *Died* March 1716.

WILKIE, JAMES [26 November 1829]. Apprentice to Alexander Pearson.—Son of John Wilkie, residing at Tannadice, Angus. *Died* 6 April 1834, aged 40, unmarried.

WILKIE, JOHN [12 June 1637]. Apprentice to Alexander Douglas.—Re-admitted, 21 November 1661. *Married* Violet Ridd. *Buried* 13 December 1669.

WILKIE, JOHN [12 June 1693]. Apprentice to George Dallas.—Son of Rev. Thomas Wilkie, Minister of Lady Yester's, Edinburgh. *Died* 26 May 1704, aged 34.

WILL, JAMES ALEXANDER [13 July 1908]. Apprentice to Horatius Bonar and William C. Hunter.—Son of James Will, Solicitor, Brechin. *Born* 15 November 1883. *Married* 5 January 1911, Bessie Kennedy (*died* 22 November 1970), younger daughter of James F. Salmon, Bolton. In R.A.S.C., 1916-19. *Died* 10 February 1952. *Firms*—Webster, Will & Co.: Symoun & Macdonald, Dumfries.

WILL, JAMES ROBERT, LL.B. [11 December 1978]. Apprentice to John Stewart Macfie and Others of Tods, Murray & Jamieson.—Son of Ronald Kerr Will, W.S., Edinburgh. *Born* 30 April 1955.

WILL, RONALD KERR [18 December 1950]. Apprentice to David Porter and Others of Davidson & Syme.—Son of James Alexander Will, W.S., Dumfries. *Born* 22 March 1918. *Married* 28 March 1953, Margaret Joyce, daughter of David Alan Stevenson, B.Sc., F.R.S.E., F.I.C.E., Edinburgh. Major, K.O.S.B. Served B.E.F. 1940, Staff College and North West Europe 1944-46. Mentioned in Despatches. Appointed Deputy Keeper of the Signet, October 1975. *Firm*—Dundas & Wilson (formerly Davidson & Syme).

WILLIAMS, Rev. HAMILTON JOHN [5 June 1823]. Apprentice to James and Donald Horne.—Son of Robert Williams of Cerne Abbas, Dorset. *Born* 1797. *Married* Margaret (*died* 1881), daughter of Thomas Taunton of Wrackleford, Dorset. Vicar of Buckland Denham, Somerset, 1830-46. Vicar of Kempston, Bedford, 1846-79. *Died* 13 December 1879.

WILLIAMS, RICHARD OLIVER MACMAHON, M.C., M.B.E.(Mil.), M.A.(Oxon), LL.B. [12 July 1948]. Apprentice to John Richardson of Scott Moncrieff & Trail.—Son of Professor J. W. Williams, M.A., D.Litt., Professor of History, University of St Andrews. *Born* 5 November 1917. *Married* 8 August 1945, Camilla Mary, daughter of Major I. Ste. C. Rose, O.B.E., Grenadier Guards. Major, Royal Signals. Served U.K., Middle East, North Africa, Central Mediterranean and North West Europe 1940-45. Awarded Croix de Guerre (France) 1944. Mentioned in Despatches 1944. Solicitor in Scotland to the Forestry Commission. *Died* 25 March 1981. *Firm*—Pearson, Robertson & Maconochie.

WILLIAMS, ROBERT DOUGLAS, M.A. [26 April 1976]. Apprentice to George Stuart Russell and Others of Strathern & Blair. *Born* 17 October 1942. *Firm*—Strathern & Blair.

WILLIAMSON, DAVID [10 March 1803]. Apprentice to Thomas Cranston.—Son of George Williamson, Messenger at Arms, Edinburgh. *Died* 1833.

WILLIAMSON, DAVID [29 May 1828]. Apprentice to Thomas Corrie and David Welsh.—Only son of Thomas Williamson, Writer in Dumfries. *Born* 1805. *Died* 21 July 1843, unmarried.

WILLIAMSON, DAVID STEWART, LL.B. [11 December 1979]. Apprentice to R. K. Watson and Others of Brodies.—Son of Kenneth Stewart Williamson, Civil Servant, Edinburgh. *Born* 6 May 1949. *Firm*—Brodies.

WILLIAMSON, JOHN [Before 1627].

WILLIAMSON, ROBERT [1609].

WILLIAMSON, THOMAS [1 December 1683]. Apprentice to John Alexander, Sen.—*Married* 25 October 1677, Jean Young (*died* 15 February 1690). *Buried* 27 July 1688.

WILSON, ALISTAIR JOHNSTON, LL.B. [3 December 1973]. Apprentice to James Thomson and Another of Fyfe, Ireland & Co.—Son of Archibald P. A. Wilson, Schoolmaster, Stobo, Peeblesshire. *Born* 19 July 1945. *Married* 1 July 1969, Linda Dorothy, daughter of Archibald R. Wood, Auctioneer, Edinburgh. *Firm*—Fyfe, Ireland & Co.

WILSON, CHARLES [21 November 1867]. Apprentice to Charles Morton.—Son of John Wilson, Farmer at Tochineal, Banffshire, Factor for the Earl of Seafield. *Born* 7 March 1842. Procurator-Fiscal at Aberdeen. *Died* at Aberdeen, 22 February 1927, unmarried.

WILSON, DAVID [28 June 1821]. Apprentice to Sir James Gibson-Craig.—Second son of John Wilson of Transy, Fife. *Died* 31 May 1830.

WILSON, EDWARD WARDLAW, M.A., LL.B. [30 July 1941]. Apprentice to Francis Chalmers and Another of Bell & Scott. *Born* 19 August 1907. *Married* 27 April 1964, Muriel Gwendolen Bingham or Ritch. Captain, R.A. Served U.K., Libya and Italy 1939-45. *Died* 16 April 1982. *Firm*—Skene, Edwards & Garson. (Retired.)

WILSON, FRANCIS, OF CROGLIN [6 December 1804]. Apprentice to Sir Henry Jardine.— Son of Ebenezer Wilson, Bookseller in Dumfriesshire. *Born* 1779. *Married* Janet Dove (*died* 26 November 1805). *Died* 15 March 1831.

WILSON, GEOFFREY CARNEGIE DOVE [26 December 1933]. Apprentice to F. J. G. Borthwick, J. G. Kirkpatrick, and Ian MacIntyre.—Son of Sir John Carnegie Dove Wilson, Advocate. *Born* 5 August 1903. *Married* 7 June 1950. Isabella Wakely or Macfarlane. *Died* 21 December 1957. *Firm*—Mackenzie & Kermack.

WILSON, HENRY [1607].—Son of Robert Wilson, of Dieppe, sometime Merchant in Edinburgh. *Married* Susanna Libberton. Deprived 27 October 1609 for not keeping an "open buith."

WILSON, HUTTON [27 June 1839]. Apprentice to James Hope, Jun.—Fourth son of James Wilson, Sheriff-Clerk of the County of Edinburgh. *Born* 25 June 1815. Depute Sheriff-Clerk of Mid-Lothian, 1843-54. *Died* 8 July 1854, unmarried.

WILSON, IAN GRAEME [22 September 1941]. Apprentice to F. P. Milligan and Another of Martin, Milligan & Macdonald.—Son of George Davie Wilson, Woollen Merchant, Edinburgh. *Born* 15 August 1911. *Married* 11 August 1954, Margaret Marion, daughter of Dr Robert H. Thomson, Uphall, West Lothian. Sergeant, R.A. Served U.K. and North West Europe 1939-45. *Died* 30 December 1980. *Firm*—Williamson & Wilson, Bathgate.

WILSON, JAMES [1627]. Signs the Acts, 26 December 1627. *Married* 1 July 1619, Janet (*died* 1649), daughter of Thomas Couper, Tailor Burgess of Edinburgh.

WILSON, JAMES [1 July 1825]. Apprentice to William Patrick.—Son of John Wilson, Vintner in Beith. *Died* 16 December 1836, aged 39, unmarried.

WILSON, JAMES [14 November 1833]. Apprentice to William Renny.—Son of James Wilson, Sheriff-Clerk of Mid-Lothian. *Born* 16 August 1809. *Died* 10 June 1866, unmarried.

WILSON, JAMES WILLIAM HASTIE, D.F.C., B.L. [12 July 1948]. Apprentice to W. Leslie Christie of Cairns, McIntosh & Morton.—Son of James Wilson, Solicitor, Kirkcaldy. *Born* 3 December 1921. *Married* 20 September 1944, Meave Corrymella Anne Allan-Burns. Flight Lieutenant, R.A.F., 1940-45. *Firm*—Gibson & Spears, Dow & Son, Kirkcaldy. (Retired 1977.)

WILSON, JOHN COLIN [23 May 1820]. Apprentice to Thomas Cranston and George Veitch.—Second son of Rev. John Wilson, Minister of Lesmahagow. *Born* 8 July 1797. *Married* 29 July 1822, Jane Ewart (*died* January 1833), daughter of Thomas Peat, W.S. *Died* 27 December 1837.

WILSON, PATRICK [5 January 1654]. Servant to John March, Advocate. *Married* 12 May 1654, Janet Cowell.

WILSON, PATRICK [18 December 1834]. Apprentice to William Young.—Son of Robert Wilson of Bowfield. *Born* 6 December 1809. *Died* 3 June 1885, unmarried.

WILSON, PETER [21 May 1829]. Apprentice to Donald Horne.—Son of William Wilson, Banker in Thurso. Commissary Clerk of Caithness, 1839-52. *Died* 11 May 1852, aged 46, unmarried.

WILSON, PETER KENNETH NOBLE, LL.B. [30 April 1973]. Apprentice to (1) George Stuart Russell and Others of Strathern & Blair, and (2) Robert John Blantyre Simpson of A. G. Cairns & Simpson.—Son of T. K. N. Wilson, Company Director, Edinburgh. *Born* 29 January 1948. *Firm*—(1) A. G. Cairns & Simpson; (2) Cowan & Stewart.

WILSON, ROBERT SYM [8 February 1816]. Apprentice to John Ferrier.—Fourth son of John Wilson, Merchant in Paisley. *Born* 6 March 1792. *Married* 26 May 1813, Eliza, daughter of James Penny of Arrad, Merchant, Liverpool. *Died* 7 May 1868.

WILSON, ROY ALEXANDER, B.A.(OXON), LL.B. [27 April 1964]. Apprentice to James Miller Thomson and Another of J. Miller Thomson & Co.—Son of Eric Moir Wilson, Farmer. *Born* 22 October 1927. *Married* 14 August 1954, Alison Mary, daughter of Dr John David Craig, Medical Practitioner. Thow Scholarship in Scots Law 1952. Solicitor in Scotland to Department of Environment (Transport). *Firm*—Allan McNeil & Son.

WILSON, THOMAS [19 July 1872]. Apprentice to James Hope and Robert Mackay.— *Born* 30 October 1835. *Married* 23 June 1864, Margaret Ewen (*died* 7 July 1910). Found *drowned* in Forth and Clyde Canal, 8 June 1878.

WILSON, THOMAS RANKIN [13 December 1910]. Apprentice to A. D. M. Black, A. W. Gifford, and C. M. Black.—Son of Thomas Jackson Wilson, S.S.C. *Born* 7 May 1886. *Married* 27 September 1916, Shiela (*died* 28 October 1952), youngest daughter of Lewis Grant, Engineer, Kirkcaldy. *Died* 12 April 1951. *Firm*—Finlay and Wilson.

WILSON, WILLIAM [Before 1633].

WILSON, WILLIAM [2 October 1697]. Apprentice to James Henderson.—*Born* 1667. *Married* 22 August 1706, Jean, second daughter of James Crokat, Merchant, Edinburgh. *Died* 16 January 1727.

WILSON, WILLIAM, OF HOWDEN [15 January 1739]. Apprentice to John Macgowan.— Eldest son of Robert Wilson, Maltman, Glasgow. *Born* 11 April 1710. *Married* (1) 3 January 1732, Mary Campbell; and (2) 24 June 1757, Margaret, daughter of Thomas Young, Merchant in Edinburgh. *Died* 18 June 1787.

WILSON, WILLIAM [12 July 1779]. Apprentice to William Wilson.—Only son of Alexander Wilson, Hosier in Glasgow. *Died* 1 March 1783.

WILSON, WILLIAM [1 July 1808]. Apprentice to, and third son of, William Wilson of Howden, W.S.—*Born* 22 September 1767. *Married* 2 August 1803, Cecilia (*died* 28 January 1837), daughter of John Gardiner, Merchant in London. *Died* 5 July 1821.

WILSON, WILLIAM [20 December 1827]. Apprentice to (1) Ralph James Dundas; and (2) James Dundas.—Eldest son of William Wilson, W.S. *Born* 9 December 1805. *Married* (1) 4 June 1845, Louisa, daughter of Colin Mackenzie of Portmore; and (2) 23 November 1876, Caroline (*died* 1882), daughter of John Dundas, W.S. Deputy Keeper of the Great Seal, 1846-52. *Died* 8 July 1880.

WILSON, WILLIAM [20 December 1937]. Apprentice to W. C. Hunter and Another of Bonar, Hunter & Johnstone.—Son of John Currie Wilson, Solicitor, Cupar. *Born* 1 June 1912. *Married* 7 June 1949, Marjorie Murray Pilkington or Russell. *Died* 25 May 1973. *Firm*—Drummond, Johnstone & Grosset, Cupar.

WILSON, WILLIAM BOLDEN [12 January 1885]. Apprentice to William Wilson, his uncle, and Ralph Dundas.—Son of Admiral Thomas Wilson, C.B. *Born* 22 October 1860. *Married* 27 July 1915, Mary Alice Dudgeon (*died* 2 March 1933), daughter of John Stein, Broomhouse, Dunbar. *Died* 11 April 1928. *Firm*—Murray, Beith, and Murray.

WILSON, WILLIAM GEDDES, M.A., LL.B. [20 December 1948]. Apprentice to Robert Francis Shepherd and Others of Shepherd & Wedderburn.—Son of William Wilson, Solicitor, Edinburgh. *Born* 9 December 1920. *Married* 29 March 1952, Isabelle, daughter of Ronald Peter Morison, Q.C. Flying Officer, R.A.F., Second World War. *Firm*—Robertson & Wilson (formerly Geddes & Wilson and Greig & Simson).

WINCHESTER, WILLIAM GRANT LUMSDEN [10 May 1879]. Apprentice to Charles Baxter.—Son of James Webster Winchester, LL.D., Deputy Inspector-General of Hospitals, Bombay Army. *Born* 31 January 1855. Clerk to the Admission of Notaries, 1888 till death. *Married* 21 January 1892, Margaret Elizabeth Robertson (*died* 11 November 1930), daughter of Thomas Collow Campbell, Bank Teller, Edinburgh. *Died* 13 March 1931.

WINRAHAM, JAMES. *See* WYNRAM, JAMES.

WISHART, ANDREW, LL.B. [12 April 1887]. Apprentice to John Patrick Wright.—Son of John Wishart, Manager, Grange Distillery, Burntisland. *Born* 25 August 1859. *Married* 25 June 1891, Agnes Helena (*died* 14 May 1948), youngest daughter of James Reidford, Farmer, Udny, Aberdeenshire. Author of *The Behring Sea Question—the Arbitration Treaty and the Award*, 1892. *Died* 11 June 1943. *Firm*—Wishart and Sanderson.

WISHART, ANDREW MICHAEL, M.A., LL.B. [24 November 1958]. Apprentice to William Watt and Others of Davidson & Syme.—Son of John Reidford Wishart, W.S., Edinburgh. *Born* 3 April 1934. *Firm*—Blair, Cadell & Macmillan (prior to amalgamation, Wishart & Sanderson and J. S. & J. W. Fraser-Tytler).

WISHART, ARCHIBALD [13 November 1817]. Apprentice to Robert Dundas.—Son of William Thomas Wishart of Foxhall. *Born* 1786. *Married* 14 July 1836, Brodie Gordon (*died* 9 February 1898), daughter of Rev. Dr James Simmie, Minister of Rothiemay. Deputy Keeper of the Register of Sasines. *Died* 7 August 1853.

WISHART, JOHN HENRY CONSTABLE, B.L. [20 July 1950]. Apprentice to John James Bonar of Bonar, Hunter & Johnstone.—Son of Ernest Henry Wishart, S.S.C., Edinburgh. *Born* 28 September 1923. *Married* (1) 14 August 1948, Margaret Stewart, daughter of John Henry Mackay, and (2) 2 January 1964, Barbro Aina, daughter of Joel Elof Källström. Sergeant, R.E.M.E. Served Europe and Middle East 1942-47. Resigned Commission. *Firms*—(1) Bonar, Hunter & Johnstone, later Bonar, Mackenzie & Kermack; (2) Constable & Co.

WISHART, JOHN REIDFORD, LL.B. [19 July 1920]. Apprentice to Andrew Wishart, his father, and Kenneth Sanderson.—*Born* 29 April 1893. *Married* 29 March 1933, Edith Douglas (*died* 15 July 1958), daughter of George Mathieson, Edinburgh. Captain R.F.A., 1914-17; wounded. *Died* 18 April 1969. *Firm*—Wishart and Sanderson.

WISHART, PATRICK, OF FOXHALL [9 July 1802]. Apprentice to James Balfour.—Fourth son of William Thomas Wishart of Foxhall, Linlithgowshire. *Born* 25 June 1776. *Married* 23 March 1807, Margaret (*died* 21 August 1849), second daughter of Alexander Robertson of Prenderguest, Berwickshire. *Died* 26 November 1831.

WOOD, SIR ALEXANDER, K.C.M.G. [8 March 1796]. Apprentice to John Wauchope.—Second son of Alexander Wood, Surgeon in Edinburgh. *Married* Christian (*died* 19 December 1863), eldest daughter of Sir William Forbes of Pitsligo, Bart. Secretary, Ionian Islands. *Died* 18 March 1847.

WOOD, ALEXANDER [30 November 1850]. Apprentice to Anderson and Trotter.—Son of Alexander Wood, Advocate. *Born* 25 May 1821. *Died* 21 May 1852, unmarried.

WOOD, ARTHUR BENJAMIN CARTWRIGHT [13 April 1885]. Apprentice to Donald Beith and Andrew Forrester.—Eldest son of Thomas Wood, Bottle-maker, sometime Provost of Portobello. *Born* 24 June 1860. *Died* 12 March 1893, unmarried.

WOOD, GEORGE JOHN [18 April 1877]. Apprentice to T. Graham Murray and J. Auldjo Jamieson.—Fourth son of Andrew Wood, M.D., LL.D., Edinburgh. *Born* 9 September 1853. *Married* 21 July 1887, Mary Balfour (*died* 19 August 1943), eldest surviving daughter of William Robertson of Auchinroath, Elginshire, and granddaughter of the Hon. Lord Ardmillan. *Died* 21 May 1932.

WOOD, GEORGE MURE [28 March 1899]. Apprentice to Sir William Stowell Haldane and William Purves.—Son of George Mure Wood, S.S.C., Edinburgh. *Born* 14 May 1876. War Service: Lieutenant R.G.A. *Died* 21 May 1957. *Firm*—G. M. Wood and Robertson.

WOOD, JOHN GEORGE [5 March 1829]. Apprentice to John Tod.—Eldest son of John Philip Wood, Auditor of Excise, Edinburgh. *Born* 5 April 1804. *Married* 16 October 1846, Margaret (*died* 21 January 1919), daughter of Lieut.-Colonel George Cadell, H.E.I.C.S. *Died* 14 September 1865.

WOOD, JOHN PHILIP, LL.D. [29 June 1871]. Apprentice to Patrick Dalmahoy and John Cowan.—Eldest son of John George Wood, W.S. *Born* 12 September 1847. *Married* 12 April 1882, Margaret Ellinor (*died* 22 November 1949), daughter of Hugh Lyon Tennant, Advocate. Professor of Conveyancing in the University of Edinburgh, 23 December 1891-1900. *Died* 14 January 1906. *Firm*—Melville and Lindesay.

WOOD, MALCOLM JAMES, LL.B. [8 December 1981*].—Son of James Wood, Civil Servant, Aberdeen. *Born* 12 September 1955. *Married* 13 September 1980, Nicola, daughter of Ian Dalrymple Ross, W.S., Edinburgh.

WOOD, ROBERT BRUCE, LL.B., LL.M.(BERKELEY) [28 May 1979]. Apprentice to H. A. Nicolson and Another of Morton, Fraser & Milligan.—Son of Thomas Loftus Wood, Company Director, St Andrews. *Born* 2 October 1951. *Married* 20 September 1975, Agnes, daughter of Robert Steel, Schoolmaster, Lundin Links. *Firm*—Morton, Fraser & Milligan.

WOODMAN, JAMES LINNING [21 November 1833]. Apprentice to Michael Linning.—Eldest son of Dr James Woodman, Physician at Bognor, Sussex. *Born* 27 September 1811. *Married* 1 March 1854, Ursilla Katherine (*died* 19 April 1910), eldest daughter of William Bruce of Symbister, Shetland. *Died* 1 February 1856.

WORDSWORTH, SAMUEL [5 March 1829]. Apprentice to (1) Archibald Crawford; and (2) Peter Couper.—Son of Samuel Wordsworth, residing in Nottingham. *Married* 21 November 1844, Frances (*died* 2 December 1884), third daughter of Robert Young, G.P.O. *Died* 24 November 1855, aged 50.

WORMALD, JOSEPH DAWSON [5 June 1862]. Apprentice to John Hope.—*Born* 4 March 1830. *Married* Mary Anderson. Struck off list of Society, 21 June 1876. *Died* 29 March 1883.

WORT, DAVID ARTHUR, M.A., LL.B. [8 May 1967]. Apprentice to James Little Mounsey and Others of John C. Brodie & Sons.—Son of Richard Spence Wort, National Youth Secretary, Y.M.C.A., London. *Born* 6 November 1926. *Married* 9 March 1957, Mavis June, daughter of Philip John Adams, Coach Builder. Served R.A.F. 1944-48. *Firm*—Melville & Lindesay.

WOTHERSPOON, ALISTAIR MUNRO COWIE, LL.B. [17 November 1952]. Apprentice to T. J. Carlyle Gifford and Others of Baillie & Gifford.—Son of Robert Wotherspoon, Solicitor, Inverness. *Born* 29 August 1926. *Married* 24 February 1953, Patricia Mary Graham, daughter of J. Graham Rankin, Edinburgh. Able Seaman, Royal Navy 1944-1947. *Died* 30 October 1970. *Firm*—Macandrew & Jenkins, Inverness.

WOTHERSPOON, JAMES ROBERT EDWARDS, LL.B. [11 December 1979]. Apprentice to William Robin Douglas and Another of Patrick & James.—Son of John Munro Wotherspoon, W.S., Inverness. *Born* 17 March 1955. *Married* 15 September 1979, Mairi Fleming Stewart, daughter of J. S. Graham, Farmer, North Berwick. *Firm*—Macandrew & Jenkins, Inverness.

WOTHERSPOON, JOHN [23 November 1827]. Apprentice to John M'Kean and James A. Cheyne.—Son of William Wotherspoon, Accountant in Edinburgh. *Died* 1852, aged 51, unmarried.

WOTHERSPOON, JOHN MUNRO, T.D., M.A.(Oxon), LL.B. [20 July 1950]. Apprentice to James Falconer Fairweather and Others of Gordon, Falconer & Fairweather.—Son of Robert Wotherspoon, Solicitor, Inverness. *Born* 24 July 1924. *Married* 30 August 1952, Victoria Avril Jean, daughter of Sir Lawrie Edwards. Lieutenant, Royal Signals. Served Europe and Far East, Second World War. *Firm*—Macandrew & Jenkins, Inverness.

WOTHERSPOON, ROBERT ALEXANDER [13 March 1849]. Apprentice to Andrew Hill.—Son of William Wotherspoon of Hillside, S.S.C. *Born* 1826. *Died* 11 April 1851, unmarried.

WOTHERSPOON, ROBERT SCOTT, B.A.(Oxon), LL.B. [17 November 1952]. Apprentice to Sir Peter Macdonald and Another of W. & J. Burness.—Son of Robert Wotherspoon, Solicitor, Inverness. *Born* 13 February 1928. *Married* 4 June 1955, Margaret Andrina, daughter of John Andrew Christopher Henderson. *Firm*—Wallace & Menzies, North Berwick.

WOTHERSPOON, WALTER SCOTT, M.A.(OXON), LL.B. [19 July 1971]. Apprentice to W. R. Milne and Others of Tait & Crichton.—Son of Robert Wotherspoon, Solicitor, Inverness. *Born* 22 August 1931. *Married* 21 August 1954, Mary Elizabeth Kelway, daughter of Ronald Robert Law. *Firm*—Macandrew & Jenkins, Inverness.

WRIGHT, JAMES [7 July 1807]. Apprentice to Sir James Gibson-Craig.—Eldest son of Rev. John Wright, Minister of Scone. *Born* 15 May 1783. *Died* 21 March 1864, unmarried.

WRIGHT, JAMES [11 July 1905]. Apprentice to Charles Drummond.—Son of John Wright, Bank Agent, Bathgate. *Born* 29 August 1882. *Married* (1) 22 November 1906, Lalla (*died* 11 May 1912), third daughter of Robert Graham Watt Irvine, Bank Agent, Kirkwall; (2) 9 December 1915, Mary Elizabeth (*died* 3 October 1952), daughter of Thomas Dale, Farmer, Scoughall, North Berwick. Provost of Bathgate, 1929-32. Mobilised in Great War as officer in 10th Batt. The Royal Scots. *Firm*—Freeman of Bathgate. *Died* 5 December 1963.

WRIGHT, JOHN [15 June 1837]. Apprentice to James Wright.—Eldest son of Rev. George Wright, Minister of Kingsbarns. *Born* 26 September 1814. *Married* 17 October 1865, Jane (*died* 20 November 1903), second daughter of John Rutherford Greig of Lethangie, Kinross-shire. *Died* 2 November 1888.

WRIGHT, JOHN PATRICK [24 March 1873]. Apprentice to John Dundas and William Wilson.—Son of James Wright, Secretary, Royal Bank of Scotland. *Born* 6 October 1846. *Married* 4 June 1872, Anna (*died* 21 December 1932), only daughter of Bethune James Walker Morison of Falfield, Fife. *Died* 19 September 1917. *Firm*—Macandrew, Wright, and Murray.

WRIGHT, PETER GRAHAM RINGLAND, B.A.(CANTAB), LL.B. [28 April 1952]. Apprentice to Simon Fraser and Another of Blair & Cadell.—Son of Norman Girvan Wright, Timber Broker, Glasgow. *Born* 10 August 1926. *Married* 20 August 1959, Agnes Robinson, daughter of John Whitelaw, Inspector of Naval Ordnance. Leading Writer, Royal Navy, 1945-47, Devonport and Far East. *Firms*—(1) Petty & Wright, Kingussie; (2) Archibald Campbell & Harley.

WRIGHT, ROBERT [22 November 1832]. Apprentice to William Young.—Son of John Wright, Builder in Edinburgh. *Born* 14 February 1807. *Died* 15 August 1846, unmarried.

WRIGHT, THOMAS GUTHRIE [23 November 1802]. Apprentice to Richard Hotchkis.— Youngest son of Charles Wright, Bookseller in Edinburgh. *Married* 22 March 1809, Mary (*died* 18 January 1857), youngest daughter of Professor John Hill, University of Edinburgh. Auditor of Court of Session, 1806-49. *Died* at Paris, 1 September 1849, aged 72.

WYLD, ROBERT STODART, OF GILSTON, LL.D. [12 December 1833]. Apprentice to Adam Gib Ellis.—Eldest son of James Wyld of Gilston, Fife, Merchant in Leith. *Born* 16 April 1808. *Married* (1) 9 October 1838, Isabella Georgina (*died* 5 May 1841), daughter of Lieut.-Colonel Maxwell of the Belgic Service; and (2) 1 November 1844, Margaret (*died* 4 October 1905), third daughter of Walter Gibson Cassels, Edinburgh. Author of *The Philosophy of the Senses*, Memoir of James Wyld of Gilston and his family (1889), and other works. *Died* 29 October 1893.

WYLIE, ALEXANDER, OF LOCHHOUSE [21 February 1856]. Apprentice to William Waddell.—Fourth son of William Wylie, residing at Paparthills, Shotts, Lanarkshire. *Born* 1 January 1828. *Married* 25 September 1866, Janet (*died* 13 July 1914), eldest daughter of Patrick Jamieson, Merchant in Edinburgh. *Died* at Pirn, Stow, 4 January 1898.

WYLIE, DAVID [Before 1606]. Signs Minute of 17 January 1606. *Married* Mariota, daughter of Richard Colville, Burgess of Edinburgh. *Died* about 1622.

WYLIE, JAMES, OF ANNATFIELD [22 November 1799]. Apprentice to Thomas Grierson.— Only son of James Wylie of Cockrigg, Mid-Lothian. *Married* 20 July 1812, Elizabeth (*died* 15 February 1865), youngest daughter of William Macfarlane, W.S. *Died* 20 April 1831.

WYLIE, JOHN [1593]. *Married* Agnes Sinclair. Writer in Chancery.

WYLIE, WILLIAM [Before 1594]. Signs the Minute of 16 December 1594. *Married* 27 December 1598, Marion Oustiane. *Died* before 1621.

WYLLIE, JOHN WILSON [29 March 1904]. Apprentice to John Ewart.—Son of James Wyllie, Chamberlain of Argyll, Inveraray. *Born* 11 March 1879. *Married* 1 June 1925, Edna Irene Callanan (*died* 23 December 1973), Pretoria. Lieutenant R.G.A. in Great War. *Died* 5 April 1953.

WYNRAM, GEORGE, OF OVERGOGAR—Son of Robert Wynram of Overgogar. Retoured heir to his father, 1610.

WYNRAM OR WINRAHAM, JAMES [1 April 1684]. Apprentice to James Hay.—*Married* 3 March 1681, Agnes Auchinleck. Sheriff-Clerk at Duns, 1692.

WYNRAM, ROBERT—Son of James Wynrame of Liberton. *Married* 24 December 1612, Maria, daughter of William Kellie, W.S. *Died* 15 January 1628.

WYNRAME, JAMES, OF LIBERTON [1606]. Signs Minute of 17 January 1606. *Married* (1) Margaret Craig; and (2) 14 June 1597, Janet Swinton, who *died* August 1635. Keeper of the Signet before 1616. *Died* April 1632.

YEAMAN, ALEXANDER [15 July 1885]. Apprentice to Alexander Howe, James S. Tytler, and William MacGillivray.—Son of John Yeaman, Jun., Forfar. *Born* 2 March 1852. *Married* 12 October 1882, Susan Christina Ursula (*died* 15 April 1920), daughter of Colonel John Wilson Auld, H.E.I.C.S. *Died* 30 March 1919. *Firm*—Lindsay, Howe, and Co.

YEAMAN, FRANCIS CAMERON, LL.B. [20 December 1937]. Apprentice to James Watt and Others of Davidson & Syme.—Son of William Yeaman, Solicitor, Edinburgh. *Born* 18 May 1913. *Married* 10 September 1942, Mary Charlotte, daughter of R. M. Johnston, Edinburgh. Gunner, R.A. Mentioned in London Gazette 1946, in recognition of gallant and distinguished service in Mediterranean area. *Firm*—Campell & Don-Wauchope.

YEAMAN, JOHN ALEXANDER, OF KILFINICHEN [12 July 1909]. Apprentice to Alexander Howe, William MacGillivray, Alexander Yeaman, W. A. MacGillivray, and James Brookman.—Son of Alexander Yeaman, W.S. *Born* 22 June 1884. *Married* 19 February 1925, Beatrice Mary, younger daughter of James Macfarlane, Farmer, Caddonfoot, Selkirk. *Died* 27 August 1974. *Firm*—Lindsay, Howe, and Co., 1910-19.

YORSTOUN, WILLIAM GRIERSON, OF GARROCH [16 May 1815]. Apprenticc to James Hope.—Son of Thomas Grierson of Garroch, Kirkcudbrightshire. *Married* 1 August 1844, Emma (*died* December 1886), only daughter of William Parker of Sunderland. *Died* 23 June 1851, aged 62.

YOUNG, ALEXANDER [Before 1549].

YOUNG, ALEXANDER, OF HARBURN [7 March 1786]. Apprentice to Alexander Orr, his uncle.—Only son of Rev. William Young, Minister of Hutton. *Born* June 1759. *Married* 6 May 1789, Sophia (*died* 1847), third daughter of William Bell of Guernsey. *Died* 3 December 1842.

YOUNG, ALEXANDER KETTLE [4 July 1809]. Apprentice to James Laidlaw.—Second son of Rev. Thomas Kettle, Minister of Leuchars. *Born* 4 February 1782. *Married* 15 July 1833, Agnes (*died* 20 July 1888), daughter of Henry Barrie, Farmer. Assumed name of Young by Royal Licence, 30 December 1834. *Died* 30 August 1841.

YOUNG, ANDREW, OF EASTFIELD [10 April 1661]. Apprentice to Richard Guthrie.—*Born* 1633. *Married* 28 April 1658, Euphan (*died* 23 May 1687), daughter of Alexander Yoole, Writer, Edinburgh. Clerk to the Incorporation of Chirurgeons. Ordinary "Writer to the Town," 1672. Treasurer, 1682-86. *Buried* 24 March 1687.

YOUNG, ANDREW RAMSAY, M.B.E. [26 March 1928]. Apprentice to Ernest M. Wedderburn, Robert F. Shepherd, and Robert W. Cockburn.—Son of John Buchanan Young, K.C., Edinburgh. *Born* 27 July 1903. *Married* 3 March 1934, Katherine Muriel (*died* 29 April 1980), only daughter of William Erskine Dommett, Civil Engineer, Examiner H.M. Patent Office. *Died* 31 May 1967.

YOUNG, ANDREW MACGREGOR, M.A., LL.B. [23 July 1951]. Apprentice to Alexander Harper and Another of Pearson, Robertson & Maconochie.—Son of Andrew White Young, W.S., Edinburgh. *Born* 17 March 1924. *Married* 30 June 1953, Irene Marion, daughter of John Mackay, Motor Engineer. Captain, Royal Signals. Served Europe, India and Far East 1939-45. *Firm*—J. & R. A. Robertson.

YOUNG, ANDREW WHITE, LL.B., F.R.S.E. [15 July 1929]. Apprentice to Ernest M. Wedderburn, Robert F. Shepherd, and Robert W. Cockburn.—Son of Thomas Young, Schoolmaster, Lanton, Roxburghshire. *Born* 19 October 1891. *Married* 19 February 1920, Margaret, daughter of Alexander D. Macgregor, Merchant, Edinburgh. Treasurer of the Royal Society of Edinburgh 1947-57. *Died* 20 July 1968. *Firm*—J. & and R. A. Robertson.

YOUNG, CHARLES [1 July 1790]. Apprentice to Alexander Mackenzie.—Son of Francis Young, Acting Collector of Excise at Haddington. *Died* 18 January 1802.

YOUNG, CHARLES [24 October 1892]. Apprentice to R. Dundas, W. J. Dundas, and G. M. Paul.—Sixth son of the Right Hon. George Young, one of the Senators of the College of Justice (Lord Young). *Born* 29 July 1869. *Married* 14 December 1898, Mary (*died* 6 April 1959), second daughter of James Hunter of Glenapp, Ayrshire. Managing Director of Houldsworths, Ironmasters. *Died* 14 January 1940.

YOUNG, CHARLES MAXWELL, LL.B. [15 July 1929]. Apprentice to William Thomson.—Son of John Maxwell, S.S.C., Edinburgh. *Born* 25 December 1902. *Married* 2 April 1931, Mary Catherine Dobie (*died* 9 November 1976), youngest daughter of Thomas M'Donald of Cameron Bank, Craigmillar. *Died* 27 January 1965. *Firm*—Young and Cruickshank.

YOUNG, DAVID MACGREGOR, M.A., LL.B. [28 July 1952]. Apprentice to R. F. Shepherd and Others of Shepherd & Wedderburn.—Son of Andrew White Young, W.S., Edinburgh. *Born* 20 November 1927. *Married* 18 May 1955, Jeanne Elizabeth, daughter of Bickham Webber, Merchant, Leith. *Firm*—J. & R. A. Robertson.

YOUNG, EBENEZER DENHOLM [11 January 1887]. Apprentice to Charles Baxter.— Eldest son of Lieut.-Colonel Samuel Denholm Young, H.E.I.C.S. *Born* 21 August 1857. *Married* (1) 20 December 1888, Jessie (*died* 26 October 1890), second daughter of David Woodburn, M.D., Camlarg, Dalmellington; and (2) 7 June 1899 (*died* 17 December 1936), Margaret Logie Hamilton, daughter of David Charles Edmondston of Buness, Shetland. *Died* 27 February 1930. *Firm*—Young and Roxburgh.

YOUNG, EDWARD [12 March 1893]. Apprentice to J. C. Brodie and T. D. Brodie.—Fifth son of the Right Hon. George Young, one of the Senators of the College of Juctice (Lord Young). *Born* 16 June 1867. *Died* 5 September 1919, unmarried.

YOUNG, IVAN LAURENCE, T.D., B.A.(CANTAB), LL.B. [19 December 1938]. Apprentice to Ernest Maclagan Wedderburn and Others of Shepherd & Wedderburn.—Son of Andrew Laurence Francis Young, Whisky Broker, Edinburgh. *Born* 3 April 1914. *Married* 16 October 1952, Elizabeth Moir, daughter of John Stanley Gartshore, Railway Supplies and Steel Merchant, Toronto, Canada. Major, R.A. Served U.K., France, Middle East and Italy 1939-45. *Firm*—Blair, Cadell & Macmillan (formerly Blair & Cadell).

YOUNG, JAMES [16 July 1888]. Apprentice to James H. Jameson.—*Born* 8 July 1856. *Married* 26 July 1883, Margaret Welsh (*died* 25 September 1936), only daughter of John Turnbull, Merchant, Edinburgh. *Died* 29 February 1920.

YOUNG, JOHN, OF HARPERDEAN [Before 1547]. *Married* Janet Rhind. *Died* September 1599.

YOUNG, JOHN, OF OVER LENY [Before 1606]. Servitor to Thomas Macaulay and brother of Thomas Young of Leny, Mid-Lothian. Commissioner, 16 December 1594. *Married* Euphan, daughter of Sir Archibald Primrose. Sheriff-Clerk of Edinburgh. *Died* 13 December 1622.

YOUNG, JOHN [21 December 1786]. Apprentice to Alexander Orme.—Eldest son of Rev. Thomas Young, Cupar, Fife. *Died* 8 July 1828.

YOUNG, JOHN, O.B.E.(MIL), B.L. [4 December 1972]. Apprentice to William Lindsay and Another of Ketchen & Stevens.—Son of John Young, Miner. *Born* 27 May 1919. *Married* 17 December 1940, Joan Margaret, daughter of Arthur Marsh. Major, R.E. Served with Indian Army in Persia and Iraq and later in Palestine and Suez Canal area. Prior to qualifying in law was Senior Examiner, Inland Revenue (E.D.O. Scotland). *Firm*—Ketchen & Stevens.

YOUNG, JOHN PERCY ADAIR [13 December 1904]. Apprentice to R. R. Simpson and Alexander P. Melville.—Son of Alexander Waugh Young, Schoolmaster, Edinburgh. *Born* 28 March 1881. *Married* 25 April 1911, Jessie Mackay (*died* 19 October 1954), daughter of the Rev. Daniel Georgeson, Bowling. *Died* 23 July 1934. *Firm*—J. K. & W. P. Lindsay.

YOUNG, JOHN WILLIAM [22 July 1868]. Apprentice to (1) William Young; and (2) Laurence Davidson.—Son of William Young, W.S. *Born* 2 April 1836. *Died* at St Andrews, 28 September 1897, unmarried.

YOUNG, KENNETH GIBSON, B.A.(CANTAB), LL.B. [19 December 1938]. Apprentice to Francis George Dalziel and Others of Tods, Murray & Jamieson.—Son of Thomas Edwin Young, W.S., Auchterarder. *Born* 22 June 1913. *Married* 19 November 1941, Kathleen Veronica, daughter of John Landers, Land Agent, Brigg, Lincolnshire. Captain, R.A. Served U.K. 1939-45. *Firm*—Young & Goodman (formerly Thomas E. Young & Co. and Young & Kennaway), Auchterarder.

YOUNG, ROBERT [Before 1586].

YOUNG, ROBERT HUNTER [9 March 1843]. Apprentice to Walter Duthie.—Fourth son of David Young of Cornhill, Aberdeen. *Born* 24 August 1820. *Married* 4 March 1845, Isabella Sophia (*died* 25 August 1898), only daughter of Ewan Evely Arthur, Merchant in London. *Died* 1 December 1851.

YOUNG, THOMAS, OF CAMMO [Before 1586]. Commissioner, 16 December 1594. *Married* Isobel Bellenden (*died* 1644). *Died* 30 November 1613.

YOUNG, THOMAS, OF LENY [Before 1605].—Son of Thomas Young of Cammo, W.S. *Married* (1) Helen Lauder (*died* August 1620); and (2) (contract, 5 April 1621), Margaret, daughter of James Primrose, Clerk to the Privy Council. *Died* about 1654.

YOUNG, THOMAS, C.B.E.,, T.D., J.P. [19 December 1927]. Apprentice to James Miller Thomson of J. Miller Thomson & Co.—Son of Thomas Downie Young, Mercantile Clerk, Edinburgh. *Born* 7 November 1896. *Married* 1 September 1924, Lilias Adie (*died* 20 December 1980), daughter of Andrew Allan, Commercial Traveller. Lieutenant Colonel, R.A. (A.A.) Served U.K. 1939-45. Commanded Legal Aid Section (Scottish Command), for which awarded O.B.E. 1948. Featured prominently in the foundation of Legal Aid schemes in Scotland and England. Sheriff-Substitute of Lanarkshire at Airdrie 1955-64 and Stirling, Dumbarton and Clackmannan at Falkirk 1964-69. *Died* 8 March 1977. *Firms*—(1) J. Miller Thomson & Co. (to 1945); (2) Gray, Muirhead & Carmichael (to 1955).

YOUNG, THOMAS CAMPBELL SANDERSON, M.A., LL.B. [20 November 1950]. Apprentice to, and son of Thomas Young, W.S., of Gray, Muirhead & Carmichael. *Born* 3 August 1926. *Married* 5 November 1962, Cecilia, daughter of Alexander Wilson, Edinburgh. Served Royal Navy, 1944-46, Gibraltar, Malta and Italy. *Firm*—Gray, Muirhead & Carmichael.

YOUNG, THOMAS EDWIN, T.D. [12 July 1897]. Apprentice to (1) A. P. Purves; (2) Campbell Hossack.—Eldest son of Andrew John Young, Advocate, Edinburgh. *Born* 26 December 1873. *Married* 15 June 1909, Agnes M'Dougal, elder daughter of A. Gibson Turnbull, Solicitor, 16 Glencairn Crescent, Edinburgh. Major in 6th Black Watch; wounded in 1916. *Died* 28 February 1941. *Firm*—Thomas E. Young and Co., Auchterarder.

YOUNG, WILLIAM [17 June 1816]. Apprentice to John Tweedie.—Second son of Archibald Young, Surgeon in Glasgow. *Married* 21 January 1820, Agnes (*died* 12 September 1889), only daughter of James Gerard of Whitehaugh. Agent for Church of Scotland. *Died* 2 April 1855, aged 59.

YOUNG, WILLIAM. *See* HERRIES, WILLIAM YOUNG.

YOUNGSON, ALEXANDER [20 May 1794]. Apprentice to John Taylor.—Eldest son of Rev. Andrew Youngson, Minister of New Aberdour, Aberdeenshire. *Born* 15 April 1766. *Died* 24 February 1849.

YOUNIE, PETER GEORGE HUGH, T.D., B.L. [28 July 1959]. Apprentice to George Waddell Harvey and Another of Hunter, Harvey, Webster & Will.—Son of John Younie, Indian Civil Service (Judicial Branch). *Born* 12 August 1931. *Married* 3 March 1961, Morag Alison, daughter of John Leonard Tod. *Firms*—(1) Hunter, Harvey, Webster & Will (1960-73); (2) Cowan & Stewart.

YULE, JOHN [26 May 1818]. Apprentice to Alexander Duncan.—Second son of John Yule, Baker in Edinburgh. *Married* 11 June 1822, J. Morrison (*died* 1870), fifth daughter of Robert Brown, Westbarns, East Lothian. *Died* 15 May 1851, aged 67.

YULE, JOHN [6 March 1845]. Apprentice to John Yule.—Eldest son of George Yule, Merchant in Edinburgh. *Born* 18 March 1818. *Died* 17 April 1861, unmarried.

YULE, THOMAS [13 December 1904]. Apprentice to John Mackenzie.—Son of John Yule, residing in Edinburgh. *Born* 5 April 1859. In Volunteer Batt. The Royal Scots during Great War. *Died* 24 December 1940. *Firm*—J. W. and J. Mackenzie.

LIST OF OFFICE-BEARERS

THE LORD SECRETARIES AND KEEPERS OF THE SIGNET

Date of Commission

1363-1365.	WALTER, OF WARDLAW, ...	*Excheq. Rolls.*
1370.	JOHN LYON, ...	,,
1388.	DUNCAN PETIT, ...	,,
1392-1400.	REGINALD, OF CRAWFORD, ...	,,
1402-1404	WALTER FORSTER, ...	,,
1405.	PATRICK OF CRAWFORD, ...	,,
1423.	PATRICK HOUSTON, CANON OF GLASGOW, . . .	*Acts. of Par.*
1425.	JOHN CAMERON, BISHOP OF GLASGOW, . . .	*Excheq. Rolls.*
1426.	JOHN, OF INVERKEITHING, ...	*Reg. Mag. Sig.*
1427.	WILLIAM FOWLIS, ...	,,
1439-1440.	JOHN METHVEN, ...	*Excheq. Rolls.*
1441.	WILLIAM TURNBULL, ...	*Reg. Mag. Sig.*
1444-1448.	JOHN RAULSTON, BISHOP OF DUNKELD, . . .	,,
1449-1452.	NICHOLAS OTTERBURN, ...	,,
1453.	GEORGE SCHOIRSWOOD, ...	,,
1456-1458.	THOMAS VAUS, DEAN OF GLASGOW, . . .	,,
1458-1459.	JOHN AROUS, ARCHDEACON OF GLASGOW, . .	,,
1459-1462.	GEORGE LIDDELL, ...	,,
1463-1493.	ARCHIBALD WHITELAW, ARCHDEACON OF LOTHIAN, .	,,
1493-1503.	RICHARD MUIRHEAD, DEAN OF GLASGOW, . .	,,
1507-1517.	PATRICK PANITER, ABBOT OF CAMBUSKENNETH, .	,,
1517.	THOMAS HAY, ...	,,
1524. Mar. 6.	PATRICK HEPBURN, PRIOR OF ST ANDREWS, .	,,
1526-1542.	THOMAS ERSKINE, OF HALTON (SIR T. E., OF BRECHIN), .	,,
1542. Jan. 8.	DAVID PANITER, BISHOP OF ROSS, . . .	*Reg. Sec. Sig.*
1542. Feb. 2.	DAVID PANITER AND HENRY BALNAVES, . .	,,
1542.	DAVID PANITER, ...	,,
1558. Dec. 4.	SIR WILLIAM MAITLAND, OF LETHINGTON, YR., .	,,
1573.	ROBERT PITCAIRN, ARCHDEACON OF ST ANDREWS, .	*Reg. Mag. Sig.*
1583.	SIR JOHN MAITLAND, OF THIRLESTANE, .	,,
1591. Apr. 22.	SIR RICHARD COCKBURN, OF CLERKINGTON, .	*Privy Council.*
1596. May 28.	JOHN LINDSAY, OF BALCARRES, . . .	,,
1598. Jan.	JAMES ELPHINSTONE, LORD BALMERINO, .	,,

Reg. Mag. Sig.
Date of Commission

1608. May.	JAMES, LORD BALMERINO, AND SIR ALEXANDER HAY, OF NEWTON.
1609. 15th July.	SIR ALEXANDER HAY, OF NEWTON.

Reg. Mag. Sig.
Date of Commission

1612. 24th July.	THOMAS HAMILTON, EARL OF HADDINGTON.
1626. 8th May.	SIR WILLIAM ALEXANDER, OF MENSTRIE.
1627. 20th October.	SIR WILLIAM ALEXANDER, AND SIR ARCHIBALD ACHESON, OF GLENCAIRN.
1630. 24th March.	SIR WILLIAM ALEXANDER, AND SIR ARCHIBALD ACHESON.
	SIR WILLIAM ALEXANDER, EARL OF STIRLING.
1640. 15th March.	WILLIAM, EARL OF LANARK.
1640. 26th March.	WILLIAM, EARL OF LANARK, AND SIR JAMES GALLOWAY.
1644. January.	SIR ROBERT SPOTTESWOOD, OF NEW ABBEY.
1644. 22nd July.	WILLIAM, EARL OF LANARK. (*See* Acts of Parl. Vol. VI. i. 182.)
1649. 10th March.	WILLIAM, EARL OF LOTHIAN. (Acts of Parl. Vol. VI. ii. 273.)

[*The Commonwealth.*]

1661. 19th January.	JOHN, DUKE OF LAUDERDALE.
1680. 11th October.	ALEXANDER, EARL OF MORAY.
1682. 26th September.	ALEXANDER, EARL OF MORAY, AND CHARLES, EARL OF MIDDLETON.
1685. 10th February.	ALEXANDER, EARL OF MORAY, AND JOHN, VISCOUNT MELFORT.
1690. 22nd February.	GEORGE, EARL OF MELVILLE.
1691. 1st January.	GEORGE, EARL OF MELVILLE, AND JOHN, MASTER OF STAIR.
1692. 3rd March.	GEORGE, EARL OF MELVILLE, AND JAMES JOHNSTON.
1696. 15th January.	JOHN, LORD MURRAY.
1696. 5th February.	JOHN, LORD MURRAY, AND JAMES, LORD DESKFORD, afterwards EARL OF SEAFIELD.
1699. 31st January.	JAMES, EARL OF SEAFIELD, AND JOHN, EARL OF HYNDFORD.
1702. 6th May.	JAMES, EARL OF SEAFIELD, AND JAMES, DUKE OF QUEENSBERRY.
1702. 12th May.	JAMES, EARL OF SEAFIELD, AND JAMES, DUKE OF QUEENSBERRY.
1702. 21st November.	GEORGE, VISCOUNT TARBET, AND JAMES, DUKE OF QUEENSBERRY.
1704. 6th March.	JOHN, EARL OF ROXBURGHE.
1704. 17th October.	JOHN, EARL OF ROXBURGHE, AND JAMES, EARL OF SEAFIELD.
1705. 9th March.	JOHN, EARL OF ROXBURGHE, AND WILLIAM, MARQUIS OF ANNANDALE.
1705. 5th June.	HUGH, EARL OF LOUDOUN, AND WILLIAM, MARQUIS OF ANNANDALE.
1705. 29th September.	HUGH, EARL OF LOUDOUN, AND JOHN, EARL OF MAR.
1706. 20th June.	HUGH, EARL OF LOUDOUN, AND JOHN, EARL OF MAR.
1708. 3rd May.	JOHN, EARL OF MAR.
1709. 20th July.	JAMES, DUKE OF QUEENSBERRY, AND CHARLES, EARL OF SUNDERLAND.
1710. 20th July.	JAMES, DUKE OF QUEENSBERRY.
1710. 21st November.	JAMES, DUKE OF QUEENSBERRY, AND WILLIAM, LORD DARTMOUTH.
1713. 17th September.	JOHN, EARL OF MAR.
1714. 8th October.	JAMES, DUKE OF MONTROSE.
1715. 6th August.	CHARLES, VISCOUNT TOWNSHEND, AND RIGHT HON. JAMES STANHOPE.
1716. 3rd December.	JOHN, DUKE OF ROXBURGHE.
1725. 16th September.	THOMAS HOLLES, DUKE OF NEWCASTLE, AND CHARLES, VISCOUNT TOWNSHEND.
1727. 24th July.	THOMAS HOLLES, DUKE OF NEWCASTLE, AND CHARLES, VISCOUNT TOWNSHEND.

Reg. Mag. Sig.
Date of Commission

1730. 24th June.	THOMAS HOLLES, DUKE OF NEWCASTLE, AND WILLIAM, LORD HARRINGTON.
1741. 18th February.	JOHN, MARQUIS OF TWEEDDALE.

[*Office of Secretary of State for Scotland abolished* 1746.]

KEEPERS OF THE SIGNET

1742.	THOMAS HAY.
1746. 10th November.	ANDREW FLETCHER, OF MILTON.
1766. 4th December.	SIR GILBERT ELLIOT, OF MINTO.
1777. 6th February.	JOHN MACKENZIE, OF DELVINE, *interim*.
1777. 3rd March.	RIGHT HON. HENRY DUNDAS, AND ANDREW STUART, OF CRAIGTHORN.
1779. 23rd June.	RIGHT HON. HENRY DUNDAS.
1792. 10th August.	RIGHT HON. HENRY DUNDAS, AND ROBERT DUNDAS.
1800. 26th May.	ROBERT DUNDAS, VISCOUNT MELVILLE.
1814. 13th August.	RIGHT HON. WILLIAM DUNDAS.
1845. 12th December.	JAMES, MARQUIS OF DALHOUSIE.
1860. 22nd December.	JAMES HOPE, *interim*.
1862. 1st July.	SIR WILLIAM GIBSON-CRAIG, OF RICCARTON.
1878. 13th March.	JAMES HOPE, *interim*.
1879. 21st February.	GEORGE FREDERICK, EARL OF GLASGOW.
1890. 14th May.	CHARLES BOWMAN LOGAN, *interim*.
1890. 30th May.	DOUGLAS BERESFORD, DUKE OF MONTROSE.
1924. 11th December.	WILLIAM CAMPBELL JOHNSTON, *interim*.
1926. 1st February.	JOHN CHARLES, DUKE OF BUCCLEUCH AND QUEENSBERRY.
1935. 19th October.	ERNEST MACLAGAN WEDDERBURN, *interim*.
1936. 1st January.	WALTER JOHN FRANCIS, EARL OF MAR AND KELLIE.
1944. 4th March.	SIR SIDNEY HERBERT, LORD ELPHINSTONE.
1955. 22nd November.	HUGH WATSON, *interim*.
1956. 1st April.	WALTER JOHN, DUKE OF BUCCLEUCH AND QUEENSBERRY.
1973. 4th October.	PATRICK JAMES OLIPHANT, *interim*.
1974. 7th August.	FRANCIS DAVID, EARL OF WEMYSS AND MARCH.

DEPUTY KEEPERS OF THE SIGNET

1583.	NEIL LAYNG.
	JOHN LAYNG.
1616.	JAMES WINRAHME.
1627.	ROBERT ALEXANDER, AND JAMES LAW.
1631.	JAMES GORDON, AND JAMES LAW.
1642.	HARRY MAULE.

1649. 1st May.	MARK CASS, OF COCKPEN.
1654. 15th February.	SAMUEL MOSELY.
1656.	JOHN LOCKHART.
1658.	JAMES CRAWFORD.
1660. 28th August.	SIR PETER WEDDERBURN, OF GOSFORD.
1666. 17th November.	SIR WILLIAM SHARPE, OF STONEYHILL.
1682. 28th September.	SIR HUGH PATERSON, OF BANNOCKBURN.
1685. 30th May.	SIR HUGH PATERSON, AND GEORGE DRUMMOND, OF BLAIR.
1690. 5th May.	DAVID SCRIMGEOUR, OF CARTMORE.
1691. 24th February.	SIR JAMES ELPHINSTONE, OF LOGIE.
1692. 19th December.	SIR JAMES ELPHINSTONE, AND HENRY DOUGLAS.
1696. 8th February.	DAVID CRAWFORD.
1696. 10th April.	DAVID CRAWFORD, AND PATRICK MURRAY, OF DOLLERIE.
1699. 22nd February.	ALEXANDER OGILVIE, OF FORGLEN, ADVOCATE.
1699. 24th November.	ALEXANDER OGILVIE, AND ROBERT KENNEDY, OF AUCHTYFARDLE.
1702. 17th June.	ALEXANDER OGILVIE, AND WILLIAM DOUGLAS, OF DORNOCK.
1703. 17th July.	WILLIAM DOUGLAS, AND SIR KENNETH MACKENZIE, OF CROMARTY.
1704. 31st October.	SIR WILLIAM KER, OF GREENHEAD.
1704. 18th November.	SIR WILLIAM KER, AND SIR ALEXANDER OGILVIE, OF FORGLEN.
1705. 16th March.	SIR GILBERT ELLIOT, OF MINTO, ADVOCATE.
1705. 12th June.	SIR GILBERT ELLIOT, AND GEORGE DALRYMPLE, ADVOCATES.
1705, 27th June.	SIR WALTER PRINGLE, AND GEORGE DALRYMPLE, ADVOCATES.
1705. 4th October.	JAMES ERSKINE, AND GEORGE DALRYMPLE, ADVOCATES.
1707. 5th March.	DAVID ERSKINE, AND GEORGE DALRYMPLE, ADVOCATES.
1708. 9th March.	DAVID ERSKINE, ADVOCATE.
1709. 8th September.	DAVID ERSKINE, AND CHARLES COCKBURN, ADVOCATES.
1711. 23rd January.	SIR WILLIAM CALDERWOOD, OF POLTON, AND WILLIAM ALVES.
1711. 13th October.	WILLIAM COCHRAN, OF KILMARONOCK, AND JOHN PRINGLE, OF HAINING.
1713. 17th September.	HARRY MAULE.
1714. 7th October.	CHARLES COCKBURN, ADVOCATE.
1716. 6th July.	THOMAS PRINGLE.
1725. 18th September.	RONALD CAMPBELL.
1726. 13th September.	ALEXANDER M'MILLAN.
1742. 3rd March.	THOMAS HAY, ADVOCATE.
1746. 21st November.	ALEXANDER M'MILLAN.
1770. 30th July.	JOHN MACKENZIE, OF DELVINE.
1778. 20th June.	JOHN DAVIDSON, OF HALTREE.
1797. 20th December.	HUGH WARRENDER.
1820. 27th June.	COLIN MACKENZIE.
1828. 12th January.	RICHARD MACKENZIE, AND JAMES HOPE.
1850. 30th April.	JAMES HOPE.
1882. 17th March.	JOHN CLERK BRODIE.
1887. 15th December.	SIR CHARLES BOWMAN LOGAN.
1905. 1st June.	SIR GEORGE MORISON PAUL.
1924. 31st December.	SIR WILLIAM CAMPBELL JOHNSTON.
1935. 7th May.	ERNEST MACLAGAN WEDDERBURN.
1954. 1st January.	SIR HUGH WATSON.

1964. 9th November.   PATRICK JAMES OLIPHANT.
1975. 29th September.   RONALD KERR WILL.

UNDER OR SUBSTITUTE KEEPERS OF THE SIGNET
AND CLERKS TO THE SOCIETY

1594.   ADAM LAWTIE.
1616.   THOMAS M'AWLAY.
1647. 9th January.   JOHN NICOL.
1654. 13th March.   GEORGE CRUICKSHANK.
1660. 19th November.   ROBERT HAMILTON.
1681. 5th December.   GILBERT NICOLSON.
1682. 3rd November.   ROBERT PATERSON.
1685. 25th August.   PATRICK JOHNSTONE.
1690. 5th May.   ROBERT RUTHERFORD.
1692. 9th March.   JOHN DALRYMPLE.
1696. 9th April.   JOHN ANDERSON.
1696. 4th May.   JOHN ANDERSON, AND JOHN DALRYMPLE.
1698.   WILLIAM CRAWFORD.
1699. 21st May.   ROBERT WATSON.
1701.   WALTER TAYLOR, AND JOHN STEWART.
1704.   ALEXANDER MACLEOD.
1705. 15th June.   JOHN DALRYMPLE, AND JAMES DRUMMOND.
1707.   WILLIAM DALRYMPLE, AND HARRY MAULE.
1708. 24th December.   CHARLES MASTERTON.
1709. 9th November.   WILLIAM ALVES, AND DAVID WATSON.
1710. 2nd January.   GEORGE FALL, AND WILLIAM ALVES.
1711. 2nd November.   GEORGE KENNEDY.
1713. 23rd September.   DAVID MAULE.
1713. 16th November.   DAVID MAULE, AND CHARLES MASTERTON.
1714. 14th October.   ANDREW GRAHAM, AND JAMES GRAHAM.
1719.   HERCULES SCOTT.
1725.   JOHN PRINGLE, AND JOHN HAY.
1726.   JOHN HAY, AND ALEXANDER CAMPBELL.
1741. 26th January.   ARCHIBALD CAMPBELL, AND ALEXANDER CAMPBELL.
1742. 12th March.   JAMES HAY, AND JOHN HAY.
1744. 27th December.   ALEXANDER TAIT.
1746. 16th November.   ALEXANDER TAIT, AND JOHN WATSON.
1762. 16th November.   ALEXANDER GRAY, AND WILLIAM ALSTON.
1767. 2nd March.   GEORGE SANDY.
1785. 4th January.   JOHN HOME.
1831. 20th October.   JOHN HAMILTON.
1867. 4th October.   JOHN RICHARDSON.
1876. 6th October.   HON. JAMES WILLIAM MONCRIEFF.
1885. 19th August.   JOHN MILLIGAN.
1904. 22nd September.   JAMES HUME NOTMAN.
1931. 16th November.   JAMES MILLIGAN.

1948. 18th October.   ROBERT CARFRAE NOTMAN.
1964. 26th October.   PETER CARMICHAEL MILLAR.

ASSISTANT CLERKS AND EXTRACTORS OF THE SIGNET

1711. 21st Jan.   WILLIAM CADDELL.
1711. 7th Nov.   ANDREW GEDDES.
1712. 21st Jan.   JOHN BOGLE.
                           ROBERT MANSON.
1722. 15th Jan.   WILLIAM ROY.
1741. 9th Nov.   ROBERT KINNELL.
1768. 13th Dec.   JAMES SANDARS.
1776. 19th June.   ALEXANDER ALISON.
1805. 23rd Aug.   JOHN CAMERON.
1810. 26th Nov.   JOHN FINLAYSON.
1831. 20th Oct.   ROBERT WEBSTER.
1846. 2nd Sept.   JAMES MILLIGAN.
1876. 9th Oct.   JOHN MILLIGAN.

1885. 6th Sept.   JOHN DUNBAR DUFF.
1889. 22nd Jan.   JAMES HUME NOTMAN.
1904. 22nd Sept.   ALEXANDER LOUIS DICK PEDDIE (resigned 30th June 1919).
1919. 27th June.   JAMES MILLIGAN.
1931. 25th Nov.   ROBERT CARFRAE NOTMAN.
1949. 18th Oct.   CHARLES SNOW CAMPBELL.
1959. 19th Oct.   THOMAS DUNSIRE.
1963. 4th Dec.   PETER CARMICHAEL MILLAR.
1964. 26th Oct.   WILLIAM MACPHERSON STEEL.
1974. 12th Sept.   STEWART YOUNG MARSHALL.

FISCALS

1596. 23rd July.   ADAM COUPAR.
1599. 21st February.   HARRY BICKARTOUN.
1604. 27th March.   GEORGE MACK.
1627. 28th December.   HEW ROS.
1657. 2nd February.   WILLIAM ROS.
1666. 22nd January.   GEORGE DALLAS.
1671. 4th January.   HUGH WALLACE.
1681. 25th September.   ALEXANDER AIKENHEAD.
1683. 29th January.   ALEXANDER CHAPLANE.
1684. 20th October.   JOHN FRANK.
1686. 13th November.   WILLIAM STIRLING.
1690. 5th May.   JOHN CUNNINGHAM, OF BANDALLOCH.
1695. 19th July.   WILLIAM DALLAS.
1696. 4th May.   JOHN STRACHAN.
1697. 19th July.   WILLIAM DALLAS, AND ROBERT PRINGLE.
1699. 2nd October.   WILLIAM DALLAS, AND ALEXANDER GLASS.
1702. 16th November.   WILLIAM MENZIES.
1703. 22nd November.   ROBERT CAMPBELL.
1710. 21st December.   THOMAS BOYES.
1717. 18th February.   JOHN STEWART.
1722. 12th November.   GEORGE KENNEDY.
1723. 14th November.   JOHN DUNDAS.
1725. 8th November.   WILLIAM FORBES.
1726. 11th November.   JOHN HAMILTON, JUN.
1728. 11th November.   ARCHIBALD STEWART.
1729. 10th November.   ROBERT WALLACE, JUN.
1732. 13th November.   JOHN HAY.

1734. 11th November.   RONALD DUNBAR.
1754. 26th November.   SAMUEL MITCHELSON.
1755. 24th November.   PETER SINCLAIR.
1763. 28th November.   JOHN SMITH.
1777. 24th November.   JOHN RUSSELL.
1796. 30th May.   JAMES MARSHALL.
1807. 30th November.   PATRICK RUSSELL.
1820. 26th December.   RICHARD MACKENZIE.
1824. 26th May.   JAMES NAIRNE.
1844. 3rd July.   ALEXANDER DOUGLAS.
1851. 17th July.   ADAM GIB ELLIS.
1864. 21st November.   PATRICK DALMAHOY.
1872. 18th November.   WILLIAM RAMSAY KERMACK.
1883. 20th June.   CHARLES BOWMAN LOGAN.
1887. 20th December.   JOHN COWAN.
1892. 13th June.   ROBERT LAIDLAW STUART.
1899. 23rd November.   WILLIAM STUART FRASER.
1918. 26th June.   JAMES HOTCHKIS JAMESON.
1928. 19th November.   ALEXANDER STEVENSON BLAIR.
1935. 21st October.   JAMES FALCONER FAIRWEATHER.
1945. 15th October.   ARTHUR HENRY CECIL HOPE.
1955. 17th October.   ARCHIBALD RICHARD BURDON HALDANE.
1963. 4th February.   ALEXANDER JACKSON AMBROSE.
1973. 5th February.   GEORGE STUART RUSSELL.
1980. 26th May.   DAVID CAIRNS FULTON.

TREASURERS

1654. 13th March.   GEORGE MACK.
1659. 18th January.   JAMES ALLAN.
1662. 13th January.   DAVID WATSON.
1682. 13th November.   ANDREW YOUNG.
1686. 13th November.   JOHN FRANK.
1691. 13th July.   JOHN MACFARLANE.
1697. 15th November.   THOMAS PRINGLE.
1698. 16th August.   DAVID RAMSAY.
1699. 7th November.   JOHN LUTFUTT.
1703. 20th January.   PATRICK HOME.
1710. 21st December.   JAMES BAILLIE.
1714. 20th April.   ALEXANDER GLASS.
1722. 26th November.   ALEXANDER STEVENSON.
1732.   JOHN STEUART.
1736. 8th November.   JOHN HAY.
1746. 17th February.   ALEXANDER STEVENSON.
1755. 3rd February.   SAMUEL MITCHELSON.
1788. 27th June.   WILLIAM TYTLER.
1792. 17th December.   RICHARD HOTCHKIS.
1824. 12th March.   RICHARD MACKENZIE.

1828. 4th February.	ANDREW STORIE.
1862. 18th June.	JOHN GIBSON, JUN.
1870. 7th February.	JOHN CLERK BRODIE.
1882. 3rd April.	JOHN THOMSON MOWBRAY.
1892. 13th June.	JOHN COWAN.
1925. 25th May.	JAMES WATT.
1935. 21st October.	GEORGE FRANCIS HENDERSON.
1946. 21st October.	DONALD BOASE SINCLAIR.
1956. 15th October.	WILLIAM DOUGLAS WATSON.
1964. 1st May.	KENNETH MACRAE.
1974. 19th June.	IAN TEMPLE JOHNSTONE.

PROFESSORS OF CONVEYANCING

1816. 16th December.	MACVEY NAPIER.
1847. 12th March.	ALLAN MENZIES.
1856. 28th February.	ALEXANDER MONTGOMERIE BELL.
1866. 28th May.	JAMES STUART FRASER TYTLER.
1891. 23rd December.	JOHN PHILP WOOD.
1900. 3rd May.	JOHN LITTLE MOUNSEY.
1922. 20th June.	ERNEST MACLAGAN WEDDERBURN.
1935. 14th June.	HARRY HENDERSON MONTEATH.
1955. 4th April.	GEORGE LOVAT FRASER HENRY.
1973. 30th September.	IAIN WILLIAM NOBLE.

LIBRARIANS

1805. 9th December.	MACVEY NAPIER.
1837. 21st June.	DAVID LAING.
1879. 24th March.	THOMAS GRAVES LAW.
1904. 30th May.	JOHN PHILIP EDMOND.
1906. 18th April.	JOHN MINTO.
1935. 4th February.	CHARLES ALEXANDER MALCOLM.
1961. 21st June.	JAMES ALEXANDER CHRISTIE.
1968. 1st October.	GEORGE HODGE BALLANTYNE.

COLLECTORS OF THE WIDOWS' FUND

1803. 1st August.	SIR ADAM FERGUSON.
1806. 20th January.	FRANCIS NAPIER.
1818. 6th July.	JAMES STUART.
1828. 17th November.	WALTER COOK.
1861. 4th March.	JOHN COOK.
1892. 4th January.	CHARLES COOK.
1922. 21st June.	WILLIAM CAMPBELL JOHNSTON.
1925. 2nd February.	ANDREW GRAY MUIR.
1936. 17th June.	EUAN BARCLAY ROBERTSON.
1947. 18th June.	SIR JOHN IRELAND FALCONER.

1950. 21st June.	ALEXANDER ARCHIBLD INNES WEDDERBURN.
1951. 26th February.	HUGO JOHN PATTEN.
1956. 19th March.	WILLIAM EDGAR GRAY MUIR.
1959. 23rd March.	PATRICK JAMES OLIPHANT.
1965. 1st February.	ALEXANDER HUGH NOBLE.
1975. 10th February.	HAROLD ALEXANDER NICOLSON.

CATALOGUE OF PORTRAITS AND BUSTS IN THE SIGNET LIBRARY

List of Portraits

1. Sir HUGH PATERSON of Bannockburn, Bart., W.S., *d.* 1696.
   Deputy Keeper, 1682-89.
   Painter unknown.
   Bequeathed by Hugh James Rollo, W.S.

2. Sir HUGH PATERSON of Bannockburn, 2nd Bart., *d.* 1701.
   Painter unknown.
   Bequeathed by Hugh James Rollo, W.S.

3. GEORGE DALLAS of St Martin's, W.S., 1636-1701.
   Author of *A System of Stiles as now practicable within the Kingdom of Scotland,* 1697.
   After Sir John Baptist Medina, 1659-1710.

4. Sir JAMES STEWART of Goodtrees, 1635-1715.
   Lord Advocate, 1692-1709.
   By Sir John Baptist Medina, 1659-1710.
   Presented by John Parker, Esq.

5. JAMES ANDERSON, W.S., 1662-1728.
   Author of *Diplomata et Numismata Scotiae.*
   By John Vanderbanck, 1694-1739.

6. GEORGE DRUMMOND, 1687-1766.
   Lord Provost of Edinburgh.
   By Sir George Chalmers, *d.* 1791.
   Presented by D. B. Anderson, W.S.

7. JAMES ERSKINE, Lord Grange, 1679-1754
   Lord Justice-Clerk, 1710-34.
   By Sir John Baptist Medina, 1659-1710.
   Bequeathed by Hugh James Rollo, W.S.

8. PATRICK GRANT, Lord Elchies, 1690-1754.
   Lord of Session, 1732-54.
   By Allan Ramsay, 1713-84.
   Presented by Richard Mackenzie of Dolphinton, W.S.

9. HEW DALRYMPLE, Lord Drummore, 1690-1755.
   Lord of Session, 1726-55.
   By John Medina, *d.* 1764.
   Bequeathed by Robert Menzies, W.S.

10. ANDREW FLETCHER, Lord Milton, 1692-1766.
    Lord of Session, 1724, Lord Justice-Clerk, 1735-48.
    Keeper of the Signet, 1746-66.
    By Allan Ramsay, 1713-84.
    Bequeathed by David Laing, LL.D., Librarian of Signet Library.

11. THOMAS HAY, Lord Huntington, *d.* 1755.
    Keeper of the Signet, 1742-46; Lord of Session, 1754-55.
    Copy by Cosmo Alexander, 1724-73.
    Presented by Miss Hay.

12. The Rt. Hon. ROBERT BLAIR of Avontoun, 1741-1811.
    Lord President of the Court of Session, 1808-11.
    By Sir Henry Raeburn, 1756-1823.

13. The HON. DAVID HUME, 1757-1838.
    Baron of Exchequer, 1822-32.
    Author of *Commentaries on Criminal Law*.
    By Sir Henry Raeburn, 1756-1823.

14. The Rt. Hon. CHARLES HOPE of Granton, 1763-1851.
    Lord President of the Court of Session, 1811-41.
    By Sir John Watson Gordon, *P*.R.S.A., 1788-1864.

15. Sir JAMES GIBSON-CRAIG of Riccarton, Bart., W.S., 1765-1850.
    By Colvin Smith, 1795-1875.
    Presented by James T. Gibson-Craig, W.S.

16. ALEXANDER DOUGLAS of Chesterhouse, W.S., 1780-1851.
    By Sir John Watson Gordon, *P*.R.S.A., 1788-1864.
    Bequeathed by his son, Alexander Sholto Douglas, W.S.

17. The Rt. Hon. DAVID BOYLE, 1772-1853.
    Lord President of the Court of Session, 1840-52.
    By Sir John Watson Gordon, *P*.R.S.A., 1788-1864.

18. DAVID WELSH of Collin, W.S., 1789-1857.
    By Sir John Watson Gordon, *P*.R.S.A., 1788-1864.
    Presented by Mrs Scott Skirving of Collin.

19. JOHN WHITEFOORD MACKENZIE, W.S., 1794-1884.
    Attributed to Sir John Watson Gordon, *P*.R.S.A., 1788-1864.
    Presented by Thomas Yule, W.S.

20. JOHN CLERK BRODIE of Idvies, C.B., LL.D., W.S., 1811-88.
    Deputy Keeper of the Signet, 1882-87.
    By Sir George Reid, *P*.R.S.A., 1841-1913.

21. JOSEPH GRANT, W.S., 1793-1873.
    By W. Smellie Watson, R.S.A., 1796-1874.
    Presented by Miss Katherine Wallace.

22. Sir Charles B. Logan, LL.D., W.S., 1837-1907.
      Deputy Keeper of the Signet, 1887-1905.
      By Sir George Reid, *P*.R.S.A., 1841-1913.

23. Sir George M. Paul, W.S., 1839-1926.
      Deputy Keeper of the Signet, 1905-24.
      By Sir James Guthrie, *P*.R.S.A., 1859-1933.

24. Sir William Campbell Johnston, LL.D., W.S., 1860-1938.
      Deputy Keeper of the Signet, 1924-35.
      By J. B. Anderson, A.R.S.A.

25. James Steuart, W.S., 1802-86.
      By Sir John Watson Gordon, *P*.R.S.A., 1788-1864.
      Presented by Miss Sylvia Steuart.

26. Andrew Storie, W.S., 1767-1862.
      Treasurer of the Society, 1828-62.
      By Sir John Watson Gordon, *P*.R.S.A., 1788-1864.
      Presented by Miss Penelope Swan.

27. Thomas Graham Murray, W.S., 1816-91.
      By Sir George Reid, *P*.R.S.A., 1841-1913.
      Presented by Viscount Dunedin.

28. William Scott of Teviotbank, W.S., 1782-1841.
      By Sir John Watson Gordon, *P*.R.S.A., 1788-1864.
      Presented by Miss Gertrude E. Scott.

29. Sir Ilay Campbell of Succoth, LL.D., 1734-1823.
      Lord President of the Court of Session, 1789-1808.
      By David Martin, 1737-98.
      Lent by Sir George Campbell of Succoth.

30. Alexander J. Russell, W.S., 1814-87.
      By Sir George Reid, *P*.R.S.A., 1841-1913.
      Presented by Miss M. Russell.

31. John Campbell of Stonefield, *d.* 1801.
      Lord of Session, 1762-1801.
      By Sir Henry Raeburn, 1756-1823.
      Presented by Kenneth Sanderson, W.S.

32. Sir Walter Scott, 1771-1832.
      By Colvin Smith, R.S.A., 1795-1875.
      On permanent loan from the Scottish National Portrait Gallery.

33. Sir John Hamilton of Orbieston, *d.* 1664.
      Justice-Clerk, 1636-49.
      Painter unknown.
      Presented by Lord Hamilton of Dalzell.

34. Sir ERNEST MACLAGAN WEDDERBURN, O.B.E., D.Sc., LL.D., 1884-1958.
         Deputy Keeper of the Signet, 1935-54.
         By David Ewart, A.R.S.A., 1901-65.

35. Sir HUGH WATSON, LL.D., W.S., 1897-1966.
         Deputy Keeper of the Signet, 1954-64.
         By Sir William O. Hutchison, R.S.A., 1889-1970.

36. PATRICK JAMES OLIPHANT, W.S., 1914-79.
         Deputy Keeper of the Signet, 1964-75.
         By Alberto Morrocco, R.S.A.

List of Busts

1. GEORGE VEITCH of Ratho Bank, W.S., 1787-1826.
         By George Joseph, *d.* 1850.
         Presented by Trustees of W. F. Pitcairn.

2. JOHN GIBSON, W.S., 1789-1879.
         By Sir John Steell, R.S.A., 1804-91.
         Presented by his grandson, J. Gibson.

3. THOMAS GRAHAM MURRAY of Stenton, LL.D., W.S., 1816-91.
         By George Webster.
         Presented by his son, Viscount Dunedin.

4. COLIN MACKENZIE of Portmore, 1770-1831.
         Deputy Keeper of the Signet, 1820-28.
         By Thomas Campbell, 1790-1858.

5. JOHN FULLERTON, 1775-1853.
         Senator of the College of Justice.
         By Sir John Steell, R.S.A., 1804-91.
         Presented by A. Palmer Douglas of Mingard.

6. ANDREW STUART of Craigthorn and Castlemilk, *d.* 1801.
         Keeper of the Signet, 1777-79.
         By Christopher Hewetson.
         Presented by Mrs Stuart Stevenson.

7. Sir WALTER SCOTT, 1771-1832.
         By John Saunders (executed 1865).